Methods in
Immunology
and Immunochemistry

VOLUME II
Physical and Chemical Methods

Advisory Board:

Methods in
IMMUNOLOGY
and IMMUNOCHEMISTRY

Edited by

CURTIS A. WILLIAMS

THE ROCKEFELLER UNIVERSITY
NEW YORK, NEW YORK

MERRILL W. CHASE

THE ROCKEFELLER UNIVERSITY
NEW YORK, NEW YORK

Volume II

Physical and Chemical Methods

1968

A C A D E M I C   P R E S S   New York and London

574.2902'8
WIL

ACADEMIC PRESS INC.
111 Fifth Avenue, New York, New York 10003

United Kingdom Edition published by
ACADEMIC PRESS INC. (LONDON) LTD
Berkeley Square House, London W.1

LIBRARY OF CONGRESS CATALOG CARD NUMBER: 67-22779

PRINTED IN THE UNITED STATES OF AMERICA

Contributors to Volume II

Numbers in parentheses indicate the pages on which the authors' contributions begin.

JOHN R. CANN (1, 6, 76), Department of Biophysics, Medical Center, University of Colorado, Denver, Colorado

KEITH M. COWAN (81), Immunological Investigation Section, Plum Island Animal Disease Laboratory, Greenport, New York

LYMAN C. CRAIG (119), The Rockefeller University, New York, New York

MERRILL W. CHASE (249, 282, 365), The Rockefeller University, New York, New York

BARUCH J. DAVIS (38), Cell Research Laboratory, Mt. Sinai Hospital, New York, New York

HELAINE DONAHUE (163, 343), Department of Microbiology, School of Medicine, Washington University, St. Louis, Missouri

JUSTINE S. GARVEY (183), Division of Chemistry and Chemical Engineering, California Institute of Technology, Pasadena, California

LEWIS I. GIDEZ (305), Albert Einstein College of Medicine, Bronx, New York

STELLAN HJERTÉN (142, 149), Institute of Biochemistry, University of Uppsala, Uppsala, Sweden

TE PIAO KING (135, 154, 160, 161), The Rockefeller University, New York, New York

J. KOHN (20), Department of Pathology, Queen Mary's Hospital, London, England

CHARLES A. LEONE (174), University of Kansas, Lawrence, Kansas

LAWRENCE LEVINE (317), Graduate Department of Biochemistry, Brandeis University, Waltham, Massachusetts

J. RUSSELL LITTLE (163, 343), Department of Microbiology, Washington University School of Medicine, St. Louis, Missouri

BERNARD MACH (328), Institute of Molecular Biology, University of Geneva, Geneva, Switzerland

HANS J. MÜLLER-EBERHARD (57), Scripps Clinic and Research Foundation, La Jolla, California

WILLIAM T. MURAKAMI (317), Graduate Department of Biochemistry, Brandeis University, Waltham, Massachusetts

LEONARD ORNSTEIN (38), Cell Research Laboratory, The Mt. Sinai Hospital, New York, New York

C. KIRK OSTERLAND (57, 409), Department of Preventive Medicine and Public Health, Washington University School of Medicine, St. Louis, Missouri

JERKER PORATH (67), Institute of Biochemistry, University of Uppsala, Uppsala, Sweden

M. D. POULIK (25), Department of Pediatrics, Wayne State University School of Medicine, Detroit, Michigan

SAMUEL RAYMOND (47), William Pepper Laboratory, University of Pennsylvania, Philadelphia, Pennsylvania

ROY E. RITTS, JR. (228), Head, Section of Microbiology, Mayo Clinic, Rochester, Minnesota and Washington University School of Medicine, St. Louis, Missouri

RODES TRAUTMAN (81), USDA Agricultural Research Service, Animal Disease and Parasite Research Division, Plum Island Animal Disease Laboratory, Greenport, New York

JOSÉ URIEL (73), Institut de Recherches Scientifiques sur le Cancer, Villejuif, France

CURTIS A. WILLIAMS (19, 249, 282), The Rockefeller University, New York, New York

Preface

The rapid growth of research in immunochemistry and immunology warrants the initiation of an open-end treatise dealing with methodology. The increasing number of applications of immunological methodology to problems in other areas of biology dictates an organization, content, and style which will be helpful to the nonspecialist and specialist alike. Our aim, therefore, has been to open our colleagues' notebooks to bring together detailed procedures that are hard to retrieve from original literature. But the presentation and discussion of reliable methods are intended to provide confidence and guidance, not rigidity. The solution of research problems often demands inventive modifications and sometimes the development of new and specialized approaches. Accordingly, contributors were asked to include not only the details of procedures they had found most satisfactory in their own laboratory, but also critical remarks about common pitfalls and interpretation of results, references to alternative methods, and mention of applications to other problems. While not all topics are easily suited to this format, we feel that insofar as our general objectives are achieved, these volumes represent high potential energy.

Other publications have appeared with similar titles. Some are intended primarily for teaching purposes, others have appeared as reports of symposia. Many are excellent aids to workers in laboratories. None we have seen to date, however, encompasses the scope of the present volumes. Volume I is concerned with typical preparative methods employed in handling antigens, antibodies, and laboratory animals. Volume II presents general chemical and physicochemical methods of great usefulness for immunological research. Volume III is devoted to techniques for the analysis of the antigen-antibody reaction, both *in vitro* and *in vivo*. Volume IV includes methods and interpretations of approaches to the study of the immune response. Unavoidably, some important general topics as well as many specific methods had to be postponed for subsequent volumes, which will treat hypersensitivity, transplantation, immunogenetics, immunity to parasites, and histochemistry, in addition to updating material already presented and introducing new fields of interest.

vii

It would clearly be impossible to compile high quality material of this scope without the enthusiastic support and creative advice of the advisory editors. Their contributed sections, their help in suggesting topics and authors, and in some cases their assistance with the editing is not only greatly appreciated by us but, we are certain, will be appreciated by the users of these volumes.

CURTIS A. WILLIAMS
MERRILL W. CHASE

New York, New York
March, 1968

Topical Listing of Contents

Chapter 6. Electrophoresis

Chapter 7. Ultracentrifugation

Appendix I

Appendix II

Appendix III

Contents of Other Volumes

Methods in
Immunology
and Immunochemistry

VOLUME II
Physical and Chemical Methods

CHAPTER 6

Electrophoresis

A. Factors Governing the Rate of Migration of Charged Particles in an Electric Field* †

Electrophoresis refers to the movement of charged particles and macromolecular ions under the influence of an electric field. Depending on the sign of their net charge, these substances migrate either to the cathode or to the anode. Differences in migration velocities provide a powerful means for the analysis and separation of substances which are difficult to fractionate by other methods. The migration velocity of a particle, when the electric field acting on it is 1 volt cm^{-1}, is called its electrophoretic mobility. The dimensions of mobility are in cm^2 sec^{-1} volt^{-1}, and its sign is the same as that of the net electrical charge on the particle. Although in a given medium the mobility is a characteristic property of the particle, it generally varies with the composition of the solution. Thus, the mobility of a protein such as γ-globulin or serum albumin depends on the pH, the ionic strength, and the nature of the supporting electrolyte. An understanding of this behavior ultimately depends on the establishment of a theoretical relationship between the mobility and various molecular parameters such as electrical charge and frictional coefficient, and the elucidation of the dependence of these parameters on the composition of the solvent medium. The theory of electromigration is considered in detail in several excellent reviews,[1-4] and only a brief survey will be presented here.

A uniform electric field of intensity E will exert a force, QE, on an

* Section 6,A was contributed by John R. Cann

† Contribution No. 241 from the Department of Biophysics, Florence R. Sabin Laboratories, University of Colorado Medical Center, Denver, Colorado.

[1] H. A. Abramson, L. S. Moyer, and M. H. Gorin, "Electrophoresis of Proteins and the Chemistry of Cell Surfaces," Chapters 1, 5, and 6, Reinhold, New York, 1942.

[2] H. Mueller, in "Proteins, Amino Acids and Peptides as Ions and Dipolar Ions" (E. J. Cohn and J. T. Edsall, eds.), Chapter 25, Reinhold, New York, 1943.

[3] J. Th. G. Overbeek, Advan. Colloid Sci. 3, 97 (1950).

[4] J. Th. G. Overbeek and J. Lijklema, In "Electrophoresis Theory, Methods, and Applications" (M. Bier, ed.), Chapter 1. Academic Press, New York, 1959.

isolated particle of charge Q suspended in a perfect insulator. The particle will be accelerated until the opposing frictional force exerted by the surrounding viscous medium just balances the electrical force, after which time the particle will move with a constant velocity, v, given by the relation

$$QE = fv \tag{1}$$

where f is the frictional coefficient of the particle. The frictional coefficient may be obtained from the diffusion coefficient, D, by means of the Einstein relationship,

$$D = \frac{kT}{f} \tag{2}$$

where k is Boltzmann's constant, and T is the absolute temperature. The electrophoretic mobility, μ, for a particle of arbitrary shape is then given by the relation

$$\mu = \frac{v}{E} = \frac{Q}{f} = \frac{QD}{kT} \tag{3}$$

If the particle is a sphere of radius a, the frictional coefficient is given by Stoke's law as $6\pi\eta a$, where η is the coefficient of viscosity of the medium. The radius of the particle may be eliminated by introducing the potential at the surface of the sphere, ψ_0, which is equal to Q/Da, where D is the dielectric constant. The mobility of the sphere is then given by

$$\mu = \frac{D\psi_0}{6\pi\eta} \tag{4}$$

Equations 3 and 4 are developed for charged particles in an insulator and must be modified for application to electrophoretic experiments on macromolecular ions in electrolyte solutions. The additional fundamental concept required for understanding electromigration in electrolyte solutions is that of the ionic atmosphere. As a consequence of the electrostatic force between the charge on the particle and the ions of the electrolyte, there are, on the average, more ions of unlike than of like sign in the neighborhood of the particle. In other words, the particle may be regarded as being surrounded by an ionic atmosphere of opposite charge. The presence of this ionic atmosphere results in electrophoretic mobilities which are smaller than those predicted by equations 3 and 4 for a medium which is a perfect insulator. Three factors contribute to this difference. First, the ionic atmosphere lowers the value of the potential at the surface of the particle. One may visualize this effect by considering that the ionic atmosphere shields the charge on the particle from the applied electric field; that is, it decreases the effective charge and, thus, the migration velocity. The second effect arises from the fact that the applied field also acts upon the ions of the ionic atmosphere. Since the charge of the ion cloud is opposite in sign to the charge of the particle, the force exerted by the electric field on the ion cloud tends to move it in a direction opposite to that of the particle, thus decreasing the migration velocity of the particle. This effect is referred to as the *electrophoretic effect* or *electrophoretic friction*, since it effectively increases the frictional force acting on the particle. Finally, the electric current continually carries new ions to and from the environment of the particle. This exchange of ions distorts the otherwise spherically symmetrical ion atmosphere because the ions approaching the particle require a finite time before their distribution can adjust itself to the field distribution near the particle. Similarly, the ions leaving the atmosphere cannot instantaneously assume a random distribution. As a result, the ionic atmosphere will trail behind the moving particle, thereby producing an electrostatic retarding force which decreases the velocity of the particle. The production of an asymmetrical ionic atmosphere is referred to as the *relaxation effect*. All three of these effects increase with increasing ionic strength of the solvent medium. Thus, other things remaining constant, the electrophoretic mobility is expected to decrease when the ionic strength of the solvent medium is increased.

Henry considered the electromigration of a nonconducting particle of arbitrary radius, a, in an electrolytically conductive medium. Assuming that the relaxation effect is negligible, he found the electrophoretic mobility to be given by the relation

$$\mu = \frac{D}{4\pi\eta}\left[\zeta + 5a^5\int_\infty^a \frac{\psi(r)}{r^6}\,dr - 2a^3\int_\infty^a \frac{\psi(r)}{r^4}\,dr\right] \qquad (5)$$

where $\psi(r)$ is the potential in the ionic atmosphere, and ζ is the zeta potential—that is, the potential at the surface of shear. A few words of explanation with regards to the zeta potential are in order. A layer of water may adhere so firmly to the particle that it cannot be set into motion either by an applied electric field or by motion of the liquid. Thus, the adhering layer of water must be considered as forming a part of the particle, and the potential determining the rate of electromigration is then taken as the potential at the boundary of the fixed and free liquid—that is, the surface of shear. The zeta potential is determined by the charge inside this surface. This charge is not necessarily identical with the net charge of the particle, since some of the ions of the ionic atmosphere may be present within the surface of shear, thereby reducing the electrophoretic charge below that which would be determined analytically, as, for example, by acid-base titration.

On the assumption that the zeta potential is small and that the interionic attraction theory of Debye and Hückel is applicable,* equation 5 reduces to

$$\mu = (\mathrm{D}\zeta/6\pi\eta)g(\mathfrak{K}a)$$
$$Q = \mathrm{D}\zeta a(1 + \mathfrak{K}a)$$
$$g(\mathfrak{K}a) = 1 + \frac{\mathfrak{K}^2a^2}{16} - \frac{5\mathfrak{K}^3a^3}{48} - \frac{\mathfrak{K}^4a^4}{96} + \frac{\mathfrak{K}^5a^5}{96}$$
$$- \left(\frac{\mathfrak{K}^4a^4}{8} - \frac{\mathfrak{K}^6a^6}{96}\right)e^{\mathfrak{K}a}\int_{\infty}^{a}\frac{e^{-t}}{t}dt \quad (6)$$
$$\mathfrak{K} = (8\pi N\epsilon^2/1000\,\mathrm{D}kT)^{1/2}\sqrt{\Gamma}$$

where ϵ is the elementary charge; N is Avogadro's number; Γ is the ionic strength ($\Gamma = \frac{1}{2}\sum^{i} Z_i^2 C_i$, where Z_i is the charge of the ith ion whose molar concentration is C_i); and $1/\mathfrak{K}$ the "thickness" of the ionic atmosphere. Values of $6/g\ (\mathfrak{K}a)$ for various values of $\mathfrak{K}a$ are presented in Table I. As anticipated, equations 6 predict that the electrophoretic

TABLE I
HENRY'S FACTOR FOR SPHERES

$\mathfrak{K}a$	$6/g(\mathfrak{K}a)$	$\mathfrak{K}a$	$6/g(\mathfrak{K}a)$
0	6.000	5	5.173
1	5.844	10	4.843
2	5.631	25	4.38
3	5.450	100	4.11
4	5.298	∞	4.00

mobility of a macromolecular ion will decrease as the ionic strength of the solvent medium is increased. In the limit of infinitely high ionic strength the mobility approaches zero, since the zeta potential vanishes.* It is, perhaps, even more instructive to examine the other limiting situation of zero ionic strength. According to the above discussion we

---

* The use of the Debye-Hückel theory introduces an inconsistency into the development of the theory of electromigration insofar as it involves the assumption that the zeta potential is equal to the potential at the surface of the particle. However, this may not be too serious at very low ionic strengths where only a negligible part of the charge in the double layer might be included within the surface of shear.

would expect the effects of the ionic atmosphere in retarding migration velocity to vanish as the ionic strength approaches zero. In other words, in the absence of electrolytes the macromolecular ion should behave as predicted for one suspended in a perfect insulator,* and equations 6 do, in fact, reduce to equation 4 in the limit of zero ionic strength.

Usually, of course, mobility measurements are made at ionic strengths in the range 0.01 to 0.1 M not only because of the inherent properties of proteins and their interactions but also because of the need to suppress undesirable phenomena accompanying both moving-boundary and zone electrophoresis at low ionic strengths.

The theory of electromigration outlined above is a valuable guide to understanding the dependence of electrophoretic mobilities, whether determined by moving-boundary or zone electrophoresis,† on the composition of the solvent medium. Thus, the mobility of a protein molecule is expected to depend on its net electrical charge corrected for ions contained within the surface of shear, its size and shape (frictional coefficient), and the ionic strength of the solvent medium. The type of buffer electrolyte is also important, since the net charge is determined not only by the state of ionization of the acidic and basic groups on the protein, which is a function of the pH of the medium, but also by the binding of buffer ions other than H^+ by the protein molecule. Binding of H^+ and other small ions can also affect the frictional coefficient through changes in either conformation or state of aggregation. The combined use of electrophoresis and a hydrodynamic method such as ultracentrifugation or viscosity measurements may sometimes be indicated in order to evaluate the relative importance of changes in net charge and frictional coefficient with changes in electrolyte environment. Finally, the theory predicts that the mobility will decrease with increasing ionic strength. Although this is generally found to be the case, occasionally a protein, such as aldolase in phosphate buffer, will exhibit just the opposite behavior. This deviation is usually interpreted in terms of binding of buffer ions other than H^+ (as are deviations of electrophoretic from titration charges), but in some instances other factors such as changes in frictional coefficient could conceivably be important. In any event, when quoting a value for electrophoretic mobility it is

---

* In thinking about this problem it is helpful to recall that macromolecular ions carry very little of the electrical current in electrolyte solutions but all of the current when the solvent medium is a perfect insulator.

† In computing electrophoretic mobilities from zone electrophoretic experiments, migration velocities must be corrected for electroösmotic flow and tortuosity of the supporting medium under conditions such that retardation due to adsorptive effects and molecular sieving is negligible.

imperative to state the conditions of pH, ionic strength, and buffer composition.

B. Moving-Boundary Electrophoresis*

1. INTRODUCTION

In the moving-boundary method of electrophoresis, an electric field is applied to an initially sharp boundary between a solution of macromolecular ions and a buffer. The formation of multiple moving boundaries is observed if the solution of macromolecular ions is heterogeneous with respect to net charge. This method was described by Lodge[1] and was developed to a high degree of perfection for the study of transference numbers of inorganic electrolytes by MacInnes and Longsworth.[2] The first application to the study of proteins was made by Picton and Linder,[3] but precise measurements on purified proteins and complex biological materials were not possible until Tiselius introduced his adaptation of the moving-boundary method.[4] This advance, combined with Longsworth's[5] introduction of the ingenious schlieren scanning technique and cylindrical lens arrangement of Philpot and Svensson for observing and recording refractive index gradients in the electrophoresis cell, has made moving-boundary electrophoresis a powerful tool for the study of biological systems.

2. PROCEDURES

The construction and operation of the Tiselius electrophoretic apparatus as modified by Longsworth and the interpretation of electrophoretic patterns are described in detail in several reviews.[6-9] Only the most essential features need be touched upon here. Basically the Tiselius cell is a U-tube, rectangular in cross section, with end walls of high optical

* Section 6,B was contributed by John R. Cann.

[1] O. Lodge, *Rept. Brit. Assoc. Advan. Sci.* **56**, 389 (1886).

[2] D. A. MacInnes and L. G. Longsworth, *Chem. Rev.* **11**, 171 (1932).

[3] H. Picton and S. E. Linder, *J. Chem. Soc.* **61**, 148 (1892).

[4] A. Tiselius, *Trans. Faraday Soc.* **33**, 524 (1937). *Biochem, J.* **31**, 1464 (1937).

[5] L. G. Longsworth, *Ind. Eng. Chem. Anal. Ed.* **18**, 219 (1946).

[6] R. A. Alberty, *J. Chem. Educ.* **25**, 426 (1948); **25**, 619 (1948).

[7] R. A. Brown and S. N. Timasheff, *in* "Electrophoresis Theory, Methods and Applications" (M. Bier, ed.), Chapter 8. Academic Press, New York, 1959.

[8] L. G. Longsworth, in "Electrophoresis Theory, Methods and Applications" (M. Bier, ed.), Chapters 3 and 4. Academic Press, New York, 1959.

[9] J. R. Cann, *in* "Treatise on Analytical Chemistry" (I. M. Kolthoff and P. J. Elving, eds.), Part I, Vol. 2, Chapter 28. Interscience, New York, 1961.

quality to permit observation of boundaries by changes in the refractive index along the length of the cell. The cell is composed of three sections which may be slid relative to one another so that sharp initial boundaries can be formed by shearing action. An initial boundary between the dialyzed protein solution and buffer is formed in each of the two limbs of the U-shaped channel, with the denser protein solution underneath. The upper ends of the two limbs are connected to electrode vessels designed to prevent products of the electrode reaction from reaching the boundaries. The use of silver–silver chloride electrodes immersed in strong chloride solution ensures against formation of gaseous products at either electrode. The application of a potential across the two electrodes will cause the boundary corresponding to a given charged protein ion to rise in one limb of the cell and descend in the other. The boundary will migrate toward the anode if the protein is negatively charged (alkaline to isoelectric pH) and to the cathode if it is positive (acid to isoelectric pH). A solution containing a single macromolecular component will show a single moving boundary, and one containing n components will show n moving boundaries. The resolution of a two-component system is illustrated in Fig. 1. Electrophoresis is usually carried out at 0.5° to 2° in order to suppress undesirable effects arising from thermal convection. Field strengths of 4 to 10 volts cm^{-1} and times of electrophoresis of 1 to 6 hours are generally employed.

The boundaries are recorded photographically by using the schlieren scanning technique or a cylindrical lens arrangement. Examples of the types of electrophoretic patterns shown by protein solutions of varying complexity are presented in Fig. 2. By convention, the patterns have been rotated 90 degrees from the position in which they were photographed. The direction of migration is shown by the arrows labeled to indicate whether the boundaries are rising (r) or descending (d). The vertical line at the tail of the arrow indicates the position of the initial boundary. The ordinates in the patterns are proportional to the refractive index gradients (and therefore concentration gradients) at the heights in the cell given by the abscissa. The small ϵ and δ boundaries reflect departures from ideality and can be ignored as far as the determination of apparent composition is concerned. The patterns of a complex mixture are well illustrated by those presented in Fig. 2 for serum, showing a leading boundary corresponding to albumin and four globulin boundaries designated as α_1-, α_2-, β-, and γ-globulin. Actually, both physicochemical and biological studies have shown that the various globulin boundaries do not correspond to single components but rather to families of protein ions whose members possess about the same electrophoretic mobilities at pH 8.6.

For ideal electrophoresis—that is, the limiting case in which conductance and pH effects of the protein are negligible—the area under a given boundary in the electrophoretic pattern is proportional to the concentration of the corresponding protein ion. Thus, the apparent composition of a mixture such as serum can be determined by measuring the areas of the various peaks in its pattern. The relative concentration of a given component is then equal to the ratio of the area under its

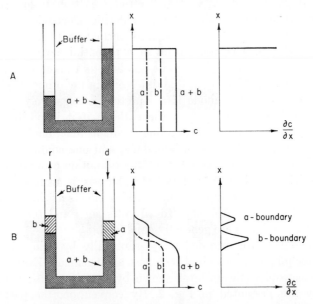

Fig. 1. Resolution of a mixture of two electrophoretic components, a and b, under ideal conditions. Diagrammatic representation of the boundaries in the U-shaped electrophoresis cell and plots of concentration, c, and concentration gradients, $\partial c/\partial x$, as functions of height, x, in the descending limb of the cell: (A) initial conditions; (B) conditions after application of electric field for a time sufficient to resolve completely the moving boundaries corresponding to components a and b. Original mixture contains 1 part of a and 2 parts of b. Mobility of b is greater than that of a. From J. R. Cann, in "Treatise on Analytical Chemistry" (I. M. Kolthoff and P. J. Elving, eds.), Part I, Vol. 2, Chapter 28. Interscience, New York, 1961.

peak to the total area exclusive of the ϵ or δ boundary. The photographic record is placed in an enlarger, the projected image of the pattern traced on a sheet of paper, the base line drawn,[10] and the position of the initial boundary recorded. In the case of incomplete resolution of peaks, as with serum, arbitrary separation is accomplished either by constructing

[10] L. G. Longsworth, in "Methods in Medical Research" (A. C. Corcoran, ed.), Vol. 5, p. 63. Year Book Publishers, Chicago, 1952.

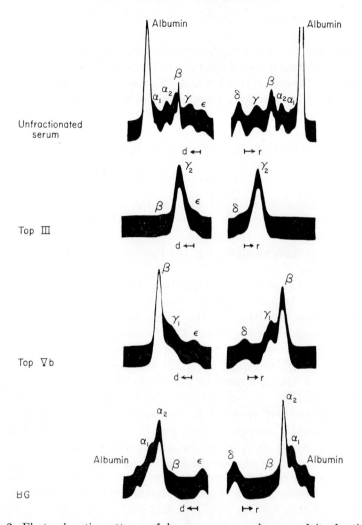

Fig. 2. Electrophoretic patterns of human serum and some of its fractions in sodium diethylbarbiturate buffer at pH 8.6, ionic strength 0.1. The fractions were obtained by the method of electrophoresis-convection as shown in Vol. II, p. 78. Fractions are designated as "Top" after fractionations III or Vb; globulin BG was precipitated from residual material in the apparatus by adding one volume of saturated ammonium sulfate. From J. R. Cann and M. H. Loveless, *J. Allergy* **28**, 379 (1957).

bell-shaped curves for each peak such that their ordinates at every point add up to the experimental curve[8,11] or by dropping an ordinate from the lowest point between adjacent maxima in the pattern to the base

[11] L. G. Longsworth, *Chem. Rev.* **30**, 323 (1942).

line.[8,12] The areas enclosed by the peaks are then measured with a polar planimeter.

The enlarged tracings are also used to calculate the distances moved by the various boundaries during electrophoresis. If a boundary is symmetrical, the distance through which the maximum ordinate has moved may be used. However, for an asymmetrical peak the boundary position is given by the first moment of the gradient curve, although the ordinate which bisects the area may be used for many purposes. The mobilities are calculated from these distances, Δx cm, by means of the relation.

$$\mu = \Delta x \cdot A \cdot \mathcal{K}_P / Git$$

where A is the cross-sectional area of the electrophoresis channel in square centimeters, and G is the product of the magnifications of the Tiselius camera and the photographic enlarger. $\mathcal{K}_P$ is the conductance of the dialyzed protein solution, i is the current in amperes, and t is the time in seconds.

The above evaluation of composition and mobilities assumes ideal electrophoresis. Actually, the patterns shown in Fig. 2 reveal several departures from ideality: (1) the rising and descending patterns are not mirror images of each other—that is, they are nonenantiographic; (2) the distances moved by the rising boundaries are greater than for the corresponding descending ones; (3) small concentration boundaries, designated as ϵ and δ, appear in the region of the cell near the initial boundaries; and (4) the area enclosed by the rising boundaries is generally less than that enclosed by the corresponding descending ones. The Dole theory[8,13] accounts rather well for these departures from nonidentity and serves as a guide for interpretation of the patterns. An important consequence of nonideal behavior is that the apparent electrophoretic composition differs from the true composition. Experiments on mixtures of known composition have verified the theoretical prediction that the deviation between apparent and real composition can be minimized by analysis of the descending rather than the rising patterns. Also, the choice of buffer and other supporting electrolytes is important, since departures from ideality increase with increasing mobilities of salt ions which carry charges identical in sign with the net charge on the macromolecular ion. Thus, for proteins at pH's alkaline to their isoelectric points, diethylbarbiturate gives the least error, and phosphate and chloride ions give the greatest error. Sodium diethylbarbiturate buffer of ionic strength 0.1 and pH 8.6 has been widely used for electrophoretic

[12] A. Tiselius and E. A. Kabat, *J. Exptl. Med.* **69**, 119 (1939).
[13] V. P. Dole, *J. Am. Chem. Soc.* **67**, 1119 (1945).

analysis of serum and plasma because it helps to minimize nonideal effects and, perhaps even more important, gives the best resolution of the boundaries. Finally, Dole's theory indicates that ideality is approached as the protein concentration is decreased and the ionic strength increased. (For routine analyses the protein concentration should not exceed 2%, w/v, in buffers of ionic strength 0.1.) Consequently, apparent compositions are often extrapolated to zero protein concentration and infinite ionic strength to obtain "true" electrophoretic composition. (A plot of composition versus ratio of protein concentration to ionic strength is convenient for this purpose.) For some problems, it is desirable to prepare artificial mixtures of the materials to be analyzed and construct calibration graphs of known versus apparent composition.

Departures from ideality also alter migration velocities, owing to production of conductance gradients and pH gradients across the moving boundaries. The electrophoretic mobility of a protein showing a single moving boundary may be calculated directly from the displacement of the descending boundary and the conductance of the dialyzed protein solution. With mixtures, however, this method gives the correct mobility only for the most rapidly moving component, the displacements of all the other boundaries giving values that are smaller than the corresponding mobilities. Consequently, the pH-mobility curve, and hence the isoelectric point of a given component of a mixture, should be determined, if possible, on material that has been separated from the other components.

3. CRITERIA OF PURITY

Under maximum conditions of sensitivity of the schlieren optics and at a protein concentration of 2 gm per 100 ml, a component representing as little as 0.5% of a mixture can often be detected. With interference optics[14] even smaller quantities should be detectable. However, when the mobilities of the minor components approach that of the major component, the former may be present to the extent of several percent and remain undetected because of failure of the boundaries to be resolved. Often only a small shoulder on the main peak may be evident even after a long time of electrophoresis. Sometimes, however, resolution into multiple boundaries may occur after prolonged electrophoresis with countercompensation to keep the moving boundary in the electrophoresis cell.

When testing for heterogeneity, it is first necessary to establish whether the material migrates as a single boundary over a wide range of pH

[14] L. G. Longsworth, *Anal. Chem.* **23**, 346 (1951).

and ionic strength. Thus, two serum mucoproteins[15] have about the same mobilities and are thus poorly resolved at pH 8.4, ionic strength 0.1, but have widely different mobilities and are therefore well resolved at pH 4.5, ionic strength 0.1. Ovomucoid shows a single boundary at pH 8.6 and 4.1, ionic strength 0.1, but five well-resolved boundaries at pH 4.2, ionic strength 0.01.[16-18] Even when a protein shows a single boundary over a wide range of pH and ionic strength,—for example, γ-globulin—it may nevertheless be heterogeneous as revealed by reversible boundary spreading. The techniques and theory of reversible boundary spreading have been described by Alberty[19] and by Brown and Cann.[20]

Finally, resolution of electrophoretic patterns into multiple moving boundaries does not necessarily indicate heterogeneity, since protein–protein and protein–solvent interactions can also give rise to multiple peaks. The latter type of interaction, illustrated in Fig. 3, accounts for the resolution of the patterns of a variety of proteins in acidic media containing acetic acid and other carboxylic acid buffers.[21,22] Furthermore, recent theoretical developments[23] reveal that highly cooperative interactions of a single macromolecular species with an uncharged constituent of the solvent can give rise to enantiographic patterns showing two moving boundaries even when equilibrium is established instantaneously. In practice, such patterns could easily be misinterpreted as indicating a mixture of two stable, noninteracting components. A similar situation pertains to isomerizing systems, $A \rightleftharpoons B$, in which the half-time of interconversion is of the order of the time of electrophoresis. In this case the patterns may show three peaks.[24] Systems of the type $A + B \rightleftharpoons C$ may show three peaks even for instantaneous establishment of equilibrium.[25] Fortunately, there is an unambiguous method for distinguishing between interactions and true heterogeneity. The protein disappearing

[15] J. W. Mehl, Humphrey, J. and R. J. Winzler, *Proc. Soc. Exptl. Biol. Med.* **72**, 106 (1949).

[16] E. Fredericq and H. F. Deutsch, *J. Biol. Chem.* **181**, 499 (1949).

[17] M. Bier, J. A. Duke, R. J. Gibbs, and F. F. Nord, *Arch. Biochem. Biophys.* **37**, 491 (1952).

[18] M. Bier, L. Terminiello, J. A. Duke, R. J. Gibbs, and F. F. Nord, *Arch. Biochem. Biophys.* **47**, 465 (1953).

[19] R. A. Alberty, *J. Am. Chem. Soc.* **70**, 1675 (1948).

[20] R. A. Brown and J. R. Cann, *J. Phys. Colloid Chem.* **54**, 364 (1950).

[21] J. R. Cann and R. A. Phelps, *J. Am. Chem. Soc.* **79**, 4672 (1957).

[22] J. R. Cann, *J. Am. Chem. Soc.* **83**, 4784 (1961). References to earlier papers are given in this article.

[23] J. R. Cann and W. B. Goad, *J. Biol. Chem.* **240**, 148 (1965).

[24] J. R. Cann and H. R. Bailey, *Arch. Biochem. Biophys.* **93**, 576 (1961).

[25] G. A. Gilbert and R. C. Ll. Jenkins, *Proc. Roy. Soc.* **253A**, 420 (1959).

across the peaks is isolated, and the resulting fractions are analyzed electrophoretically under conditions identical with those used in the original separation. If the apparent heterogeneity is due to interaction, the fractions will behave like the unfractionated material and show two peaks. In the case of inherent heterogeneity, each fraction should produce a single boundary. This test is also applicable to mixtures of inherently different macromolecules in which each component interacts with the solvent.

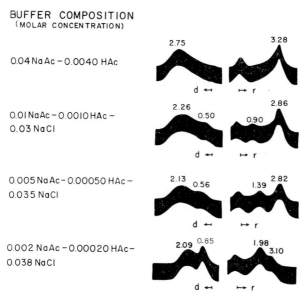

BUFFER COMPOSITION
(MOLAR CONCENTRATION)

0.04 NaAc - 0.0040 HAc

0.01 NaAc - 0.0010 HAc - 0.03 NaCl

0.005 NaAc - 0.00050 HAc - 0.035 NaCl

0.002 NaAc - 0.00020 HAc - 0.038 NaCl

FIG. 3.   Electrophoretic patterns of bovine γ-pseudoglobulin in media containing varying concentration of acetate buffer, pH 5.7 From J. R. Cann and R. A. Phelps, *J. Am. Chem. Soc.* **79**, 4672 (1957).

4. APPLICATIONS AND CRITIQUE

The abundant results obtained with the Tiselius apparatus as modified by Longsworth have contributed significantly to the rapid progress made in the past two decades in the various branches of biochemistry and medicine. For example, the electrophoretic demonstration of Tiselius[4] that rabbit antibodies to ovalbumin are associated with the γ-globulin fraction of the serum proteins has led to important advances in the understanding of the nature of antibodies and the specific antigen–antibody reaction. Since human γ-globulins separated from plasma by Cohn's ethanol fractionation procedure[26-28] (see Chap. 3,A,2) contain a variety of antibodies which have been concentrated fifteen to thirty times,[29] they have proved useful clinically to attenuate and suppress infectious diseases. Electrophoretic analyses of sera led to the recognition of agammaglobulinemia,[30] a pathological condition characterized by increased susceptibility to infection and failure to give the usual immunological response to the most intensive antigenic stimulation. The tissues and sera of patients suffering from this disease contain little, if any, γ-globulin.

a. Protein Interaction

In their elegant studies on soluble antigen–antibody complexes, Singer and his co-workers[31] used moving-boundary electrophoresis in conjunction with ultracentrifugation to evaluate equilibrium constants and other thermodynamic parameters of antigen–antibody reactions, and to establish the bivalency of precipitating antibody and the validity of the lattice theory of specific precipitation. Other applications of the moving-boundary method to specific protein–protein interactions include the first unambiguous physical demonstration[32,33] of a Michaelis-Menten complex between a proteolytic enzyme, pepsin, and its macromolecular substrate (serum albumin), physical demonstration and characterization of trypsin–trypsin inhibitor complex,[34] studies on complexing of ribonucleic acid with proteins,[8] and discovery of the transition of serum albumin between the N (slow) peak and the F (fast) isomer in acidic media ("N–F transition").[35]

b. Interaction of Proteins with Small Molecules

Moving-boundary electrophoresis has also provided important information on the interaction of proteins with salt ions and other constituents

[26] H. F. Deutsch, R. A. Alberty, and L. J. Gosting, *J. Biol. Chem.* **165**, 21 (1946).

[27] J. L. Oncley, M. Melin, D. A. Richert, J. W. Cameron, and P. M. Gross, Jr., *J. Am. Chem. Soc.* **71**, 541 (1949).

[28] M. Cohn, H. F. Deutsch, and L. R. Wetter, *J. Immunol.* **64**, 381 (1950).

[29] J. F. Enders, *J. Clin. Invest.* **23**, 510 (1944).

[30] R. A. Good, R. L. Varco, J. B. Aust, and S. J. Zak, *Ann. N.Y. Acad. Sci.* **64**, 882 (1956).

[31] S. J. Singer and D. H. Campbell, *J. Am. Chem. Soc.* **74**, 1794 (1952); see Cann (ref. 9) and Brown and Timasheff (ref. 7) for other references to the work of Singer and co-workers on soluble antigen–antibody complexes.

[32] J. R. Cann and J. A. Klapper, Jr., *J. Biol. Chem.* **236**, 2446 (1961).

[33] J. R. Cann, *J. Biol. Chem.* **237**, 707 (1962).

[34] J. Sri. Ram, L. Terminiello, M. Bier, and F. F. Nord, *Arch. Biochem. Biophys.* **52**, 451 (1954); see also Brown and Timasheff (ref. 7).

[35] K. Aoki and J. F. Foster, *J. Am. Chem. Soc.* **79**, 3385 (1957); see Cann (ref. 9) and Brown and Timasheff (ref. 7) for other references to the work of Aoki and Foster on the N-F transition.

of the solvent medium. It is pertinent to mention studies on the binding of small anions by γ-pseudoglobulin.[36] Isoelectric point determinations have demonstrated that the order of increasing binding is $Cl < Br < NO_3 < ClO_4$, which is also the order of increasing effectiveness of these anions in causing aggregation of the protein at pH 3. Longsworth and Jacobsen[37] were the first to note that the electrophoretic patterns of some proteins at pH values acid to their isoelectric points are suggestive of interaction between various forms of the protein in solution. Cann and his co-workers[21,22] pursued this matter and observed that a variety of proteins, including γ-globulin, display nonenantiographic electrophoretic patterns in acidic media containing acetate or other carboxylic acid buffers. The nature of the patterns depends on the concentration of buffer in the solvent medium. Increasing the concentration at constant pH and ionic strength results in progressive and characteristic changes, notably in the appearance and growth of fast-moving peaks at the expense of slow ones. Fractionation and other measurements have shown that the peaks in a given pattern constitute a reaction boundary modified in some instances by mild convective disturbances. Evidence has been advanced to support interpretation of these observations in terms of reversible complexing of the protein molecules with undissociated buffer acid with concomitant subtle structural changes which increase the net positive electrical charge on the protein but do not change its frictional coefficient significantly. A theoretical basis for this interpretation has recently been provided[23] by a moving-boundary theory of electrophoretic transport of interacting systems of the type $P + nHA \rightleftharpoons P(HA)_n$, where P represents a macromolecular ion in solution, and $P(HA)_n$ its complex with n moles of an uncharged constituent, HA, of the solvent medium. It is assumed that the $P(HA)_n$ complex migrates with a greater electrophoretic mobility than the uncomplexed macromolecule and that equilibrium is established instantaneously. Numerical solution of the conservation equations by means of a digital computer shows that under appropriate conditions the electrophoretic patterns will resolve into two moving peaks as a result of the production of gradients of HA concentration in the electrophoresis column. The computations predict the essential features of the electrophoretic behavior of proteins in acidic media containing varying concentrations of carboxylic acid buffer. The agreement between observed and computed electrophoretic patterns is illustrated by Figs. 3 and 4 for bovine γ-pseudoglobulin at pH 5.7.

These theoretical gains are making understandable what in the past

[36] J. R. Cann and R. A. Phelps, *J. Am. Chem. Soc.* **77**, 4266 (1955).
[37] L. G. Longsworth and C. F. Jacobsen, *J. Phys. Colloid Chem.* **53**, 126 (1949).

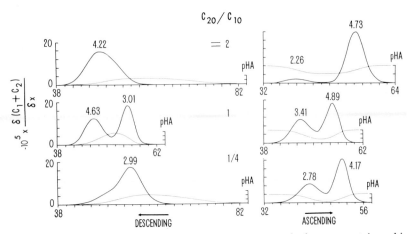

Fig. 4. Theoretical electrophoretic patterns computed for a protein which complexes with n moles of undissociated buffer acid, HA, according to the reaction $P + n\mathrm{HA} \rightleftharpoons P(\mathrm{HA})_n$. It is assumed that the complex, $P(\mathrm{HA})_n$, migrates with a greater electrophoretic mobility than the uncomplexed protein, P, and that equilibrium is established instantaneously.

The theoretical electrophoretic patterns (solid line) are plots of gradient of protein concentration, $\delta(C_1 + C_2)/\delta x$, against position in the electrophoresis column. C_1 and C_2 represent the molar concentration of P and $P(\mathrm{HA})_n$, respectively; and x, position. Patterns are shown for three values of C_{20}/C_{10}, which is the ratio of concentration of $P(\mathrm{HA})_n$ to that of P in the initial equilibrium mixture. $(C_{20}/C_{10}) = KC_{30}^n$, where K is the equilibrium constant of the reaction, and C_{30} is the initial concentration of HA. Thus, reading from the bottom to the top of the figure (C_{20}/C_{10} increasing from $\frac{1}{4}$ to 2) shows the effect of increasing concentration of HA on the electrophoretic patterns. In this way, the computed patterns are brought into correspondence with experimental ones (Fig. 3) obtained for increasing concentration of acetic acid.

Each pattern is accompanied by a plot (dotted line) of pHA (logarithm of the reciprocal of HA concentration) against position in the electrophoresis column to illustrate that resolution into two peaks results from the production of gradients of HA concentration in the electrophoresis column.

The following values were used for the various parameters: $K^{1/n} = 10^4$, $n = 3$, $C_{10} + C_{20} = 1.4 \times 10^{-4}$ M; $\mu_1 = 3 \times 10^{-5}$ cm^2 sec^{-1} volt^{-1}; $\mu_2 = 5 \times 10^{-5}$; $D_1 = D_2 = 3.14 \times 10^{-7}$ cm^2 sec^{-1}, $D_3 = 5.5 \times 10^{-6}$, $E = 10$ volts cm^{-1}. μ_1 and μ_2 are the mobilities of P and $P(\mathrm{HA})_n$; D_1, D_2, and D_3, diffusion coefficients of P, $P(\mathrm{HA})_n$, and HA; E, electric field strength. Time of electrophoresis, about 5.7×10^3 seconds. Migration velocities per unit field, $10^5 \times v$ cm^2 sec^{-1} volt^{-1}, are shown above corresponding peaks. From J. R. Cann and W. B. Goad, $J.$ $Biol.$ $Chem.$ **240**, 148 (1965).

was uninterpretable. This, in turn, has increased the power of moving-boundary electrophoresis as a tool for investigating biological systems. For example, theoretical calculations suggest that the electrophoresis of purified antibody against an uncharged hapten in a solvent containing the appropriate concentrations of the hapten (for example, p-amino-β-

phenyl lactoside) might yield important information concerning the mechanism of the antigen–antibody reaction. Thus, if the antibody–uncharged hapten complex has an electromobility different from that of the uncombined antibody molecule, the electrophoretic patterns will show at least two peaks at concentrations of hapten such that one-fourth to one-half of the antibody combining sites are caused to react.

c. FRACTIONS

In addition to the above applications, moving-boundary electrophoresis has proved to be an indispensible analytical method for following the fractionation of complex biological tissues and fluids (Fig. 2) and characterization of highly purified proteins. In fact, it is the only method which permits highly precise measurements of electrophoretic mobilities and isoelectric points and, in addition, mobility distribution functions in the case of those proteins that migrate as a single boundary but are nevertheless heterogeneous as revealed by reversible boundary spreading. Furthermore, the relatively recent introduction of interference optics[14] has provided a sensitive and precise method for characterization and analysis of proteins at low concentration, determination of the concentration of small amounts of a given component in a mixture, study of boundary spreading, and analysis of low-molecular-weight substances. Although there have been several interesting applications of moving-boundary electrophoresis to the analysis of mixtures of low-molecular-weight substances such as adenosine phosphates[38] and amino acids,[14] the apparent compositions calculated from the electrophoretic patterns are subject to much larger errors than in the case of macromolecular ions due to exaggerated departures from ideality. In such cases, zone electrophoresis is by far the preferred method of analysis.

Moving-boundary electrophoresis can be used for fractionation as well as analysis of complex mixtures and has proved especially valuable for identification of the particular boundary corresponding to a protein with a certain biological activity. But fractionation is often hampered by the occurrence of convection in the electrophoresis cell. Furthermore, with few exceptions the quantities of resulting fractions are too small for both physicochemical and biological characterization. Also, separation of components that do not differ greatly in mobility—for example, γ_1- and γ_2-globulins—is not possible. Finally, fractionation of very small quantities of material is not possible, since a certain minimum change in density across a moving boundary is required to assure gravitational stability. In contrast, zone electrophoresis often allows complete separa-

[38] R. M. Bock and R. A. Alberty, *J. Biol. Chem.* **193**, 435 (1951).

tion of zones containing different electrophoretic components, stabilization against convection being achieved either by use of a porous solid supporting medium such as filter paper or starch, or by electrophoresis in a density gradient. Zone electrophoresis on a supporting medium also enjoys the important advantages of simple, inexpensive apparatus, fairly simple procedures for isolation of fractions, and adaptability to either large-scale or micro separation. It must be stressed that these advantages are gained at the sacrifice of accuracy and precision, particularly with respect to the determination of mobilities. This loss of accuracy, however, is a serious consideration only if one wishes to use zone electrophoresis for identification and characterization of biocolloids and other charged substances in the same way as in moving-boundary electrophoresis. The supporting medium presents several sources of difficulty for the determination of mobilities: (1) purely geometrical effect of the structure of the medium which makes the charged particles and electric current travel through tortuous channels, (2) superposition of electroösmotic transport of the solution as a whole upon electrophoretic migration, (3) interaction between the supporting medium and the migrating substances by adsorption, and (4) molecular sieve effects. Adsorption and molecular sieving may not always be a disadvantage, however. Differences in extent of reversible adsorption and/or differences in size of different migrating species possessing the same electrophoretic mobilities would be expected to result in resolution of the electrophoretic pattern into multiple zones, thereby revealing an inhomogeneity which might otherwise go undetected. For example, Li[39] has found that some adrenocorticotropic hormone preparations, although appearing to behave as single proteins in moving-boundary electrophoresis, are actually inhomogeneous, as demonstrated by zone electrophoresis on filter paper. On the other hand, adsorptive effects may lead to quite misleading results, since adsorption of a substance on the supporting medium decreases its migrating rate. This would seem to be the case with C-reactive protein which migrates at a rate which is different during moving-boundary electrophoresis than during zone electrophoresis on starch.[40] This protein, which appears in the serum during certain acute infections and which reacts with the C-polysaccharide of the pneumococcus, has the mobility of a β-globulin during free electrophoresis and of a fast γ-globulin during starch electrophoresis.

Finally, the same caution must be exercised in interpreting zone electrophoretic patterns as moving-boundary patterns. As pointed out

[39] C. H. Li, *Acta Endocrinol.* **10**, 255 (1952).
[40] H. F. Wood, M. McCarty, and R. J. Slater, *J. Exptl. Med.* **100**, 71 (1954).

above, moving-boundary patterns may show multiple peaks arising from interaction of the protein with the solvent medium. Likewise, the theory of zone electrophoresis of interacting systems[41] reveals that under appropriate conditions a single macromolecule, interacting reversibly with an uncharged constituent of the solvent, can give two zones despite instantaneous establishment of equilibrium. This important prediction has been verified experimentally.[42] Fortunately, with certain precautions,[43] fractionation provides an unambiguous method for distinguishing between interactions and inherent heterogeneity.

[41] J. R. Cann and W. B. Goad, *J. Biol. Chem.* **240**, 1162 (1965).
[42] J. R. Cann, *Biochemistry* **5**, 1108 (1966).
[43] J. R. Cann and W. B. Goad, *Arch. Biochem. Biophys.* **108**, 171 (1964).

C. Analytical Zone Electrophoresis

1. INTRODUCTION*

Many supporting matrices have been employed for zone electrophoresis. The object of all of them is to confine a buffer in which material to be electrophoretically resolved is freely soluble and to prevent convection currents due to heat production in the electric field. Ideally the matrix should remain uncharged, minimizing electroendosmotic buffer flow, and it should have minimal adsorptive attraction for the soluble substances in the system.

The choice of a supporting matrix for analytical zone electrophoresis is therefore likely to consist of compromises between the desirable and undesirable general physical properties and the restrictions of the experimental objectives. Aside from simple electrophoretic distribution of protein, the objectives might include special analysis (such as radioactivity, biological or biochemical activity, chemical characteristics) or special resolution.

For simple analysis of electrophoretic distribution of any detectable property or activity, cellulose acetate membranes seem the least cumbersome and most dependable support for small sample volumes. Paper strips or agar gels offer no advantages, apart from greater capacity if elution of components is an objective, and in many cases they impose certain disadvantages. Paper is still widely employed in high-voltage electrophoresis, for studies in solution chemistry and ionophoresis, and for peptide mapping (the "fingerprint" technique of electrophoresis fol-

* Section 6,C,1 was contributed by Curtis A. Williams.

lowed by chromatography, in the perpendicular direction[1]). The only other advantage to paper strips is that a large body of early zone electrophoresis work was thus performed, and mobilities of many materials under defined conditions are reported in the literature. Among the better general treatments of paper electrophoresis are those by Wunderly[2] and Smith.[3]

Zone electrophoresis in agar, initially introduced by Gordon *et al.*,[4] was employed by Grabar and Williams for immunoelectrophoresis,[5] for which it was well suited (see Chap. 14,E, Vol. III). For simple zone electrophoresis, however, it offers no unique advantages except for comparison studies with immunoelectrophoresis. For detailed discussion of this method, see Wieme.[6] The techniques are basically as described for immunoelectrophoresis in Chap. 14,E, Vol. III.

Special resolution is obtained in hydrolyzed starch gels and in polyacrylamide gels because they behave not only as anticonvection supports but also as molecular sieves. For analytical purposes, developments in these techniques seem most promising. They are described in Sections 6,C,3, 6,C,4, and Section 6,C,5, following the description of electrophoresis on cellulose acetate membranes in Section 6,C,2.

---

[1] M. Efron, *in* "Chromatographic and Electrophoretic Techniques" (I. Smith, ed.), Vol. II, pp. 158–189. Heineman, London, 1960.

[2] C. Wunderly, *in* "Electrophoresis" (M. Bier, ed.), pp. 179–223. Academic Press, New York, 1959.

[3] "Chromatographic and Electrophoretic Techniques," (I. Smith, ed.), Vol. II, Heineman, London, 1960.

[4] A. H. Gordon, B. Keil, K. Sebesta, O. Knessl, and F. Sorm, *Collect. Czech. Chem. Commun.* **15**, 1 (1950).

[5] P. Grabar and C. A. Williams, *Biochim. Biophys. Acta* **17**, 67 (1955).

[6] R. J. Wieme, "Agar Gel Electrophoresis." Elsevier, Amsterdam, 1965.

2. CELLULOSE ACETATE MEMBRANE (CAM) ELECTROPHORESIS*

The principles of cellulose acetate membrane (CAM) electrophoresis are essentially the same as those of filter paper electrophoresis, but modified techniques and apparatus are required because of the differences in chemical composition and structure.[1,2]

* Section 6,C,2 was contributed by J. Kohn.

[1] J. Kohn, *Clin. Chim. Acta* **2**, 297 (1957).

[2] J. Kohn, "Chromatographic and Electrophoretic Techniques" (I. Smith, ed.), Vol. 2, Chapter 3, p. 84, London, 1968 (in press).

a. Apparatus

Horizontal buffer tanks, with a bridge capable of accommodating strips not exceeding 8 to 10 cm in length, can be used. Filter paper wicks providing electrical contact from the CAM strip to the buffer should not exceed 4 to 5 cm. The Shandon Universal Electrophoresis Apparatus (after Kohn) is particularly convenient for CAM electrophoresis and immunoelectrophoresis, and forms the basis of the following description. The assembling and setting up of the apparatus is carried out according to instructions provided, but water cooling is usually not necessary; and simpler bridges are now available. A power supply, preferably with a constant-current device, and capable of delivering up to 25 ma and 400 volts, is required.

CAM strips now available from British, German, Italian, and American sources are supplied in various sizes and differ slightly in their characteristics.* The procedure described here applies mainly to the Oxoid and the German Sartorius strips. Minor modifications of procedure recommended for the Italian and American CAM are provided by the manufacturers.

b. Procedure

i. *Preparation of CAM Strips*

The CAM is cut into required lengths and widths (for small-scale electrophoresis, 9 to 12 cm × 2 to 3 cm). For microelectrophoresis, 7 × 2 cm is adequate. CAM sheets instead of individual strips are strongly recommended. The application line and legend are marked on the strips with nondiffusible ink or a soft grease pencil.

ii. *Impregnation of the Strips*

Any buffer can be used; for serum proteins barbital buffers (pH 8.2 to 8.6, 0.05 to 0.07 M) are recommended. It is essential that the strip first be floated on the surface of the buffer, and only subsequently submerged; otherwise air will be trapped in the membrane pores, delaying impregnation. Any existing camber or curling should be flattened out by pressing the moistened strip between glass plates placed in the buffer.

---

* United Kingdom: (Oxoid) Oxo Ltd., London E. C. 4. United States (Oxoid and Cellogel) Consolidated Laboratories, Chicago Heights, Illinois; Millipore Filter Corporation, Bedford, Massachusetts; Gelman Instrument Company, Ann Arbor, Michigan. Germany: Sartorius-Membranfilter GmbH, Gottingen. Italy: (Cellogel) Soc. Chemetron Chimica, Milan.

The impregnated CAM strips are lightly blotted twice between sheets of filter paper. No excess moisture or white opaque spots indicating dry areas should be evident.

iii. Placing the Strips in Position

The shoulder pieces supporting the membrane are covered with buffer moistened sheets of filter paper (e.g., Whatman No. 3) in such a manner that one edge dips into the buffer. This filter paper connection should be changed daily. The impregnated and blotted CAM strips are gently stretched across the gap from one shoulder piece to the other. The ends should overlap the filter paper connections by about 1 cm. Good electrical contact is made by pressing the CAM strip against the filter paper. The adhesion of the strips to the moist filter paper is sufficient to hold the strip in position. A blank CAM strip about 1 cm wide is placed as the first and last strip of each load. Dental forceps with curved tips are most convenient for handling the strips at all stages.

iv. Application of Sample

The sample is applied with the buffer-impregnated strip in position as a straight streak by means of a micropipet, disposable capillary tube, or any other suitable device capable of delivering small volumes. Linear application is achieved by moving the pipet backward and forward along the edge of a ruler or a special guide until the desired volume is delivered. Special types of applicators which facilitate the procedure have recently been introduced. Generous margins, approximately 5 to 7 mm, should be left on both sides of the applied sample. The optimal position of the application line should be determined for each substance and buffer system; usually one-third to one-half of the distance from the cathode end. If several samples are to be run simultaneously for comparative purposes, they may be applied to wide (e.g., 6–10×20 cm) CAM sheets, which have recently been made available.

For electrophoresis of serum proteins using 10×2.5-cm strips, the sample volume may vary from 0.5 to $3\,\mu$l. For Ponceau S. staining, about $1\,\mu$l is adequate. For glycoprotein and lipoprotein staining (see below), transfer immunoelectrophoresis (see Vol. III, Chap. 13), enzyme separation, and particularly for micropreparative electrophoresis, larger samples, up to 4 to $5\,\mu$l/cm of length of application line, are applied. For electrophoresis of serum it is recommended that aqueous 0.1% bromophenol blue be added to the sample.* The dye combines with the

---

* Use 0.25 ml. per milliliter of serum to avoid dye excess.

albumin and thus monitors the displacement of this rapidly migrating fraction.

v. Conditions

Constant current is preferable in most instances, as the danger of overheating is practically eliminated. As a rule, 0.4 to 0.5 ma/cm of width should not be exceeded. With 0.05 to 0.07 M barbital buffer, this should result in an initial potential gradient of 25 volts/cm of strip (voltage at the terminals, not actual voltage across the strip), which will gradually fall off during the run. Under these conditions a separation pattern of serum proteins 5 to 6 cm long should be obtained within 90 to 120 minutes. With shorter strips, suitable buffers, and higher potentials, satisfactory separation can be obtained even within 30 minutes. The fastest fraction should not be permitted to migrate beyond 0.5 to 1.0 cm from the end of the strips to avoid distortion of the band by the hydrostatic flow of the buffer. After the electrophoretic run is completed, the strip is removed and further processed.

vi. Fixing and Staining

The strip is transferred directly into a fixing denaturant bath—for example, 5% trichloroacetic acid or 3% sulfosalicylic acid for about 15 minutes. The drying and subsequent staining and washing times are not critical within reasonable limits.

(a) *Proteins*. Any protein staining solutions not containing a CAM solvent can be used, but aqueous solutions are preferred. The dye concentrations should be approximately 0.2%. If an alcoholic staining solution is used, the last wash must be aqueous, such as 5% acetic acid.

Ponceau S. is particularly suitable for staining general protein.

1. Fix the strips for 5 to 10 minutes in 5% trichloroacetic acid.
2. Transfer the strips to staining solution (0.2% Ponceau S in 3% trichloroacetic acid) for 5 to 10 minutes.
3. Wash the strips in 5% acetic acid with a few changes, or transfer to consecutive washes of a few minutes each until background is colorless.
4. Blot the CAM and dry it at room temperature, preferably between filter paper sheets under pressure—for example, in a book.

Nigrosine is recommended for very small amounts of protein.

1. After electrophoresis, fix the strips by drying them at 80° to 100° or in 5% trichloroacetic acid. (No fixing is necessary after immunodiffusion on CAM. Remove the membrane from the eluting bath, blot, and transfer into the staining solution.)

2. Stain the strips for about 1 to 2 hours in 0.002% nigrosine in 2% acetic acid. (CAM can conveniently be left in the staining bath overnight.)

3. Rinse the strips in tap water, blot, and dry at room temperature.

(b) *Lipoproteins.* The commonly used lipoprotein stains are unsatisfactory. The ozone-Schiff technique,[3] however, gives satisfactory and reproducible results. It may also be used for filter paper strips. The electrophoretic separation is performed in the usual manner, a somewhat larger sample being used than for ordinary protein analysis. After separation is completed, the strip is dried in a hot-air oven, the temperature not exceeding 80°, and then placed in an ozonization chamber. This consists of a larger jar or glass tank with closely fitting lid into which is placed a small glass container with barium peroxide. A small quantity of concentrated H_2SO_4 is added, and the lid of the chamber is quickly closed. After about 15 to 30 minutes the strip is removed from the ozonization chamber, rinsed in 0.001 N HCl, and placed in Schiff's (Feulgen) stain until the lipoprotein bands acquire maximum color intensity—usually in about 10 to 15 minutes, but the staining time is not critical. The strip is then transferred to three consecutive 0.5% HNO_3 (Analar) baths, for about 15 minutes each. A final rinse in 0.001 N HCl is recommended, after which the strip is blotted and dried at room temperature.

The demonstration of enzyme activity may be achieved by placing the electrophoretic strip with the separated fractions in contact with a CAM strip impregnated with the substrate and a suitable color reaction system.[4]

Clearing the strips is achieved by immersion in a suitable oil, such as Ondina oil 17 (Shell), or by treatment with swelling agents (German and Italian strips).

c. GENERAL REMARKS

CAM electrophoresis is a reliable, reproducible, rapid, and adaptable technique. Analysis may be made by visual inspection, scanning, or elution. Absolute transparency of the cleared strips makes possible quite accurate evaluation by scanning. For certain purposes CAM may be completely dissolved. Extended shoulder pieces permit the use of smaller (5 to 7 cm $\times$ 1½ to 2 cm) strips. Besides serum proteins, it can be used for the separation of hemoglobins,[5] isoenzymes,[6] peptides,[7] nucleic

[3] J. Kohn, *Nature,* **189,** 312 (1961).

[4] H. Barnett, *J. Clin. Pathol.* **17,** 567 (1964).

[5] L. J. Graham and B. W. Grunbaum, *Am. J. Clin. Pathol.* **39,** 567 (1963).

[6] B. W. Meade and S. B. Rosalki, *J. Clin. Pathol.* **17,** 61 (1964).

[7] L. G. Goodwin, C. R. Jones, W. H. G. Richards and J. Kohn, *Brit. J. Exptl. Pathol.* **44,** 551 (1961).

acids,[8] and indoles, for immunoelectrophoresis, for micropreparative purposes, and for the isolation of certain biologically active substances. Since relatively few hydroxyl groups are present, there is minimal absorption and hence almost complete absence of tailing; thus a sharp separation of fractions with negligible background values is obtained. This is particularly valuable for studies involving isotopes or biological activities. Some large molecules and certain groups of substances that do not separate well on filter paper can be resolved on CAM. The sensitivity of the method is relatively high. For example, 5 μg of protein in a 0.1μl sample of interstitial fluid gives a separation pattern with nigrosine staining showing seven distinct fractions.

Essentially the principles and conditions employed for CAM electrophoresis are similar to those used for paper electrophoresis. The most common error, however, is the use of paper electrophoretic techniques without modification instead of the procedures recommended especially for CAM.

[8] V. Gebicki, J. M. Gebicki and S. Freed, *Anal. Biochem.* **13**, 505 (1965).

3. STARCH GEL ELECTROPHORESIS*†

a. Introduction and Theoretical Considerations

The classical free-boundary electrophoresis of Tiselius will probably remain unsurpassed for determination of mobilities of proteins. The method is not suited, however, for complete separation of the components present in a protein mixture or for preparative procedures. Several new techniques have been devised to separate protein components; these are known collectively by the term "zone electrophoresis." In these techniques a narrow zone of sample protein is stabilized by various means—density gradient, filter paper, starch grain, synthetic polymer beads such as Pevikon, or gel media (agar, acrylamide, or starch). On electrophoresis, mixed proteins separate into discrete zones. The gel techniques used[1] can be divided into nonsieving (for example, agar and agarose), and those with sieving effect (for example, acrylamide and starch).

* Section 6,C,3 was contributed by M. D. Poulik

† This investigation was supported in part by Public Health Service Grants AI 05785, from the National Institute of Allergy and Infectious Diseases, and HE 07495, from the National Heart Institute, and in part by the Children's Leukemia Foundation of Michigan.
[1] J. F. Frederick, (ed.), *Ann. N.Y. Acad. Sci.* **121**, 305 (1964).

Despite the fact that the migrating components must pass *through* the gel matrix in each type of gel, there is a fundamental difference between the two types of gel. The physical impediment of the starch gel matrix is of such magnitude that the separation obtained is due to the molecular size and the charge of the protein. This physical impediment, according to Smithies,[2,3] reflects the thermal motion of the polysaccharide chains of the gel. These chains are unlikely to be static or rigid. Consequently the distance between the neighboring chains is constantly varied. More time is required for the larger protein molecules to pass through the smaller pore, and larger molecules, accordingly, will be more retarded than smaller ones and consequently better separated. The degree of retardation varies, however, not only with the size of the molecule[2] but also with the concentration of the starch.[3] The resolution can be further increased by a proper choice of buffers, among which the discontinuous system of buffers has proved to be particularly useful.[4] Other systems of buffers have also been employed.[5] The starch gel technique is endowed with high resolving power, and Smithies[6] was able to separate normal serum into fifteen to seventeen components. The "new" components were related to the classical electrophoretic fractions of Tiselius by a combination of filter paper electrophoresis (first dimension) and starch gel electrophoresis (second dimension) by Poulik and Smithies.[7]

Further applications of starch gel electrophoresis were made possible by preparing the gel in buffers containing a dissociating agent.[8,9] Separation of structural subunits of polypeptide chains of proteins has been achieved in such gels, since the continuous presence of the dissociating agent is a prerequisite for their solubility and also for their separation.[10] Immunochemical analysis of the components separated in the regular gels (made in buffers in the absence of urea) and in urea gel is also feasible.[11] Recently a two-dimensional method for structural character-

[2] O. Smithies, *Advan. Protein Chem.* **14**, 65 (1959).

[3] O. Smithies, *Arch. Biochem. Biophys. Suppl.* **1**, 125 (1962).

[4] M. D. Poulik, *Nature* **180**, 1477 (1957).

[5] O. Prokop, and G. Bundschuh, "Die Technik und die Bedeutung Haptoglobine und GM-gruppen in Klinik und Gerichtsmedizin." Walter de Gruyter and Co., Berlin, 1963.

[6] O. Smithies, *Biochem. J.* **61**, 629 (1955).

[7] M. D. Poulik, and O. Smithies, *Biochem. J.* **68**, 636 (1958).

[8] M. D. Poulik, *Biochim. Biophys. Acta* **44**, 390 (1960).

[9] O. Smithies, G. E. Connell, and G. H. Dixon, *Am. J. Human Genet.* **14**, 14 (1962).

[10] M. D. Poulik and G. M. Edelman, *Protides Biol. Fluids* **9**, 126 (1961).

[11] M. D. Poulik, *Protides Biol. Fluids* **11**, 385 (1963).

ization of products obtained by enzymatic digestion has been developed which utilizes regular starch gel in the first dimension, and starch gel prepared either in urea or in urea and mercaptoethanol in the second dimension.[12]

Although electrophoresis can be conducted with the gel in either the vertical or the horizontal position, vertical gel electrophoresis has gained great acceptance because of its superior resolving power and the possibility of applying larger samples. Therefore this method will be described in detail. For the purpose of the two-dimensional technique, however, the starch gel is held usually in the horizontal position during each stage of electrophoresis.

b. CONVENTIONAL (VERTICAL) STARCH GEL ELECTROPHORESIS[13]

i. Equipment*

(a) A plastic *electrophoretic tray* measuring $32 \times 12 \times 0.6$ cm, or having slightly different dimensions (Fig. 1, A), with removable end plates needed during molding and setting of the gel. The end plates are then removed so that the terminal blocks of gel can make direct contact with the buffer or buffer wicks.

(b) *Slot-former.* A plastic cover having slightly larger dimensions than the tray, containing a form for casting eight to ten application slots (Fig. 1, B and C). The original Smithies cover (Fig. 1, C) incorporates slots sawed in the Lucite to cast ridges of gel to serve as separators between adjacent slots. The plane cover (Fig. 1B) is more flexible and allows use of interchangeable, differently spaced slot-formers to provide up to twelve slots (Fig. 2); separation ridges of petrolatum jelly, just molten, are laid down after the slot-former has been removed from the gel.

(c) Two *electrode vessels*, also made of plastic, each having two compartments of the same dimensions. Each compartment is filled to the same level by adding 250 ml of buffer. In use, electrical contact between the two compartments of each vessel is made by a thick filter paper wick (one sheet of paper such as Fisher No. 9-800). The electrodes

---

[12] M. D. Poulik, *Nature* 198, 752 (1963).

[13] O. Smithies, *Biochem. J.* 71, 585 (1959).

* The equipment described is obtainable from the Grafar Company, P.O. Box 7788, Detroit, Michigan; from Otto Hiller, P.O. Box 1294, Madison, Wisconsin; and from Buchler Instruments, Fort Lee, New Jersey.

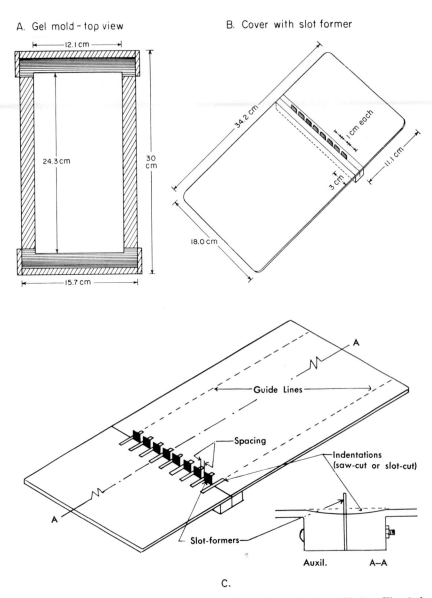

A. Gel mold – top view

B. Cover with slot former

C.

FIG. 1. Lucite equipment. *A*, schematic dimensions of gel mold (see Fig. 2 for side view of resulting cast block). *B*, view of a plane Lucite cover with a slot-former in position. *C*, original Smithies cover showing the grooves.

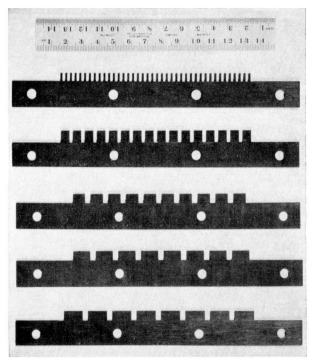

Fig. 2. Various slot-formers can be used with the plane gel lid, suitable for a variety of purposes, as by running triplicate samples. The narrow slots work well with high-voltage, low-temperature runs. The principal requirement is precision in cutting the holes prior to milling the slot-forming tips.

are made of platinum wire (gauge No. 28) about 20 cm in length, fashioned into spirals.

(d) A *stand* to position the two electrode vessels (Fig. 3). One vessel is placed on the base plate of the stand, and the other rests on the top plate.

(e) A *power supply* capable of delivering up to 400 volts, such as Model IP-32, from the Heath Company, Benton Harbor, Michigan. For certain other purposes, such as high-voltage runs in the cold room described below, a power supply to deliver 1000 volts is needed.

(f) A *slicing tray* having the inner dimensions $27 \times 11.8 \times 0.3$ cm, and a *Plexiglas plate* ($25 \times 13 \times 1.5$ cm) of slightly greater dimensions than the starch gel. After the gel has been transferred to the slicing tray, this plate holds the gel and prevents its buckling during slicing. The gel block is sliced along its length with a dermatome knife (Brown-Blair) or a thin, taut piano wire.

ii. Materials

(*a*) *Starch.* Specially hydrolyzed starch of high quality is manufactured by the Connaught Medical Research Laboratories, Toronto, Canada. The starch concentration to be used is stated and varies with the batch. This product, labeled "Starch-Hydrolyzed," is available through the Fisher Scientific Company.

(*b*) *Buffers.* A large variety of buffers is now available. To accomplish best a desired separation of proteins, it is advisable to try at least two different buffers before deciding on the buffer of choice. A useful discontinuous buffer system is the following.[4*] One buffer is used for preparing the gel, the other for filling the electrode vessels. The "gel" buffer is made with 9.2 gm of Tris (Sigma 121, Sigma Chemical Company, St. Louis, Missouri), and 1.05 gm of citric acid (monohydrated) dissolved in a liter of distilled water, pH 8.5 to 8.6. The second, or "tank," buffer, used in the electrode vessels, is composed of 18.5 gm of boric acid and 2.5 gm of NaOH (pellets) dissolved in 1 liter of distilled water.

(*c*) *Dyes and decolorizing solutions.* Amido Black 10B dye (Bayer, Leverkusen, Germany) or Buffalo Black NBR (Allied Chemicals, New York) proved best for staining routine gels for proteins. A staining solution containing 6 gm of Buffalo Black dissolved in a mixture of methyl alcohol (405 ml), distilled water (405 ml), and glacial acetic acid (90

* Modifications of the original buffer have been used with vertical starch gel electrophoresis, in connection with the use of high voltage at low temperature, as listed below (see Section C,3,b,*v*).

		Barrett *et al.*[a]	Bearn[b]
1. Tank buffer	Boric acid	23.5 gm/liter (0.38 *M*)	11.89 gm/liter
	Lithium hydroxide · H_2O	4.196 gm/liter (0.1 *M*)	2.1 gm/liter
2. Tris–citric buffer	Tris (Sigma 121)	1.94 gm/liter (0.016 *M*)	6.29 gm/liter
	Citric acid · H_2O	0.693 gm/liter (0.0033 *M*)	1.6 gm/liter
3. Gel buffer	One part (1) plus 9 parts (2), pH 8.0.		

[a] R. J. Barrett, H. Friesen, and E. B. Astwood, *J. Biol. Chem.* **237**, 432 (1962).

[b] A. Bearn, personal communication.

ml) is filtered through two layers of gauze and is then ready for use.* The decolorizing solution has the same formula, except that dye is omitted. This same dye mixture is used also for staining urea-starch gel and urea–mercaptoethanol–starch gel, but the decolorizing solution used with the latter is a 1 to 2% solution of acetic acid, best diluted from glacial acetic acid in tap water at 70° to 80°.

A most useful adjunct for the decolorization of gels is the automatic "washing machine" developed by Pert et al.[14] In this apparatus the decolorizing solution is continuously regenerated by being pumped through a column of activated charcoal which removes the dye. The clear decolorizing solution then returns to the decolorizing chamber. It is advisable to have two separate decolorization machines when the laboratory is doing work with both kinds of gels (those with and without urea), since the water-clear urea gels are made nontransparent in the methanol–water–acetic acid mixture but remain perfectly transparent in the acetic acid–water mixture. The latter state is desirable to facilitate photography.

iii. Preparation of the Gel

Every batch of the hydrolyzed starch contains specifications for the optimal concentration necessary for preparation of starch gel in *borate* buffers. The stated concentration should be increased by about 5 to 10% when Tris–citrate buffer is used. It may be necessary to raise the stated concentration by 10 to 15% for the preparation of urea–starch gel, particularly so when it is prepared in alkaline buffers. It is advisable to determine the necessary concentration beforehand for each new batch of hydrolyzed starch.

The appropriate amount of starch is weighed out, and 500 ml of buffer is added. The suspension is mixed with a magnetic rod to remove metallic iron and then passed through gauze into a 1-liter Erlenmeyer flask. The starch is then heated over a Bunsen burner and constantly mixed by agitating the flask by hand. The starch becomes quite viscous, and a common error is to stop heating at this point. Heating should be continued until the starch becomes less viscous and more transparent. At this stage, the gel is degassed under vacuum for a short time,† and

---

* An alternative procedure used in staining immunoglobulins on urea–starch gel utilizes more dilute dye and longer contact time (Chap. 5,B,2).

[14] J. H. Pert, E. R. Engle, K. R. Woods, and M. H. Slesinger, *J. Lab. Clin. Med.* **54**, 572 (1959).

† A nylon T-tube inserted in the line to the water pump permits fingertip control during the process of degassing.

the clear gel is poured into the tray, the bottom of which is coated with a thin layer of mineral oil.

Five to ten minutes is allowed to elapse before the cover (also coated with mineral oil, save the immediate region of the slot-former) is applied on the warm gel. The slot-former is introduced first in such a way as to avoid bubble formation at the surfaces, by bending the cover. The cover is then gently lowered on the gel and secured in position by flat weights, each 13 cm in width.

iv. Application of the Sample

After standing overnight (or at least for 5 to 6 hours), the cover is freed at the edges with a thin spatula and then removed by gentle

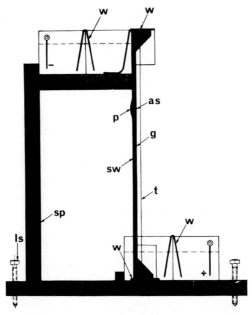

Fig. 3. Vertical starch gel electrophoresis apparatus: sp—supporting stand; t—tray; g—starch gel; p—petrolatum jelly at application site; as—application slots; sw—Saran Wrap; w—paper wicks connecting the electrode vessels, and the gel with the electrode vessels; ls—leveling screws. The position of electrode vessels and electrodes is self-explanatory. See text for further details.

rocking. The slots are walled off with hot petrolatum jelly to prevent spilling and flowing of the sample on the surface of the gel (see Fig. 3). With the aid of a Pasteur pipet, samples (0.05 ml) are applied to the slots, which are then filled with slightly more of the sample. The slots are covered with warm petrolatum jelly, and the gel surface is enclosed in Saran Wrap (Dow Chemical Company, Midland, Michigan). The end plates of the tray are then removed, and the tray is placed upright in the lower electrode vessel with application slots closer to the upper electrode vessels. The exposed upper surface of the gel is connected with the buffer in the upper electrode vessel with a wick of filter paper, as shown in Fig. 3. The gel is leveled perfectly in both vertical and horizontal planes with a spirit-level. This step is very important for the outcome of the run.

v. Electrophoretic Conditions

The positive pole (Fig. 3) is at the bottom compartment. A voltage gradient of 4 to 5 volts/cm is applied for 18 to 20 hours, and the electrophoretic run is conducted at room temperature. In the summer it may be necessary to cool the gel with a fan if an air-conditioned room is not available.*

vi. Staining, Decolorizing, and Recording of Results

After termination of the run, the gel is cooled in a refrigerator (4° to 6°) for about ½ to 1 hour and then removed from the gel tray and placed on the slicing tray. It is divided into two complete sheets, an upper and a lower, with a dermatome knife.† One half of the gel is then placed in a shallow plastic staining dish, overlaid with dye solution, and stained for 1 to 2 minutes. After the dye has been poured off, the gel is transferred to the tank of the decolorizing machine and washed for 2 to 3 hours. Finally it is placed in a container and decolorized overnight in a fresh decolorizing solution. Gels so treated are ready to be photographed. In this laboratory each gel is photographed by

---

* For the purpose of effecting faster separations (typically in 4 hours), thereby limiting the extent of diffusion of migrating proteins, the same apparatus can be used in a cold room, cooled by two fans during the run. Necessary modifications are (1) power supply for 1000-volt output; (2) buffer at temperature of the cold room; (3) filter paper bridges of two double folds of filter paper (23 × 19 cm cut from Whatman No. 3 paper) soaked in tank buffer, compressed slightly, and overlaid with polyethylene sheeting (23 × 13 cm) to avoid evaporation; (4) baffles to divert air draughts of the fans from the surfaces of the upper and lower electrode vessels; (5) a starting voltage gradient of 9 volts/cm along the block, secured with wicking described, input of 800 volts and 60 to 70 ma, and avoiding manual resetting of input voltage. Modified buffers, as given in footnote to Section b,ii(b), are employed; the buffer system used by Bearn has proved to be very suitable.

† For special purposes, divisions into third or even quarter thickness may be made by using Lucite frames of corresponding height as guides for the slicing knife.

two different methods: (1) with a Polaroid camera (MP-3) on positive-negative film (55 P/N); and (2) with an Exa camera, equipped with a Macrokillar lens (Thayer) on high-contrast 35-mm film (Kodak). A Wratten 25 A red filter is used in each case for better results. Prints are made on Kodabromide paper (F-2 or F-5).

c. UREA–STARCH GEL AND UREA–MERCAPTOETHANOL–
   STARCH GEL ELECTROPHORESIS[8]

i. Equipment and Materials

The same equipment, materials, and sample handling are used as described above. The *urea* is Fisher certified chemical urea. In urea–starch gel, and especially with use of alkaline buffers in conjunction with urea–starch gel, it is necessary to increase the amount of starch in order to prepare a gel of sufficient strength (see Section b,*iii*).

ii. Buffers

Only two buffers will be described here. *Formate buffer:* A stock solution (1 *M* formic acid, 0.2 *M* sodium hydroxide, pH 3.2) used in the preparation of the starch gel is made by mixing 39 ml of 97% formic acid (Eastman Kodak Organic Chemicals, Rochester, New York), or 37.4 ml of 99% formic acid, with 200 ml of 1 *N* sodium hydroxide, and diluted with distilled water to 1 liter in a volumetric flask. (Twenty-five milliliters of the stock solution is mixed with 275 ml of distilled water prior to preparation of the urea–starch gel.) The electrode vessel buffer is prepared by mixing 136 ml of formic acid (90%) and 51.2 gm of sodium hydroxide pellets to a final volume of 16 liters. The pH of the buffers is usually 3.0 to 3.4.

Discontinuous system of buffers: Buffers are prepared as described in Section b,*ii*(b).

Buffers containing urea and mercaptoethanol: Both acid and alkaline buffers may be prepared with mercaptoethanol. Three hundred milliliters of the buffer are prepared from 25 ml of stock solution, 1.8 ml of 2-mercaptoethanol,[9] and water to 300 ml. No mercaptoethanol is added to the buffer in the electrode vessels. The *Tris–citrate buffer* is prepared in a similar way. To 1.8 ml of 2-mercaptoethanol is added 298.2 ml of buffer. Likewise, no mercaptoethanol is added to the borate buffer in the electrode vessels.

iii. Preparation of the Gel

The weighed-out starch is poured into a 500-ml Erlenmeyer flask. The solid urea (240 gm) is sieved to remove larger aggregates and is added in small amounts to the starch powder. The materials are mixed by vigorous shaking after each new addition. Thorough mixing is absolutely necessary to minimize clumping of the starch and hence its loss. The mixture is transferred to a 2-liter thick-walled suction flask. The buffer (300 ml) is then added in small portions, with vigorous mixing between additions. The flask is placed in a suitable large water-bath at 70°, where the starch suspension is heated for 10 to 15 minutes with vigorous mixing at 5, 7, 10, 13, and 15 minutes after submersion. The suspension becomes very viscous but at 10+ minutes the viscosity decreases and the gel becomes quite translucent. After 15 minutes the gel is degassed for a short period of time, until all bubbles are removed. The gel is then poured into the tray, the bottom plate of which has been coated with mineral oil. After 5 minutes, the cover with the slot-former is introduced into the slightly viscous gel (see Section b,*iii*) and secured with weights. The gel will set within the next 10 to 18 hours as a strong, water-clear gel.

The preparation of the gel is the same when alkaline buffers are employed. Alkaline gels are quite sticky, however, and are difficult to remove from the electrophoretic tray for cutting and staining procedures. Such gels should be loosened from the tray by introducing thin piano wire under the whole gel (lengthwise) and cutting the gel off the Plexiglas plate. Subsequent handling is the same as for conventional gels.

iv. Electrophoresis in Urea–Formate–Starch Gel*

Electrophoresis in the urea–formate–starch gel is carried out with the standard arrangement, except that the electrodes are reversed. A voltage of 180 to 190 volts across the electrodes corresponding to current of 25 to 30 ma and a voltage gradient of 4 to 5 volts/cm is applied at room temperature for 16 to 20 hours. The position of the "brown line" developing as the borate buffer passes through the gel can be used as an index of electrophoresis and is very helpful in determining the length of the experiment when Tris–citrate buffer is used in the gel.

v. Staining the Gel

The gels are stained in similar fashion as indicated in Section b,*vi*, but are decolorized in warm 1 to 2% acetic acid, with frequent turning of the gel to speed the removal of excess dye. The gels are usually left overnight in a large volume of 1 to 2% acetic acid. Thus, treated gels remain transparent and are photographed by transmitted light (by placing them on an X-ray viewer) with the same equipment as described in Section b,*vi*.

* Cf. Chap. 5,B,2, Vol. I.

d. Two-Dimensional Starch Gel Electrophoresis

This specialized method was developed for several reasons: (1) to detect the presence of metastable polymers, or isomers; (2) to study the structural makeup of fragments of proteins obtained by proteolytic digestion; (3) to separate constituent polypeptide chains of polymerized multichain proteins (for example, myeloma γA-globulins, ceruloplasmin); and (4) to improve separation.

Several combinations are possible in two-dimensional gel electrophoresis. For example, in studying the structural makeup of subcomponents of enzymatic fragments,[12,15] a combination of vertical starch gel, urea–starch gel, and urea–mercaptoethanol–starch gel electrophoresis was used. In this technique, chemical reaction(s) (for example, dissociation and/or reduction) are performed in the gel prior to the electrophoretic separation, which is then conducted in the presence of the dissociating and/or reducing agent(s). These methods can be extended by conducting immunoanalysis on such gels.[16] Some details of the latter technique follow and more can be found in Poulik.[16]

The material is first separated by conventional vertical starch gel electrophoresis in the discontinuous system of buffers (first dimension). The sample is applied in especially large application slots, each holding 0.1 to 0.15 ml of the test solution. Three of the slots in the middle of the gel are filled with 8% solution, and the adjacent five slots with the same solution diluted 1:3. Such an arrangement ensures excellent separation and keeps the protein zones straight. (The straightness of the zone is of paramount importance for the outcome of the electrophoretic pattern of the second dimension.) The gels are run at room temperature at a voltage gradient of 4 to 5 volts/cm for 18 to 20 hours. After termination of the run, the portions of the gel in which the diluted material was run are removed, sliced in half, and stained with Amido Black 10B in order to locate the zones and establish the quality of separation.

Electrophoresis in the second dimension is performed in specially made plastic trays measuring $200 \times 280 \times 6$ mm and accommodating the same amount of gel as was used for the vertical starch gel apparatus (500 ml). The gels are prepared the same way as described in Section c,iii, but one may elect to use urea–starch gel or urea–mercaptoethanol–starch gel. After pouring, the warm gels are covered with a glass plate (6 mm thick) of slightly greater dimensions than the tray and left to set at room temperature. Slots 6 mm wide are cut out *across* the gel about

[15] M. D. Poulik, *Protides Biol. Fluids* **12**, 400 (1965).
[16] M. D. Poulik, *Ann. N.Y. Acad. Sci.* **121**, 420 (1964).

5 to 6 cm from the intended *anodal* end of the gels by means of a double-blade cutter (180 × 6 mm). With the same cutter, starch blocks bearing the protein components under investigation are cut out from the *unsliced* center portion of the first-dimension run and are *transferred* into the slots prepared in the second-dimension tray. All air bubbles must be removed at the cut surfaces of the receiving slots and the transferred block.

The gels are then covered with Saran Wrap to prevent evaporation

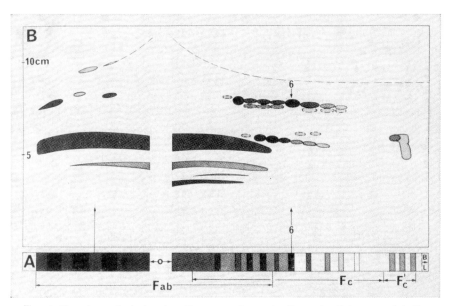

Fig. 4. Drawings of electrophoretic maps of papain-digested γG-immunoglobulins. *A*, one-dimensional pattern of subcomponents of fragments (Tris–citrate buffer, pH 8.3). *B*, map of the subunits of the subcomponents after electrophoresis in the second dimension (urea–starch gel, pH 3.0).

and are left at room temperature for 4 to 5 hours. During this "reaction" time, the transferred blocks become transparent as the concentration of the urea in the starch blocks reaches equilibrium with the urea–starch gel. Dissociation and/or reduction is now proceeding in the urea or urea–mercaptoethanol gel. It should be noted that, since the gels are degassed prior to pouring into the trays, reduction will occur in relative lack of oxygen. Also, no alkylation of mercaptoethanol will be necessary, since electrophoresis is conducted in the continuous presence of the reducing agent. The reduction proceeds at approximately pH 7.0. By means of a double set of filter paper wicks the gel is connected with the buffer in the electrode vessels. A typical second-dimension electrophoretic run is performed in horizontal position. The wicks and the gel are then covered tightly with Saran Wrap to prevent evaporation during the run. After electrophoresis at room temperature and a voltage gradient of 4.5 to 5.0 volts/cm for 16 hours, the gels are cooled at 4° for 1 to 1.5 hours and then sliced. One half is stained with Amido Black and decolorized in 1 to 2% acetic acid. The other half may be used for further immunological analysis.

Results obtained in this way with the human γG-immunoglobulins[12] are shown diagrammatically in Fig. 4. Papain-digested γ-globulin fraction II (Cohn) is separated into a number of zones by electrophoresis in the first dimension (strip A). The Fab fragment, in addition to its major part, contains also three minor subcomponents, migrating in the cathodal portion of this fragment. The Fc fragment can be separated into ten to eleven subcomponents of which the sixth, counting anode-wise, stains most intensely (marked 6 in Fig. 4). The F'c fragment affords three subcomponents under these conditions. On dissociation and electrophoresis in the second dimension (urea–starch gel) the major part of the Fab fragment migrates as a long single band, owing to the heterogeneous nature of the starting material. Each of the three subcomponents of this fragment is now clearly separated, one of them showing the presence of two subunits. Each subcomponent of the Fc fragment is separated into two or three subunits. The F'c subcomponents assume a characteristic constellation. Further definition is found as the result of dissociation *and reduction* and electrophoretic separation in the presence of the dissociating and reducing agents.[12] Such results demonstrate the advantages of using two-dimensional separations, in which single bands found on one-dimension runs can be shown to contain more than one component. Detailed maps are given by Poulik.[17]

[17] M. D. Poulik, *Methods Biochem. Analy.* 14, 455 (1966).

4. DISC ELECTROPHORESIS, ACRYLAMIDE GEL COLUMNS*

a. INTRODUCTION

An analytical technique of high resolution in the separation of the components of protein mixtures is often of great utility in immunological and immunochemical studies. For many such purposes, disc electrophoresis has been a method of choice.[1-13] Below is a condensed description

* Section 6,C,4 was contributed by Baruch J. Davis and Leonard Ornstein.
[1] G. M. Kunitake, R. M. Nakamura, B. G. Wells, and D. L. Moyer, *Fertility Sterility* 16, 120 (1965).
[2] G. F. Kalf and M. A. Grece, *Arch. Biochem. Biophys.* 107, 141 (1964).
[3] P. Stelos, Y. Yagi, and D. Pressman, *J. Immunol.* 93, 106 (1964).

of one of the more frequently used versions of the basic techniques. For further details on theory, apparatus construction, and practice, see the literature.[14,15]

The polyacrylamide gel column, formed in a suitable container (for example, cylindrical glass tubing), is composed of three layers: (1) a large-pore gel (sample gel) containing the sample ions in which electrophoretic concentration of these protein ions is initiated; (2) a large-pore gel (spacer gel) in which electrophoretic concentration of the sample ions is completed; and (3) a small-pore gel in which electrophoretic separation takes place. The large-pore gels serve primarily as anticonvection media, while the small-pore gel serves as a sieving as well as an anticonvection medium. Electrophoresis is ordinarily performed with the column in a vertical position, with the sample gel uppermost; the column is attached at the upper end to an upper buffer reservoir, and the lower end immersed in a lower reservoir of buffer. Electrodes are placed in each reservoir, and the polarity is set so that the sample ions migrate toward the small-pore gel. A voltage is applied for a specified time. The gel is then removed from the container and placed for a period of time in a solution of protein fixative and stain. Unbound dye is removed from the gel by electrophoresis or (more slowly) by washing, and the gel is then preserved in a suitable solution.

b. APPARATUS

The following apparatus is used: (1) Containers for the gel columns made from glass tubing of suitable dimensions—for example, length about 60 mm and internal diameter about 5 mm. (2) A stand for supporting the gel tubes vertically during preparation of the gels (Fig.

[4] M. Hagman, in "Pollen Physiology and Fertilization" (H. F. Linskers, ed.), pp. 242–250. North-Holland, Amsterdam, 1964.

[5] M. L. Heideman, Biochemistry 3, 1108 (1964).

[6] W. Fitschen, Immunology 7, 307 (1964).

[7] R. J. Morris, J. R. Spies, and E. J. Coulson, Arch. Biochem. Biophys. 110, 300 (1965).

[8] R. F. Riley, M. K. Coleman, and Y. Hokama, Clin. Chim. Acta 11, 530 (1965).

[9] J. T. Seto and Y. Hokama, Ann. N.Y. Acad. Sci. 121, Art. 2, 640 (1964).

[10] A. Friedman and D. Koffler, Federation Proc. 22, Part 1, 544 (1963).

[11] F. Paraskevas and J. W. Goodman, Federation Proc. 23, Part 1, 454 (1964).

[12] P. Stelos, A. L. Grossberg, O. A. Roholt, and D. Pressman, Federation Proc. 23, Part 1, 454 (1964).

[13] J. P. Vaerman, H. H. Fudenberg, L. B. Johnson, and W. J. Mandy, Federation Proc. 23, Part 1, 558 (1964).

[14] L. Ornstein, Ann. N.Y. Acad. Sci. 121, Art. 2, 321 (1964).

[15] B. J. Davis, Ann. N.Y. Acad. Sci. 121, Art. 2, 404 (1964).

1), in which the tubes, set in rubber caps having a recess of appropriate size, are secured at the upper ends. (3) Buffer reservoirs made of plastic containers, the upper one being tapped and grommeted for insertion of the gel tubes (Fig. 2). (4) Power supply and inert electrodes. (5) Destaining tubes for electrophoretic destaining, about 10 mm longer than

FIG. 1. Gel tube stand and viewer (Canalco).

the gel tubes and about 1 mm greater in internal diameter, constricted at one end. The apparatus can be purchased from Canalco, Bethesda, Maryland, or made according to instructions published elsewhere.[15]

c. REAGENTS*

Twelve reagents are required: (1) acrylamide (Eastman 5521)† (2) N,N'-methylenebisacrylamide (Eastman 8383) (Bis); (3) tris(hydroxymethyl)-aminomethane (Sigma Trizma base)‡; (4) N,N,N',N'-tetramethylethylenediamine (Eastman 8178) (Temed); (5) riboflavin (Eastman 5181); (6) 1 N hydrochloric acid (HCl), reagent grade; (7)

---

* Reagent kits are also available from Canalco, Bethesda, Maryland.
† Distillation Products Industries, Division of Eastman Kodak Company, Rochester, New York.
‡ Sigma Chemical Company, St. Louis, Missouri.

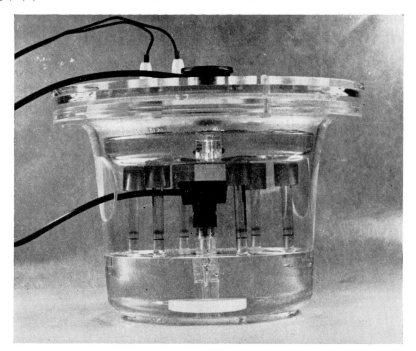

Fig. 2. Disc electrophoresis apparatus (Canalco). Six 3-µl samples of human serum are shown during separation (two of which are illustrated in Fig. 3, *B* and *C*). A thin dark disc of free bromophenol blue dye and, above it, the thicker disc of albumin–bromophenol blue complex is visible in each tube. Heavy leads connect the power supply to electrodes in the upper and lower reservoirs; a pair of thin leads on top lead to a safety switch.

ammonium persulfate, reagent grade; (8) glycine (ammonia-free); (9) glacial acetic acid; (10) the dye Amido Schwarz, known also as naphthol blue black; (11) bromophenol blue; (12) sucrose.

d. Solutions

i. Stock Solutions

Solutions (Table I) are prepared in distilled water, filtered, and stored in brown glass bottles in a refrigerator. The solutions last for several months.

ii. Working Solutions

Working solutions (Table II) should be prepared on the day of use, except the persulfate, which should be stored in a refrigerator and used within a week. The dye is added to the acetic acid; the mixture is stirred and filtered. This solution can be reused a number of times.

TABLE I
STOCK SOLUTIONS

(A)		(B)	
1 N HCl	48 ml	1 N HCl	(approx) 48 ml[a]
Tris	36.6 gm	Tris	5.98 gm
Temed	0.23 ml	Temed	0.46 ml
Water to	100 ml	Water to	100 ml
(pH 8.9)		(pH 6.7)	
(C)		(D)	
Acrylamide	28.0 gm	Acrylamide	10.0 gm
Bis	0.735 gm	Bis	2.5 gm
Water to	100 ml	Water to	100 ml
(E)		(F)	
Riboflavin	4 mg	Sucrose	40 gm
Water to	100 ml	Water to	100 ml

[a] pH adjusted by titration with 1 N HCl.

TABLE II
WORKING SOLUTIONS[a]

Small-pore solution 1	Small-pore solution 2	Large-pore solution	Stock buffer solution for reservoirs[b]
1 part A	Ammonium persulfate,	1 part B	Tris, 6.0 gm
2 parts C	0.14 gm	2 parts D	Glycine, 28.8 gm
1 part water	Water to 100 ml	1 part E	Water to 1 liter
pH 8.9 (8.8–9.0)		4 parts F	pH 8.3
		pH 6.7 (6.6–6.8)	
	Wash solution for destaining and storing gels	*Fixative–stain solution*	
	Glacial acetic acid 70 ml	Amido Schwarz 1 gm	
	Water to 1 liter	7% acetic acid 100 ml	

[a] See Table I for stock solutions A–F.

[b] Up to twelve samples may be run with 500 ml of 1:10 dilution of stock buffer i.e., 0.005 M Tris, 0.0383 M glycine, before it is discarded.

e. PROCEDURE

Two procedures can be used. The protein solution usually is introduced into the large-pore solution prior to its polymerization, as described in step 2 below. In instances in which the protein sample may contain substances that prevent gelation of the gel mix (or where vinyl polymerization may affect the sample), an alternative procedure can be used: 40% sucrose solution replaces the gel sample in step 3 below, and one proceeds to step 8; the space provided by the 40% sucrose is later used for placing the sample, as will be described.

Step 1. Stock solutions and small-pore solution 2 are removed from the refrigerator and brought to room temperature before use.

Step 2. A sample gel solution composed of about 0.15 to 0.20 ml of large-pore solution and about 3 to 4 μl of serum, or an equivalent protein mixture containing about 200 μg of protein, is gently but thoroughly mixed. Sample gel mixes are protected from strong light. The sample is added to the well of a rubber stopper attached to the tube stand. The total amount of protein in the sample usually should not exceed 200 μg. When a protein solution is more dilute than serum but more concentrated than 0.3 mg %, a more concentrated large-pore solution is prepared, and the sample gel solution is made by dilution with the protein sample. If the concentration of the protein is less than 0.3 mg %, the volume of the sample gel is increased to accommodate an amount of protein solution containing about 200 μg, and correspondingly longer gel tubes are used.

Step 3. After the stopper wells have been filled with sample solutions, *clean* glass gel tubes are inserted into the wells in precisely vertical position.

Step 3 (alternate). The gel sample is replaced with 40% sucrose, and the procedure continues with step 8 and then step 8 (alternate).

Step 4. A thin water layer is placed on top of the gel solution. This is accomplished by means of a 1- or 2-ml syringe equipped with a 25-gauge hypodermic needle, with the piston removed. The barrel is filled with distilled water, and the needle is introduced into the top of the gel tube so that the tip rests against the wall and the hub against the top of the tube. The water will flow slowly and evenly down the *clean* inner wall of the tube and will form a layer smoothly on top of the denser sample gel solution. A 3- to 4-mm layer is adequate.

Step 5. The tube stand is placed directly under or in front of and within a few inches of a daylight fluorescent bulb for about 15 to 30 minutes, in order to photopolymerize the sample gel solution.

Step 6. After gelation, the tube stand is removed from the light. It is inverted so that the water layer and the adjacent small fraction of inhibited gel solution will flow down the walls and drain. The tube is rinsed twice with a mixture of 1 part B, 1 part E, and 6 parts H_2O, and then drained.

Step 7. A spacer gel is prepared by adding about 0.15 ml of large-pore solution to the gel tubes. This solution is over-layered with water as in step 4, and the stand is again placed near the fluorescent light as in step 5 for about 20 to 30 minutes. When a very dilute protein sample is used, and the sample gel volume, and therefore the height, is increased, the height of the spacer gel column must be increased proportionately.

Step 8. After photopolymerization of the spacer gel solution, and while the inverted tubes are draining, a small-pore gel solution is prepared by mixing equal volumes of small-pore Solutions 1 and 2. The tubes are half filled with this solution, and the tube stand is rocked and tilted so that the tube walls and spacer gel surface are washed. The solution is thoroughly drained from the tubes, and the wash procedure is repeated once more. After draining, the tubes are completely filled so that a bead of solution rests on top of each tube. Each tube is then capped, by means of forceps, with a previously cut 10-mm square of Saran Wrap.* No air bubbles should be trapped under the film. The tubes are protected from strong light and permitted to stand for about 30 minutes, at the end of which time electrophoresis can be performed.

The gel time of this small-pore gel mixture is about 15 to 20 minutes. The time between the preparation of the small-pore gel solution and the capping of the tubes should not exceed 10 minutes, and the gel solution should reside undisturbed in the gel tubes for at least 5 to 10 minutes prior to the onset of gelation.

If the gel time differs from the stated limits when gel is prepared from fresh reagents, it can be corrected by making minor adjustments in the concentration of Temed.

Step 8. (alternate). Following step 8 the gel tubes are removed from the tube stand, the sucrose is drained from the tubes, and this volume is rinsed with large-pore gel solution. If the rinsed surface of the spacer gel is not reasonably smooth and flat, the gel tubes, small-pore gel down, are placed back in the tube stand, and a column (about 4 mm high) of large-pore gel solution is added on top of the spacer gel. This gel solution, when water-layered and photopolymerized, forms a smooth flat surface upon which the sample will be placed, as described in step 10.

Step 9. When polymerization is complete, following step 8 or step 8 alternate, the gel tubes are removed from the tube stand, caution being exercised to avoid stressing and distorting the gel column to prevent inadvertent separation from the gel tube wall. Removal is accomplished by pressing and tilting the tube against one side of the flexible cap wall so as to provide a space through which air can enter the hollow of the cap as the gel tube is removed. Polymerization is usually inhibited in a small zone, 0.5 to 1.0 mm in height, of the sample gel adjacent to the base of the stopper well. Any watery solution is removed by inverting the gel tubes, sample gel down, and touching the open end to absorbent material.

Step 10. Electrophoresis should preferably be started within 1 hour after the separation gel has been prepared. The tubes, sample gel upper-

* Dow Chemical Company, Midland, Michigan.

most, are inserted into the grommets of the upper buffer reservoir, and this reservoir is filled with about 200 ml of the stock buffer solution (Table II) diluted ten-fold with distilled water. One milliliter of 0.001% bromophenol blue in water is usually stirred into the upper buffer. Any air spaces in the gel tubes above the sample gel are displaced with buffer by means of a pipet. Next a hanging drop of buffer is placed on the bottom of each gel tube to prevent trapping of bubbles, and the upper reservoir is then lowered so that the bottoms of the gel tubes are immersed about ¼ inch in the buffer (also about 200 to 500 ml of one-tenth strength) of the lower reservoir.

When a sample is omitted (see alternative procedure), the gel tubes, spacer gel uppermost, are attached to the upper buffer reservoir, and about 200 ml of one-tenth strength buffer solution is added. Air bubbles in the gel tubes are displaced with a pipet. One-tenth milliliter of sample solution, diluted to give about 200 μg of protein, is mixed with about 0.1 ml of 20% sucrose, and the mixture (or an appropriately small volume of concentrated sample, if the sample is denser than the one-tenth strength buffer) is introduced with a fine pipet through the buffer solution and into the gel tubes to a point about 4 mm above the surface of the spacer gel. The sample is gently expelled so as to layer between the gel surface and the less dense buffer solution above. The gel tubes must be carefully adjusted to a vertical position so that the protein solution is evenly distributed across the face of the gel.

Step 11. The power supply is connected, cathode to the upper reservoir, and the current is adjusted to about 5 ma per tube. The running time is determined empirically. For whole serum this is about 30 minutes at 5 ma per tube, the disc of bromophenol blue dye migrating about 30 mm into the separation gel. (When the sample solution is not gelled but rather is layered above the spacer gel, the current initially should not exceed 2 ma per tube to prevent convective losses. After the sample enters the spacer gel, the current is increased to 5 ma per tube.)

At room temperature and 5 ma per tube, the temperature in the sample region is about 35° to 40°C. If heat-labile substances are to be analyzed, lower current and cooling should be considered.

Step 12. At the completion of electrophoresis, the power supply is turned off, and the buffer solutions are decanted. If fewer than twelve samples are run, the buffer solutions may be reused, but the upper and lower buffer solutions must not be pooled or the positions reversed in the apparatus in future runs.

Step 13. The gel tubes are removed from the upper reservoir, and the gels removed from the tubes by rimming under water. The water lubricates the gel surface and helps to prevent mechanical damage to the gel by the rimming wire or needle. The wire is slowly introduced into the bottom of the gel tube between the small-pore gel and the tube wall for a distance of about 5 to 10 mm. while the gel tube is continuously rotated. The wire is then withdrawn with a slight pressure against the gel, stretching the gel so that it protrudes about 2 mm beyond

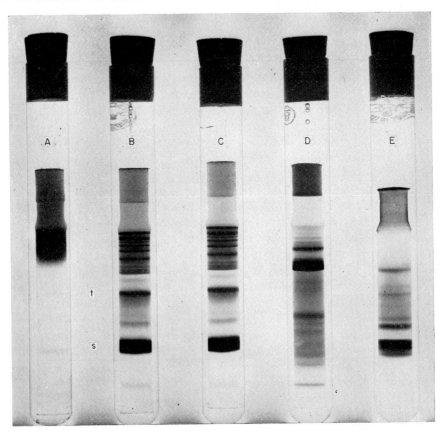

Fig. 3. Finished gels in test tubes, photographed on the viewer illustrated in Fig. 1. A, poliomyelitis immune globulin (human). Note contaminating traces of serum albumin, s, and transferrin, t, as well as small amounts of low-mobility material in sample and spacer gels. B and C, whole human serum, haptoglobin type 2-2, illustrating typical resolution and reproducibility. Very small amount of protein trapped in sample gels. D, aqueous extract of the isopod *Oniscus asellus* (sow bug). Note large amount of protein trapped in sample gel. E, ammonium sulfate (0 to 30% saturated) fraction of aqueous extract of edible mushroom. Extract inhibited polymerization of sample gel; therefore the alternate method, steps 8 and 10, were used.

the end of the tube. The needle is then withdrawn completely. It is then introduced into the other end, and a continuous rimming action is again applied as the needle advances until the gel slips out of the tube.

Step 14. Each gel is immersed in at least 2 ml of fixative–stain solution for a minimum of 1 hour. At the end of 1 hour, the fixative–stain solution is decanted and saved, and the gels are rinsed for a few minutes in tap water.

Step 15. Electrophoretic destaining is usually done in the same apparatus. The gels, sample gel uppermost, are placed in the destaining tubes which have been attached by their unconstricted ends to the upper buffer reservoir. The ends of the separation gels should wedge firmly against the walls of the constricted ends of the tubes. The spaces above, below, and around the gels are filled with wash solution by means of a pipet. About 200 to 500 ml of wash solution is added to each reservoir, and 20 to 30 μl of fixative–stain solution is mixed into the lower reservoir. The electrodes are connected, cathode to *lower* reservoir. On applying a voltage the unbound dye migrates up the gels into the upper reservoir. Destaining is completed in 20 to 40 minutes at a current of 10 to 15 ma per tube.

Step 16. At the completion of destaining, the power supply is shut off, the wash solutions are decanted, and the gels are transferred to small test tubes containing wash solution for inspection and storage (Fig. 3).

Step 17. If destaining is done by washing, the gels are immersed in the fixative–stain solution for about 10 minutes. The fixative–stain solution is decanted and replaced by wash solution, which is repeatedly changed until destaining is completed (within 1 to 2 days).

5. ACRYLAMIDE GEL ELECTROPHORESIS*

a. INTRODUCTION

Acrylamide gel as prepared for electrophoresis[1] is a transparent, flexible, and elastic gel easily and reproducibly made from a highly soluble monomer mixture which is compatible with buffers of all kinds. The neutral gel shows no electroendosmosis but can be chemically modified to incorporate positively or negatively charged groups into the gel structure for ion exchange effect.[2] The gel is inert and unreactive to proteins,

* Section 6,C,5 was contributed by Samuel Raymond.

[1] S. Raymond and L. Weintraub, *Science* 130, 711 (1959).
[2] S. Raymond and M. Nakamichi, *Anal. Biochem.* 3, 23 (1962).

buffers, enzymes, and a wide variety of histochemical techniques. Acrylamide gel demonstrates molecular sieve effects; the gel concentration can be adjusted over a tenfold range (3 to 35%) so as to exclude or admit proteins of high and low molecular size. The acrylamide gel pattern is similar to the starch gel pattern in serum protein sequence but differs significantly from the paper or agar gel electrophoresis pattern because of molecular sieve effects.

Contrasting with these favorable properties, there are some disadvantages. The unpolymerized monomer mixture is reactive toward free hydroxyl, sulfhydryl, and amino groups; therefore proteins cannot be incorporated into the monomer mixture before polymerization without danger of loss or denaturation of protein.[3] The gel absorbs in the ultraviolet below 350 mμ and, as ordinarily prepared, liberates ultraviolet-absorbing materials on extraction with aqueous buffers. The cut surface of a "sliced" gel exhibits a granular appearance which makes it unsuitable for staining and examination of patterns. The gel undergoes significant dimensional changes on dialysis and during staining procedures. Finally, acrylamide gel as ordinarily prepared in buffer solutions does not adhere well to glass or plastic surfaces, so that some modification of techniques is necessary when one is carrying out immunodiffusion or immunoelectrophoresis in acrylamide gel.[*]

b. APPARATUS

The properties of acrylamide gel can best be utilized for electrophoresis and immunoelectrophoresis by preparing the gel in the form of a flat slab in a specially designed electrophoresis cell, shown in Fig. 1.[4] The flat slab configuration provides the maximum surface for control of the heat generated in the cell through the use of internally cooled plates in direct contact with the faces of the slab. A number of samples can simultaneously be applied to the slab and run concurrently. In this way errors due to dimensional changes in the gel pattern, which may vary from one gel to another, can be avoided.[5] Two-dimensional gel electrophoresis can be carried out on the flat slab.[6] This technique not only affords a greatly increased degree of resolution as compared to a one-dimensional pattern, but in addition provides information concerning

[3] P. Bernfeld and J. Wan, *Science* **142**, 678 (1963).

[*] Much of the experimental work reported here was supported by grants from the National Institutes of Health; the development of the apparatus described was supported by the E-C Apparatus Corp., Philadelphia, Pennsylvania.

[4] S. Raymond, *Clin. Chem.* **8**, 455 (1962).

[5] A. C. Peacock, S. L. Bunting, and K. G. Queen, *Science* **147**, 145 (1965).

[6] S. Raymond and B. Aurell, *Science* **138**, 152 (1962).

the size, shape, and molecular relationships of proteins analyzed together on the slab. The flat configuration also makes transmission densitometry easier. Microgram samples can be analyzed effectively on such a slab; it can also be used for larger scale work including preparative methods with capacity up to 50 mg of protein, as in the elution-convection process[7] for recovery of purified proteins in concentrated form from the gel pattern.

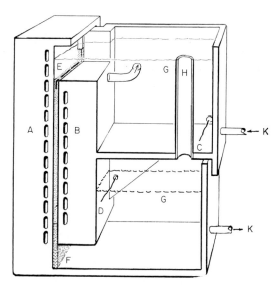

Fig. 1. Vertical gel electrophoresis cell, diagrammatic cross section. *A, B,* cooling plates; *C, D,* electrodes; *E,* slots for samples; *F,* sponge strip supporting gel slab; *G, G,* levels of buffer in electrode chambers; *H,* buffer overflow tube; *K,* buffer recirculation connections (to pump).

c. Procedure

i. General Considerations

Although significant improvements in resolution have been obtained in starch gel techniques using discontinuous buffer systems, such techniques have proved to be of less value in acrylamide gel electrophoresis. If the buffer concentration, the pH, and the conductivity are held constant within the gel, the resulting patterns are much easier to interpret because there is uniform field strength throughout the migration path. It may be useful to employ a discontinuous buffer system for concen-

[7] S. Raymond, *Science* **146,** 3642 (1964).

trating dilute protein samples before permitting them to enter the gel where resolution takes place. For such purposes it is possible to adapt the discontinuous buffer system of Ornstein[8] to the flat slab technique as originally described.

With a uniform buffer system, the interpretation of an acrylamide gel electrophoresis pattern is based on the concepts of electrophoretic mobility of the proteins and pore size of the gel. The latter can be prepared in a wide range of pore sizes for the estimation of molecular parameters. By running the electrophoresis in two directions under identical conditions of buffer composition and field strength in both directions, changing only the pore size of the gel in going from the first direction to the second, one can eliminate the effect of electrophoretic conditions from the experiment, leaving only the pore size itself as the effective pattern determinant. Under these circumstances, if the change in pore size had no effect, all components would lie on a diagonal straight line passing through the origin. Deviations from such a straight line demonstrate that the protein components observed are differentially affected by the change in pore size.

ii. Preparation of Gel

The gel is formed by a free radical mechanism, initiated by an oxidizing agent (for example, ammonium persulfate) or photochemically (via riboflavin), which results in the copolymerization of monomer and cross-linking agent dissolved in aqueous buffer solution. The reaction is promoted by a tertiary amine (DMAPN, dimethylaminopropionitrile; or Temed, tetramethylethylenediamine). In acid solutions the tertiary amine concentration must be significantly increased in order to provide a sufficient concentration of the free amine. Since polymerization is inhibited by molecular oxygen, it is necessary to exclude oxygen from the free surface of the monomer solution until gelling is complete. Where the solution is in contact with oxygen, the exposed layer of solution to a depth of several millimeters will remain unpolymerized. A small bubble trapped within the polymerizing solution will inhibit a much larger volume of solution immediately surrounding the bubble, thus causing a large defect in the gel.

A standard mixture of 95% acrylamide and 5% methylenebisacrylamide (Cyanogum for electrophoresis, E-C Apparatus Co., Philadelphia, Pennsylvania) is generally useful and forms a gel of optimal physical properties. The electrophoretic pore size can be varied by varying the total concentration. Altering the proportion of cross-linking agent has

[8] L. Ornstein, *Ann. N.Y. Acad. Sci.* **121**, 321 (1964).

very little effect on pore size until it is reduced to less than 1%,[9] but such gels are difficult to handle.

The monomer mixture may be made up as a single stock solution containing everything but the persulfate catalyst. The solution is stable for months at room temperature if certain reactive buffer components (for example, glycine) are avoided. A suitable recipe for serum proteins[5] is: TEB buffer—Tris 1.08 gm, Na_2EDTA 0.925 gm, boric acid 5.50 gm, water to 1 liter, pH 8.3 to 8.4; gel solution—buffer 1 liter, Cyanogum 50 gm, DMAPN 4.0 ml. To prepare the gel, dissolve 0.16 gm of ammonium persulfate (AP) in 160 ml of gel solution, mix rapidly, and pour immediately into the electrophoresis cell. Other buffers, including formate, acetate, citrate, Veronal, glycine, and borate, have been used effectively at pH's from 2 to 10. Other gel concentrations, from 3 to 35%, have been used to obtain less or more molecular sieve effect.

iii. One-Dimensional Analysis of Serum Protein

Prepare a 5% gel in pH 8.4 TEB buffer as described above. Insert an eight-place slot-former. Circulate cooling water at 0° through the coolant channels. When gelling is complete, turn the cell to the vertical position, fill it with TEB buffer, remove the excess gel and the slot-former, and apply a prerun of 20 minutes at 200 volts. Discontinue the voltage while applying 15 μl of undiluted serum to each sample slot. Continue the electrophoresis at 200 volts for 5 hours without recirculation of the buffer. The current should be 80 ma initially, decreasing to 25 ma at the end of the run.

When the electrophoresis run is completed, discard the buffer, remove the gel slab, and mark it appropriately, using a toothpick dipped in 5% albumin applied lightly to the surface of the gel. Stain the gel for 1 hour in a solution of 1% Amido Black 10B in a solvent mixture consisting of 10 parts of methanol, 10 parts of water, and 1 part of acetic acid. Destain in an electrophoretic destainer or by washing in the solvent mixture. This procedure gives excellent resolution of the major protein components in serum.

iv. Two-Dimensional Gel Electrophoresis[6]

First, prepare a one-dimensional pattern using the procedure just described or a variant of it. The second step varies according to the purpose of the experiment and the information desired.

[9] J. F. Jongkind, J. H. Wisse, and H. Bloemendal, *Protides Biol. Fluids* **10**, 77 (1962).

(a) *Identity Pattern.* It is sometimes desirable to demonstrate that a series of zones in a protein pattern are real components of the sample mixture and not artifacts introduced by the electrophoresis process. This is particularly desirable when a zone is spread out diffusely along the migration path. This appearance may be due to trailing or to distribution of electrophoretic mobilities within the protein component concerned (for example, γ-globulin). For experimental decision of this question, remove the gel slab, and excise a longitudinal strip, 6 mm wide, from the pattern,

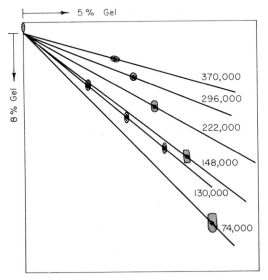

Fig. 2. Two-dimensional gel electrophoresis pattern. Sample—crystalline bovine serum albumin and lactic dehydrogenase. Diagonal hatching—albumin monomer and polymers. Cross-hatching—LDH isoenzymes. Diagonal lines through origin correspond to designated molecular weights.

including the original point of application and extending out through the zone of interest. Replace the strip transversely in the electrophoresis cell in the position normally occupied by the sample slots. Pour in a monomer solution identical to that used in the first direction. When the gel is formed, proceed with electrophoresis, using the same experimental conditions as before. After staining, the pattern will consist in a series of small spots lying on a diagonal line extending from the origin out to the fastest moving component. If all electrophoretic conditions are identical in both the first and second directions, and if there has been no interaction or chemical change within the components of the first pattern or between them and the gel itself, all the spots will lie exactly on a line at a 45° angle to the initial direction. Any protein zones lying off the diagonal demonstrate some type of interaction, the nature of which can often be deduced from further electrophoretic experiments.

(b) *Concentration Variable.* This technique demonstrates components differing in molecular size. It gives essentially the same information as is obtained from gel filtration methods, but it is easier and more convenient experimentally if the components all migrate in the same direction in an appropriate buffer. To carry out this procedure, proceed as described in the preceding paragraph, using a higher concentration of gel in the second direction. It is advisable to run the second electrophoresis for a longer time to compensate for the slower average migration rate of proteins in gels of higher concentration. The resulting pattern can be interpreted by drawing a series of straight lines through the origin covering the pattern field. Each line corresponds to a single molecular size. By including proteins of known molecular size, the pattern field can be calibrated internally to estimate the molecular size of an unknown (Fig. 2).

(c) *Other Variables.* The effect of changes in pH, buffer concentration or composition, temperature, and other experimental variables can be demonstrated simultaneously on a complete series of proteins. For example, a change in pH from 9.2 to 8.6 affects all the components of a bovine serum albumin mixture equally.

v. Discontinuous Systems

(a) *Discontinuous buffer systems* use two different buffers forming either a Kohlrausch boundary behind the sample[8] or a conductivity boundary ahead of the sample.[10] The objective is to concentrate the protein sample into a very thin layer before it enters the running gel, where pH, conductivity, and ionic composition are uniform. It is often convenient although not essential to stabilize the buffer boundary by using a separate gel for each buffer.

(b) *Discontinuous gel systems* include (i) those which merely serve to stabilize a discontinuous buffer system, and (ii) those in which a second gel increases the electrophoretic resolution by the molecular sieving effect. A 5% gel following a 3% gel will completely exclude high

[10] S. Hjertén, S. Jerstedt, and A. Tiselius, *Anal. Biochem.* **11**, 219–223 (1965).

molecular weight lipoproteins but will pass haptoglobins, thus separating components of these two classes which would otherwise not be separable by electrophoretic means alone.

(c) *A procedure* for use in the cell of Fig. 1 follows: (1) Form a supporting gel plug as described in Section *vi*. (2) With cell vertical, form a 7% running gel in tris-HCl buffer pH 8.9. Overlay with water

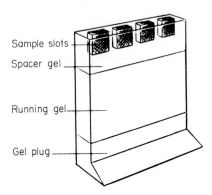

Sample slots

Spacer gel

Running gel

Gel plug

FIG. 3. Stacked-gel System for discontinuous gel electrophoresis described in the text.

leaving space for spacer gel and sample slots above the gel. (3) With cell horizontal, form a spacer gel and sample slots as in Section c,*ii*, in tris-HCl buffer pH 6.7.* (4) Fill buffer chambers with tris-glycine pH 8.3.† (5) Dialyze protein samples against spacer buffer and fill sample slots completely. (6) Apply 200 volts until samples have entered running gel, then increase to 400 volts. Do not recirculate buffer. The final gel appears as in Fig. 3.

vi. Large-Pore Gels

As noted above, acrylamide gel can be prepared in a wide range of gel concentrations. For high-molecular-weight proteins, a low concentration provides a large-pore gel. Gels below approximately 5% in total concentration are structurally weak and difficult to handle, but this difficulty can be overcome by the following technique, which will be described in its application to lipoprotein electrophoresis.

* Cf. buffer No. 38, Appendix II.
† See Table II, Section C,4,d,*ii*.

The vertical electrophoresis cell described above is supported at an angle of 30°. Fifty milliliters of Tris–EDTA buffer solution (pH 9.0) containing 8% Cyanogum and 0.1% each of AP and Temed is poured into the cell, forming a layer 3 cm deep at the bottom of the gel space. The 8% gel after polymerization forms a support for the 3% gel subsequently poured but does not take part in the electrophoresis pattern itself. After the supporting gel is fully polymerized, the cell is returned to the horizontal position, and 180 ml of a 3% Cyanogum solution (including catalysts) is poured into the cell. After 2 hours, the excess gel above the slot-former is removed, and the cell is returned to the upright position. The buffer compartments are filled with buffer, buffer circulation is begun, and a prerun of 15 minutes at 150 volts is applied before the slot-former is removed.

For lipoprotein patterns, 20 μl of a serum sample prestained with Lipid Crimson (one-half volume of 1% dye in diethylene glycol) is placed in each 1-cm slot. The current is then applied for $2\frac{1}{2}$ hours at 150 volts with buffer recirculation, the temperature being maintained at 20°. At the end of this time the visible pattern includes one or more red bands in the β-lipoprotein region and diffuse bands in the α-lipoprotein and albumin region.

For subsequent operations the gel is "stiffened." First, the buffer is drained, and the cell is placed in the horizontal position; the upper cooling assembly is removed, and the excess gel is trimmed from the pattern. The remaining gel is covered with 120 ml of buffer containing 10% Cyanogum and 0.1% Temed, omitting the persulfate. After 45 minutes, 30 ml of 0.5% ammonium persulfate is mixed with the gel solution. A cover is placed over the gel pattern to exclude air, permitting the stiffening gel to polymerize uniformly. During this procedure acrylamide monomer diffuses into the 3% gel and polymerizes there to convert the soft weak 3% gel into an approximately 8% gel which can be handled easily.

vii. Analysis of the Pattern

The most general procedure is to fix and stain the pattern by immersing it in a denaturing solvent containing a protein stain (e.g., 1 gm of Amido Black, 250 ml methanol, 250 ml water, and 50 ml acetic acid) for 1 hour or more. The excess dye is removed by washing with the same solvent, or by electrophoretic destaining. Destaining equipment using stainless steel electrodes produces a brown stain (ferric compounds) in solutions containing chloride or acetic acid; platinum electrodes, however, produce a clear gel in less than 30 minutes.

Enzymes are often demonstrated by allowing substrates to diffuse into the gel to produce a colored end-product, e.g., a tetrazolium reaction. Procedures requiring diffusion of enzymes into the gel usually fail because the protein diffuses too slowly.

Radioactive components can be detected by autoradiography. For quantitative analysis, however, the gel should be sliced into sections of equal size which may be dissolved in 30% H_2O_2 at 50°. Samples may then be mixed with suitable fluor solutions for scintillation counting. Alternatively, gel may be stained and then only the appropriate bands cut out, dissolved, and counted.[11]

viii. Recovery of Separated Components from Acrylamide Gel

Unlike starch gel, acrylamide gel is stable against freezing-thawing, but other techniques for recovery can be used. Dialysis following excision of the appropriate zone is facilitated by grinding the gel with eluting buffer (e.g., in a tissue grinder). Electrophoretic elution, which may be faster for larger proteins, is effected either along the original direction of migration or transverse to it. Several column designs have been described in which zones migrate out the end of the column and are successively collected in a stream of buffer flowing across the end of the column. These methods require a long time to move the slower components off the column and a large volume of buffer to collect each zone. Transverse electrophoretic elution can be combined with the electro-convection effect to recover and reconcentrate many components simultaneously.[7,12,13]

The above procedures are applied to undenatured proteins (i.e., before staining). After staining, proteins are denatured and insoluble, but they can usually be redissolved and eluted in buffers above pH 10.5. It is not essential to elute components from the gel for use as antigens. The gel containing the antigen can be homogenized and injected directly for immunization. The gel itself is non-antigenic and in some cases may act as an effective adjuvant.[13,14]

[11] R. W. Young and H. W. Fulhorst, *Anal. Biochem.* **11**, 389 (1965).
[12] W. C. Ng and J. R. Brunner, *J. Dairy Sci.* **49**, 96–98 (1966).
[13] N. G. Anderson, *Fed. Proc.* **15**:4 (1956).
[14] M. Weintraub and S. Raymond, *Science* **142**, 1677–1678 (1963).

D. Preparative Zone Electrophoresis

1. ZONE ELECTROPHORESIS ON POWDER BLOCKS*†‡

a. GENERAL CONSIDERATIONS

Block electrophoresis represents one of the simplest preparative electrophoretic methods. It was originally described by Kunkel and Slater[1] in 1952 and has since found wide application in biochemical and medical research. Its chief applications in the immunological laboratory are: (1) isolation of immunoglobulins and separation of immunoglobulin fragments; (2) isolation of complement components; and (3) isolation of certain carbohydrate and protein antigens.

The primary advantage of block electrophoresis over other forms of preparative electrophoresis is the simplicity of the apparatus. Other advantages are that two or more samples may be separated simultaneously on one block, and that the separated material is eluted from the area of the block wherever it is located at the end of the experiment. Elution does not require that a protein zone traverse the full distance through the supporting medium, as is necessary in column electrophoresis. Possible disadvantages of the method are its comparatively limited capacity, which cannot be increased to that of large electrophoresis columns (see Section D,2).[2] Further, elution of blocks is handled manually and cannot readily be automated.

b. THEORETICAL CONSIDERATIONS

General theory of electrophoresis is discussed in Section A. The theory of zone electrophoresis has been treated exhaustively by Kunkel and Trautman.[3] Only a few points of immediate practical importance will be discussed here. Separation of solutes in an electric field is based on their relative rates of migration. The rate of migration varies with the pH. For each solute a characteristic relation exists between mobility

* Section, 6,D,1 was contributed by Hans J. Müller-Eberhard and C. Kirk Osterland.

† This is publication No. 145 from the Division of Experimental Pathology, Scripps Clinic and Research Foundation, LaJolla, California.

‡ This work was supported in part by grant AI-05617 from the U. S. Public Health Service, National Institutes of Health, Bethesda, Maryland.

[1] H. G. Kunkel, and R. J. Slater, *Proc. Soc. Exptl. Biol. Med.* **80**, 42 (1952).

[2] J. Porath, *Arkiv Kemi* **11**, 18 (1957).

[3] H. G. Kunkel and R. Trautman, *in* "Electrophoresis" (M. Bier, ed.), Chapter 6. Academic Press, New York, 1959.

and pH (pH-mobility curve). To achieve optimal separation of two proteins, for instance, a pH should be chosen at which the rates of migration of the two proteins differ maximally.

To achieve separation of components into discrete zones, convection in the solution must be minimized. Powders of various solid materials have been used successfully as stabilizing or anticonvection media. Such a zone electrophoresis system thus consists of a solid and a liquid phase, only the latter being available for the electrophoretic migration of the solute. A solid supporting medium forces a migrating solute molecule to take a tortuous path, its actual distance of migration therefore being greater than the observed one.[3] Accordingly, mobility measurements require corrections, or they may be carried out by comparison with a component of known mobility in free solution (cf. Section B,4,c).

The supporting medium affects the composition of the system, and thus the electrophoretic process, by determining the ratio between liquid and solid phase, the extent of zone spreading, and the magnitude of electroösmosis. The larger the proportion of free liquid in the block, the greater is the resemblance of the prevailing conditions to those of free solution electrophoresis. A larger free liquid content permits formation of a narrower initial zone and a greater degree of resolution of the material to be separated. Zone spreading during electrophoresis is not caused by diffusion but is related to the chemical and physiochemical nature of the supporting medium; it is proportional to the distance that a zone has migrated. Negative charges of the supporting medium induce a flow of the aqueous phase through the block from the anode to the cathode, in which case the point of application is no longer identical with the point of zero migration. When electroösmosis occurs, the point of zero migration is indicated by the position of a neutral solute in the block, such as neutral hexose, which may be added to the sample and detected subsequently in the block eluates by the anthrone reagent.*

The electrophoretic resolution of two components is proportional to the difference of their mobilities and to the distance of their migration. It is inversely proportional to the width of the initial zone and to the extent of zone spreading during migration.

c. Methodology

i. Preparation of the Powder

The following supporting media may be used: potato starch,[1] polyvinyl chloride resin,[4,5] or a copolymer of polyvinyl chloride and poly-

---

* Ortho-nitroaniline, electrically neutral between pH 7 and 9, has been used as a colored (but highly toxic) marker.

[4] H. J. Müller-Eberhard and H. G. Kunkel, *J. Exptl. Med.* **104**, 253 (1956).

[5] H. J. Müller-Eberhard and H. G. Kunkel, *Clin. Chim. Acta* **4**, 252 (1959).

vinyl acetate.[6] The desired supporting medium is washed in a 2-liter funnel with sintered-glass filter (coarse), first with distilled water, then with several liters of electrophoresis buffer. Equilibration with buffer is particularly important when starch is used, since this material has ion exchange properties. When Pevikon, a copolymer of polyvinyl chloride and polyvinyl acetate is used, thorough washing with water is needed to remove particles that are small enough to pass the sintered-glass filter. If these particles are not removed initially, they will later cause the block eluates to have a turbid appearance.

ii. Pouring the Block*

A thick, homogeneous suspension of washed supporting medium in buffer is poured into a supporting arrangement consisting of a glass plate (50 × 30 cm or, for larger blocks, 50 × 60 cm) and two Lucite bars (50 × 1.5 × 1.5 cm) placed on the glass plate along its 50-cm sides. Plate and bars are covered with thin polyethylene sheeting.† For removal of excess fluid, packs of thick filter paper are tightly attached to the other two sides of the glass plate and anchored with suitable weights. This process can be advanced by careful blotting of the excess fluid on the surface as the powder settles. When the block has solidified, it sometimes has a coarse and foamy surface. This is corrected by smoothing the surface with a wide spatula.

iii. Application of the Sample

A narrow slit is prepared with a spatula at a site approximately 10 cm away from the cathodal end of the block. A 3-cm margin should be left on either side of the slit. To obtain a narrow initial zone, the area around the slit is moistened with several drops of buffer prior to application of the sample. Maximally, 10 to 20 ml of serum or the equivalent of any other test solution may be applied to a 50 × 30-cm block, and 20 to 40 ml of serum to a 50 × 60-cm block. The slit is then closed with a spatula, and the block surface is covered with polyethylene sheeting. Care should be taken to prevent the trapping of air bubbles between block surface and cover.

iv. Electrophoresis*

The filter paper packs are removed, and the block is transferred to the cold room, where its ends are connected with the electrode troughs by means of buffer-soaked towels. Bridges are established to the outer electrode vessels by inverted U-tubes (ca. 35–40 mm I.D.) bearing an

[6] H. J. Müller-Eberhard, *Scand. J. Clin. Lab. Invest.* **12**, 33 (1960).
* See Appendix III for further technical details.
† A thickness of 0.0015 inches is satisfactory.

air-evacuating tube. A potential gradient of 3 to 4 volts/cm is applied as measured on the block, and the period of electrophoresis is chosen according to the migration rate of the components in the sample. For human serum, electrophoresis is carried out for 20 to 25 hours on a 30-cm plate.

v. Recovery of Fractions

At the end of the experiment, the block is disconnected, and filter paper is placed on both ends for a few minutes. The cover is then removed, and the block is cut into 1.5-cm-wide segments from which the solute is eluted by displacement filtration. One of two methods may be used. A segment is first pressed onto the bottom of a small sintered-glass funnel (coarse), then overlaid with a few milliliters of buffer. The funnel is then inserted into a suction bottle. On application of vacuum, the solution is pulled down into a test tube placed below the funnel outlet. Or elution is achieved by pressing the segment into a plastic cylinder which is equipped with a perforated bottom plate covered with wire mesh and a Whatman No. 3 filter paper disc. A few milliliters of buffer is added, and the plastic elution device is placed inside a 40-ml centrifuge tube. The liquid is centrifuged out of the supporting medium at 4° and 300 g for 10 minutes, and thereafter recovered from the centrifuge tube.

The eluates may be analyzed for protein content by the Folin, biuret, or ninhydrin method or by ultraviolet absorption.* Carbohydrate constituents may be determined by any of the conventional carbohydrate assays for neutral hexose, hexosamine, hexuronic acid, and neuraminic acid.[4,5] Recovery of serum proteins from Pevikon blocks (see below) was 98%.

d. CHOICE OF SUPPORTING MEDIUM

For most purposes, the originally proposed supporting medium, potato starch, suffices. However, there are instances where the use of potato starch is disadvantageous. Such is the case when material after its electrophoretic separation is to be analyzed for carbohydrate constituents. Eluates from starch blocks are heavily contaminated with carbohydrates derived from starch. Starch should also be avoided for the separation of serum if the resulting fractions are to be screened for complement components. Almost all sera contain natural antibody to starch, which, after application of the serum to the starch block, will trigger a reaction which may lead to inactivation of most of the components of the complement system. In these cases a more inert supporting medium is required, such as the commercially available polyvinyl resins.

* Barbital absorbancy at 280 mμ can be cancelled by temporary acidification when the material to be scanned permits this (Appendix II, p. 387).

Pevikon C-870,[*6] which is a copolymer of polyvinyl chloride and polyvinyl acetate, has been used in this and other laboratories for several years with good results. Its advantages over starch are: (1) It is a chemically defined synthetic resin. (2) It does not interfere with carbohydrate determinations. (3) It is a nonswelling medium; all the liquid in a Pevikon block represents free water which is available for the electrophoretic process. Both starch and Pevikon blocks which are connected with the buffer troughs contain approximately 50% liquid. In the starch block only half of this amount is free liquid; the other half is bound in the starch granule. (4) The surface charge of Pevikon is very low at pH 8.6 and ionic strength 0.1, generating an electroösomotic cathodal flow of 0.6 mobility unit.

In certain instances, a supporting medium that causes a greater electroösmotic cathodal flow may prove superior. In the case that the mobility difference between two proteins is small so that separation can be expected only after migration of the two components over a greater distance, separation may be obscured or completely prevented by zone spreading, the extent of which is proportional to the distance migrated through the supporting medium. Under these circumstances, a larger electroösmotic backflow may greatly facilitate separation of the two components by reducing their rate of migration through the block and thus zone spreading. A number of polyvinyl resins, among them Geon 426†[4,5] exhibit properties that give rise to electroösmotic cathodal flow of more than 4 mobility units. These latter resins have been successfully used in work with relatively rapidly migrating substances, such as free neuraminic acid or neutral hexoses in borate buffer.

e. Examples of Applications in Immunology

i. Immunoglobulins

Preparative block electrophoresis is ideally suited for the isolation of the immunoglobulin fraction from serum. Serum is subjected to electrophoresis in barbital buffer, pH 8.6, ionic strength 0.05 (0.044 M),‡ for 20 hours at 4° with a potential gradient of 3.5 volts/cm. After protein analysis of the eluates, the immunoglobulin fraction can be recognized as the most slowly migrating globulin fraction (Fig. 1). By pooling all eluates

---

* Stockholms Superfosfat Fabriks A.-B., Stockholm, Sweden. Distributor in the United States: Mercer Chemical Corporation, New York, New York.

† B. F. Goodrich Company, Los Angeles, California.

‡ Borate buffers of pH 8.6 are listed in Appendix II—No. 7 diluted 1:2 (0.044 M) or No. 9 diluted 1:2 (0.055 M) are appropriate for the block and its electrode vessels; the outer electrode vessels are filled with phosphate buffer, pH 7.5, ionic strength = 0.2 (buffer No. 33B prepared at double strength).

between the cathodal end of the serum protein spectrum and the inter-beta-gamma valley, a fraction is obtained containing γG-, γA-, and γM-globulin. This material is free of other serum globulins and may be utilized for the production of polyvalent antisera to γ-globulin, for conjugation with fluorescein or ferritin, and as starting material for the isolation of γA and γM by subsequent Sephadex filtration (G-200) or DEAE chromatography (see Chap. 9,B and 9,C). Pathological γ-globulins such as myeloma proteins or macroglobulins may readily be isolated by block electrophoresis, under the above described conditions. Their con-

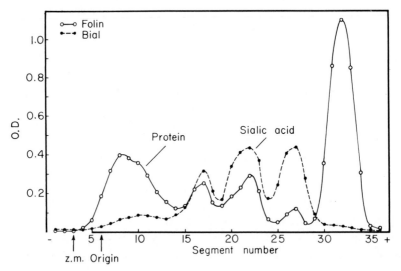

Fig. 1. Separation of human serum by zone electrophoresis at pH 8.6 with a copolymer of polyvinyl chloride and polyvinyl acetate (Pevikon C-870) as supporting medium. (z.m. = point of zero migration.)[6]

centration in serum is usually so great, and that of normal γ-globulin usually so small, that the pathological proteins can be obtained in a highly purified form (at least 95%) by electrophoresis only. In most other cases, however, it is necessary to combine preparative electrophoresis with another separation technique such as chromatography, gel filtration, or zone ultracentrifugation in order to obtain a highly purified product (see Chap. 7). It is also possible to separate normal γG-globulin (Cohn fraction II) into a continuous spectrum of molecular species differing in their electrophoretic mobility. After electrophoresis, this spectrum may be divided into arbitrary groups of γG-globulin, each possessing a characteristic mean electrophoretic mobility.[4]

ii. Immunoglobulin Fragments

Another, more recent application of block electrophoresis is the separation of the Fab and Fc fragments which arise from papain treatment of γG-globulin. To obtain well-separated fragments, it is essential to begin with a pure sample of γG-globulin. Whenever possible, the γ-globulin population with the slowest electrophoretic mobility should be selected, since the fragments of slowly migrating γ-globulins can be separated more widely on electrophoresis than those of fast-moving γ-globu-

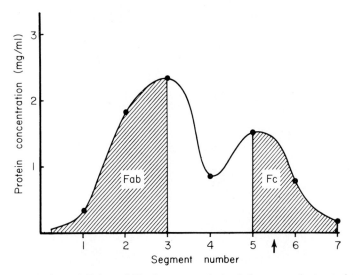

Fig. 2. Separation of Fab and Fc fragments derived from papain-treated human γG-globulin by zone electrophoresis at pH 8.6 with potato starch as supporting medium. Arrow indicates the origin; the anode was at the right; shaded areas indicate eluates that contain pure fragments.

lins. The protein is enzymatically digested according to Porter's method,[7] 4 hours of incubation being sufficient for most γ-globulins (see Chap. 5, Vol. I). Myeloma proteins are usually split completely with papain into Fc and Fab fragments. In the case of normal human γG-globulin, however, there is often some protein which remains undegraded. It is advisable to eliminate the undegraded protein prior to block electrophoresis by filtering the sample through Sephadex G-100. Two peaks are obtained. The first represents unsplit γG-globulin and is discarded.

The γ-globulin digest is applied to a starch or a Pevikon block and is subjected to electrophoresis in barbital buffer, pH 8.6, ionic strength

[7] R. R. Porter, *Biochem. J.* **73**, 119 (1959).

0.05 (0.044 M), for 20 hours at 4° with a potential gradient of 3.5 volts/cm. Elution is accomplished as described above, and the eluates are analyzed by the Folin procedure. Two protein peaks can be seen, with an intervening trough (Fig. 2). The protein in the trough represents overlapping Fc and Fab fragments. To obtain pure fragments, it is necessary to use only those eluates that correspond to the maxima of the two protein peaks and to the adjacent extreme ends of the protein curve (indicated in Fig. 2 as shaded areas under the curve).

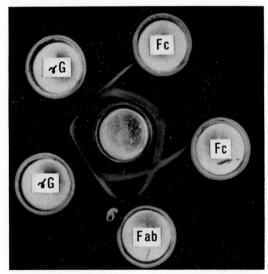

Fɪɢ. 3. Ouchterlony plate analysis demonstrating purity of human Fab and Fc fragments separated by block electrophoresis. Center well contains rabbit antihuman γG-globulin.

Assessment of purity of the fragments is made by agar diffusion analysis (see Chap. 14,C,3, Vol. III). The Fc and Fab fragments are placed in adjacent wells with unsplit γG-globulin in wells on either side, as shown in Fig. 3. When an antiserum prepared against whole human γG-globulin is placed in the center well, the typical pattern of purified fragments should be obtained. The Fc and Fab fragments give precipitin lines which cross each other, thus showing nonidentity, whereas the γG-globulin line shows partial identity with both Fc and Fab fragments.

iii. Ferritin-Labeled Immunoglobulin

Block electrophoresis may also be applied to the purification of ferritin–γ-globulin conjugates. These conjugates have become powerful tools in immuno-electron microscopy. After conjugation of γ-globulin with ferritin according to standard methods, the reaction mixture contains, in addition to the conjugate, free ferritin and unconjugated γ-globulin (see Chap. 4,B, Vol. I). These three components can be readily separated by Pevikon block electrophoresis at pH 8.6 in barbital buffer, under the conditions described above. Free ferritin moves rapidly with α-globulin mobility, while ferritin-conjugated γ-globulin migrates with a mobility intermediate to that of ferritin and unconjugated γ-globulin. By holding a light source underneath the block, one can clearly see from above the two separated color bands, the anodal band corresponding to free ferritin, the cathodal to the conjugate. The conjugate is isolated by cutting out the cathodal color band and by eluting it in bulk.

iv. Complement

Pevikon block electrophoresis constitutes an essential part of the isolation procedure for several complement components of human serum. These procedures are described in detail in Chap. 16,B, Vol. III and will be mentioned only briefly here. One of the subcomponents of the first component of complement, C'1q,[8] is one of the most basic proteins of human serum. Being an asymmetrical molecule with a sedimentation rate of 11S, it passes Sephadex G-200 with the exclusion fraction together with macroglobulins and γ-globulin aggregates. Subsequent Pevikon block electrophoresis at pH 6 in phosphate buffer, ionic strength 0.1,[*] permits complete separation of C'1q from the other proteins. While the latter migrate from the point of application toward the anode, C'1q moves toward the cathode.

In a similar fashion, purification of the second and fourth components of human complement[8] is facilitated by Pevikon block electrophoresis. The second component is eluted from carboxymethylcellulose together with γ- and α2-globulins. The fourth component of complement is eluted from TEAE cellulose, also contaminated with γ- and α2-globulin. Since both the second and the fourth components are β-globulins, subsequent electrophoresis on Pevikon blocks leads to the removal of the α2- and γ-globulin contaminants. In the case of the second component, electrophoresis is carried out in phosphate buffer, pH 6, ionic strength 0.05, containing 0.002 M EDTA. For purification of the fourth component, barbital buffer, pH 8.6, ionic strength 0.05 (0.044 M), is used. An electro-

---

[8] H. J. Müller-Eberhard, *Adv. Immunol.*, **8**, 1 (1968).
[*] Buffer No. 33B, Appendix II.

phoresis step is also employed in the isolation procedures of the third, fifth, eighth and ninth components of complement.[8]

v. Carbohydrates

Electrophoresis on polyvinyl blocks has been utilized for the study of carbohydrate compounds. Two examples may be cited: the comparative analysis of streptococcal carbohydrate prepared with *Staphylococcus albus* enzyme and with phage-associated lysin (see Chap. 1,B,3, Vol. I).[9] Both preparations of this streptococcal antigen were analyzed simultaneously on the same polyvinyl block (Geon 426); 0.1 M sodium borate buffer, pH 9, was used. They were found to differ electrophoretically and to be heterogeneous with respect to charge. The physicochemical heterogeneity could be correlated to some extent with the antigenic heterogeneity of each preparation.

Since borate buffer interacts with carbohydrates and hence causes neutral carbohydrate molecules to acquire an electric charge, this buffer was used for the separation of monosaccharides derived from the carbohydrate moiety of immunoglobulins. With either Pevikon C-870 or Geon 426 as supporting medium, acid hydrolyzates of γG- and γM-globulin were subjected to electrophoresis in 0.05 M sodium borate, pH 9.2, at 4° for 12 hours with a potential gradient of 8 volts/cm.[4,5] The best resolution was observed when the concentration of each carbohydrate component in the test solution did not exceed 1 mg/ml and when the initial band at the site of application was not wider than 0.5 cm. To achieve this, 2 ml of solution was applied to a slit 6 to 8 cm in length. To check the width of the initial band of the colorless carbohydrate solution, one drop of phenolphthalein was added to the sample. Under these conditions, mannose, galactose, and glucose can be quantitatively separated from each other. Galactose and fucose also separate, but their zones overlap. With this method it was demonstrated that the main neutral hexose sugars in the γG carbohydrate moiety are mannose and galactose and that γM-globulin contains, in addition, considerable amounts of fucose.

vi. Protein-Activity Correlation

Block electrophoresis is well suited for examining the correlation between protein and activity distributions. In the area of immunology, the following examples may be quoted. Analysis of electrophoretic fractions of certain human sera showed that the Gm antigenic character

[9] R. M. Krause, *J. Exptl. Med.* **108**, 803 (1958).

correlated with the distribution of γG-globulin, while the Inv antigenic character was found to be present in all types of immunoglobulins.[10] Rheumatoid factor activity was found initially to correlate with the distribution of γM-globulin.[11] One of the purity criteria of isolated complement components is the complete correlation between the distribution of hemolytic activity and of the protein after block electrophoresis.

Radioactively labeled proteins are widely used today in immunology. Radioactive labels can readily be introduced into antigens, specific antibodies, and purified complement components. Since results obtained with these materials are often based exclusively on radioactivity measurements, it is essential to establish that the radioactive label is not associated with possible contaminants. Block electrophoresis may be used to demonstrate that the radioactivity resides in the protein component which was intended to be labeled.

[10] M. Harboe, C. K. Osterland, M. Mannik, and H. G. Kunkel, *J. Exptl. Med.* **116**, 719 (1962).
[11] E. C. Franklin, H. R. Holman, H. J. Müller-Eberhard, and H. G. Kunkel, *J. Exptl. Med.* **105**, 425 (1957).

2. COLUMN ELECTROPHORESIS*

a. GENERAL CONSIDERATIONS

The great variety of column designs may make a selection of type difficult for those who are not particularly familiar with these electrophoretic techniques. Proper handling of some of the columns may require training, but most of them are simple to operate. Advantages over block methods should be emphasized, particularly the ease of temperature control, packing, and flow of solutions. The simplicity of collecting the fractionated material is also an attractive feature of column procedures. Trial experiments may be made in small columns, and in most cases conditions can be transposed to almost any scale of interest.

Each apparatus is usually designed to meet specific requirements. Some may be suited for small-scale preparations; others permit easier separations of large samples. Among the more advanced designs, we find those allowing compensatory flow of buffer to adjust electrophoresis migration of a component to the most desirable column position or to nullify electroendosmotic flow.

b. SMALL-SCALE PREPARATIONS

A simple and easily operated column used in the author's laboratory will be described. It is recommended for exploration of buffer systems

* Section 6,D,2 was contributed by Jerker Porath

and anticonvection media to be used for large-scale columns and for preparative fractionation of 5 to 200 mg of sample in 0.2 to 2 ml of solution.

i. Apparatus

The apparatus (Fig. 1) is essentially an inverted U-tube system connecting the two electrode vessels.* One of the limbs consists of the elec-

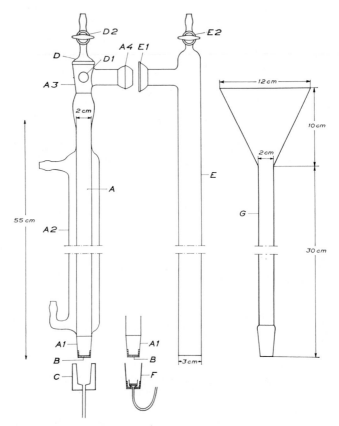

Fig. 1. Electrophoresis column tube and accessories described in the text.

trophoresis column, A, with accessories for easy manipulations, and the other, E, serves as a connecting part. The electrophoresis column (55 × 2 cm) is provided with a cooling jacket, A2, to provide temperature control. A female (No. 19) ground joint, A1, at the lower end of the tube joins

*This apparatus is produced commercially by Mr. Nils Larsson, Salgvagen 4, Uppsala, Sweden.

the collecting funnel, C. The plug, B, is dropped inside A and pressed into the slightly conical seat at the end of the tube. The plug is cut from a plate of porous plastic to fit exactly the end of A.* Since the plug has the form of a small cup with a thin bottom, it will support the column without causing extensive temperature rise. The arrangement shown in F may also be used when continuous removal of buffer during electrophoresis is desired. A female (No. 24) ground joint, A3, makes possible liquid connection and disconnection between the two limbs. A short side arm (diameter 1.6 cm) is fused to the tube at a circular hole in the joint. A top piece, D, fits into A3. A hole, D1, in the male joint corresponds to the side arm opening in A3. Liquid connection is accomplished by turning D to the coinciding position of the two openings. The tube above the stopcock, D2, is connected to a buffer reservoir when the column is washed or fractionated material is to be collected.

The side tube, E, is attached to A by the ball joint A4–E1. The lower parts of the column (A) and side tube (E) are placed in two electrode vessels (glass beakers or plastic jars of 2- to 5-liter capacity). If desirable, direct contact between column and catholyte or anolyte (which may contain harmful electrode products) can be avoided by bridges to secondary buffer reservoirs. Short thin platinum wires wound around glass or plastic rods serve well as electrodes. The dimensions of the wires are not critical.

In a column of the size described here, electrophoresis may be performed with 500 to 1000 volts at 25 to 50 ma if materials such as Sephadex† or cellulose are used to suppress convection.

ii. Anticonvection Materials

Sephadex G-25 is an excellent convection suppressor for electrophoresis of proteins or polynucleotides. Fine-grade Sephadex G-25 is better than coarse grade and permits flow rates sufficiently high for most purposes. After the beads have been allowed to swell for 2 hours in the buffer to be used, they may be transferred as a suspension to the column tube. In alkaline solutions, slight but definite electroendosmosis occurs, presumably caused by trace quantities of carboxyl groups fixed to the dextran matrix of the gel. Since only a small portion of these groups are exposed on the surface, adsorption of macromolecular solutes will be negligible.

---

* Polystyrene available from Porous Plastic Ltd, Dagenham Docks, Essex, England, under the trade name Vyon.

† Cross-linked dextrans available from Pharmacia Ltd., Uppsala, Sweden; Pharmacia Fine Chemicals, Inc., Box 1010, Rochester, Minnesota; or other subsidiary companies.

The absence of significant irreversible adsorption of proteins in common buffer systems is extremely important in zone electrophoresis. It should be mentioned, however, that lipids or lipoproteins sometimes accumulate on top of the columns in gel filtration experiments. Sephadex G-25 shares another weakness with other similar gel material including starch grains. A large fraction of the current is carried by ions which move in regions inaccessible to the proteins. For this reason the capacity of such columns for large molecules is lower than cellulose columns of the same conductivity.

Dextran gels with more expanded network structure such as Sephadex G-100 or G-200, or corresponding agar, agarose, or polyacrylamide, can be used to superimpose molecular sieving on electrophoretic migration (see Chap. 9).

Cellulose powder* may be used to achieve higher capacity per unit bed volume and also when molecular or ion sieving effects encountered on Sephadex and similar gel materials are undesirable.[1] Adsorption may sometimes be disturbing, but certain washing procedures should decrease the adsorption on ethanolyzed cellulose powder.[2]

Among other anticonvection agents, agar or agarose should be mentioned. They require equipment of other types.[3,4] Gorkin et al. have successfully used polymethacrylate,[5] and we have occasionally used plastic powders. The reader may be further informed elsewhere.[4]

c. Procedure for Serum Fractionation on Sephadex G-25

Sephadex G-25, fine grade, is allowed to swell for 2 hours in barbital buffer, pH 8.6, ionic strength 0.1.† The plug, B (Fig. 1), is deaerated in the buffer with the aid of vacuum and transferred to the column tube. The funnel, G is positioned in joint A3 on top of the tube, and the suspension of Sephadex is poured into the tube. After settling, the upper surface is made even and perfectly horizontal. Satisfactory zone movement during liquid flow should be checked by passing a narrow band of a colored substance (for example, dinitrophenylethanolamine) through the column. The tube is closed by replacing the funnel by the top piece, D, and the side tube is connected. The apparatus is transferred

---

* Commercially available from Grycksbo Pappersbruk, Grycksbo, Sweden.
[1] J. Porath, Sci. Tools 11, 21 (1964).
[2] S. Sorof, E. M. Young, R. A. McBride, and C. Binder, Sci. Tools 11, 27 (1964).
[3] S. Hjerten, J. Chromatog. 12, 510 (1963).
[4] J. Porath, and S. Hjerten, Methods Biochem. Anal. 9, 197 (1962).
[5] V. Z. Gorkin, A. A. Avakyan, I. V. Verevkina, and N. N. Kommissarova, Vopr. Med. Khim. 8, 638 (1962) [reprinted in Federation Proc. 22, 4 Part II (translation supplement) 619 (1963)].
† Buffer No. 7 or No. 9, Appendix II, used undiluted.

to buffer-filled electrode vessels, and liquid is drawn into the side tube by vacuum at *E2* with *A3–D1* kept closed. Liquid above the surface of the Sephadex bed is removed by a capillary tube inserted from the top through *D2*, and 1 ml of serum sample is allowed to drain into the column, through the same tube, followed by 1 ml of a dinitrophenylethanolamine solution and 2 ml of buffer. The upper part of the column limb is then filled with buffer, the stopcock *D2* is closed, and the top piece, *D*, is turned to make liquid connection to the side tube. The surface levels in the electrode vessels are then equalized.

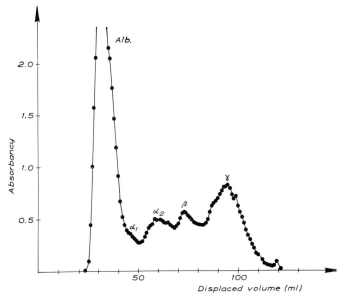

Fig. 2. Electrophoretic fractionation of human serum on 50×2-cm column of Sephadex G-25 in Veronal buffer, ionic strength 0.1, pH 8.6. Protein distribution was determined by the Folin-Lowry method.

Electrophoresis is started with a current of about 140 ma (500 volts across the electrodes). Electroendosmotic flow must be compensated by adding buffer to the cathode vessel until there is about 4-cm difference in level between the vessels. This should be sufficient to keep the yellow zone stationary. The electrolyte solution is periodically mixed. After 30 hours the power is shut off, the side arm disconnected, and the elution device, *C*, connected to *A*, and the column placed on a fraction collector. Elution is started with a flow rate of 1.7 ml/hour. The eluate solution may also be transported with a peristaltic pump via an absorptiometer (for example, LKB-UVI-CORD) to the fraction collector.

Figure 2 shows the protein distribution pattern obtained in the actual collected fractions. The UVICORD elution curve is similar except for a deviation in the albumin peak due to a contaminant in the dinitrophenylethanolamine (presumably dinitrophenol). The dye eluted far behind the γ-globulins and is not shown in the diagram.

After passage of the colored zone another experiment may be started on the same column. A column may be used repeatedly, but it is advisable to include a bacteriostatic agent (sodium azide, 2% butanol, or chloroform) in the buffer.

d. Large-Scale Preparations

A large-size compact apparatus is now commercially available.* The separation compartment consists of an externally and internally cooled

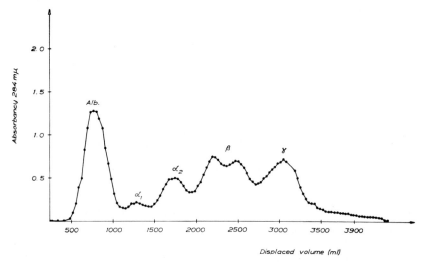

Fig. 3. Electrophoretic fractionation of 200 ml of human serum on cellulose powder. Electrolyte: 0.1 M Veronal, pH 8.6 with 0.002 M NaN₃; Separation time: 47 hours. Voltage: 425 volts. Current: 665 ma.

annular tube. The buffer in the electrode compartments is continuously mixed without disturbing the column bed. While electrophoretic fractionation is in progress, substances that have migrated to the bottom may be removed by countercurrent buffer flow through special outlets. Preparative column electrophoresis compares very favorably with continuous-flow methods when components of low mobilities, such as immuno-globulins, are to be separated.

* LBK-Produkter, Stockholm, Sweden.

Figure 3 illustrates the fractionation of 200 ml of serum on cellulose powder. The pattern corresponds exactly to that obtained in small-scale experiments with the apparatus described above (Section b, *i*, and Fig. 1) under otherwise comparable conditions. Samples exceeding 1000 ml have been successfully fractionated on cellulose columns. Although cellulose powder is considered to be a superior anticonvection support, Sephadex G-25 permits excellent separations of 25- to 250-ml samples.

3. PREPARATIVE ELECTROPHORESIS IN HORIZONTAL GELS*

Electrophoresis in horizontal gels (starch, agar, agarose, or acrylamide) has been widely used as an analytical tool. Recently, improvements in recovery have been introduced for preparative purposes.[1] After the electrophoretic run, the recovery of separated material from the gels is cumbersome and usually incomplete.†

a. GENERAL METHOD

By means of the device schematically represented in Fig. 1, some of these difficulties have been overcome.[2] It combines in a single run

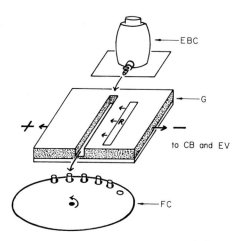

FIG. 1. Schematic representation of the apparatus used for preparative electrophoresis in a horizontal gel. *EBC,* elution buffer container; *G,* preparative gel layer; *EV,* electrode vessel; *CB,* gel connecting bridge; *FC,* fraction collector.

* Section 6,D,3 was contributed by José Uriel.

[1] P. M. Townseley, *Can. J. Biochem. Physiol.* **37**, 1025 (1959).
† For a preparative adaptation of electrophoresis on polyacrylamide, see Section D,5.
[2] S. Avrameas, and J. Uriel, *Nature* **202**, 1005 (1964).

the electrophoretic separation of the sample and the simultaneous recovery of resolved components by continuous elution. Two troughs are cut in the gel layer across the direction of the electrical field. One of them, the starting reservoir (R), is filled with the material to be separated. The other, the anodic collecting reservoir, serves for the elution of fractions. A continuous flow of electrolyte from a container runs through the trough to a fraction collector. When a potential difference is applied across the gel, all negatively charged molecules move toward the anode and successively approach the collecting trough where they are drained off the gel by the flow of the electrolyte and finally recovered in the fraction collector.

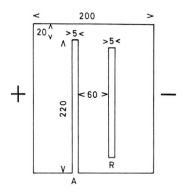

FIG. 2. The surface of the horizontal gel layer, showing position of the two troughs. R, starting reservoir; A, collecting trough. Distances are in millimeters.

The critical variable of the procedure is the distance between the two parallel troughs. This distance must be great enough to ensure resolution of the mixture, but short enough to permit the majority of the constituents to reach the collecting reservoir in a reasonable period of time (up to 8 hours). A prior analytical run must serve as a guide.

For recovery of cationic or electroösmotically moving proteins, as for the separation in agar of immunoglobulins from whole antisera, the second trough parallel to the starting reservoir is cut on the cathodic side and used for elution in the same manner as the anodic collecting reservoir. Isoelectric components at a given pH or those which for any other reason remain in the vicinity of the starting reservoir must be recovered from the gel by conventional methods. It may be possible to effect elution of such fractions by changing the experimental conditions of the electrophoretic run (pH of the buffer, gel support, etc.).

A potential gradient up to 8 volts/cm at room temperature is permissible for horizontal gels (agar, agarose, and acrylamide) no more than 8 to 10 mm thick. With special cooling systems these limits can be increased. The amount of material which can be separated in each experiment depends on the size of the gel layer. With a plate of the dimensions represented in Fig. 2 and a gel layer 8 mm thick, up to 250 mg of material can be separated in a single run.

b. APPARATUS

Details of the electrophoresis-elution unit* are given in Fig. 3. As far as possible, a single buffer solution is used to make the preparative

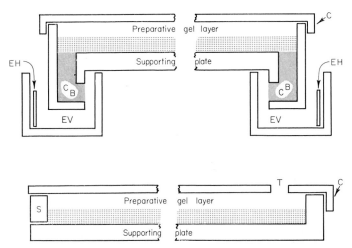

FIG. 3. Cross sections of the electrophoresis-elution unit, parallel and perpendicular to the electric field, upper and lower, respectively. *C*, cover plate; *EH*, electrode holder; *CB*, connecting bridge; *S*, removable side support; *B*, slit for insertion of the elution buffer tubing; *EV*, electrode vessel.

gel layer and the connection bridges (*CB*) as well as to fill the electrode vessels (*EV*), and the elution buffer container. Agar connecting bridges are preferable for reasons of economy, but the bridges can be also made of the same gel as the horizontal plate.

c. PROCEDURE

Preparative electrophoresis of adenosine nucleotides in agarose gel serves as an example of a procedure. Agarose gel† is prepared at 0.8% in sodium citrate–citric acid buffer, 0.025 M pH 4.8.‡ Connecting bridges

---

* Available from APELAB, 35, rue des Ecoles, Bagneux, Seine, France.
† Agarose powder is available from several commercial sources; see footnote, p. 149.
‡ Dissolve 2.42 gm of citric acid·H_2O and 3.97 gm of sodium citrate·$2H_2O$ per liter.

to the electrode vessels are prepared with buffered agarose at 1.2%. A quantity of melted agarose solution is poured on the supporting plate sufficient to obtain a horizontal layer 8 mm thick. When the gel is firm, the troughs are cut according to the pattern shown in Fig. 2.

A solution of adenosine mono-, di-, and tri-phosphates (AMP, ADP, and ATP), containing 5 mg of AMP and 2 mg of ADP and ATP per milliliter, is added to an equal amount of melted agarose (1.6% in sodium citrate buffer, 0.05 M, pH 4.8), mixed, and poured into the starting reservoir. Sodium citrate buffer, 0.05 M, pH 4.8, is used for elution

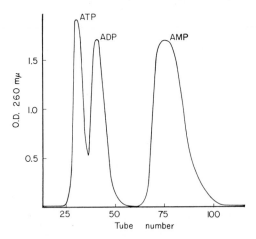

Fig. 4. Preparative electrophoresis of three adenosine nucleotides.

at a flow rate of 1.5 ml/min. A potential gradient of 5 volts/cm, as measured at the edges of the agarose plate, is applied during 4 hours in a cold room at 5°. The separation obtained is shown in Fig. 4.

4. ELECTROPHORESIS-CONVECTION*†

a. INTRODUCTION

Electrophoresis-convection is a mild physical method for fractionation of proteins in solution which utilizes a combination of electrophoretic and convective transport of the components to achieve separation.[1-4]

* Section 6,D,4 was contributed by John R. Cann.

† Contribution No. 241 from the Department of Biophysics, Florence R. Sabin Laboratories, University of Colorado Medical Center, Denver, Colorado.

[1] J. G. Kirkwood, J. *Chem. Phys.* **9**, 878 (1941).

[2] L. E. Nielsen and J. G. Kirkwood, *J. Am. Chem. Soc.* **68**, 181 (1946).

[3] J. G. Kirkwood, J. R. Cann, and R. A. Brown, *Biochim. Biophys. Acta* **5**, 301 (1950).

A large number of relatively homogeneous fractions are obtained in quantities sufficient to permit thorough physicochemical and immunological characterization. On the other hand, the fractionation cell can be scaled to handle either small or large quantities of material.[5] In addition to minimizing the risk of denaturation during fractionation, electrophoresis-convection possesses the advantage that the proteins do not come into contact with supporting media which might react with the sample or contaminate the fractions.

Investigations of experimental conditions for fractionation procedures were carried out by Brown et al.,[6,7] and a semicontinuous modification has been described.[8]

b. Apparatus and Principles of the Method

The principles of electrophoresis-convection are illustrated diagrammatically in Fig. 1 and may be described as follows: the cell, consisting of two reservoirs, A and B, connected by a narrow vertical convection channel, C, is filled with the protein solution to be fractionated. On application of a horizontal electric field, E, differential transport of the mobile components across the channel produces a horizontal density gradient. Under the influence of gravity, the dense solution near the far wall of the channel descends into the bottom reservoir, thereby initiating convective circulation in the channel. Superposition of the horizontal electrophoretic transport and the vertical convective transport causes movement of the mobile components from the top to the bottom reservoir at rates depending on their electrophoretic mobilities. Consequently, the top reservoir is enriched with respect to slow components and the bottom reservoir with respect to fast components. To avoid contamination of the protein solution by electrolysis products, the walls, D, of the convection channel are constructed of semipermeable membranes separated from the electrodes by buffer solution. The electric field across the channel is maintained by an electric current carried by the ions of the buffer electrolyte, to which the membranes are per-

[4] J. G. Kirkwood, J. R. Cann, and R. A. Brown, *Biochim. Biophys. Acta* **6**, 606 (1951).

[5] J. R. Cann, and J. G. Kirkwood, *Cold Spring Harbor Symp. Quant. Biol.* **14**, 9 (1950).

[6] R. A. Brown, J. B. Shumaker, Jr., J. R. Cann, and J. G. Kirkwood, *J. Am. Chem. Soc.* **73**, 4420 (1951).

[7] R. A. Brown, J. B. Shumaker, Jr., S. N. Timasheff, and J. G. Kirkwood, *J. Am. Chem. Soc.* **74**, 460 (1952).

[8] S. N. Timasheff, J. B. Shumaker, Jr., and J. G. Kirkwood, *Arch. Biochem. Biophys.* **47**, 455 (1953).

meable. The exterior buffer solution is replenished by a circulatory system at a rate sufficient to prevent electrolysis products from reaching the membranes, thus assuring constant pH. Operation of the electrophoresis-convection apparatus is carried out at 4° to dissipate heat.

Separation of a mixture such as serum into constituent proteins possessing discrete mobilities and isoelectric points is accomplished by successive immobilization of its components and transport of the mobile ones from the top to the bottom reservoir. The most alkaline or acidic

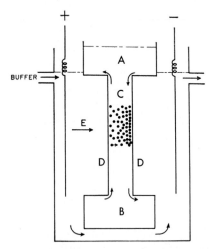

Fig. 1. Schematic representation of the electrophoresis-convection apparatus. Under the influence of the electric field, E, the protein molecules in the convection channel, C, migrate to the right. The resulting dense solution near the right-hand membrane descends into the bottom reservoir, B, thereby inducing convective circulation in the channel. The net result is differential transport of mobile proteins from the top reservoir, A, into the bottom reservoir.

component is the first to be immobilized by operating at its isoelectric pH. The transport process leaves pure immobile component in the top reservoir. However, only about half of the immobile component is so isolated, the remainder being in the bottom reservoir and channel mixed with all the other components. Consequently, several successive stages of operation are necessary for complete separation. The bottom cut from the last stage is a concentrate of the mobile components. The process is repeated until the mixture is resolved. By using an apparatus permitting semicontinuous operation, separation can be accomplished in a single stage.

c. FRACTIONATION OF γ-GLOBULINS

The following method is used routinely in the author's laboratory to prepare γ_2-globulin (γG) for physicochemical investigations. Serum diluted with 1 volume of buffer, or a 3% solution of its globulin fraction prepared by $(NH_4)_2SO_4$ precipitation (see Vol I, Chap. 3,A,2), is equilibrated by dialysis against phosphate buffer, ionic strength 0.1, pH 7. The separation is carried out on 150 ml of protein solution in the standard-size apparatus (Cann and co-workers[9]) with an electric current of 0.65 ampere, which corresponds to a field strength of about 2 volts/cm. The solution removed from the top reservoir after 48 hours of operation contains pure γ_2-globulin.

A modified procedure is used to fractionate a protein such as γ_2-globulin. While showing a single moving boundary in the Tiselius apparatus, γ_2-globulin is nevertheless heterogeneous and reveals a mobility distribution by reversible electrophoretic boundary spreading. Fractionation is carried out at a pH displaced by an arbitrary amount from the mean isoelectric point of γ_2-globulin. Transport in the apparatus leads to redistribution of the protein ions such that the fractions withdrawn from the top and bottom reservoirs possess mobility distributions differing from that of the original protein depending on the operating pH. A set of fractions possessing the desired mean mobilities and isoelectric points can be obtained by appropriate choice of operating pH. The guiding principle is that transport proceeds to a stationary state in which the top fraction is isoelectric at the operating pH.

d. ANTIBODY-CONTAINING FRACTIONS OF SERUM

The modified procedure is used for studies on the distribution of antibodies among the serum proteins. If successive stages of fractionation are carried out at different pH levels near the isoelectric point of γ_2-globulin, a number of γ_2-globulin fractions possessing different mean electrophoretic mobilities can be obtained. As the operating pH is progressively lowered, fractions rich in β-globulin can be similarly obtained. Usually the pH is lowered stepwise between about pH 8 and 5 at intervals of about 0.5 pH unit. It is sometimes desirable at a given stage in the fractionation to carry out two or three successive operations at the same pH before proceeding. Serum, which has been diluted with 1 volume of buffer and then dialyzed against buffer, serves as the starting material for the first stage. The protein solution removed from the top reservoir at the end of each stage is set aside for subsequent characterization.

[9] J. R. Cann, R. A. Brown, and J. G. Kirkwood, *J. Biol. Chem.* **181**, 161 (1949).

The solution from the bottom reservoir and channel serves as the starting material for the succeeding stage, the original volume being restored with buffer before dialysis. The final bottom fraction is separated into albumin and α-globulin fractions by $(NH_4)_2SO_4$ precipitation. (See Fig. 2 of Section B for the electrophoretic patterns of a serum and some of its fractions obtained as described herein.) Operating conditions are: (1) phosphate buffers, ionic strength 0.1, pH 8.1 to 5.5, with an electric current of 0.65 ampere for standard-size cell and operating time of 48 hours; and (2) for the last stage of fractionation, $0.1M$ acetate buffer at pH 5.3 and 0.7 ampere for 72 hours. These conditions serve as a guide for the fractionation of other biological materials. In general, the protein concentration should not exceed 3.5%; the ionic strength may be lower than 0.1 if so dictated by the electrophoretic properties of the system under investigation, but osmotic transport of solvent into the channel from the external buffer solution may be troublesome at sufficiently low ionic strengths.

e. APPLICATIONS

In addition to the analysis and fractionation of human serum proteins mentioned above, bovine γ-globulin,[9] and diphtheria antitoxin,[10] several other interesting biological systems have been studied by electrophoresis convection. These include the egg white proteins, conalbumin[11,12] and ovomucoid[13]; insulin[14,15]; and ragweed allergen.[16] Another useful application is the fractionation of substances forming soluble complexes.[15,17]

[10] J. R. Cann, J. G. Kirkwood, R. A. Brown, and O. J. Plescia, *J. Am. Chem. Soc.* **71**, 1603 (1949).

[11] R. A. Phelps, and J. R. Cann, *Arch. Biochem. Biophys.* **61**, 51 (1956).

[12] S. N. Timasheff and I. Tinoco, Jr., *Arch. Biochem. Biophys.* **66**, 427 (1957).

[13] M. Bier, L. Terminiello, J. A. Duke, R. J. Gibbs, and F. F. Nord, *Arch. Biochem. Biophys.* **47**, 465 (1953).

[14] S. N. Timasheff, R. A. Brown, and J. G. Kirkwood, *J. Am. Chem. Soc.* **75**, 3121 (1953).

[15] S. N. Timasheff, and J. G. Kirkwood, *J. Am. Chem. Soc.* **75**, 3124 (1953).

[16] M. H. Loveless, and S. N. Timasheff, *Arch. Biochem. Biophys.* **58**, 298 (1955).

[17] S. J. Singer, S. N. Timasheff, and J. G. Kirkwood, *J. Am. Chem. Soc.* **74**, 5985 (1952).

CHAPTER 7

Preparative and Analytical Ultracentrifugation*

A. Introduction

In consequence of the availability of practical ultracentrifugation instruments in the last decade, tremendous advances have been made in both the theoretical and practical aspects of determining various molecular parameters, and in the development of procedures for the mild concentration and purification of biologically or chemically active agents. This chapter presents a systematic approach to such concentration, purification, and characterization of the macromolecular agents that engage the attention of immunochemists, and it illustrates that the different methods in use are complementary and not competitive.

The ultracentrifuge should be used at the very beginning of an investigation without any misconception that the biological agent under investigation has to be "pure" before certain fundamental molecular parameters can be established.

The quantitative application of preparative techniques and the general relationships between analytical and preparative procedures are emphasized at the expense of theoretical considerations. The basic mathematical relationships given in Section G constitute a summary for reference and possible further amplification of the few text equations given, and are not intended to be a development of theory. The reader is referred to standard treatises[1-5] for details and to a recent review[5a] for the impact of digital computers on ultracentrifugation.

* Chapter 7 was contributed by Rodes Trautman and Keith M. Cowan.

[1] T. Svedberg and K. O. Pedersen, "The Ultracentrifuge." Oxford Univ. Press, London (Johnson Reprint Corporation, New York), 1940.

[2] H. K. Schachman, in "Methods in Enzymology" (S. P. Colowick and N. O. Kaplan, eds.), Vol. IV, p. 32. Academic Press, New York, 1957.

[3] H. K. Schachman, "Ultracentrifugation in Biochemistry." Academic Press, New York, 1959.

[4] H. Fujita, "Mathematical Theory of Sedimentation Analysis." Academic Press, New York, 1962.

[5] J. W. Williams, "Ultracentrifugal Analysis in Theory and Experiment." Academic Press, New York, 1963.

[5a] R. Trautman, Fractions, No. 2 (1966) (Beckman Instruments, Inc.).

1. INSTRUMENTS REQUIRED

Ultracentrifugation is the *quantitative* application of centrifugal force to solutions of molecules or particles. It does not necessarily mean using high-speed equipment, elaborate optical systems, or only sedimentation. The *drive* is the power unit which spins the *rotor* holding *cells* or *tubes* which contain the *solution* of molecules or *suspension* of particles. In a *preparative run* the contents of the tubes are analyzed after the centrifugation period, whereas in an *analytical run* the solute distribution along a radius in the cell is observed during centrifugation. In a *continuous-flow run,* input and/or output of material occurs during centrifugation.

Ultracentrifuge instrumentation reached a highly useful plateau in the 1950's, with development of commercial equipment capable of producing forces up to 200,000 times gravity in solutions of practical volume. Besides the interchangeable electric drive it includes: (1) swinging-bucket rotors, (2) angle rotors, (3) analytical rotors accommodating up to four cells, (4) temperature devices with range and control from 0° to 40°, (5) cells with thicknesses covering a factor of 10 in sensitivity, and (6) wedge quartz windows permitting several cells to be used simultaneously. Some additional equipment that is useful, but not necessary, includes (1) a two-dimensional comparator with printing desk calculator, (2) interference and absorption optical systems, (3) a gradient-forming device, (4) hand refractometers, and (5) a recording spectrophotometer with flow cell and fraction collector. Current instruction manuals are good, and some manufacturers offer training courses as well as excellent field engineering service.

2. TEN PRINCIPLES

The ultracentrifuge can be operated without a detailed understanding of theory; in fact, theoretical treatment is not available for many of the complex arrangements of rotors, cells, and solutes or solvents used in the major methods shown in Fig. 1.[6] However, in designing experiments to utilize the systematic relative motion caused by the centrifugal field in the presence of diffusion, it is helpful to be cognizant of the following ten principles underlying the application of centrifugal force.

a. MAJOR METHODS

Six major ultracentrifugation methods are used to exploit differences in size, shape, mass, or density of molecules or particles in a solution

[6] R. Trautman, *in* "Instrumental Methods of Experimental Biology" (D. W. Newman, ed.), p. 211. Macmillan, New York, 1964.

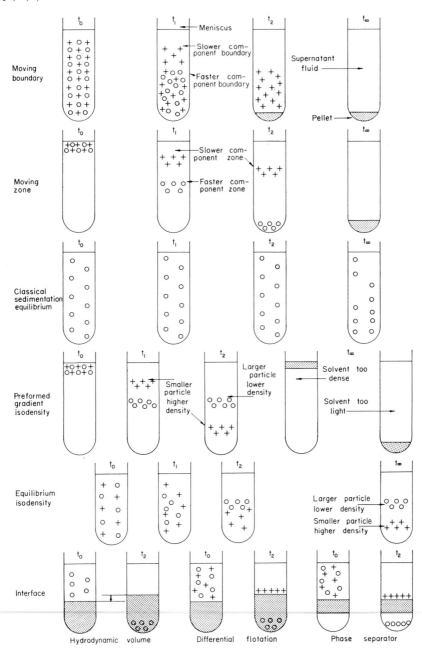

FIG. 1. Methods of ultracentrifugation. Either preparative or analytical centrifuges can be used, and tubes or cells can have various shapes. In all figures, circles represent hypothetical particles faster (larger or more symmetrical) but less dense than particles marked as crosses. t_0, initial loading; t_1, t_2, two successive times during centrifugation; t_∞, equilibrium. From Trautman (ref. 6), reprinted courtesy The Macmillan Company.

(Fig. 1). "Moving boundary" and "moving zone" are *velocity* methods based on size or shape differences; "classical sedimentation equilibrium" and "equilibrium isodensity" exploit mass differences at *thermodynamic equilibrium;* "preformed gradient isodensity" and "equilibrium isodensity" (besides its use mentioned above, and also called "field-formed gradient isodensity") are based on buoyant *density* differences; and the "interface" methods exploit differential penetration of, and selective denaturation by, *immiscible fluids.*

b. REDISTRIBUTION DETECTION

The reason for applying centrifugal force is to cause redistribution of solute and solvent. Eight major assays are available to reveal this redistribution, and each has its own conversion factor to give mass concentration. *Biological, chemical,* and *radioactivity assays* are based on specific activity. *Schlieren optics, interference optics,* and *refractometry* are based on relatively nonspecific changes in the index of refraction. *Absorption optics* and *light-scattering optics* are based on extinction and light-scattering coefficients, which in part are specific.

Optical assays performed during centrifugation provide extensive "data" because of the continuous registration along a cell radius; yet this does not necessarily make them superior to activity or optical assays performed after the centrifugation on fractions collected from a tube. Six methods of *fractionation* of tube contents are illustrated in Fig. 2. Prior to fractionation, it is sometimes useful to examine the tubes, after a preparative run, in a darkened room for light-scattering zones by means of a narrow beam of light entering at right angles. Colored bands and boundaries should also be noted under general illumination. Examples of optical assays are shown in Fig. 3.

c. S-RATE

Centrifugal force causes particles in solution to attain a *terminal velocity* which increases with differences in their size, mass, or density relative to the solution, and decreases both with viscosity of the solution and deviations from spherical shape. The *sedimentation coefficient* (abbreviated as s-rate) is an operational quantity computed from an observed terminal velocity which is divided by the strength of the centrifugal field. The practical unit is S (for Svedberg), equal to 10^{-13} second. Values of s-rate are usually converted to standard conditions of infinite dilution in water at 20° and denoted either as $s_{20,w}^0$ or merely $s_{20,w}$. In the moving-boundary method, the level in the cell or tube representing the *boundary position* in a broad boundary region is chosen so that its s-rate is equal to the s-rate of the particles in the *plateau* solution ahead where the concentration is

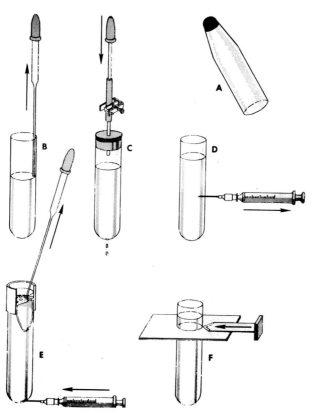

FIG. 2. Fractionation methods after preparative centrifugation. Fractionation should be done at temperature of run to avoid convection. Arrows show direction of fluid or air flow. Only *F* requires special equipment. *A*, decantation. *B*, removal with a Pasteur pipet whose tip must be kept at the meniscus so that a mixture of air bubbles and solution is withdrawn. Foam is broken, after transfer to calibrated tube, by centrifugation, as in a desk-top clinical centrifuge, for accurate measurement of volume. *C*, drip-out method. The tube must be sealed at the top before it is punctured with a needle. The speed of the drops is governed by the screw clamp, and final emptying (or freeing clogged puncture) is done by squeezing the bulb after covering the hole at the top with finger. *D*, syringe withdrawal method, after puncture. *E*, Flow-out-top method, accomplished by slow injection of a dense sucrose solution in bottom. *F*, tube slicer method, useful for separation into two fractions with large numbers of tubes. From Trautman (ref. 6), reprinted courtesy The Macmillan Company.

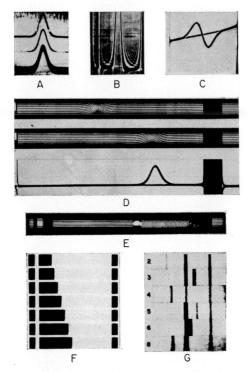

Fig. 3. Major optical assays in analytical ultracentrifugation. (*A–C*) Phase-plate schlieren optics are widely used and are most rugged, versatile, and sensitive to heterogeneity. *A,* moving-boundary method. Comparison of three schlieren diaphragms: wire, phase-plate, and bar, from top to bottom. *B,* phase plate at high magnification in vertical dimension (15° angle). *C,* isodensity equilibrium method for bovine serum albumin, initially at 1 mg/ml in ρ 1.28 CsCl, double-sector cell, 56,100 rpm for 24 hours at 25°. (*D, E*) Rayleigh interference optics are more precise than schlieren optics for measurements of concentration, but are complicated to use and limited in application. In *D,* the moving-boundary method is applied to bushy stunt virus, 5 mg/ml, 14,290 rpm. The top pattern represents 96 minutes, the middle pattern represents 128 minutes. The bottom comparison phase-plate schlieren pattern was made at 130 minutes, 80° angle. A double-sector cell is required. *E,* classical sedimentation equilibrium method for sucrose at 54 mg/ml, 35,600 rpm (sapphire windows), in a short column (4.5 mm). (*F, G*) Absorption optics are most easily automated with a scanning photocell and are most promising for specificity. Densitometer tracings are required for accurate measurements if absorption films are used. *F,* moving-boundary method, showing a single component at successive times during run: purified poliomyelitis virus at 0.2 mg/ml, 23,150 rpm, 2 minutes between exposures (154 S). *G,* isodensity equilibrium method for bacteriophage in ρ 1.50 CsCl at 27,690 rpm for 12 hours at 20°. The dense phage in the right-hand band was added as a marker in the several runs shown. The middle common band is normal λ-bacteriophage, whereas the third band in each photograph is a transducing phage which has a variable density in the series of lysates. From Trautman (ref. 6), reprinted courtesy The Macmillan Company.

constant with respect to radius but changes with time. Correspondingly, in the moving-zone method the *zone position* is chosen so that it moves at the average s-rate of the individual particles in the zone.[7] The s-rate of an active agent can be determined without prior purification and with a smaller percentage of error than that of the assay.

d. DIFFUSION

Movement of any one particle by centrifugal force is superimposed on the particle's *Brownian motion,* which is much larger. Brownian movement itself can result in a net displacement of particles, such *diffusion* increasing with abruptness of concentration changes and decreasing with solution viscosity, particle size, and deviations from spherical shape. Both diffusion and centrifugal *transport* occur in almost all ultracentrifuge runs. Diffusion is used to advantage in (1) determining mass by methods of either classical sedimentation equilibrium or equilibrium isodensity, (2) obtaining a sufficiently broad boundary to quantitate the concentration in the moving-boundary method, and (3) establishing a density gradient in the field-formed isodensity method. Diffusion limits the degree of resolution in determinations of heterogeneity.

e. CENTRIFUGAL FORCE

The gravitation-like *centrifugal* force acts at a distance on particles in solution and is proportional to the radius and the square of the (angular) speed. It neither breaks chemical or hydrogen bonds nor aligns asymmetric particles. Thus, the ultracentrifuge does not remove nucleic acid from nucleoprotein or lipid from lipoproteins. Any association or dissociation of molecules that may occur is due to *mass action effects* on the chemical equilibrium as a result of changes in concentration, and not to centrifugal force per se.

f. CONVECTION

An increase of solution density with radius due to changes in solute composition provides a bulk solution stability which is magnified by the centrifugal field; but compression density gradients do not provide stability, and *density inversions* result in convection.

g. SOLVATION

The *density* of a particle or molecule (its mass divided by its volume) is operationally determined in the ultracentrifuge as the density of a solution in which the particle neither sediments nor floats. The density

---

[7] V. N. Schumaker and J. Rosenbloom, *Biochemistry* **4,** 1005 (1965).

of a particle in solution includes contributions from both the *dry* particle and its *solvation mantle* (for example, protein of partial specific volume 0.75 ml/gm and with hydration of 0.2 ml/gm would have an actual density of $1.2/(0.75 + 0.2) = 1.26$ gm/ml). If the solvation mantle takes up salt, sucrose, or other solvent components to the same concentration as they are present in the bulk solution, the centrifugal force on the solvation mantle is numerically the same as its buoyant force. Thus, in many situations only the *anhydrous molecular weight* and the *dry density* (reciprocal of partial specific volume) need to be considered. However, the size and shape of the solvated particle governs the frictional force, and the *solvated particle density* governs possible penetration into immiscible organic fluids.

h. RESOLUTION

In velocity methods, *detection* and *resolution* of contaminants are increased with speed, cell depth (in direction of migration), and concentration. In the equilibrium isodensity method, resolution is independent of speed but is dependent on the material used for establishing the gradient.

i. DURATION OF RUNS

The *time required to sediment* (or float) any given particles in velocity methods (moving boundary and moving zone) is related almost directly to the volume used and inversely to the square of the speed used; with increase in temperature the time decreases roughly in proportion to the viscosity. In equilibrium methods, the *time required to reach* (within a given closeness to) *equilibrium* in a negligible gradient density (classical sedimentation equilibrium) is proportional to the square of the column depth, is inversely proportional to the diffusion coefficient, and is essentially independent of the speed. In an appreciable density gradient (equilibrium isodensity), however, such time is inversely proportional to both the fourth power of the speed and the first power of the s-rate determined without a gradient.

j. NONIDEALITY

Complications encountered in establishing an elementary theory of ultracentrifugation are of seven types: (1) *geometrical complications,* due to using various shaped cells in a nonuniform field of force; (2) *solvation* and *specific binding,* due to interactions, at equilibrium, with the solvent and other solutes; (3) *concentration dependence,* due to interactions with other particles of the same type and other sedimenting solutes at the finite concentrations used; (4) *electrical charge effects,* due to the electrical field set up by relative displacement of oppositely charged constituents; (5) *mass action*—chemical conversion due to association or dissociation reactions; (6) *pressure dependence,* due to the elevated hydrostatic pressure with depth of the solution; and (7) *heterogeneity,* due to the *paucidispersity* and *polydispersity* of the solutes.

3. APPLICATION OF ULTRACENTRIFUGATION

The idealized application of ultracentrifugal methods to an immunochemical problem can be traced through the sequence indicated in Fig. 4. At the start, it is assumed that the phenomenon of interest has been explored to the extent of establishing a relatively quantitative assay for the agent (for example, its activity has been found to be inversely proportional to the end-point dilution). Further, the active agent must be reasonably stable for a few hours at some temperature between 0° and 40°.

Block 1 of Fig. 4 lists the centrifugations to be done and the information that may be derived from preparative swinging-bucket rotor runs, analyzed by assays of activity. The resultant s-rate and density data are necessary to interpret analytical ultracentrifuge patterns of the crude material used to determine the physical characteristics of contaminants (block 3). All this information may then be utilized to develop rational purification and concentration procedures of noncentrifugal (block 4) or centrifugal (block 5) types. Large-scale ultracentrifugation methods may be required, as indicated in block 6. Once the agent is purified, the analytical ultracentrifuge is used for precise measurements of four major types, as indicated by the subdivisions of block 7.

The centrifugation methods shown represent interplays between preparative and analytical procedures. A valuable attribute of ultracentrifugation is the ability to give not only molecular parameters but also concentration and purification of the agents. Once these molecular parameters are obtained, it is possible to determine a conversion factor relating the original biological assay with concentration of the agent, in terms either of weight (specific activity) or of the numbers of particles involved (molar activity). This is indicated in block 8 of Fig. 4 and is the logical end of the sequence.

B. Moving-Boundary Methods

1. PURPOSE

The moving-boundary method (Fig. 1) is by far the most frequently used centrifugation technique, commonly referred to as a pelleting or

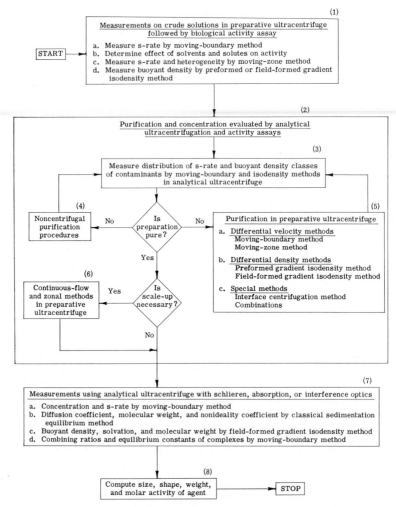

Fig. 4. Flow chart of application of ultracentrifugation to agents of immunochemical interest. The blocks numbered 1 to 7 show the interrelationship of complementary preparative and analytical ultracentrifugation runs, based on the methods outlined in Fig. 1 for separating an agent with biological activity. Block 8 indicates the final computation of the physical parameters of the agent and the conversion factor between its concentration and its activity.

clarifying preparative procedure or conventional analytical ultracentrifugation. As generally applied, the solute is originally uniformly distributed throughout the tube or cell; that is, a concentration *plateau* exists initially (Fig. 1, t_0). On application of a sufficient centrifugal field, *transport* (net movement of solute with respect to solvent) of the solute occurs. Depending on the relative densities of solute and solvent, transport may be toward the bottom of the tube (*sedimentation*) or toward the top of the tube (*flotation*). As centrifugation and subsequent transport proceed, a boundary develops between two adjacent plateaus, or multiple boundaries may be formed with complex systems (Fig. 1, t_1 and t_2). When the centrifugation period and force are sufficient, pelleting of the solute results (Fig. 1, t_∞). In addition to transport, *convection* may occur. This is a bulk movement of the fluid, both solvent and solute together. A slight density gradient prevents radial convection, even in angle rotors, but not the desired convection perpendicular to a radius in such rotors. With crude preparations the boundaries themselves are frequently adequate to stabilize the transport.

Since particles in the plateau are not directly visible, the moving-boundary method relies on observing a boundary between the *supernatant fluid* and the plateau by using some colligative property of the solution. In the boundary region there will be other processes besides centrifugation taking place; for example, with diffusion, individual particles may move opposite to the field, and, with chemical reaction, they may convert from one complex to another. Even so, a *boundary position* may be computed from the concentration distribution which moves with the same s-rate as do particles ahead in the plateau region where the solute concentration is constant with radius. In the quantitative moving-boundary procedure, it is necessary to select conditions that will move the initial boundary (usually from the meniscus) to an appropriate position in the cell or tube, determine its precise location, and compute the s-rate and concentration of particles present.[8]

A relationship exists between the average s-rate, s^* (in Svedbergs), of a particle and the time, t'' (in hours), required to sediment a hypothetical test particle through any particular portion of a tube of any initial volume (*fill*) in a given rotor.[9,10] The use of this relationship is greatly facilitated if the rotor characteristics are expressed as a quantity called $\overline{ST}$ ("S-T-bar") which can be tabulated as a function of volume measured from the bottom of the tube (Table I). In term of $\Delta\overline{ST}$, the difference between $\overline{ST}$ values for any volume under consideration, s^*t'' can be written

$$s^*t'' = \Delta\overline{ST}\ [(rpm)_{max}/(rpm)]^2 \tag{1}$$

where (rpm) is the symbol for (angular) speed used. The units of speed, revolutions per minute, will be denoted rpm. The manufacturer's maxi-

[8] R. Trautman and S. S. Breese, Jr., *J. Phys. Chem.* **63**, 1592 (1959).

[9] C. de Duve and J. Berthet, *Nature* **172**, 1142 (1953).

[10] R. Trautman, *in* "Ultracentrifugal Analysis in Theory and Experiment" (J. W. Williams, ed.), 203. Academic Press, New York, 1963.

TABLE I
ROTOR CHARACTERISTICS FOR COMPUTATION OF s-RATES IN PREPARATIVE ULTRACENTRIFUGATION

Spinco Model E rotors

	AN-D	AN-E
$\overline{ST}{}^a$	16.4	22.8
Sector Vol. (ml) — 2°	0.4	1.0
Sector Vol. (ml) — 2.5°	0.5	1.25
Sector Vol. (ml) — 4°	0.8	2.0
Optical thickness (mm)	12	30
Max. speed (rpm)	59,780	50,740
$10^3\,g$	260	187

Spinco Model L rotors — $\overline{ST}{}^a$ (Svedberg hours)

Vol. (ml)	50	SW-39	40	40.2	40.3
13.5			120	131	81
10	66		75	100	62
6.5	32				
6	30				
5	27	94	45		
4	23	71	39	69	43
3	20	51	35	53	35
2	18	33	28	38	28
1	14	17	21	25	22

Vol. (ml)	30	SW-25.1	21
94			440
40			125
38.5	210		
35	170	379	
30	124	301	100
25	104	236	
20	88	181	80
15	71	131	
10	55	87	65
5	41	50	

Spinco Model L rotors — parameters

	50	SW-39	40	40.2	40.3	30	SW-25.1	21
Max. speed (10^3 rpm)	50	40	40	40	40	30	25	21
Number of tubes	10	3	12	12	18	12	3	10
Max. ml/tube	10	5	13.5	6.5	6.5	38.5	35	94
Angle	20°	90°	26°	40°	20°	26°	90°	18°
RCF^b in $10^3\,g$ — Top	103	78	68	63	86	50	37	30
RCF^b in $10^3\,g$ — Middle	151	125	105	102	114	78	54	44
RCF^b in $10^3\,g$ — Bottom	198	173	145	143	143	106	90	59

Oak Ridge Zonal BIV

Vol. (ml)	$\overline{ST}{}^a$
1685	159
1600	135
1400	98
1200	73
1000	55
800	40
600	28
400	17
200	8

Max. speed (10^3 rpm)	40
Number of tubes	4 connected sectors
Max. ml/tube	1685
Angle	90°
RCF^b in $10^3\,g$ — Top	33
RCF^b in $10^3\,g$ — Middle	62
RCF^b in $10^3\,g$ — Bottom	91

International Equipment Company, 259 rotor, 384 bucket

200-ml bottle Vol. (ml)	$\overline{ST}{}^a$	15-ml tube (989 carrier) Vol. (ml)	$\overline{ST}{}^a$
200	38,300	15	37,400
180	33,500	10	22,400
160	29,300	5	14,300
140	25,400	1	5,800
120	21,600	0.5	3,800
100	17,900	0.4	3,300
80	14,300	0.3	2,700
60	11,200	0.2	2,000
40	8,100	0.1	1,100
20	4,700		

	200-ml bottle	15-ml tube
Max. speed (10^3 rpm)	2	2
Number of tubes	6	42
Max. ml/tube	200	15
Angle	90°	90°
RCF^b in $10^3\,g$ — Top	0.60	0.60
RCF^b in $10^3\,g$ — Middle	0.80	0.80
RCF^b in $10^3\,g$ — Bottom	1.06	1.06

^{a} $\overline{ST}$ values are in Svedberg hours.
^{b} RCF denotes relative centrifugal force.

mum rated speed is $(rpm)_{max}$. No correction has been made for rotor expansion or for variability in tube sizes. Table I is applicable to angle as well as swinging-bucket rotors and to both cylindrical tubes and sector-shaped cavities. For example, suppose the analytical ultracentrifuge is to be used to assay the amount of 19 S class materials in serum. With the Spinco AN-D rotor the time at top speed for complete traverse of the cell would be $t'' = 16.4/19 = 0.8$ hour. It would still be quite short at 52,640 rpm $[(16.4/19)\ (59,780/52,640)^2 = 1.2$ hours], the speed commonly used at 20°. Refinements in the table and in the s-rates used can be made as necessary. Preparative examples follow.

2. SELECTION OF PREPARATIVE ROTOR, SPEED, TIME, AND TEMPERATURE

Suppose a sample contains material of known s-rate, and it is desired to pellet this agent by centrifugation. As an example, suppose it is desired to obtain the 19 S antibody from a serum with little contaminating 7 S antibody, and also to obtain the 7 S antibody free from the 19 S component in as high a yield as possible. We should like to select centrifugation conditions where the 19 S antibody will just be pelleted. If the centrifugation proceeds too long, the pellet will contain an excess amount of 7 S antibody and a concomitant decrease in that component above the pellet. If centrifugation is inadequate, a relatively poor recovery of 19 S antibody will occur in the pellet and the fluid above will be contaminated with 19 S material.

Procedure. Select the rotor on the basis of the amount of material to be centrifuged. In the example, assume that approximately 100 ml of serum is available, so the Spinco No. 40 rotor would be selected by using 13.5 ml per tube. Compute the centrifugation time at maximum speed, at room temperature (20°), and with full tubes to just pellet the 19 S component. From Table I and Eq. (1), sedimentation from meniscus to the bottom corresponds to $\Delta \overline{ST} = 120 - 0$, $t'' = 120/19 = 6.3$ hours.

Adjustments. If the computed time is too short to be practical, a lower speed will provide a longer centrifugation time. If the computed time is too long, decrease the volume and substitute mineral oil to completely fill the tubes. If the computed time is too long for a labile material to retain activity at 20°, a lower temperature will have to be selected, and the time or speed will have to be altered upward to compensate for the lowered s-rate caused mainly by the increase in viscosity of the water. (A rule of thumb is that the s-rate increases approximately 3% per degree centigrade for water. All refrigerated centrifuges can be operated at any temperature, and the operator should change the setting as desired. Note that in ones without direct measurement of rotor temperature, the refrigerated chamber must be 10 to 20 degrees colder than the rotor to maintain it constant.) Recompute the time for the rotor, temperature, and speed finally chosen.

Although the example presented is somewhat idealized, it illustrates a rational approach to the selection of centrifugation conditions for preparative purposes of either the pelleting or clarifying type.

3. SUPERNATANT-PELLET METHOD FOR DETERMINATION OF S-RATE OF UNKNOWNS

Procedure. Fill the swinging-bucket rotor tube with crude starting material. Centrifuge at constant speed and temperature for a known time (approximated as the period between reaching two-thirds of the operating speed on both acceleration and deceleration). Fractionate the tube contents after the centrifugation period into at least the supernatant and resuspended pellet. Assay the fractions. Repeat the run, changing the time or speed, or both, to find the time, t'', for which the active agent has *just* completely gone into the pellet or bottom fraction of known volume. Compute s^*, using Eq. (1).

Example. Consider Table II, which represents hypothetical data obtained on just two fractions from three swinging-bucket runs of an

TABLE II
SAMPLE CALCULATION OF s-RATE OF IMMUNOLOGICALLY ACTIVE AGENT BY THREE CENTRIFUGATIONS AT 20° IN SPINCO SW-39 ROTOR AT 36,000 RPM

Fraction	Per cent activity recovered after:		
	4 hours	6 hours	8 hours
Top 4 ml	20	1	0.4
Bottom 1 ml	80	99	99.6

From data: time t'' to *just* empty top 4 ml = 6 hours.

From Table I for top 4 ml: $\Delta \overline{ST} = 94 - 17 = 77$.

From Eq. (1): $s^* = \left(\dfrac{77}{6}\right)\left(\dfrac{40,000}{36,000}\right)^2 = 16 \text{ S}$

immunologically active agent. The top 4-ml fraction extends from 5 ml to 1 ml. From Table I the corresponding $\overline{ST}$ values are 94 and 17 for the SW-39 rotor. From the data presented, an s-rate of 16 S is calculated from Eq. (1). From this simple procedure the general s-rate class of the agent of concern is readily established.

Notes. The *partition cell* has a sector-shaped centerpiece and a central partition (either fixed and perforated, or moving and solid) which permits fractionation into just two compartments after centrifugation in the analytical rotor.[11] It was developed before the swinging-bucket rotor and should be considered superseded when the swinging bucket is used as described in the next section. However, classical errors committed with the two-compartment cell are also possible with the supernatant-pellet method above and can be specified as follows.

(1) Only two fractions are taken. This limitation not only prevents establishing a plateau but usually results in activity being found in both compartments. The computed s-rates have too large an error because of the biological assay error. (2) A plateau does not exist because centrifugation was too long. The s-rates computed will be too low (for example, see third time (8 hours) in example above, Table II), since activity detected in the upper compartment was due to boundary spreading, convection, or general contamination. (3) Total recovery is low because the agent was inactivated or adsorbed to the partition. The computed s-rate probably refers to something else. A check must be made on the total recovery in all experiments of this type.

4. PRECISE BOUNDARY LOCATION IN PREPARATIVE RUNS

A more precise determination of s-rate than that given by the supernatant-pellet method requires stopping the centrifuge before the boundary reaches the bottom of the tube. Therefore, techniques for precise boundary location have become quite elaborate.[8,12,12a] In principle many measurements in any one tube are combined to yield a single value of the boundary position. In all procedures, it is essential to have a reasonable movement of the boundary, yet still be able to demonstrate a plateau; hence the boundary should be centrifuged one-half to two-thirds the length of the solution column.

Procedure. In a cylindrical preparative tube, a slight density gradient to prevent radial convection is needed only if the agent has been partially purified. Sucrose is used for this purpose as follows: For a Spinco SW-39 tube put 150 mg of sucrose into each of two containers, and add 3 ml and 6 ml of the sample to give 50 mg/ml and 25 mg/ml of sucrose, respectively. Transfer 1 ml of the former to each of three centrifuge tubes, layer 2 ml of the latter solution on each, and then 2 ml of the sample. Slight agitation with a saw-toothed wire blurs the density steps into a smooth gradient of sucrose with the agent uniformly distributed.

[11] D. A. Yphantis, *in* "Ultracentrifugal Analysis in Theory and Experiment" (J. W. Williams, ed.), p. 227. Academic Press, New York, 1963.
[12] G. H. Hogeboom and E. L. Kuff, *J. Biol. Chem.* **210**, 733 (1954).
[12a] K. Strohmaier, *Anal. Biochem.* **15**, 109 (1966).

Use both slow acceleration (~2000 rpm/min by manually advancing speed dial) and slow deceleration (by not using brake).

A series of fractions of the tube contents are collected, usually by aspiration (Fig. 2B) or drip-out (Fig. 2C), and assayed. Either the volume or the radius of the fractions is needed. The latter is established by aligning the tube against a millimeter scale. In the SW-39 rotor, the tip of the tube is 9.8 cm from the center of rotation, and, by matching the bottom of the tube with this point, the new meniscus levels are recorded as samples are removed.

Computation. If a large number of data points are available, make a plot of concentration against radial distance. Check that a plateau exists and that the total recovery is reasonable. Approximate the boundary position as the location of the half-concentration point. Compute the s-rate in Svedbergs from Eq. (1) if volumes and $\overline{ST}$ values are used, or from the equivalent relationship in terms of radius as

$$s^* = \left[\frac{2.303(10^{13})}{60\omega^2}\right]\left(\frac{\log \bar{r} - \log r_a}{t'}\right) \tag{2}$$

where common logs to the base 10 are used, $\bar{r}$ and r_a are the distance (in any units) from the boundary position and the starting level (usually the meniscus), respectively, t' (in minutes) is the time, and $\omega = 2\pi$ $(rpm)/60$ is the angular velocity (in sec^{-1}). It is possible to determine the boundary position even when a small number of fractions are collected. A detailed sample calculation has been given.[6]

Correction to standard conditions can be made if the viscosity, η, and density, ρ, are measured on the solution just below the boundary. The equation is

$$s_{20,w} = \left(\frac{1 - \bar{v}\rho_{20,w}}{1 - \bar{v}\rho}\right)\left(\frac{\eta}{\eta_{20,w}}\right)s^* \tag{3}$$

where $\bar{v}$ is the partial specific volume. This is usually assumed, but it is measurable by using density determinations as a function of concentration or is calculable from the amino acid composition as shown in a detailed example by Schachman.[2] The correction factors for various concentrations of sucrose at 5° and 20° for two assumed particle densities are given in Table III.[13,14]

[13] F. Y. Bates, Polarimetry, saccharimetry and the sugars. Circular 440, U.S. Government Printing Office, Washington, D.C., 1942.

[14] C. de Duve, J. Berthet, and H. Beaufay, *Progr. Biophys. Biophys. Chem.* **9**, 325 (1959).

TABLE III

FACTORS FOR CONVERTING s-RATES MEASURED IN SUCROSE TO $s_{20,w}$ VALUES

| Percent sucrose in H$_2$O | | At 5° | | | | At 20° | | | |
(w/w)	(w/v)$_{20°}$	ρ (gm/ml)	η/η_w	Correction factor[a] $\bar{v}=0.50$	$\bar{v}=0.75$	ρ (gm/ml)	η/η_w	Correction factor[a] $\bar{v}=0.50$	$\bar{v}=0.75$
0	H$_2$O	0.99999	1.000	1.51	1.52	0.99823	1.000	1.00	1.00
5	5.089	1.0201	1.135	1.75	1.84	1.0179	1.145	1.17	1.22
10	10.381	1.0408	1.352	2.13	2.34	1.0381	1.336	1.39	1.52
15	15.887	1.0624	1.656	2.67	3.10	1.0592	1.593	1.70	1.95
20	21.619	1.0846	2.079	3.44	4.23	1.0810	1.947	2.12	2.59
25	27.589	1.1077	2.684	4.55	6.02	1.1036	2.451	2.74	3.58
30	33.810	1.1315	3.602	6.28	9.04	1.1270	3.192	3.66	5.18
35	40.295	1.1563	5.067	9.09	14.5	1.1513	4.330	5.11	7.97
40	47.058	1.1819	7.585	14.0	25.4	1.1765	6.18	7.52	13.2
45	54.114	1.2083	12.33	23.6	49.9	1.2025	9.40	11.8	24.1
50	61.478	1.2359	22.00	43.6	114	1.2296	15.47	20.1	50.0
55	69.164	1.2641	44.30	91.1	324	1.2575	28.14	38.0	124

[a] $s_{20,w} = $ (correction factor)s_{obs}.

5. POINTERS ON OPTICS, MEASUREMENT OF PLATES, AND COMPUTATION OF ANALYTICAL RUNS

Since photographs are taken during analytical centrifugation, there is an opportunity to obtain the boundary position at several times. These data are combined to give a single value of the s-rate along with its standard error computed from the internal consistency of the measurements. The optical patterns also contain information as to the initial concentration of the sedimenting or floating particles. Detailed instructions for assembling and loading the cells and operating the ultracentrifuge can be obtained from the instruction manuals. Here, some pointers will be given that are frequently overlooked or misunderstood by routine users.

Optics. The *elevation* of the base line in schlieren optical patterns is due to the compression gradient in the solvent and its concomitant index of refraction gradient. A downward *tilt* is due to window distortion. The *curvature* of the base line at the top and bottom of the cell is due to redistribution of the buffer or salts present. The use of double-sector centerpieces with solvent in one side will eliminate nonspecific optical effects. The menisci from the two sectors will superimpose if the same Chaney syringe (Microchemical Specialties, Berkeley, California) is used to fill first the solution side, then, after rinsing with the solvent, the solvent side. It is possible to slide the phase-plate across the optical track to center the pattern on the viewing screen, especially when high magnifications are used (low phase-plate angles, say 15°, as in Fig. 3*B*). The four possible combinations of upright or inverted peaks which are either sedimenting or floating have been described.[15] Biphasic schlieren patterns must be obtained in zone methods (for example, as in Fig. 3*C*).

Timer and temperature. Start the photographic mechanism and timer during acceleration at two-thirds of the final operating speed. This procedure will ensure that movements of peaks can be directly compared on a light box by aligning menisci of corresponding frames. Make all runs at a predetermined temperature, say 4.0°, 20.0°, or 37.0°, using the temperature-control device to adjust the temperature of a precooled or preheated rotor as well as to measure and to control it.

Measurement. The appropriate formula for combining measurements in any one frame depends on the optical registration used.[10] This could be an interference optics photograph (upper strips of Fig. 3*D*), a densitometer tracing of an absorption optics film (Fig. 3*F*), or a schlieren photograph (Fig. 3*A, B,* or lowest strip in *D*). As a first approximation

[15] J. A. Faucher and J. V. Koleske, *Science* 147, 1152 (1965).

the boundary position is, respectively, the point with closest fringe spacing, the location of the half-concentration point, or the position of the maximum ordinate taken as the crossover point of the phase-plate schlieren fringe pattern under the peak. The requirement of a plateau on either side of the peak can be relaxed for steep (sharp) boundaries. More sophisticated computation of the boundary position, $\bar{r}$, as the radius of gyration is generally not practical without a computer. However, it is convenient to align the photographic plate on a two-dimensional comparator such that the origin of the abscissa scale starts at the center of rotation as if it could be seen on the plate.[16] This is done by first computing the distance to the center of the rotor reference hole on the plate as $x_{ref} = M_0 M_e r_{ref}$, where M_0 is the magnification of the schlieren optics camera lens, M_e is the magnification (or, more properly, the conversion factor from comparator scale units to centimeters) of the comparator, and r_{ref} is the reference hole center (Spinco AN-D or AN-E rotors). Then set the comparator to x_{ref}, and slide the plate so that the center of the rotor reference hole image is under the cross-hairs.

Computation. Plot log $\bar{r}$ against the time, t' (in minutes), for each frame measured. With multicomponent patterns draw the best straight lines through the data such that all lines intersect at the position corresponding to the meniscus. The time at the intersection is the *zero time correction* and should be less than a minute if the timer was started at two-thirds operating speed and there was no convection. Determine the slope of each line, and compute the s-rate, s^*, from Eq. (2) and the $s_{20,w}$ from Eq. (3). For a single-component pattern, the s-rate computed by Eq. (2) refers not to the initial concentration, c^0, but to a diluted value, c, given by $c = (x_a/x)^2 c^0$, where x is the boundary position at the median time of the data used.

C. Moving-Zone Methods

1. PURPOSE

The moving-zone method is based on velocity separation of a band or zone of a faster component completely free of slower components in one cycle of centrifugation (Fig. 1). In general, this is accomplished by layering a small sample over a density gradient. The faster sedimenting components will move further in the gradient than will those of lower s-rates. The density gradient is not used to provide isodense conditions but is used to stabilize against density inversions which would otherwise result as particles sediment into fresh solvent and increase

[16] R. Trautman, *J. Phys. Chem.* **60**, 1211 (1956).

its density. Just as there are both preparative and analytical versions of the moving-boundary method (MB), there are both versions of the moving-zone method (MZ). The analytical MZ method has recently been termed "band centrifugation" and has been mainly applied to nucleic acid studies.[17] The preparative MZ method has been widely used for virus purification,[18] for separating 19 S and 7 S antibodies,[19,20] and for studies on enzymes.[21]

2. COMPARISON OF VELOCITY METHODS

It is convenient to consider the characteristics of the MB and MZ methods in comparative terms, but the reader should not imply quality judgment, as the methods are complementary rather than competitive.

1. Larger sample volumes can and must be used in the MB method.

2. Only faster migrating materials are removed from the environment of the active agent in the MB method, whereas the agent moves into the solvent in the MZ method. With interacting or labile systems this difference may be either advantageous or disadvantageous. For example, consider an attempt to measure the s-rate of the 22 S rheumatoid factor complex. The moving-boundary method in the analytical ultracentrifuge reveals two peaks (19 S and 22 S), but in a moving-zone procedure only the 19 S is obtained (besides the other serum components). The reason for this is that, as the faster component (22 S) moves into the sucrose solution, it dissociates into its 7 S and 19 S components. In the moving-boundary method the 22 S moves in the presence of 7 S and so does not dissociate.

3. A density gradient must be provided to stabilize against convection in the MZ method. Some of the complications of the moving-zone procedure have been discussed by Brakke,[22] who indicates that sedimentation in a density gradient is not completely ideal in the sense that convection still occurs even in sector-shaped cells. In band centrifugation, self-generating density gradients are used.

4. Corrections of observed s-rates to standard conditions in the MZ method are larger and require estimates of (1) the particle density,

[17] J. Vinograd, R. Bruner, R. Kent, and J. Weigle, *Proc. Natl. Acad. Sci. U.S.* **49**, 902 (1963).

[18] M. K. Brakke, *Advan. Virus Res.* **7**, 193 (1960).

[19] E. C. Franklin, H. R. Holman, H. J. Müller-Eberhard, and H. G. Kunkel, *J. Exptl. Med.* **105**, 425 (1957).

[20] H. G. Kunkel, *in* "The Plasma Proteins" (F. W. Putnam, ed.), Vol. I, p. 279. Academic Press, New York, 1960.

[21] R. G. Martin and B. N. Ames, *J. Biol. Chem.* **236**, 1372 (1961).

[22] M. K. Brakke, *Arch. Biochem. Biophys.* **107**, 388 (1964).

(2) the varying solvent composition traversed by the moving zone, and (3) osmotic and solvation changes in the particle.

5. Each component may be obtained pure in the MZ method, whereas a faster sedimenting component is never free of slower ones in the MB method. Thus, absorption optics may not be applicable for a small, faster component in the presence of highly absorbing, slow, sedimenting materials in the MB method.

6. Heterogeneity of biological activity and determination of s-rates can be made with less precise assays in the MZ method.

7. Prior purification is not required for the MB method, but it may be necessary with the MZ method if the sample cannot be diluted or if there is a very high concentration of lower s-rate contaminants. For example, it is difficult to prepare pure 19 S globulins in the MZ method with whole serum because of the presence of relatively high concentrations of other proteins.

8. The agent can be concentrated in the MB method, but it is always diluted in the MZ method.

3. CONSEQUENCES OF THE REQUIRED DENSITY GRADIENT

Droplet sedimentation. The preformed density gradient used in the moving-zone process stabilizes against "turnover" convection caused by particles sedimenting into regions devoid of particles. However, it does not stabilize against droplets of solutions settling from the initial sample caused by an appreciable difference in diffusion rates between the gradient material (for example, sucrose) and the sample components (for example, serum proteins).[23,24] The initial sample zone receives more sucrose from below than it loses protein. The density, therefore, increases to values higher than the local density below the zone, and convection in the form of small droplets develops in less than 1 minute. This "raining down" of visible droplets is quite dramatic, as well as disastrous. The main *practical* ways of prevention are the use of very dilute solutions, slight blurring of the interface between sample and gradient, or the use of a very large density difference between the sample and the gradient ("density shelf").[25] The inverse sample gradient is not practical, especially if "synthetic boundary-forming caps"[25a] are used to empty the sample during acceleration.

[23] M. K. Brakke, *Arch. Biochem. Biophys.* **55**, 175 (1955).

[24] N. G. Anderson, *Exptl. Cell Res.* **9**, 446 (1955).

[25] H. Svensson, *in* "A Laboratory Manual of Analytical Methods of Protein Chemistry" (P. Alexander and R. J. Block, eds.), Vol. I, p. 125. Pergamon Press, Oxford, 1960.

[25a] L. Gropper and O. Griffith, *Anal. Biochem.* **16.** 171 (1966).

Production of gradient. Gradient-forming devices can be employed to make continuous gradients of either linear or nonlinear shape.[25,26] In any gradient it is important to have a continuous density distribution, and the rather extensive use of discontinuous steps is obsolete. When using the layer method for loading, make the end layers just one-half the volume of intervening ones, and stir slightly by twirling a saw-toothed wire, or allow the gradient material to diffuse overnight before layering the sample and centrifuging.

Preparation and use of density gradient column for density determination. Density is one of the most difficult *absolute* measurements to make, but it can be determined simply by *relative* procedures.[26] Prepare a density gradient in a 100-ml graduated cylinder by layering 50 ml of an appropriate mixture of *m*-xylene ($d_4^{20} = 0.86$) and bromobenzene ($d_4^{20} = 1.50$) to have a density of 1.2 gm/ml over 50 ml of pure bromobenzene. This particular gradient column would not be suitable if solutions of densities of less than 1.25 gm/ml or greater than 1.45 gm/ml were under study. Stir the boundary region, or let it stand overnight before use. Draw out short lengths of capillary tubing to make micropipets, and use a rubber bulb (with a small air hole) on the pipet. Draw the aqueous solution into the pipet, uncover the hole, insert the pipet below the gradient meniscus, cover the hole, eject a small droplet of material, and withdraw the pipet, knocking off the droplet at the meniscus. Record the level of the drop when it comes to rest. Repeat the procedure with standard salt solutions. Compute the density of the unknown by linear interpolation between the positions of the standards.

The density of the standard solutions can be determined (1) on large volumes with a hydrometer, (2) by weighing in a pycnometer, (3) by conversion of refractive index measurement, or (4) by using handbook values for saturated solutions. A layer of mineral oil on the standards will not interfere with their use and will ensure constant density for months.

4. PRECISE S-RATE MEASUREMENT METHOD

This sucrose gradient procedure is that of Martin and Ames,[21] who developed it for enzyme studies. It has been used by Andersen and Vannier[27] for skin-sensitizing antibody investigations. The method uses the SW-39 swinging-bucket rotor and a 4.6-ml linear gradient extending from 5% (w/v, 0.146 M) to 20% (0.584 M) cold sucrose in 0.05 M Tris-HCl buffer at pH 7.5. Layer a sample of 0.1 to 0.2 ml which contains not more than 2% (w/v) protein. Accelerate the rotor for 10 seconds;

[26] G. Oster and M. Yamamoto, *Chem. Rev.* **63**, 257 (1963).
[27] B. R. Andersen and W. E. Vannier, *J. Exptl. Med.* **120**, 31 (1964).

then start a separate timer, and advance the speed dial to 39,000 rpm. Record the speed as a function of time. If it is linear, the timer may be started in subsequent runs when two-thirds operating speed is reached. Centrifuge for 17 hours at 39,000 rpm at 3°. (If the agent is stable enough, use room-temperature solutions and centrifuge at 20°.) Decelerate without the brake, and stop the timer at two-thirds of the operating speed, since deceleration is very nearly linear. As many fractions as possible should be obtained by dripping out the bottom or by forced flow out of the top (Fig. 2). The fractions are assayed to determine the center of the zone of activity. The average s-rate, s^*, is calculated from the movement represented by the distance or volume between the center of the starting zone and the center of activity, from Eq. (1) or Eq. (2). The correction of s^* to 20° in water by Eq. (3) can be made by determining the composition (density and viscosity) of the gradient at a midpoint between initial and final zones (see Table III).

Other sophisticated procedures are available to compute s-rates. For example, an s-rate scale can be constructed for each point in the tube so that $s_{20,w}$ values can be read off directly.[27a] It should be noted that the $s_{20,w}$ calculation requires a knowledge of the particle density, so with unknown systems calculated values may be subject to large errors. It also assumes that the sucrose gradient measured at the end is the same as at the beginning. Another procedure uses reference substances, and the s-rate of the unknown activity is obtained by interpolating between the standards.[28] The Martin and Ames gradient[21] has a very nearly linear distance-versus-time property, since the increased centrifugal field is offset by the decrease in s-rate due to the increase in sucrose.

5. SEPARATION OF 7 S AND 19 S ANTIBODIES

a. Sucrose Gradient Method

A variety of procedures have been utilized for the separation of antibodies in human and animal sera.[20] In all of these the swinging-bucket rotor (SW-39) is used with a 10 to 40% (w/v) sucrose gradient in isotonic saline. In the simplest procedure the gradient is formed by successively layering with a pipet 1 ml of 40%, 2 ml of 25%, and 1 ml of 10% cold sucrose solutions. A saw-toothed wire is twirled in the tube to blur the two boundaries. In most experiments, however, it is advantageous to form a continuous gradient. This can be done simply by placing 10% sucrose in a small mixing chamber and by means of a syringe attached to a capillary tube adding 40% sucrose continuously to the mixing chamber. At the same time another capillary tube from

[27a] B. S. Bishop, Natl. Cancer Inst. Monograph 21, 175 (1966).
[28] P. A. Charlwood, *Anal. Biochem.* 5, 226 (1963).

the mixing chamber to the bottom of the centrifuge tube delivers sucrose of progressively increasing concentration. After formation of the gradient, 0.5 ml of cold diluted serum (at least a 1:2 dilution) is layered on the top. The serum boundary is blurred by gentle stirring with the pipet tip. Centrifugation is begun as quickly as possible and proceeds at 35,000 rpm for 18 hours at 10°. The 19 S component will be close to the bottom of the tube, and the 7 S component will be in the upper half. Serial fractions are taken from the bottom of the tube by drip-out (Fig. 2C). A stopper at the top of the tube with or without a pressure device aids in controlling the outflow rate from the tube (Fig. 2C).

b. SALT GRADIENT METHOD

The 19 S and 7 S antibodies have also been separated by use of a gradient composed of $NaNO_3$ and KBr.[29] The gradient is prepared from room-temperature saturated $NaNO_3$ and KBr solutions by placing 2.5 ml of 75% (v/v) saturated KBr in the SW-39 tube and layering on 1.5 ml of 65% (v/v) saturated $NaNO_3$. The boundary in this very slight gradient is blurred with a saw-toothed wire, and up to 1 ml of undiluted serum is layered on top. Centrifugation is at 37,000 rpm for 20 hours at 20°. The tube contents can be fractionated by the drip-out method, giving the 19 S component in the bottom 1 ml, and the 7 S component in the next 2.5 ml.

Successful separation has also been obtained by using this gradient with the Spinco No. 40.2 angle rotor. In this case, after the gradient solutions and sample have been loaded, the tubes are filled with mineral oil to prevent tube collapse, and centrifugation is at 35,000 rpm for only 18 hours at 20°. The advantage of centrifuging twelve samples in the No. 40.2 rotor versus three in the SW-39 rotor is that many different samples can be studied at once or all fractions obtained from one previous three-tube SW-39 run may be recycled.

The KBr-$NaNO_3$ gradient utilized here provides a high-density shelf that even accommodates undiluted bovine serum, which has a relatively high protein content, with minimal droplet sedimentation. The two salts are chosen because of their differing viscosity but similar density properties to give almost a constant s-rate which is reduced to one-seventh the normal s-rate. Zone sharpening results because the particles first entering the gradient will be slowed down while the particles of the same component sedimenting in the less dense sample zone tend to "catch up." Thus, this procedure might be considered a combination of both

[29] K. M. Cowan and R. Trautman, *J. Immunol.* **94**, 858 (1965).

the moving-boundary and moving-zone methods. Variations in the concentrations, volumes, and times used should be considered in applying this recently introduced procedure to other systems.

D. Isodensity Methods

1. PURPOSE

The methodology for purification and characterization of an unknown agent will be dependent on a knowledge of not only its s-rate but also its density. Thus, isodensity determination should be one of the first measurements made on the agent. Basically the principle is to find the density of the solution in which the agent neither sediments nor floats when subjected to a centrifugal field. This isodensity is also called its *buoyant density* or *isopynic value*. Refer to Section C,3 for techniques for solution density measurement.

Some of the general features of isodensity procedures are as follows: (1) If a tube is filled uniformly with the agent in a solvent of approximately the buoyant density, the size of the agent will determine the time it takes for the particles to reach their isodense position, but their mass will determine how tightly they will band; (2) concentration as well as purification can be achieved without pellet formation; and (3) since all particles of a particular component initially present contribute to the final zone, isodensity methods can be micromethods for density heterogeneity determinations as well as concentration assays. The general disadvantages are: (1) the gradient substance may inactivate the agent or adversely affect the assay; and (2) the gradient substance usually has to be removed after centrifugation by dialysis or gel filtration.

There are two major methods, the preformed gradient isodensity (PI) and field-formed gradient isodensity (FI) methods. Both are frequently used in the preparative ultracentrifuge, but the latter is more common in analytical ultracentrifugation. The preformed gradient isodensity method uses a density gradient set up initially in the tube. It is generally applicable to large particles which reach their isodense positions in a reasonably short time—that is, a few hours before the gradient has changed much. Droplet sedimentation is usually not a problem because of the very high densities used, but it could be a problem when isolating low-density materials in the presence of dense contaminants. The field-formed gradient method uses the centrifugal field itself to form the density gradient by redistributing the gradient solute, but it takes 8 hours for the gradient to reach classical sedimentation equilibrium in a 1-cm depth. The method can be used for all sizes of particles; those of $s_{20,w}$ about 10 S take 18 hours to reach equilibrium in their zone width.[30] It is also called equilibrium isodensity.

The general advantages of the preformed over the field-formed method are: (1) the agent can be made to move into fresh solvent; (2) much shorter centrifugation periods are needed; (3) almost any density range can be used; and (4) the starting sample can be placed either underneath or on top of the gradient; for example, if contaminating substances should be heavier than the agent, place the sample underneath the gradient. Specific disadvantages are: (1) a smaller volume of starting sample usually is used; (2) the time to terminate the centrifugation is somewhat important because the gradient will eventually redistribute; (3) substances can cross over before reaching their final position (see example in Fig. 1); (4) some components may not have moved to their isodensity levels by the end of the experiment, making buoyant density determinations inaccurate; and (5) loading of tubes is much more complicated than in the field-formed method, which is the ultimate in simplicity.

2. PREFORMED GRADIENT ISODENSITY METHOD FOR DETERMINATION OF DENSITY OF UNKNOWNS

Preliminary procedure. Either the Spinco SW-39 swinging-bucket or the No. 40.2 angle rotor may be used. Buffered solutions of selected densities—for example, 1.10, 1.15, and 1.20 gm/ml—are prepared with salts, sucrose, heavy water, or other materials which may be required to maintain activity. After the tubes are half-filled with the selected solutions, layer 0.5 ml of a solution of 1.05 gm/ml density, and finally layer 2.5 ml of the sample (use mineral oil to fill tubes of the No. 40.2 rotor). Centrifuge for 8 hours at 40,000 rpm at 20° unless the agent is unstable at this temperature. Fractionate the tube contents into two portions, and assay for activity. Let ρ_1 be the highest initial density which permitted the agent to enter, and ρ_2 the lowest density which prevented the agent from entering. As a first approximation, the buoyant density, ρ_0, is $\rho_0 = (\rho_1 + \rho_2)/2$.

Refined procedure. Prepare two tubes, one with 1 ml of sample adjusted to $\rho_0 - 0.05$ layered on 4 ml of solution of ρ_0 density, and the second with 4 ml of ρ_0 solution layered on 1 ml of sample adjusted to $\rho_0 + 0.05$. Centrifuge for 18 hours at 40,000 rpm, and collect at least five fractions. Assay for both biological activity and density. Average the density of the most active fraction from each of the two tubes for the final value of ρ_0.[31]

[30] M. Meselson and G. M. Nazarian, *in* "Ultracentrifugal Analysis in Theory and Experiment" (J. W. Williams, ed.), p. 131. Academic Press, New York, 1963.
[31] A. Polson and J. Levitt, *Biochim. Biophys. Acta* **75**, 88 (1963).

3. FIELD-FORMED GRADIENT ISODENSITY METHOD IN PREPARATIVE AND ANALYTICAL RUNS

Procedure. Adjust the sample to the nominal buoyant density of the agent. Fill the tubes (preparative) or cells (analytical) with the minimum volume usable, since the time to reach equilibrium varies as the square of the column depth, being 8 hours for 1 cm. Centrifuge for 8 to 24 hours, usually at top speed of the rotor used. With the preparative centrifuge assay fractions for activity and density, but with the analytical centrifuge take schlieren or absorption optical pictures every hour to establish when equilibrium is reached (see Fig. 3C for a schlieren optical picture of bovine serum albumin at equilibrium in the field-formed isodensity method).

Notes. By using either marker substances for interpolation or an absolute calibration, the density of the unknown zones is determined. The larger the molecular weight, the narrower the equilibrium zone will be in both the preparative and analytical versions. See Vinograd and Hearst[32] for tables of density versus refractive index and equilibrium density gradient values for commonly used salts.

At the high salt concentrations used in the analytical ultracentrifuge, the combined elevation of the base line due to hydrostatic compression and the redistribution of the gradient material may move the pattern off the plate. To circumvent this, slide the phase-plate across the optical track (toward the rear of Model E), use negative wedge windows on the cells, and in extreme cases move the light source toward the rear of the ultracentrifuge for the schlieren optics, or toward the front for the absorption optics.

Many corrections are necessary to convert isodensity values and band widths to partial specific volume and anhydrous molecular weight.[32] It should be noted, however, that even without making detailed computations differences between particles can be easily detected and may have biological significance.

4. COMBINED METHODS IN A SINGLE TUBE FOR VIRUS PURIFICATION AND CONCENTRATION

The purification and concentration of foot-and-mouth disease virus involves moving-boundary, moving-zone, isodensity, and interface penetration methods.[33] By biological assay of preparative fractions, foot-

[32] J. Vinograd and J. E. Hearst, *Fortsch. Chem. Org. Naturstoffe* **20**, 372 (1962).
[33] H. L. Bachrach, R. Trautman, and S. S. Breese, Jr., *Am. J. Vet. Res.* **25**, 333 (1964).

and-mouth disease virus was determined as having at 20° an s-rate of 140 S and a density of 1.43 gm/ml. Concentration and purification in the SW-25.1 swinging-bucket rotor could be achieved by layering 25 ml of virus-containing fluid onto 5 ml of CsCl solution of density 1.42 (chosen slightly less than the isodensity) and centrifuging at 4° for 4 hours at 25,000 rpm ($s^* = 75$ S). The virus sediments (moving-boundary method) to the CsCl solution, which has a steep gradient because of the initial layering. The virus enters the CsCl layer as a moving zone, bands near the bottom of the tube, and is collected by dripping out. The virus is thus separated from overlaying protein and lipoprotein zones as well as larger, more dense material.

A short dialysis lowers the density enough to permit layering the virus solution on an immiscible organic fluid which itself is layered on a 1.42 density CsCl solution in a Spinco SW-39 tube (Fig. 1). The organic mixture of density 1.09 gm/ml is 30% (v/v) chloroform and 70% (v/v) di-2-ethylhexyl sebecate ("Octoil-S," a diffusion pump oil, Consolidated Vacuum Corp., Rochester, New York). In the 3½-hour centrifugation at 4° at 37,000 rpm (overall $s^* = 30$ S), the virus sediments out of the upper solution as in the moving-boundary method, penetrates the organic phase, enters the CsCl solution, and bands in the field-formed gradient.

With this, as with all the other procedures given, the investigator must be prepared to change conditions slightly if, for example, zones do not move far enough in velocity methods or are too high in the tube in isodensity methods.

E. Separation of Subcellular Particles

The architecture of the mammalian cell has been beautifully revealed in sections by electron microscopy, but the elaboration of detailed bio-chemical processes in such a complex structure requires study of isolated subcellular particles or organelles. Centrifugation procedures have been developed to a rather sophisticated level, but since there is an enormous heterogeneity in size, density, and lability to ordinary chemicals, no one procedure gives all the metabolically active organelles both pure and in large yield.[34] The proper identification should be confirmed by electron microscopy, chemical composition, or activity. Speeds and times should be changed as necessary, as there are variations from organ to organ and from host to host.

[34] N. G. Anderson, *Phys. Techniques Biol. Res.* **3**, 300 (1956).

1. CONVERSION OF "NUMBERS OF g's" TO THE MINIMUM APPARENT S-RATE

A composite picture of the separation procedures which involve moving-boundary, moving-zone, and isodensity methods is shown in Fig. 5. Double arrows indicate centrifugation steps, and single arrows indicate manipulation such as adding reagents or decanting.

The time and "number of g's" usually given for centrifugation in the cold have been expressed as an s-rate in Fig. 5. This represents the minimum s-rate of a hypothetical particle which traversed from meniscus to the bottom of the tube at the speed and time used. The $\overline{ST}$ table (Table I) should be used to compute actual times and speeds for the particular volume and rotor used. Note that the s-rate in the tube of actual particles will be less than their $s_{20,w}$ value, since they sediment in a solvent effectively at the temperature and composition of the gradient midway between starting level and final zone.

To convert a procedure given in relative centrifugal force (RCF) and time to the minimum s-rate class (s^*) that would sediment from the meniscus to the tube bottom, use the RCF entries at the bottom of Table I. Guess what rotor, tubes, and volume were probably used, if they were not specified, and select one of the rotors of comparable capacity. In Eq. (1) the $\Delta\overline{ST}$ value is for maximum fill, and the ratio of the RCF value in the table to the given RCF value is the square of the speed factor. For example, say the procedure called for centrifuging in the cold at 600 g for 10 minutes. If we assume that 200-ml bottles were used in the International No. 259 rotor, the $\Delta\overline{ST}$ from Table I is 38,300. Equation (1) yields $s^* = (38300/0.17)\ (800/600) = 3.10^5$ S. This is the calculation for the moving-boundary step from 3 to 4 in Fig. 5.

2. DIFFERENTIAL CENTRIFUGATION METHOD

A cell suspension, usually about 20 to 50 % (w/w), is made in Tris-HCl buffer, pH 7.2, and with sucrose to a final concentration of 0.25 M (8.5% w/w) to preserve isotonicity, avoiding lipid solvents to preserve ribosomes on microsomal membranes, but in 0.01 M $MgCl_2$ to preserve ribosomes themselves (step 1, Fig. 5). Homogenization[35] and subsequent operations are usually done in the cold (0° to 5°).

Steps 4 through 8 are the classical differential centrifugation procedures representing the moving-boundary method used to pellet successively lower and lower s-rate classes. The resuspended pellets are thus

[35] N. G. Anderson, Natl. Cancer Inst. Monograph 21, 1 (1966).

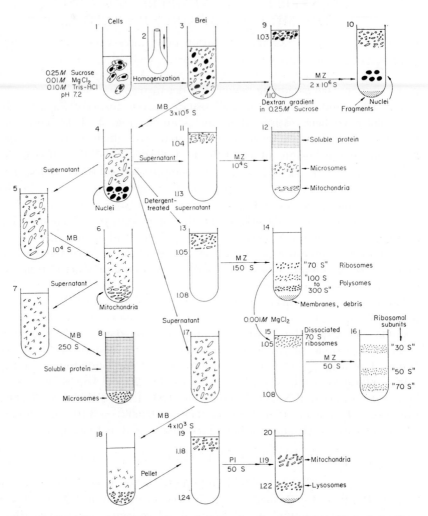

Fig. 5. Centrifugal methods for isolation of cell particulates. Steps 1 to 8 are the classical methods of differential centrifugation which result in contaminated moving-boundary-method pellets. The other steps shows moving-zone or isodensity methods. Concentration of detergents, Mg⁺⁺, sucrose, and buffers are important in either retaining integrity or purposely dissociating the organelles. The s-rate figures under the double-arrowed centrifugation steps represent the minimum apparent s-rate class that would sediment from top to bottom at the temperature of the run. Use Table I to compute speeds and times for any particular rotor selected. Further detail is given in Sections E,2–E,4.

contaminated with all the other components. It is, however, useful to concentrate certain classes of particles before separation in the much more refined moving-zone methods. If a step is repeated by resuspending the pellet and recentrifuging, it is called *washing* the precipitate. If a low-speed centrifugation is used, it is called *clarification*.

3. MOVING-ZONE METHODS

Generally, a sucrose gradient is used that starts at 10% (w/w), 1.04 gm/ml density. If the sample was prepared without sucrose for some special purpose, then it may be sufficiently dilute to be layered without density inversion on only 5% sucrose (1.02 gm/ml density). With the zonal rotor a 10 to 40% sucrose gradient above a "cushion" of 55% sucrose is convenient to keep most substances from pelleting on the rotor wall and to allow loading and unloading while the rotor is spinning at low speed.[35]

Nuclei. Steps 9 and 10 represent a moving-zone centrifugation in a dextran gradient extending from 0 to 30% w/w dextran in 0.25 M sucrose and 0.006 M $CaCl_2$. Dextran is used so that the gradient will be isotonic throughout, which is essential to preserve the metabolic activity of the purified nuclei.[36]

Soluble protein, microsomes, and mitochondria. After the nuclei are removed in step 4, the supernatant is centrifuged in steps 11 and 12 as a moving-zone procedure in a 10 to 30% (w/w) sucrose gradient in the presence of Mg^{++} to preserve the ribosomes on the microsomes. The "soluble" protein is considered to be those protein particles of less than 250 S. This one step, 11 to 12, gives a much higher purity of the three main classes of particles than do steps 5, 6, 7, and 8 of the differential centrifugation procedure.

Polysomes and ribosomes. The nuclei-free supernatant (step 4) may be treated with detergent or equivalent to free the polysomes and ribosomes from the microsomal membranes. Moving-zone centrifugation at steps 13 and 14 is done in a shallow sucrose gradient extending from 13 to 20% (w/w). The polysomes appear as components of s-rates between 80 and 300 S. The main band of 70 S ribosomes can be dialyzed against the very low Mg^{++} concentration buffer to cause dissociation. Steps 15 and 16 represent a recycle of moving-zone centrifugation used in steps 13 and 14 but for a longer time or higher speed to yield the 30 S, 50 S, and 70 S ribosomal subunits.

[36] W. D. Fisher and G. B. Cline, *Biochim. Biophys. Acta* **68**, 640 (1963).

4. PREFORMED GRADIENT ISODENSITY METHOD

Mitochondria and lysosomes. A concentrated pellet of mitochondria, lysosomes, and intact microsomes is prepared in steps 17 to 18 from the nuclei-free supernatant as indicated by step 6, in the moving-boundary method which depletes the microsomes. This resuspended pellet is centrifuged in a preformed gradient isodensity procedure (in steps 19 and 20).[37] This is not a velocity procedure, but the 50 S value is useful for selecting the rotor, speed, and time. The mitochondria band at a density of 1.19, and the lysosomes at 1.22 gm/ml. Any contaminating ribosomes will be at the bottom of the tube.

Some of the early procedures combined moving-zone and isodensity methods in the same tube (for example, steps 12 and 20). It should be noted that in the velocity procedure the mitochondria start ahead of the ribosomes. In the isodensity method the ribosomes catch up and pass through the zone of mitochondria. In a combination procedure the time to stop the centrifugation is usually extremely important.

F. Classical Sedimentation Equilibrium Methods

1. PURPOSE

After the agent has been purified, its diffusion coefficient and molecular weight may be determined by the classical sedimentation equilibrium method. This method is carried out at high dilution, at reasonable ionic strength, and, in the ideal situation, with complete thermodynamic equilibrium. The method relies on the balance between sedimentation and diffusion. Many short-cut procedures have been introduced; however, one must decide what information is desired from the experiment before using a method that precludes the possibility of obtaining data on one of the items of interest. Thus, molecular weight heterogeneity is very difficult to determine in currently popular ultrashort columns.[38]

2. ARCHIBALD METHOD TO USE THE APPROACH TO EQUILIBRIUM

A uniform solution of the agent is used to fill a double-sector cell of the analytical ultracentrifuge. Starting at 15,000 rpm, observe the boundary as it separates from the meniscus. After it is part way out, accelerate to top speed. Use the equations of Section G to reduce the comparator data. From the plot of the equivalent of the schlieren pattern height at the meniscus against the difference in concentration between

[37] C. de Duve, *Sci. Am.* **208**, 64 (1963).
[38] D. A. Yphantis, *Biochemistry* **3**, 297 (1964).

that at the meniscus and the initial concentration, it can be ascertained if the solute is heterogeneous, nonideal, or associating, and an estimate of the molecular weight can be obtained.[16]

3. PRECISE MOLECULAR WEIGHT DETERMINATION

For the definitive run, the previously filled cell is shaken to redistribute the agent and is recentrifuged at a speed which will give, at equilibrium, a concentration at the bottom of the cell about three times that at the top. The approach to equilibrium can be used to compute the diffusion coefficient.[39] From the equilibrium photograph, the precise weight average molecular weight is computed, and estimates are made of nonideality, heterogeneity, and association coefficients.[40]

G. Summary of Mathematical Formulas

The centrifugal force per unit mass (centrifugal acceleration) (cm/sec^2) at a distance r (cm) from the center of rotation is $\omega^2 r$, where the angular velocity, ω (radians/sec), is determined from the speed (rpm) in revolutions per minute (rpm) as

$$\omega = (2\pi/60)(rpm) \tag{1a}$$

Popularly, the magnitude of centrifugal force compared to gravitational force on the same particle is called *relative centrifugal force* (RCF)

$$RCF = \omega^2 r/g = [2\pi(rpm)/60]^2(r/980) = 1.119(10^{-5})r(rpm)^2 \tag{2a}$$

where g is the gravitational acceleration, 980 cm/sec^2. Even though RCF is dimensionless, it is usually denoted as $\times g$ or just g, representing so many times gravity.

The velocity per unit centrifugal field is called the sedimentation coefficient (s-rate) (sec), given by

$$s = [1/(\omega^2 \bar{r})](d\bar{r}/dt) = (1/\omega^2)(d \ln \bar{r}/dt) \tag{3a}$$

where $\bar{r}$ is the position of a moving boundary or zone representing the particles, and t (sec) is the time. It is customary to express s-rates in Svedbergs, S, by multiplying by 10^{13}, since $1\ S = 10^{-13}$ sec. The apparent (or average) s-rate, s^* (in Svedbergs), of a particle moving from $\bar{r} = r$ to $\bar{r} = r_b$ in the time t is

$$s^* = (10^{13}/t) \int_0^t s\, dt = [10^{13}/(\omega^2 t)] \ln (r_b/r) \tag{4a}$$

[39] F. E. LaBar and R. L. Baldwin, *J. Phys. Chem.* **66**, 1952 (1962).
[40] E. T. Adams, Jr., and D. L. Filmer, *Biochemistry* **5**, 2971 (1966).

Combination of these equations, converting to time t'' (hours), gives

$$s^* t'' = \left[\left(\frac{10^{13}}{4\pi^2} \right) \frac{\ln(r_b/r)}{(rpm)^2_{\max}} \right] \left[\frac{(rpm)^2_{\max}}{(rpm)^2} \right] = \left(\frac{10^{13}}{60^2 \cdot 980} \right) \left[\frac{\ln r_b/\bar{r}}{(RCF)'/r'} \right] \quad (5a)$$

The first factor in square brackets in the middle member is the definition of $\overline{ST}$ which can evidently be tabulated (Table I) as a function of the volume between the tube bottom at $r = r_b$ and a meniscus at r for various volumes of fill. Because of the log function in the numerator, the relationship of text Eq. (1) holds for differences $\Delta \overline{ST}$. In the right-hand member $(RCF)'$ is the relative centrifugal force computed at radius r', usually taken as the tube bottom and called $(RCF)_{\text{tip}}$.

A dry particle of mass m (gm) of any shape which displaces a volume v (ml) when present at a concentration of p (% by weight) has an apparent volume φ (ml/gm) of

$$\varphi \equiv v/m = (V - V^0)/m = (1/\rho^0)[1 - 100(\rho - \rho^0)/(p\rho)] \quad (6a)$$

where V and ρ are the volume (ml) and density (gm/ml) of solution, and superscript ^{0} means solvent. The partial specific volume $\bar{v}$ (ml/gm) is the change in volume per infinitesimal change in mass of solute at constant temperature (T), pressure (P), and mass of solvent (m^0), and is determined from φ by

$$\bar{v} \equiv (\partial V/\partial m)_{T,P,m_0} = \varphi + \frac{d\varphi}{d \ln[p/(100 - p)]} \quad (7a)$$

If the particle solvation is h (ml) of density d (gm/ml), the solvated particle density, ρ' (gm/ml), is

$$\rho' = \frac{m + hd}{v + h} = \frac{1 + Hd}{\bar{v} + H} \quad (8a)$$

where H (ml/gm) is the specific hydration, h/m.

The diameter, $2a_0$ (cm), of the equivalent sphere having the same volume as the *solvated* particle is implicitly

$$(4/3)\pi a_0^3 = v + h \quad (9a)$$

Acting on the solvated particle are the centrifugal force, $f_c = (m + hd)\omega^2 r$; the buoyant force, $f_b = -(v + h)\rho\omega^2 r$; and the friction force, $f_f = -6\pi\eta a_0(f/f_0)\omega^2 rs$, where η (poise) is the coefficient of viscosity of the solution, (f/f_0) is the friction factor (a dimensionless measure of deviation from spherical shape), and $\omega^2 rs$ (cm/sec) is its velocity. In sedimentation velocity experiments the net force per particle $f_c + f_b + f_f = 0$;

hence

$$s = \frac{(2a_0)^2(\rho' - \rho)}{18\eta(f/f_0)} = \frac{(2a_0)^2[(1/\bar{v} - \rho) + H(d - \rho)/\bar{v}]}{18\eta(f/f_0)(1 + H/\bar{v})}$$
$$= \frac{M[(1 - \bar{v}\rho) + H(d - \rho)]}{6\pi\eta a_0 N(f/f_0)} \tag{10a}$$

where the molecular weight, $M = Nm$, is the *dry* weight (gm/mole) of Avogadro's number N (6.023×10^{23} particles/mole) of particles. (The interpretation of the right-hand member when $d = \rho$—that is, when the solvated particle (the kinetic unit) has the density of its solvation mantle equal to the density of the bulk solution—is that the centrifugal force on the solvation mantle is exactly balanced by its buoyant force; hence an anhydrous molecular weight can be determined. Note that the a_0 refers to the radius of the kinetic unit.)

To compare s-rates obtained under varying conditions of temperature, density, viscosity, and solvation, it is convenient to define a standard state and convert observed s-rates to its hypothetical conditions. Define the standard s-rate, $s_{20,w}$, as

$$s_{20,w} \equiv \left[\frac{M(1 - \bar{v}\rho)}{6\pi\eta a_0 N(f/f_0)}\right]_{20°,\text{water}} \tag{11a}$$

where ρ and η are values for water at $20°$, and $\bar{v}$, a_0, and (f/f_0) refer to the particle as if it could exist in water (frequently not the case for biologicals). Combination of Eq. (10a) and Eq. (9a), replacing s by s_{obs} (observed), gives

$$s_{20,w} = \left(\frac{\rho'_{20,w} - \rho_{20,w}}{\rho'_T - \rho_T}\right)\left(\frac{\eta_T}{\eta_{20,w}}\right)s_{\text{obs}} = \left(\frac{1/\bar{v} - \rho_{20,w}}{1/\bar{v} - \rho_T}\right)\left(\frac{\eta_T}{\eta_{20,w}}\right)s_{\text{obs}}$$
$$= \left(\frac{1 - \bar{v}_{20}\rho_{20,w}}{1 - \bar{v}_T\rho_T}\right)\left(\frac{\eta_T}{\eta_{20,w}}\right)s_{\text{obs}} \tag{12a}$$

where various assumptions are required for the three equations represented: all require a_0 and f/f_0 to be constant, regardless of the hydration, H; the middle and right-hand members both require, in addition, that $d = \rho$; and the middle member alone requires further that $\bar{v}$ is constant. If η and ρ are measured on the fraction representing the plateau solution just below the boundary in the moving-boundary method, then s_{obs} can be the observed s^*; but if they refer to the solvent, then a series of measurements of s^* at constant temperature must be extrapolated to infinite dilution of all solutes to give s_{obs}. The viscosity ratio can be calculated as

$$\eta_T/\eta_{20,w} = (\eta_{T,w}/\eta_{20,w})(\eta_{T'}/\eta_{T',w}) \tag{13a}$$

where $\eta_{T,w}/\eta_{20,w}$ is the handbook value of the ratio of the viscosities of water at the temperature, T, of the run and at 20°, and the ratio of the viscosity, $\eta_{T'}$ to that of water, $\eta_{T',w}$, can usually be determined at any convenient temperature, T'.

In the moving-zone method the s-rate varies with the composition of the gradient encountered. From Eqs. (3a) and (12a),

$$s_{20,w} = \left\{ \left(\frac{\rho'_{20,w} - \rho_{20,w}}{\eta_{20,w}} \right) \left[\frac{1}{\ln \bar{r}/r_a} \int_{r_a}^{\bar{r}} \frac{\eta \, dr}{(\rho' - \rho)r} \right] \right\} s^*$$

$$= \left\{ \left(\frac{1/\bar{v} - \rho_{20,w}}{\eta_{20,w}} \right) \left[\int_{r_a}^{\bar{r}} \frac{\eta \, dr}{(1/\bar{v} - \rho)r} \right] \Big/ \ln \bar{r}/r_a \right\} s^* \qquad (14a)$$

The first form is the most general, but it is useful only if the particle density, ρ', is constant—that is, if the solvation mantle excludes the gradient substance. The second form, however, involves evaluation of the same integral, but now the reciprocal of $\bar{v}$ is used for the "density." The integral can be evaluated numerically for any gradient in which η and ρ are known as a function of r for various assumed values of $1/\bar{v}$.

The Einstein-Sutherland equation is

$$D = RT/[6\pi\eta a_0 N(f/f_0)] \qquad (15a)$$

where D (cm²/sec) is the diffusion coefficient, frequently expressed in Ficks, F $(1 \text{ F} = 10^{-7} \text{ cm}^2/\text{sec})$; R is the gas constant $(8.314 \times 10^7$ ergs/°C/mole); and T is the absolute temperature $(293.16 + \text{tempera-}$ ture in degrees centigrade). Elimination of (f/f_0) between Eqs. (11a) and (15a) gives the Svedberg equation:

$$M = (10^{-6} RT)\{s/[D(1 - \bar{v}\rho)]\} = 243.7\{s/[D(1 - \bar{v}\rho)]\} \qquad (16a)$$

whereas elimination of a_0 between Eqs. (10a) and (15a) gives

$$f/f_0 = \left[\frac{10^{27}R^2T^2}{162\pi^2N^2\eta^3} \right] \left(\frac{\rho' - \rho}{D^2s} \right) = 1018 \left(\frac{\rho' - \rho}{D^2s} \right) \qquad (17a)$$

where in both equations s is in Svedbergs, D is in Ficks, and numerical values on the right are for water at 20°.

If a volume V_1 of solution of known density ρ_1 is mixed with a volume V_2 of density ρ_2, the density, ρ, of the mixture will be

$$\rho = (V_1\rho_1 + V_2\rho_2)/(V_1 + V_2) = 1 + [V_1(\rho_1 - 1) \\ + V_2(\rho_2 - 1)]/(V_1 + V_2) \qquad (18a)$$

if there is additivity of volume. A more precise relationship is

$$1/\rho \equiv \bar{v} = (p_1\bar{v}_1 + p_2\bar{v}_2)/100 \qquad (19a)$$

where p_1 and p_2 are the percentages by weight of the solvent and solute, respectively. In terms of the concentration, c_2 (gm/ml),

$$\rho = \rho_1 + c_2(1 - \bar{v}_2\rho_1) \tag{20a}$$

Since 1 ml of water at $4°$ weighs 1 gm, ρ is numerically equal to the density relative to water at $4°$ (frequently denoted d_4^{20}). In terms of the specific gravity at $t°$, which is the mass of a substance divided by the mass of an equal volume of water at $t°$ (denoted d_t^t), ρ is

$$\rho = d_4^t = d_t^t(d_4^t)_w \tag{21a}$$

The initial concentration, c^0, of a component whose concentration, c_p, is measured in the plateau at some radius, r_p, after movement of a boundary from r_a is

$$c^0 = c_p(\bar{r}/r_a)^2 = \int_{r_a}^{r_p} (r/r_a)^2(\partial c/\partial r) \, dr \tag{22a}$$

Direct determination of the integral on the right can be done by a simplified plate-reading procedure by reading schlieren ordinates, $y = y_{soln} - y_{solv}$, equally spaced on a radius-cubed scale, Z, given by

$$Z = 1000(x/160)^3 \tag{23a}$$

where x is the radial coordinate (mm) on the plate. The initial concentration is computed from

$$c^0 = F_x F_y(x_a/160)^2 \tan \theta \Sigma y \, \Delta Z \tag{24a}$$

where $F_x = 160/(3000 \, M_0 M_e)$, $F_y = 1/(a'b'M_c M_e\alpha)$, a' and b' (cm) are the cell thickness and optical lever arm, respectively, θ is the phase-plate angle, M_c is the magnification of the cylindrical lens, x_a is the comparator distance to the meniscus, and α is the specific refractive increment (usually taken as 0.000186 ml/mg for albumin).

There is no net flow of solute through the meniscus or out of the bottom of the cell; hence in the Archibald method

$$\omega^2 rsc - D(\partial c/\partial r) = 0 \tag{25a}$$

By adding and subtracting c^0 and using Eq. (16a), Eq. (25a) can be written

$$q_a = M(c_a - c^0) + Mc^0 \tag{26a}$$

where

$$q_a = [(\partial c/\partial r)_{r_a}/(\omega^2 r_a)]/(1 - \bar{v}\rho) \tag{27a}$$

and

$$c_a - c^0 = - \int_{r_a}^{r_p} (r/r_a)^2 (\partial c/\partial r) \, dr \tag{28a}$$

Equation (28a) can be evaluated directly by using the cube scale (see Eq. 24a). The slope of Eq. (26a) at $c_a - c^0 = 0$ is the z-average molecular weight:

$$\bar{M}_z \equiv \frac{\Sigma c_i M_i^2}{\Sigma c_i M_i} \tag{29a}$$

and the slope of the chord between intercepts is the weight average molecular weight:

$$\bar{M}_w \equiv \frac{\Sigma c_i M_i}{\Sigma c_i} \tag{30a}$$

The variance of the molecular weight distribution is

$$\sigma_m^2 = \bar{M}_w \bar{M}_z - \bar{M}_w^2 \tag{31a}$$

At classical sedimentation equilibrium between $r = r_a$ and $r = r_b$,

$$\bar{M}_w = \left[\frac{2RT}{\omega^2(1 - \bar{v}\rho)} \right] \left[\frac{c_b - c_a}{c^0(r_b^2 - r_a^2)} \right] \tag{32a}$$

Point-by-point values along the cell are

$$M_z = \left[\frac{RT}{\omega^2(1 - \bar{v}\rho)} \right] \left\{ \frac{\partial[(1/r)\partial c/\partial r]}{\partial c} \right\} \tag{33a}$$

and

$$M_w = \left[\frac{2RT}{\omega^2(1 - \bar{v}\rho)} \right] \frac{\partial \ln c}{\partial r^2} \tag{34a}$$

A zone at r_0 at isodensity equilibrium has a net solvated molecular weight, M_s, with net solvation parameter, Γ_1', of

$$M_s = M(1 + \Gamma_1') = \left(\frac{RT}{\omega^2} \right) \left[\frac{\rho}{r(d\rho/dr)} \right]_{r_0} \left(\frac{1}{\sigma^2} \right) \tag{35a}$$

where σ^2 is the variance of the (Gaussian) concentration profile (2σ is the distance between inflection points) and the equilibrium density gradient is computed from tables for common salts. The density at band center, ρ_0, is related to $\bar{v}$, Γ_1', and the partial specific volume of the gradient component, $\bar{v}_1$, by

$$\rho_0 = (1 + \Gamma')/(\bar{v} + \Gamma_1' \bar{v}_1) \tag{36a}$$

Charge effects can be reduced by using 0.1 M KCl as the supporting electrolyte.

CHAPTER 8

Dialysis and Ultrafiltration *

A. Introduction

Dialysis is a separation process that depends on the differential transport of solutes of different sizes across a porous barrier separating two liquids when the driving force is a concentration gradient only. It is usually used to separate solutes too large to diffuse through the barrier from those small enough to diffuse freely through it. Ultrafiltration, sometimes called reverse osmosis, is a more complicated process in that the solvent and solutes up to a certain critical size are forced through the barrier by considerably higher pressure on one side of the porous barrier than on the other. Thus, there is always a flow of solvent moving through the barrier in the same direction as the smaller solutes that are able also to pass through the membrane. This sets it apart from dialysis where, owing to osmosis, there is usually a certain net movement of solvent in the direction opposite to the movement of solute. This has a practical aspect, since in dialysis the membrane never becomes plugged, whereas ultrafilters usually become more or less plugged as the filtration proceeds.

Both dialysis and ultrafiltration are very simple to accomplish. The most important item in both operations is the porous barrier, but it is far from the only consideration, since the success of the operation will depend also on the physical arrangement, the temperature, the solvent, the pH, the nature of the solutes, and other factors. The various factors are often strongly interdependent.

B. The Membrane

For dialysis in biochemical work the most widely used membrane is commercially available in the form of extruded cellulose casing manufactured not primarily for dialysis but for the sausage industry. The technical requirements in the latter ensure the production of an amazingly reproducible thin, strong casing, free from fixed charges. Although other porous materials can and have been used, this short treatment will consider only cellulose casing, usually spoken of as cellophane.

* Chapter 8 was contributed by Lyman C. Craig.

Currently, in the United States, two grades of Visking casing are marketed.* One, their dialysis casing, is cast from specially prepared viscose and treated for dialysis work. It is supposed to be more reliable and to permit a faster rate of dialysis than the so-called Seamless cellulose tubing. In the author's experience both grades are reliable and useful, the latter because it is less porous than the former. In their brochure the Visking Co. lists the sizes in the dialysis grade shown in Table I. Both types are

TABLE I
SIZES OF VISKING "DIALYSIS" CASING AVAILABLE

Identity	Approx. inflated diameter (wet) (cm)	Wall thickness (mm)	Lengths available (feet)
8 DC	0.62	0.05	100 or 1500
20 DC	1.55	0.02	100 or 1000
27 DC	2.1	0.025	100 or 1000
36 DC	2.8	0.02	100 or 1000
1⅛ SS	4.7	0.04	50 or 500
3¼ SS	8.13	0.09	50 or 500

marketed in rolls put up in polyethylene plastic bags to prevent their drying out. They contain a certain amount of glycerine to prevent their becoming too hard and small amounts of impurities most of which are easily removed by washing in water or dilute acetic acid. Where materials sensitive to trace metals are involved it may be advisable to wash the casing in Versene solution before use. Once a membrane has been wetted, it should never be permitted to dry out again. Otherwise, the porosity will decrease and pinholes may be formed. The porosity throughout a given roll usually will be very uniform, but only if the roll is preserved carefully. It will change only slowly over a period of months if kept in the polyethylene bag and stored in a cold room.

A survey of the literature will reveal that there is no unanimity of opinion regarding the best way to evaluate membranes and their relative porosities. In the past, the most accepted approach to this problem has involved the measurement of the flow of water through unit area under a recorded pressure. A formula established many years ago then permits the mean pore diameter to be calculated.[1] For precision dialysis, there are certain obvious objections to such calculations. It is difficult to know the exact nature of the so-called pores. For ultra-filtration this is not as serious,

* Manufactured by the Visking Co., 6733 West 65th Street, Chicago, Illinois.
[1] J. D. Ferry, *J. Gen. Physiol.* **20**, 95 (1936).

a consideration, so long as the solute is retained. Moreover, wet cellophane is really a gel, deformable under pressure.

The most reliable way of measuring pore size for dialysis work is through the study of actual dialysis rates of solutes of known size under standard conditions. An arrangement can be employed whereby a solution of known concentration is placed on one side of the membrane and pure solvent on the other. Both are stirred, and the solvent side is changed with sufficient frequency that the diffusion across the membrane takes place against essentially zero concentration. The solution side will be called the retentate, and the low-concentration side will be called the diffusate. In this arrangement, at a given temperature and for an ideal pure solute the rate of diffusion will follow first-order kinetics. A plot of the logarithm of the concentration in the retentate against time will give a straight line. Relative porosities can be derived from the differences in the slopes of the lines for solutes of different known sizes, or more simply by comparing the times when the concentration has been reduced by half—that is, the 50% escape times.

C. Apparatus

1. THE ANALYTICAL DIALYSIS CELL

Dialysis is ordinarily thought to be a slow process, requiring overnight or sometimes days to accomplish. It need not be with the proper arrangement. Moreover, it has seldom in the past been used as a discriminating tool capable of rather precise quantitation. The simple apparatus shown in Fig. 1 permits determinations in a relatively short time which can be of surprising precision. The principle of this cell depends on the provision of the maximum dialysis area for a given small volume of solution and with stirring of the solutions both inside and out in a completely reproducible way.[2]

A length of wet cellophane casing is pulled over the lower part of a glass collar, about 5 cm in length, carefully fire-polished on the lower end and slightly larger than the wet inflated casing. The casing is tied off with silk thread (size 20 suture silk) at a distance from the glass collar sufficient to provide about 50 cm² of dialyzing area. That part of the membrane pulled over the glass collar is allowed to dry and thus fix the membrane tightly on the glass collar, but the dialyzing area below the collar is always kept wet.

The retentate solution, approximately 0.5 ml, is placed inside the sac, and a glass tube previously sealed and rounded off at the bottom is lowered

[2] L. C. Craig and W. Konigsberg, *J. Phys. Chem.* **65**, 166 (1961).

inside the sac. It is only slightly smaller than the dialysis tubing and is of such size that it barely spreads the solution over the entire inside membrane surface. It must not fit too tightly. The solvent for the diffusate, about 5 ml in volume, is placed in the outside cuvette, which is of such inside diameter that when in place, as shown in Fig. 1b, the solvent will reach the glass collar and cover all the outside of the membrane. The cuvette is enlarged at the top for a distance of about 1 cm so that it will extend a short distance over the lower end of the collar.

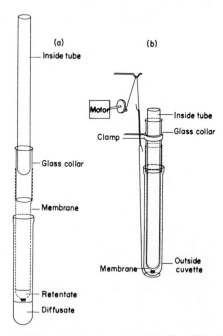

FIG. 1. Schematic drawing of a thin-film dialysis cell.

Stirring is accomplished by a small motor with a gear reduction that provides 10 to 20 rpm and whose shaft carries an eccentric. A nylon string attached to the eccentric can be passed over a bent glass rod and attached to a wire with the lower end formed as a loop fitting around the bottom of the cuvette. The movement of the eccentric causes the cuvette to be raised and lowered a few millimeters on each revolution. The pistonlike effect causes efficient stirring even on the inside by virtue of the flexibility of the membrane. The temperature can be controlled by lowering the assembly into a constant-temperature water bath.

Prior to making a run, the assembly is prepared, and the membrane is washed with several changes of pure solvent until no blank is obtained by the analytical method to be used. If optical density is to be used, cellophane usually gives a persistent low blank—for example, an optical density of about 0.020 at 280 mμ with a 1-cm light path.

For the run, the solution is placed inside, and the time is recorded. At arbitrary recorded intervals the diffusate is set aside and replaced with solvent. When most of the solute has diffused through the membrane, the retentate solution as well as the diffusate is removed and its concentration determined. The membrane is kept wet and preserved for the next run. Many determinations can be made with the same membrane.

Following a run and determination of the solute concentrations, the total recovery is calculated. Then a plot can be constructed, as shown in Fig. 2. If the solute is of known size and purity, this plot serves as a cali-

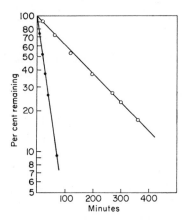

FIG. 2. Plot of escape rates of two solutes, one twice the molecular weight of the other.

bration against which that obtained in the same membrane with other similar solutes can be compared. Commercially available test solutes include bacitracin (molecular weight 1400), insulin (molecular weight 6000, monomer), and ribonuclease (molecular weight 13,600).

Not all pure solutes give straight-line escape plots, in which case the type of escape plot given can be interpreted to indicate association, dissociation, or slow conformational rearrangement. This behavior has been discussed more fully elsewhere.[3,4] More often than not, a deviation is an indication of impurity in the preparation. In fact, this type of dialysis is a very informative way of testing a preparation for purity.

This apparatus is ideal for equilibrium dialysis for the analysis of hapten–antibody reactions (see Chap. 18,B, Vol. III) because of the very rapid equilibration between diffusate and retentate. Equilibrium dialysis

[3] L. C. Craig and T. P. King, *Methods Biochem. Anal.* **10,** 175 (1962).
[4] L. C. Craig, *Advan. Anal. Chem. Instr.* **4,** 35–74 (1965).

with this apparatus has been used to study the complex formation between oxytocin and neurophysin.[5] Washed tubing can be autoclaved in water to prepare for dialysis with sterile retentate; changes in porosity must be measured if critical values are needed.

2. SMALL-SCALE PREPARATIVE DIALYSIS

The simplest and most popular way of carrying out this kind of dialysis is to form a sac from the appropriate cellophane casing after wetting it or soaking it in dilute acid or, in the case of metal-sensitive solutes, with Versene solution. The knot can be formed by tying the tubing itself or by a silk thread. The solution to be dialyzed is placed inside the bag, and a knot is tied above the solution. The closed bag is then placed in a large volume of water or the solution against which the solution is to be dialyzed. Stirring of the outside solution is desirable, or a flowing stream of water may be employed if water is the solvent.

The objection to this type of dialysis is that it is slow and a certain risk of loss of valuable solute is involved. Many times investigators have found that solute thought not to be dialyzable has in some way managed to pass through the membrane.

In the first place, the knot may leak. A double knot will reduce this possibility if the second knot is a little removed from the first one. Solution accumulating between the knots indicates a leak in the first knot.

The second possibility is that the membrane is faulty and has pinholes. Preliminary testing of the sac by putting it under hydrostatic pressure has been recommended. If this is done, a pressure greater than the order of 30 to 40 cm of water should be avoided. Higher pressures, as will be shown later on, make the membrane more porous. A moderate pressure of 30 to 40 cm of water is sufficient to reveal pinholes.

A third possibility arises from pressure building up in the closed sac during dialysis, owing to the osmotic flow of water. To avoid this, the knot closing the bag should be tied some distance above the solution with the casing collapsed completely. The volume of solution inside the sac can then increase two- or threefold without pressure building up inside the sac. If pressure builds up inside, the membrane can be stretched in such a way that it becomes much more porous. Pressure on the membrane should always be avoided in dialysis work unless the solute of interest is very much larger than the limiting pore size of the membrane.

The apparatus shown in Fig. 1, or a modification of it, offers a reliable and rapid preparative dialysis arrangement for smaller volumes. The capacity can be greatly increased by making the apparatus longer or

[5] J. E. Stouffer, D. B. Hope, and V. du Vigneaud, in "Perspectives in Biology" (Cori, Foglia, Leloir, and Ochoa, eds.), p. 75. Elsevier, New York.

by reducing the size of the center tube and even by withdrawing it completely. The latter slows the rate of dialysis accordingly. A convenient modification is shown in Fig. 3, in which a graduate cylinder placed over a magnetic stirrer serves as the dialysis bath. Here the movement of the outside solution can be adjusted so that the suspended sac attached to the glass collar is caused to move and thus stir the retentate. Where several solutions are to be dialyzed simultaneously, the graduate cylinder can be replaced by a tall vessel with a cover of a stiff polyethylene sheet. A number of holes of appropriate sizes can be cut through the plastic cover through which the dialysis sacs attached to the glass collars can be sus-

FIG. 3. Small-scale preparative dialysis modification.

pended. The holes through the plastic are of such size that the flared tops of the glass collars will not pass through them. In Fig. 3 this is shown for a single dialysis sac.

The advantages of this type of dialysis sac are several. Each sac can be tested prior to use and used repeatedly for a considerable time, particularly if it is stored under 0.01 N acetic acid in the cold room between uses. Increase of volume due to osmotic flow does not significantly increase pressure on the membrane. Sampling of the retentate from time to time to follow the course of the dialysis can be accomplished conveniently.

For dialysis of somewhat larger amounts of solution a number of devices are commercially available.* There is not space for discussion of their relative merits in this short treatment. More extensive reviews can be found in the literature.[4,6–8]

3. COUNTERCURRENT DIALYSIS

It is interesting that so little effort has been made to design a rapid countercurrent dialyzer for laboratory use. A number of advantages would appear to result from such an apparatus if it were available. These would include a saving of time, the use of higher temperatures permissible because of the shorter time the solution is exposed to the membrane, and better control over possible losses. Higher temperatures should lead to more effective removal, particularly where solute binding is involved.

Recently, an attempt has been made to design such a dialyzer.[9] It has given promising results but has not been widely tested in other laboratories as yet. It takes advantage of the thin-film principle for achieving higher transfer rates with a given porosity. A schematic drawing of the apparatus is shown in Fig. 4. The countercurrent flow of the solutions on each side of the membrane as a thin film is achieved by two concentric glass tubes approximately 0.5 mm apart with the dialysis membrane between them. Channeling of the outer solution is avoided by rotation of the outer glass tube. The flow of the solutions is precisely regulated by a suitable pump. Temperature regulation is provided for by a stream of water from a constant-temperature bath passed through an outer jacket. The jacket is not shown in the drawing.

Table II is an example of data on the performance of this type of dialyzer. It would seem to be especially useful for removing salts or solutes like urea from the solutions of high ionic strength so often found useful in chromatography and countercurrent distribution. For a full description of the dialyzer the original paper[9] must be consulted. With more extensive testing, improvements can now be mentioned.

The improvements include the use of a larger pair of concentric tubes so that the membrane is stretched and under a degree of tension. This

* For example, the Technicon (Technicon Instruments Co., Chauncey, New York); the Hoch (National Instruments Laboratories, 12300 Parklawn Drive, Rockville, Maryland).

[6] S. B. Tuwiner, "Diffusion and Membrane Technology," ACS Monograph No. 156, Reinhold, New York, 1962.

[7] C. J. O. R. Morris and P. Morris, in "Separation Methods in Biochemistry," pp. 771–805. Interscience, New York, 1963.

[8] R. E. Stauffer, in "Separation and Purification" (A. Weissberger, ed.), Vol. 3, Part I, 2nd ed., pp. 65–119. Interscience, New York, 1956.

[9] L. C. Craig and K. Stewart, Biochemistry 4, 2712 (1965).

permits a closer fit of the outer tube so that the annular space between the two tubes can be of the order of 0.3 mm. With such a small clearance, the inside tube must be precision ground and polished.

Another improvement involves a reduction in diameter of the inside tube at the point where it extends through the glass collar holding the

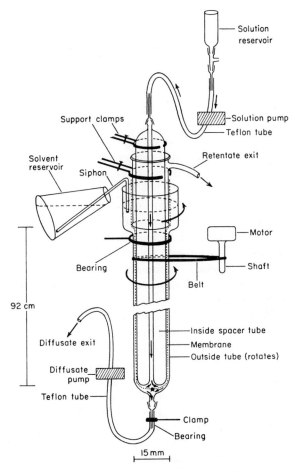

FIG 4. Schematic drawing of a thin-film countercurrent dialyzer.

membrane. The retentate reaching this point is then picked up by a thin Kel-F tube (No. 24) attached to a pump and passed to a fraction collector. The retentate exit spout is thus eliminated and the hold-up at the top of the column greatly reduced.

With these improvements, it was found that under tests comparable to

TABLE II

DIALYSIS DATA OBTAINED WITH THE THIN-FILM COUNTERCURRENT DIALYZER
AT 25° AND THE INTERMEDIATE PUMP SETTING

	Size 18			Size 20		
	Exit flow rate (ml/min)		Re-moval (%)	Exit flow rate (ml/min)		Re-moval (%)
Solutes	Re-tentate	Dif-fusate		Re-tentate	Dif-fusate	
Tryptophan $(2.46 \times 10^{-3}\,M)$	0.45	1.19	91.6	0.45	1.32	93.9
Sucrose 6%	0.52	1.42	82.6	—	—	—
Sucrose 30%	0.75	1.37	72.7	—	—	—
Bacitracin $(1.92 \times 10^{-3}\,M)$	0.46	1.20	60.7	0.48	1.48	67.4
Subtilin $(2.42 \times 10^{-3}\,M)$	0.46	1.28	30.0	0.45	1.43	44.2
1 M NaCl	0.54	1.25	99.4	0.56	1.46	99.4
3% sat. $(NH_4)_2SO_4$	0.50	1.20	96.9	0.56	1.45	98.5
50% sat. $(NH_4)_2SO_4$	0.86	1.18	91.8	0.94	1.43	91.5

those given in Table II bacitracin could be removed to the extent of 97%
on a single pass as compared to 67.4% in Table II. It was even more
convincing to find that a pulse of tritiated water showing 10^8 cpm would
emerge with a count no higher than background. Thus, the quantitative
transfer to the diffusate stream achieved at a differential flow rate of
retentate/diffusate streams of $\frac{1}{3}$, and in a single pass with a residence
time in the dialyzer of 6–8 minutes, suggests interesting possibilities in
tritium exchange studies. The dialyzer has been shown to be an effective
tool for this and in other binding studies.

The transfer efficiency has also been shown in another way with practical implications. The dialyzer could be operated cocurrently by reversing
the flow of the diffusate stream. In this case, the effluent diffusate could
be picked up at the top of the column by a thin Kel-F tube passing to a
pump. When this stream was adjusted to be 10 times the rate of flow of
the retentate stream it would remove 90% of the salt from the retentate
on a single pass. This choice of operation was found to be preferable for
the first step in desalting concentrated salt solutions where strong
osmotic flow of solvent into the retentate would occur and thereby cause
pressure problems.

4. ULTRAFILTRATION

Ultrafiltration membranes of standardized porosities designed for
particle retention are available, allowing sterile filtration (Chap. 2,C,5,
Vol. I). A discussion of this type of filter will not be given. Collodion mem-

branes on alundum thimbles have been employed (Chap. 1,B,6 and 1,D,1, Vol. I). A recently developed type, which retains solutes, deserves special mention. It is claimed by the Amicon Corporation which developed it that its gel structure permits a relatively rapid diffusion flow of water when appropriate pressure is applied to the solution. The filter membrane is a supported synthetic ion exchange membrane with positive and negative charges so balanced that their sum is neutral. Several membranes are available with different solute retention characteristics, "Diaflow" membranes UM 1, UM 2, and UM 3. They are claimed to retain solutes larger than 10,000, 1,000, and 350 in molecular weight, respectively. Several different filtration devices are offered* for these membranes depending on the volume of solution to be filtered. The simplest is a hypodermic syringe modification. The others provide for efficient stirring of the solution contacting the filter. An intermediate size filter operates under pressures up to 50 psi and a larger model up to 100 psi. These ultrafilters are excellent devices for concentration of dilute protein solutions. Performance data are available from various bulletins of the company. For studies dealing with the concentration of protein solutions by this method, see Blatt et al.[10]

A useful and simple type of ultrafilter can be made from the same cellophane casing used in dialysis. Its porosity for the most porous tubing can be such as to hold back everything above 30,000 in molecular weight, or 10,000 for the least porous tubing. The arrangement shown in Fig. 5 is more or less self-explanatory. The lower end of the casing is closed by a knot. The upper end is slipped over a glass tube. A one-hole rubber stopper sliced through to the hole surrounds the membrane and glass tube. When the stopper is inserted into the mouth of the suction flask, an airtight seal supporting the tubing results. A vacuum up to the range of 150 mm Hg can be used. This type of filtration can run unattended for hours (see Chap. 9,E for a slightly different description). Berggård has made comparisons of this type of ultrafiltration with dialysis.[11]

The apparatus shown in Fig. 5 was suggested by Berggård for use with size 8 DC Visking casing because it is small enough not to require support around the casing. Casings of larger diameter require support. This can be provided by placing the wet casing inside a tube made of gauze.†

Another way of supporting the larger tubing is shown in Fig. 6. Here

* Available from The Amicon Corporation, 280 Binney St., Cambridge, Massachusetts.
[10] W. F. Blatt, M. P. Feinberg, H. B. Hopfenburg, and C. A. Saravis, Science 158, 224 (1965).
[11] I. Berggård, Arkiv Kemi 18, 291 (1961).
† Scholl Manufacturing Co., New York.

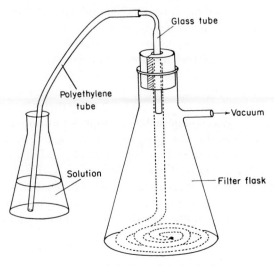

FIG. 5. Schematic drawing of an ultrafiltration device.

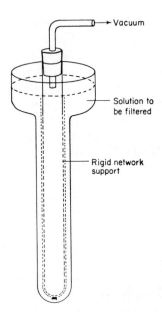

FIG. 6. Schematic drawing of an ultrafiltration device with inner support.

the rigid network or support is placed inside the cellophane bag, and the solution is filtered from the outside to the inside.*

D. Methods for Altering Porosity

Dialysis can be a more discriminating separation process than ultra-filtration except in a few cases as, for example, in an extremely high-pressure filtration process being developed for the removal of salt from sea water. In both cases the porosity of the membrane is of little concern where very large solutes are to be separated from very small ones. The limiting porosity does become important, however, when a more discriminating separation is to be undertaken. For such a purpose it is obvious that a way of altering the pore size will be required so that it will be optimum for the range of molecule to be studied. Also needed is a

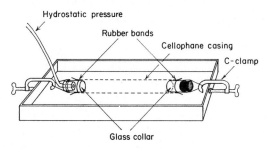

FIG. 7. Device for controlled stretching of cellophane membranes.

suitable way of determining pore size. This requirement has already been discussed.

The porosity of cellophane casing can be altered easily to allow passage or rejection, in dialysis, of solutes ranging in molecular weight from 100 to 100,000.[2] This can be accomplished by a stretching process carried out on the wet casing, by causing the membrane to swell with a strong $ZnCl_2$ solution or to become less porous by acetylation. It is interesting that the most selective membrane in the filtration process for desalination of sea water is cast from acetyl cellulose.

Mechanical stretching can either reduce the porosity or increase it, depending on the way the stretching is done. The apparatus shown in Fig. 7 is convenient for controlling the degree of stretching. In this equipment a length of the casing is firmly held at each end by being slipped over glass

* L.K.B. Instruments Inc., Stockholm; and Rockville, Maryland.

collars and held in place with rubber bands. The glass collars are tied by nylon cords to small C clamps hooked over each end of the stainless-steel trough filled with water. When the clamps are tightened, the casing is stretched linearly. This reduces the diameter of the casing and the pore size as well, up to a size that would reject a solute of roughly half that barely rejected by the unstretched membrane.

If during the linear stretching hydrostatic pressure is also applied through the tube, the casing becomes larger in diameter as well as longer. It also becomes more porous, up to a limiting pore size permitting a solute twice as large to pass as the unstretched casing would permit. The stretched membranes retain the altered porosity after a short time for relaxation.

Visking size 20 DC can be stretched in this way so that it will allow ovalbumin (molecular weight 45,000) to pass slowly in dialysis at 40°. It will not permit serum albumin (molecular weight 66,000) to pass. When, however, the membrane is soaked for 10 to 15 minutes at 25° in 64% $ZnCl_2$ and the salt is washed out, the membrane will allow even the dimer of serum albumin to pass slowly. Intermediate porosities can be obtained by a shorter treatment or by a lower concentration of $ZnCl_2$.

In the $ZnCl_2$ solution the casing becomes very plastic and is easily deformed. This can be avoided by making a sac held by a glass collar as in Fig. 1, or preferably by leaving the bottom open until after the treatment and then tying it off. The center expander tube slipped into place can then be used to hold the membrane in place when it is dipped into the $ZnCl_2$ solution and during the washing operation following the $ZnCl_2$ treatment. The $ZnCl_2$-treated membranes have less mechanical strength than the less porous membranes.

Acetylation to reduce the porosity is a simple procedure. The sac is attached to the glass collar as shown in Fig. 1 and washed with dry pyridine to remove the water. It is then filled with a 25% solution of acetic anhydride in pyridine and suspended in the solution. Heating at 60° for about 7 hours will reduce the porosity of Visking size 18 seamless cellulose, previously linearly stretched, to the point where it will nearly reject amino acids.[11] Intermediate porosities can be obtained by a shorter period of acetylation or by a lower temperature. Following acetylation the pyridine and acetic anhydride can be removed by several hours of soaking in 0.01 N acetic acid. The acetylated membranes are stable except in concentrated urea solutions or at a pH below 3 or above 9.

Table III gives the different Visking casings and modifications found suitable for various ranges of molecular weights in the thin-film dialyzer. These estimates are based on 50% escape times of a few hours.

[12] L. C. Craig and A. Ansevin, *Biochemistry* **2**, 1268 (1963).

TABLE III

VISKING CASING SUITABLE FOR THIN-FILM DIALYSIS OF VARIOUS
MOLECULAR SIZES

Casing	Range of molecular weights
18 DC untreated	6,000–12,000
18 DC stretched	2,000–6,000
18 DC stretched linearly and acetylated	100–2,000
20 DC untreated	12,000–20,000
20 DC stretched linearly + circularly under pressure	20,000–45,000
20 DC ZnCl₂ treated	45,000–135,000

CHAPTER 9

Chromatographic Separations of Macromolecules on Porous Gels and Cellulose Ion Exchangers

A. Introduction*

In recent years there have been many developments for a more effective separation of substances of biological interest. Two of the most commonly used techniques are the chromatographic separations carried out on selectively porous gels and on cellulose ion exchangers. It is the purpose of this chapter to give some of the experimental details on the use of these two techniques only.

One would be remiss not to mention that the classical procedures of salt and alcohol precipitations still have much merit for the initial fractionation of a crude biological mixture. Precipitation procedures have selectivities different from those of the chromatographic procedures, and initial fractionation reduces the complexity of the mixture to be separated by chromatography. This is helpful since the resolution obtained by column chromatography is concentration-dependent, a fact that applies particularly to cellulose ion exchange columns and somewhat less to columns of porous gels. It is therefore good strategy, for the separation of a complex mixture, to use first the precipitation techniques, second the chromatographic techniques with porous gels, and third cellulose ion exchangers. The joint use of these techniques will permit the isolation of most proteins and peptides in high states of purity.

* Section 9,A was contributed by Te Piao King.

B. Chromatography on Gels

1. CHROMATOGRAPHY ON CROSS-LINKED DEXTRAN GELS (SEPHADEX)†‡

a. GENERAL CONSIDERATIONS

Porath and Flodin[1] first showed that separation of solutes mainly on the basis of their molecular size differences can be carried out readily on

† Section 9,B,1 was contributed by Te Piao King.

‡ Pharmacia Fine Chemicals, Inc., 800 Centennial Avenue, Piscataway, New Market, New Jersey.

[1] J. Porath and P. Flodin, *Nature* 183, 1657 (1959).

columns of aqueous gels of cross-linked dextrans. Dextrans of different degrees of cross-linkages are available commerically under the trade name of Sephadex. Sephadex gels are suitable for fractionation of solutes with molecular weights from several hundred to several hundred thousand. Several reviews are available on the principle of this process as well as on its range of applications.[2-4]

i. Exclusion Limit

One possible interpretation of the separation process on Sephadex columns is as follows. Large solutes that cannot enter the gel pores will emerge first at the void volume, V_0, which is the volume of liquid surrounding the gels in the column. Small solutes, which can penetrate the gel pores freely, will be retarded and emerge at a volume $V_0 + V_i$, where V_i is the volume of liquid inside the gel particles. Thus the region available for the fractionation of solutes with intermediate sizes lies in the volume range between V_0 and $V_0 + V_i$ in the chromatogram. As this interpretation of the process bears a resemblance to that of a hypothetical continuous countercurrent dialysis (see Chap. 8), the process has been designated as gel filtration by the original inventors.

In Table I are listed the several grades of Sephadex now available. In the first column of the table is given the approximate exclusion limit of each

TABLE I
Types and Specifications of Sephadex Gels

Type	Approximate exclusion limit (molecular weight)	Water regain (gm water per gm dry gel)	Bed volume (ml/gm)	Particle size (microns)
G-10	700	1.0 ± 0.1	2	40–120
G-15	1,500	1.5 ± 0.1	2.5–3.5	40–120
G-25: Coarse (C)	5,000	2.5 ± 0.2	5	100–300
Medium (M)				50–150
Fine (F)[a]				20–80
G-50: (C), (M), (F)[a]	10,000	5.0 ± 0.3	10	as with G-25
G-75[a]	50,000	7.5 ± 0.5	12–15	40–120
G-100[a]	100,000	10.0 ± 1.0	15–20	40–120
G-150[a]	150,000	15.0 ± 1.5	20–30	40–120
G-200[a]	200,000	20.0 ± 2.0	30–40	40–120

[a] Superfine grades (10–40 μ particle size) are available, and are being applied to column chromatography. Bed volume of G-200 Superfine is 25 ml/gm.

[2] J. Porath, Advan. Protein Chem. **17**, 209 (1962).
[3] P. Flodin, Dextran Gels and Their Applications in Gel Filtration, Dissertation, Uppsala (1962) (obtainable from A. B. Pharmacia, Uppsala, Sweden).
[4] H. Determann, Angew. Chem., Intern. Ed. **3**, 608 (1964).

grade of Sephadex. The exclusion limit refers to the smallest solute that will emerge at the void volume, V_0. In the second column is given the water regain of each grade of Sephadex. When the amount of dry Sephadex used for a column is known, the V_i of the column is equal to its dry

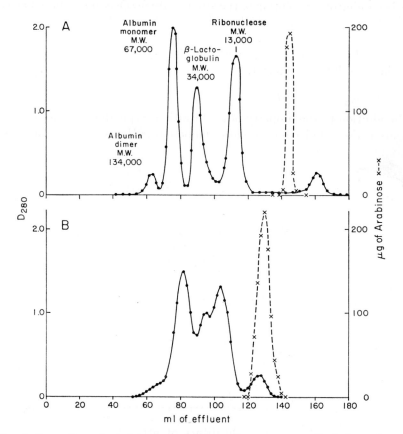

FIG. 1. Separation of a mixture of proteins and a pentose on Sephadex columns. *A*, Sephadex G-100. *B*, Sephadex G-200. In both figures the column dimensions are 0.9 × 195 cm and the eluants are 0.20*M* (NH₄)₂SO₄ + 0.05*M* Tris + 0.03 *M* HCl. About 10 to 25 mg of each protein was used. The flow rate was 12 ml/hour, and 2-ml fractions were collected. The pentose peak is represented by the dashed curve.

weight multiplied by the water regain. In the third column the swollen gel volume for each gram of dry Sephadex is given.

The chromatographic separations of an artificial mixture of proteins and a pentose on Sephadex G-100 and Sephadex G-200 columns are given in Fig. 1. Comparison of the two chromatograms shows the importance of a proper selection of the grade of Sephadex for achieving a desired separation. The three proteins—albumin monomer, β-lactoglobulin and ribonuclease—are well resolved on the G-100 column but poorly resolved on the G-200 column. On the other hand, the G-200 chromatogram showed the beginning of a resolution of the albumin dimer peak into a broad peak, suggesting the presence of higher albumin polymers. From these results it is seen that the proper grade of Sephadex for an effective separation is one whose exclusion limit is not more than four to five times the molecular weights of solutes of interest.

ii. Adsorption Properties

In addition to the property of gel filtration, Sephadex gels also possess an adsorption affinity for aromatic compounds.[5] Hence the retardation of

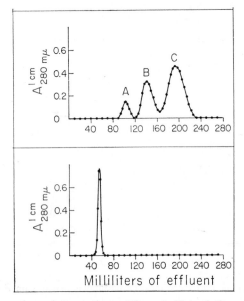

Fig. 2. Separation of a mixture of tyrocidines A, B, and C on a Sephadex G-25 column (0.9 × 150 cm). The eluant in the upper pattern was 10% acetic acid, and that in the lower pattern was 50% acetic acid. The flow rate was 10 ml/hour, and 2-ml fractions were collected. Crushed form of Sephadex was used in this figure; slightly poorer resolution was obtained with the bead form. From M. A. Ruttenberg, T. P. King, and L. C. Craig, *Biochemistry* 4, 11 (1965).

a solute on a Sephadex column may be due to its small size or to its high aromatic content. When proper cognizance of this fact is taken, the

[5] J. Gelotte, *J. Chromatog.* 3, 330 (1960).

aromatic adsorption property may be used advantageously for separation. Figure 2 illustrates this. Three tyrocidines were separated on a Sephadex G-25 column with 10% acetic acid as eluant. When 50% acetic acid was used as eluant, the selective aromatic affinity of Sephadex was completely abolished, and the three tyrocidines emerged as a single peak. These tyrocidines are homologous cyclic decapeptides, and they differ by the stepwise replacement of a single amino acid residue with a tryptophanyl residue. Tyrocidines B and C contain one and two residues of tryptophan, respectively. These two peptides are adsorbed so strongly that they are not eluted by water at all.[6]

iii. Solvent Effects

Chromatography on Sephadex columns is relatively insensitive to changes of pH and ionic strength of the eluants. When changes in the elution position of a solute do occur with varying pH or ionic strength, it usually indicates that the solute is undergoing dissociation or association with itself or other solutes present. It is also possible that the conformational alterations of a solute in different solvent environments will cause changes in its elution position. Therefore, the choice of a proper pH is dictated mainly by the stabilities of the solutes. However, eluants of moderately high ionic strength are usually preferred over distilled water. This is so for two reasons. First, the very few carboxyl groups present in Sephadex gels may display ion exchange properties with the solute in pure water such that anomalous separation or incomplete recovery of solute may occur.[5] Second, Sephadex columns of any grade higher than G-50 tend to shrink after use with water as eluant so that they become inoperable because of the decreased flow rate. An eluant of high ionic strength prevents this shrinkage.

Sephadex chromatography is generally insensitive to temperature changes except that the flow rate of a column is influenced moderately by viscosity variations of the eluant with temperatures. Therefore the choice of the operating temperature is limited only by the stability of the solute.

b. Techniques

i. Column Dimensions and Buffers

The degree of separation obtainable on a Sephadex column depends on the ratio of column height to diameter, as a column with a high ratio provides more stages of fractionation. Since it is just as easy to use a long

[6] M. A. Ruttenberg, T. P. King, and L. C. Craig, *Biochemistry* **4**, 11 (1965).

column as a short one, the use of a long column with better resolution is preferred. Two columns with the dimensions of 1 × 205 cm and 2.5 × 205 cm will meet most analytical and moderate preparative purposes.* As much as a 300-mg sample may be handled on the 1-cm column, and the sample may be applied in a volume of 1 to 4 ml. Sample volumes larger than 4 ml are to be avoided, as decreased resolution of peaks will result. The 1-cm column can be operated by simple gravity flow at a rate of 8 to 12 ml/hour. Higher flow rate will broaden the peaks. Fractions of 2-ml volumes are collected. For the 2.5-cm column quantities six times as large are used, and the flow rate is maintained below 20–40 ml/hour.

When separations of closely similar substances are called for, the recycling procedure[7] may be used, or two or three columns may be connected in series.[8] Columns longer than 2 meters are not practical for most laboratories.

When a Sephadex column is used solely for desalting of a protein solution or equilibrating it to a different buffer, the ratio of column height to diameter becomes less critical. For example, a protein solution having a volume of 10 ml or less can be desalted cleanly on a 2 × 60-cm column of Sephadex G-25 at a flow rate of 80 ml/hour.

For Sephadex G-25 and G-50 columns the eluant should have an ionic strength equivalent to about 0.1 N NaCl; for G-75 to G-200 columns the ionic strength of the eluant should be equivalent to about 1 N NaCl. Of course, any other inorganic salt may be used in place of NaCl to give the desired ionic strength. Buffer salts in the concentration range of 0.05 to 0.10 M are also included in the eluants to achieve the required buffering capacity. For purposes of desalting on G-25 columns, eluants containing volatile buffers are used, such as 0.2 N acetic acid, 0.05 N pyridine acetate, or ammonium bicarbonate; otherwise, incomplete recovery of sample may result, owing to the weak adsorption and ion exchange properties of Sephadex gels.

---

* The columns are mounted on a wall rack, and the column effluent is brought to the fraction collector through a thin polyethylene tubing (O.D. 0.075 inch, PE 200, Clay Adams Co.). The glass column has a coarse sintered-glass disk sealed at its bottom, and the exit end has a male ⑤ 12/2 ball joint; the volume between the disk and the joint is kept to the minimum to avoid mixing. A length of polyethylene tubing is pulled partly through a 4-cm length of the female ⑤ 12/2 joint. One end of the tubing is flanged by placing it near a lighted cigarette. When this flanged end is pulled tight toward the socket joint, a good seal is formed between the tubing and the glass joint tube. This female joint is then attached to the column. To avoid leakage around the ball joint, a thin silicon rubber gasket is recommended.

[7] J. Porath and H. Bennich, *Arch. Biochem. Biophys. Suppl.* **1**, 152 (1962).
[8] T. P. King and P. S. Norman, *Biochemistry* **1**, 709 (1962).

ii. Packing the Column

Sephadex G-25 and G-50 are available in two particle size ranges, but there is only one size range for the other types (Table I). A column made with the fine particle grade gives a slightly better resolution but has a slower flow rate. For most purposes the coarse grade will suffice, and it is easier to use.

After the proper column, the type of Sephadex, and the buffer have been chosen, an amount of Sephadex estimated to be 15 to 20% in excess of that required to fill the column is weighed out. The dry Sephadex is stirred up with four times the estimated bed volume of buffer in a beaker. After a settling period of 15 to 20 minutes the supernatant containing some fine particles is decanted off. This process is repeated three times; then the gel is suspended in one half the volume of buffer initially used for swelling. For G-25 or G-50 gels, this suspension may be used immediately to pack a column. For G-75 to G-200 gels, it is best to allow the gels to swell a day or two before use; otherwise the columns poured will shrink to give diminishing flow rates after use.

To pack a column free of trapped air bubbles, the empty column is first filled with buffer to a height of about 30 cm. Then a uniform suspension of the gel in the buffer is added to fill the column. After most of the gel has settled, the excess buffer is withdrawn to about 10 cm above the gel. Addition of the gel suspension is repeated until the gel column height reaches 200 cm. The packed column is connected to a reservoir, and 4 column volumes of buffer are passed through before use.

iii. Loading and Calibrating the Column

A small polyethylene plate floated on top of the column buffer minimizes any possible disturbance of the gel bed by the incoming buffer and during the application of sample to column. This plastic plate fits the column loosely and rises and falls readily with the buffer height of the column. This device also provides for a simple procedure of application of the sample to the column. The buffer in the column is withdrawn to about 2 to 3 mm above the gel bed. The sample (1 to 4 ml) is added dropwise onto the plate; then a rinse solution (1 to 2 ml) is added in a similar fashion. After being connected to a reservoir, the column is ready for elution. As long as the incoming buffer drops through a distance of less than 3 cm before hitting the plastic plate, there is little danger of mixing.

Before a new column is used, it is best to calibrate it with a known mixture of proteins and a low-molecular-weight neutral solute. This model experiment will yield information on the elution positions of solutes of known molecular weight as well as the expected peak width of homogeneous solutes. This information serves as a useful guide for estimating the approximate molecular size and the homogeneity of the unknown to be fractionated. It is appropriate to emphasize again that the molecular size so determined is only a crude estimate, since, as was mentioned earlier, the Sephadex gels also have adsorptive properties.

The best way to confirm an observed fractionation is to rerun the isolated sample on the same column. If the fractionation is authentic, the sample should appear at the same effluent position with the same peak width and with a quantitative recovery.

2. CHROMATOGRAPHY ON POLYACRYLAMIDE GELS*

a. GENERAL REMARKS

Chromatographic columns prepared from polyacrylamide gel grains can be used for the fractionation of substances largely on the basis of molecular size in a fashion similar to Sephadex columns. Polyacrylamide gels thus behave as "molecular sieves." With these gels it is possible also to desalt and to fractionate peptides, proteins, nucleic acids, and polysaccharides.[1-5]

b. PREPARATION OF POLYACRYLAMIDE SPHERES†

i. Selection of Gel Concentration

The gel grains are prepared from the monomers acrylamide and N,N'-methylenebisacrylamide. The chromatographic properties of the grains are determined by the total concentration, T, of the two monomers and by the concentration, C, of N,N'-methylenebisacrylamide, acting as a cross-linking agent. If a and b are the numbers of grams of acrylamide and N,N'-methylenebisacrylamide, respectively, added to m milliliters of

* Section 9,B,2 was contributed by Stellan Hjertén.

[1] S. Hjertén and R. Mosbach, Anal. Biochem. 3, 109 (1962).
[2] S. Hjertén, Arch. Biochem. Biophys. Suppl. 1, 147 (1962).
[3] D. J. Lea and A. H. Sehon, Can. J. Chem. 40, 159 (1962).
[4] H. G. Boman and S. Hjertén, Arch. Biochem. Biophys. Suppl. 1, 276 (1962).
[5] S. Hjertén in "Protides of the Biological Fluids" (H. Peeters, ed.) Elsevier, Amsterdam, p. 553 (1967).

† Spherical polyacrylamide grains are commercially available as Bio-Gel P from Bio-Rad Laboratories, Richmond, California. The Bio Gels P are now characterized by a high reproducibility and good physical and chemical properties.

buffer, the following relations pertain:

$$T = \left(\frac{a+b}{m} \cdot 100 \right) \% \ (\mathrm{w/v})$$

$$C = \left(\frac{b}{a+b} \cdot 100 \right) \% \ (\mathrm{w/w})$$

There is an optimum polyacrylamide gel composition for each particular fractionation problem. This composition is determined by trial-and-error experiments. However, one can roughly state that, the higher the molecular weights of the substances to be separated, the lower is the gel concentration necessary. For an estimation of a suitable gel concentration when the molecular weights of the applied substances are approximately

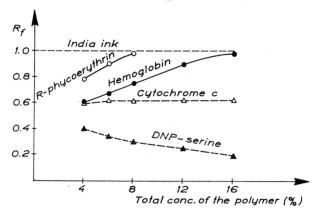

Fig. 1. The relationship between R_f value and total concentration, T, of cross-linked polyacrylamide for molecules of different size: R-phycoerythrin (molecular weight 290,000), human hemoglobin (molecular weight 68,000), cytochrome c from horse heart (molecular weight 13,000), and DNP-serine (molecular weight 271). The cross-linking concentration, C, has been kept constant and equal to 5%. India ink was used as a reference substance. This diagram can be used for a rough selection of gel concentration when the molecular weights of the substances to be separated are approximately known. Reproduced from S. Hjertén, *Arch. Biochem. Biophys. Suppl.* **1**, 147 (1962), courtesy of the publishers.

known, Fig. 1 is of help. It shows, the highest total concentration, T (for $C = 5\%$), that can be used to separate substances above a certain molecular size. Thus, it is evident that for proteins larger than phycoerythrin (molecular weight 290,000) a total concentration lower than 8% should be used. Figure 1 also shows that polyacrylamide columns permit fractionation of substances of molecular weights up to 0.5 to 1 million. For

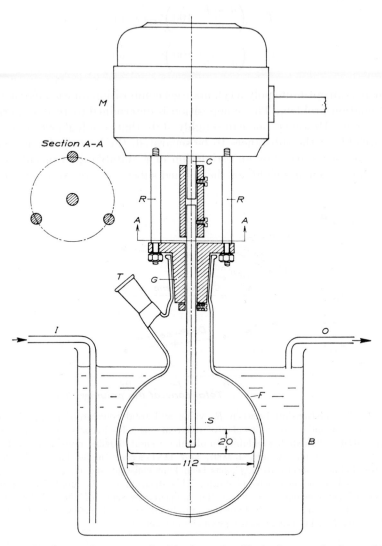

FIG. 2. Equipment for preparation of polyacrylamide (and agarose) spheres: M, d-c motor, power rating 190 watts at 3000 rpm; R, three metal rods; C, motor axis; S, blade stirrer of stainless steel (thickness 1 mm); F, round-bottom flask (reactor); T, side tube; I, inlet for water; O, outlet for water; B, beaker; G, male joint of stainless steel.

larger molecules and for submicroscopic particles the agarose columns are recommended (see Section B,3).

ii. Formation of Spherical Gel Grains

Spherical grains give a more uniformly packed bed than grains of an irregular shape, thus providing much narrower zones and, consequently, higher resolution. Another advantage is that they allow higher flow rates.

Polyacrylamide gel spheres are prepared by suspension polymerization. An aqueous solution of the monomers is dispersed into spheres in a hydrophobic liquid containing a stabilizer. The function of the stabilizer is to prevent aggregation of the spheres. In the presence of an initiator and an accelerator, bulk polymerization takes place in each of the suspended spheres. The equipment for the preparation of polyacrylamide spheres is illustrated schematically in Fig. 2. The male joint, G, is fixed to the motor, M, by three metal rods, R. Thus, vapors from the organic phase in the reactor, F, do not pass into the motor, and the risk of ignition by the commutator sparks is eliminated.

Experimental conditions for the preparation of gels of different compositions are found in Table I. For other gel compositions, the polymerization conditions can be obtained by extrapolation; sphere diameters other than those listed can easily be achieved, as there are many variable factors determining the sphere size (see below, Section c,ii). As oxygen is a polymerization inhibitor, the air in the reactor, F, is displaced with oxygen-free nitrogen. A d-c motor is preferred to an a-c motor, because it gives a stirring speed that is less dependent on the load.

Nitrogen from a tank is delivered to the reactor flask through the side tube, T, at a rate of two to four bubbles per second, as indicated by a wash bottle coupled between the tank and the reactor. The stabilizer* is added to the chloroform in the reactor flask. About half an hour of stirring is required to dissolve the stabilizer. Polybutene† (average molecular weight 440) is poured into the chloroform. After these two liquids have been mixed by stirring for some seconds the accelerator (N,N,N',N'-tetramethylethylenediamine) is added. The stirring is continued a few more seconds to distribute the accelerator uniformly.

Nitrogen is bubbled for 1 minute through the deaerated monomer

---

* Polyvinylacetate with an average molecular weight of about 20,000 and with 9% of the acetate groups replaced with hydroxyl groups has been used as a stabilizer. It is available from Wacker-Chemie, Prinzregentenstrasse 22, 8 München 22, Postfach, Germany, under the trade name Vinnapas B 17/550.

† This polymer is available from California Chemical Division, 200 Bush Street, San Francisco, California, under the trade name Oronite Polybutene, No. 8.

TABLE I
EXPERIMENTAL CONDITIONS FOR SUSPENSION POLYMERIZATION OF ACRYLAMIDE[a]

| Gel composition: | | | | | | | | | | |
Total concn., T (%)	Cross-linking concn., C (%)	Polymerization temperature	0.01 M Tris–acetic acid, pH 7.8 (ml)	Ammonium persulfate (gm)	N,N,N',N'-tetramethylethylenediamine (ml)	Chloroform (ml)	Polybutene (ml)	Polyvinylacetate (mg)	Stirring speed (rpm)	Sphere diameter (mm)
6	5	Room	300	1	1	450	150	100	490	0.07
6	5	Room	300	1	1	450	150	85	510	0.08
6	5	Room	380	1	1	390	130	70	510	0.10
6	5	Room	450	1	1	340	110	70	510	0.11
10	5	9°	300	0.5	0.5	450	150	100	525	0.04
20	5	9°	300	0.3	0.3	450	150	100	525	0.04
30	5	9°	300	0.3	0.3	450	150	80	525	0.04

[a] Organic phase: a mixture of polybutene and chloroform. Water phase: acrylamide and N,N'-methylenebisacrylamide, dissolved in 0.01 M Tris–acetic acid, pH 7.8. Initiator: ammonium persulfate. Accelerator: N,N,N',N'-tetramethylethylenediamine. Stabilizer: polyvinylacetate with a minor amount of hydroxyl groups. The values at the far right are the diameters of the majority of the polyacrylamide spheres. The polymerization temperature is the temperature of the contents of the reactor flask at the onset of the polymerization—either the temperature of the cooling water or the room temperature when the flask is not cooled (for the latter case the notation "Room" is used).

solution* containing dissolved initiator (ammonium persulfate). This solution is then poured into the reactor flask,† in which the air has now been completely replaced by nitrogen.

The stirring is then started immediately. The stirring should be continued for at least 45 minutes after the start of the polymerization.‡ The initiation is attended by a temperature rise and can therefore be detected easily (provided the reactor flask is not water-cooled) by feeling the reactor flask occasionally.§

The contents of the reactor flask are poured into a Büchner funnel, and the majority of the organic phase is sucked off. The diameter of the funnel should be large (about 20 cm) to avoid long filtration times. The spheres are washed thoroughly with ether and then with 1% acetic acid. They are then suspended in 2 liters of 1% acetic acid and transferred to a suction flask which is connected to a water pump. About half an hour of evacuation is required to remove the ether. Excessively large particles are collected on a 40-mesh sieve and discarded. "Fines" are removed by repeated decantations, first in 0.01 M Tris–acetic acid, pH 7.8, until the pH of the supernatant attains a neutral value, and then in the buffer to be used for the elution (phosphate buffers should be avoided, as they have a tendency to aggregate the gel spheres in some cases).

c. CHROMATOGRAPHIC TECHNIQUES

i. Packing the Column

It is convenient to support the column bed by a porous polyethylene disk‖ of the same diameter as the tube. Column tubes with a glass wool plug at the tip are not suitable because the gel grains can easily clog the channels in the glass wool, which results in a low flow rate.

Buffer is poured into the tube to a height of about 10 cm. Part of the buffer is sucked out rapidly through the effluent nipple at the bottom of

---

* The monomers are dissolved in 0.01 M Tris–acetic acid, pH 7.8. Any insoluble material should be removed by filtration. Deaeration is performed after addition of the initiator by connecting a suction flask with the monomer solution to a water pump for some minutes.

† In polymerization experiments with water-cooled reactor, the organic phase and the water phase should be cooled to the same temperature (that of the cooling water) before mixing.

‡ There is a lag period of 10 to 45 minutes before the onset of the polymerization after all reactants are present.

§ The beaker, B, is used for cooling with tap water. For temperatures other than that of tap water, it may be more practical to supply the reactor flask with a glass mantle for circulation of the coolant.

‖ Porous polyethylene sheets are manufactured by Porous Plastics Ltd., Dagenham Docks, Essex, England.

the tube. In this way the buffer displaces the air from the pores of the disk—a prerequisite for a low flow resistance. A uniformly packed bed is obtained by pouring a dilute suspension of the polyacrylamide spheres into the column tube.

ii. Flow Rate

The resolution decreases considerably at extremely high flow rates. Therefore the diameter of the spheres should be chosen so that the flow rate will not be higher than 3 ml/hour/cm². As the resolution is a function not only of the flow rate but also of the diameter of the spheres, it is wiser to repack the column tube with smaller spheres, if the above flow rate is exceeded, than to decrease the flow rate by lowering the pressure head. A decrease (increase) of the sphere diameter is achieved by using a larger (smaller) amount of the stabilizer, a smaller (higher) amount of the initiator and the accelerator, a higher (lower) stirring speed, and a lower (higher) polymerization temperature. Often it is enough to alter only one of these factors. When very large spheres are required in order to give extremely high flow rates, one should also increase the volume of the water phase relative to that of the organic phase.

iii. Loading the Column

The simplest way to apply the sample is by layering it cautiously under buffer on the column bed. A prerequisite is that the density of the sample be higher than that of the buffer. If such is not the case, the density can be increased by addition of some sucrose, inorganic salts, etc. The difference in density between sample and buffer must not be too large, as the starting zone may then be deformed by convection.

d. Analysis of Human Serum Proteins

The usefulness of "molecular-sieve" chromatography on polyacrylamide columns is illustrated in Fig. 3 by the fractionation of normal human serum.[5] For comparison with a similar experiment performed on an 8% agarose column, see Fig. 2 in Section B,3. The difference in elution profiles of the two chromatograms is chiefly due to the fact that the agarose column preferentially fractionates the high-molecular-weight serum proteins, while the polyacrylamide column has poorer resolution for these substances.

Acknowledgments

The author wishes to acknowledge his indebtedness to Professor Arne Tiselius for many stimulating discussions and to thank Professor Peter Hohenstein and Dr. Fredrik Eriksson, who have given valuable advice on suspension polymerization. I am also grateful to Mrs. Irja Blomqvist who has performed part of the experimental work.

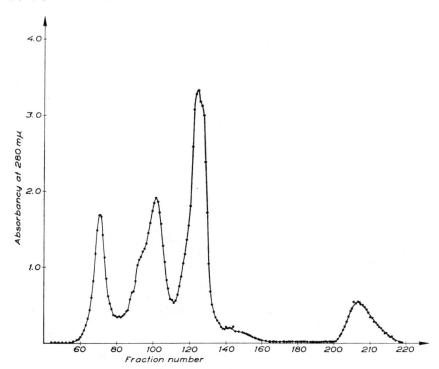

Fig. 3. "Molecular-sieve" chromatography of normal human serum on a poly-acrylamide column. Gel concentration: $T = 6\%$, $C = 5\%$. Column dimensions 1.8×87 cm. Sample volume 1 ml. Buffer 0.1 M Tris–HCl + 0.2 M NaCl, pH 8.1. Fraction volumes 1 ml. Nominal sphere diameter 0.07 mm. The flow rate was reduced with a Mariotte flask to about 2 ml/hour.

3. CHROMATOGRAPHY ON AGAROSE SPHERES*,†

a. GENERAL REMARKS

As has been mentioned in other articles in this volume, gel grains of dextran (see Section B,1) and polyacrylamide (see Section B,2) can be

* Section 9,B,3 was contributed by Stellan Hjertén.

† For preparation of agarose, see Chap. 14,G,2, Vol. III. Agarose is available commercially, not all equal in quality. Suppliers include Bausch and Lomb, Inc., Rochester, New York, Bio-Rad Laboratories, Richmond, California, and Mann Research Laboratories, New York, N.Y.; Seravac Laboratories Ltd., Maidenhead, England; Litex, Glostrup, Denmark; L'Industrie Biologique Française S. A., Gennevilliers, France; Behringwerke A. G., Marburg-Lahn, Germany; Pharmacia Fine Chemicals, Uppsala, Sweden.

Agarose gel spheres, prepared essentially as described here, are available from Bio-Rad Laboratories (Bio-Gel A, 6 grades, fractionating materials of 0.5–150 × 10^6 molecular weight) and Pharmacia Fine Chemicals (Sepharose, 2 grades, handling materials of 0.3–25 × 10^6 molecular weight).

used to advantage for chromatographic "molecular sieving" only of substances with molecular weights below one million. Agarose is a good complement to these bed materials, for this polysaccharide gel permits fractionation of substances with molecular weights ranging from about 50,000 up to several millions and of submicroscopic particles as well.[1-4] Since gel grains of agarose are only slightly compressible, an agarose column gives good flow rates even if it is long and is packed with small grains in order to yield high resolution.

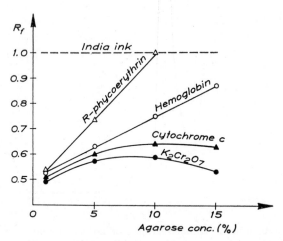

FIG. 1. The R_f values of R-phycoerythrin (molecular weight 290,000), hemoglobin (molecular weight 68,000), cytochrome c (molecular weight 13,000) and potassium dichromate (molecular weight 294) as a function of the concentration of agarose. Reference substance: India ink. If the molecular weights of the substances to be separated are approximately known, this diagram can be used for a rough estimation of the gel concentration that will give the highest resolution in each particular fractionation problem. This figure is reproduced from S. Hjertén, *Arch. Biochem. Biophys.* **99**, 466 (1962), courtesy of the publishers.

The relationship between R_f value, molecular weight, and gel concentration is illustrated in Fig. 1, which can serve as a guide for selection of a suitable gel concentration when the molecular weights of the substances to be separated are approximately known (compare Fig. 1 of Section B,2).

[1] S. Hjertén, *Arch. Biochem. Biophys.* **99**, 466 (1962).
[2] S. Hjertén, *Biochim. Biophys. Acta* **79**, 393 (1964).
[3] K. Fridborg, S. Hjertén, S. Höglund, A. Liljas, B. K. S. Lundberg, P. Oxelfelt, L. Philipson, and B. Strandberg, *Proc. Natl. Acad. Sci. U.S.* **54**, 513 (1965).
[4] S. Hjertén, *in* H. Peeters (Ed.), Protides of the Biological Fluids (H. Peeters, ed.) Elsevier, Amsterdam p. 553 (1967).

b. Preparation of Agarose Spheres

The principle for the preparation of agarose spheres is the same as that described for polyacrylamide (Section B,2). A warm agarose solution is dispersed into spheres in an organic liquid by stirring in the presence of a stabilizer; gelation is achieved by a decrease in temperature.

The equipment for the preparation of agarose spheres is the same as depicted in Fig. 2 of Section B,2. Experimental conditions for preparation of agarose spheres are given in Table I.

The agarose is dissolved in water by boiling in the reactor. This boiling is performed at the ambient atmospheric pressure for the lower agarose concentrations ($\leq 6\%$), and in a pressure cooker for the higher concentrations. In the latter case there is some risk of boiling over. To prevent this, the flask with water and agarose is connected to a water pump for evacuation. The evacuated flask is boiled for 5 minutes in the pressure cooker. The flask is then lifted out of the cooker and examined to determine whether the agarose is completely dissolved. If it is not, the flask is cautiously shaken to suspend the agarose uniformly throughout the solution, and the boiling is continued for another 5 minutes. Two or three such boilings are in general required to dissolve the agarose completely. The toluene and carbon tetrachloride mixture, containing dissolved stabilizer,* is preheated to about 50° in a water bath and added to the warm agarose solution. The stirring is then started immediately. After some minutes of stirring, tap water is run down into the beaker, surrounding the flask. As an outlet, for the cooling water, one can use a glass tube connected to a water pump. The gelation is complete after 5 minutes. The agitation is stopped, and the suspension is transferred to a Büchner funnel for removal of most of the organic phase (the diameter of the Büchner funnel should be about 20 cm; otherwise the filtration time may sometimes be unnecessarily long). The agarose spheres are washed thoroughly with ether (if these washings proceed very slowly, the spheres should be transferred to a separatory funnel for extraction with ether; three 5-minute shakings are necessary to obtain efficient washing of the spheres). The spheres are transferred to a suction flask containing 1 liter of water at a temperature of 35°. Under magnetic stirring the ether is removed by connecting the suction flask to a water pump for about half an hour.†

---

* The stabilizers sorbitan sesquioleate and polyoxyethylene sorbitan monostearate are manufactured by Atlas Chemical Industries, Inc., Chemicals Division, Wilmington, Delaware, under the trade names Arlacel 83 and Tween 61, respectively.

† If part of the agarose spheres still retain organic solvent, they will collect at the water surface. In such cases most of the water is sucked off with the aid of a piece

TABLE I

EXPERIMENTAL CONDITIONS FOR PREPARATION OF AGAROSE SPHERES[a,b]

Agarose concn. (gm agarose added to 100 ml water)	Toluene (ml)	Carbon tetrachloride (ml)	Stabilizer		Stirring speed (rpm)	Sphere size (mesh, U.S. standard)
			Type	Amount (gm)		
1	490	110	Sorbitan sesquioleate	0.5	250	30–60
2	480	120	Sorbitan sesquioleate	1.0	650	60–100
3	470	130	Sorbitan sesquioleate	1.0	1150	100–170
4	460	140	Sorbitan sesquioleate	3.5	1700	170–300
6	450	150	Sorbitan sesquioleate	1.5	1700	100–170
6	450	150	Sorbitan sesquioleate	4.5	1700	170–300
8	445	155	Polyoxyethylene sorbitan monostearate	5	1500	60–100
8	445	155	Polyoxyethylene sorbitan monostearate	12	1700	170–300
10	440	160	Polyoxyethylene sorbitan monostearate	15	1700	170–300
12	430	170	Polyoxyethylene sorbitan monostearate	25	1700	170–300
15	420	180	Polyoxyethylene sorbitan monostearate	35	1700	170–300

[a] This table has been reproduced from S. Hjertén, *Biochim. Biophys. Acta* **79**, 393 (1964), courtesy of Elsevier Publishing Company.

[b] The volume of water in which the agarose was dissolved was 300 ml. The right-hand column gives the size of the majority of the agarose spheres.

of tubing whose orifice should be kept between the bottom and top layer of the agarose spheres; ether is then added and is poured off after 5 minutes of intensive shaking. The residual ether is sucked off by means of a water pump as described above.

Excessively large particles are removed by pouring the suspension onto a large-mesh sieve, and fine particles by repeated decantation in the buffer to be used for the elution. If desired, the spheres can then be sieved to a narrower size interval, which increases the resolving power of the column.

Agarose columns have been used repeatedly, without repacking, for up to one year. The presence of antibacterial agents or EDTA in the buffer is recommended.

c. Chromatographic Techniques

Agarose gels are more rigid than many other gels and therefore have the advantage of showing little tendency to clog the bed support at the bottom

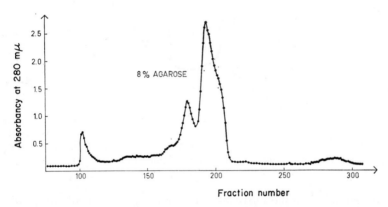

Fig. 2. "Molecular-sieve" chromatography of normal human serum on an 8% column. Sample volume 1 ml. Column dimension 2.0 × 95 cm. Nominal sphere diameter 0.05 mm. Buffer 0.1 M Tris–HCl + 0.2 M NaCl, pH 8.0. The flow rate was reduced with a Mariotte flask to about 3 ml/hour. Compare this chromatogram with that in Fig. 3 in Chap. 9,B,2.

of the column tube. Therefore almost any design of column tube can be used and the preparation and operation of the column can be performed as described for polyacrylamide columns (Section B,2).

The relation between flow rate, sphere diameter, and resolution is discussed briefly in Section B,2, with reference to polyacrylamide. The diameter of the agarose spheres can be controlled by the stirring speed and the amount of stabilizer (see Section B,2). Because of the low compressibility of an agarose gel, the flow rate can easily be increased by elution under pressure.

Chromatography on agarose columns can be used to advantage for purification of high-molecular-weight substances in serum, for fractiona-

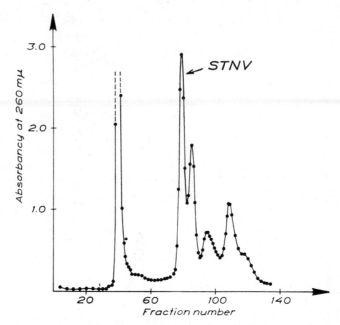

Fig. 3. Purification of satellite tobacco necrosis virus (STNV) on a 4% agarose column.[3] Column dimensions 2×105 cm. Nominal sphere diameter 0.04 mm. Buffer 0.05 M sodium phosphate (pH 7.2) $+ 0.15$ M NaCl $+ 0.001$ M MgSO$_4$. Sample volume 4 ml. Flow rate 6 ml/hour. Fraction volumes 3 ml.

tion of submicroscopic particles, and for isolation of proteins from such particles and even from whole cells.[1-4] Examples are given in Figs. 2 and 3.

ACKNOWLEDGMENTS

The author is very grateful to Professor Arne Tiselius for many valuable discussions on chromatographic size-sieving, and is also indebted to Mrs. Irja Blomqvist for skillful technical assistance.

C. Cellulose Ion Exchange Chromatography*

1. GENERAL CONSIDERATIONS

Chromatography on cellulose ion exchangers has found a wide range of biochemical applications since the introduction of CM- and DEAE-cellulose.[1] There is now available a wide variety of cellulose ion exchangers (Table I), but CM- and DEAE-celluloses remain the most popularly

* Section 9,C was contributed by Te Paio King.

[1] H. A. Sober and E. A. Peterson, *J. Am. Chem. Soc.* **76**, 1711 (1954).

TABLE I
Types of Cellulose Ion Exchangers

Designation	Ionic form	Ref.
AE (aminoethyl-)	$-O\ CH_2CH_2NH_3^+$	a
DEAE (diethylaminoethyl-)	$-O\ CH_2CH_2\overset{+}{N}H(C_2H_5)_2$	b
TEAE (triethylaminoethyl-)	$-O\ CH_2CH_2\overset{+}{N}(C_2H_5)_3$	c
Ge (guanidoethyl-)	$-O\ CH_2CH_2NH-\overset{\overset{\displaystyle NH_2}{\displaystyle \vert}}{C}=NH_2^+$	a
ECTEOLA (mixed amines)	$-\text{(undefined)}^+$	b
CM (carboxymethyl-)γ	$-O\ CH_2CH_2CO_2^-$	b
P (phosphoryl-)	$-O\ PO_3^{--}$	b
SM (sulfomethyl-)	$-O\ CH_2SO_3^-$	c
SE (sulfoethyl-)	$-O\ CH_2CH_2SO_3^-$	c

a G. Semenza, *Helv. Chim. Acta* **43**, 1057 (1960).
b E. A. Petersen and H. A. Sober, *J. Am. Chem. Soc.* **78**, 751 (1956).
c J. Porath, *Arkiv Kemi* **11**, 97 (1957).

used adsorbents. Several extensive reviews on the applications have been published.[2-5]

The separation of proteins on cellulose ion exchangers is believed to depend mainly on the electrostatic interactions of the polyelectrolyte protein with the oppositely charged adsorbent. The relative affinity of a protein therefore depends on its charge density. This affinity can be modified (1) by altering the charge of solute and/or that of the adsorbent and (2) by increasing the concentration of the buffer salts whose ions also have affinities for the adsorbent. With few exceptions most proteins do not exhibit finite adsorption equilibria between the adsorbent and the eluant of a fixed buffer composition; in such cases the protein will appear as a broad trailing peak in the chromatogram. For this reason chromatography of proteins is often carried out under a condition nearly approaching that of all or none absorption by either a stepwise or a gradient change of the eluant.

[2] H. A. Sober and E. A. Peterson, *Federation Proc.* **17**, 1116 (1958).
[3] E. A. Peterson and H. A. Sober, "Plasma Proteins," Vol. I, p. 105. Academic Press. New York, 1960.
[4] E. A. Peterson and H. A. Sober, *in* "Methods in Enzymology" (S. P. Colowick and N. O. Kaplan, eds.), Vol. 5, p. 3. Academic Press. New York, 1962.
[5] G. Semenza, *Chimia* **14**, 325 (1960).

The stepwise elution is useful for the initial group separation of proteins, since the procedure is simple and the materials are eluted as a concentrated solution. To utilize the maximum selectivity of an adsorbent, gradient elution is the method of choice, as each protein differs sharply in its requirements for the adsorption to the ion exchanger. Gradient elution also has the virtue that it suppresses the trailing of a protein peak, since an eluant of constantly increasing eluting power is being applied. With stepwise elution some trailing is unavoidable, and the appearance of another peak of the same protein may occur at the solvent front of a stronger eluant when next applied.

The stability of the protein under study usually determines the choice of pH of the starting buffer. The buffer has a concentration of about 0.01 M so as to promote the adsorption of the protein to the exchanger. Whether a cation or an anion exchanger is used depends on the charge of the protein at the selected pH. The selected pH should also be in the range where the functional groups of the ion exchanger are nearly fully dissociated, since it is within this range that the adsorption capacity of the exchanger is at its maximum. Adsorbents such as DEAE- and TEAE-celluloses all give comparable separations for acidic proteins, while adsorbents such as CM and SE are used for the basic proteins. Although each member of the same family of exchangers carries the same charge, each does differ in its affinity for a protein because of differences in the ionization properties of the exchange groups involved. A more basic anion exchanger permits the use of a starting buffer of higher concentration than that of a less basic one; this is true also for a more acidic cation exchanger. A starting buffer of as high a concentration as possible is always desirable, as it minimizes any possible protein–protein interactions as well as any possible pH changes of the eluant due to the adsorption process. When a basic buffer of low ionic strength is used with an anion exchanger like DEAE-cellulose, an additional complication arises, owing to the adsorption of dissolved carbonate ions, and its desorption with an accompanying increase of pH of the eluant may lead to separation artifacts.[6]

Chromatography on ion exchange columns is sensitive to temperature changes. This is to be expected, as the ionizations of the exchange groups and those of the solutes are temperature-dependent. An adequate temperature control of $\pm 5°$ is advisable. O'Donnell and Thompson[7] showed that the DEAE-cellulose is more basic at a higher temperature than at a lower one, and that on a DEAE-cellulose column both bovine plasma albumin and insulin are adsorbed more strongly at a higher temperature than at a lower one.

[6] W. Bjork, *J. Chromatog.* 2, 536 (1959).

[7] I. J. O'Donnell and E. O. P. Thompson, *Australian J. Biol. Sci.* 13, 69 (1960).

2. TECHNIQUES

a. CLEANING THE CELLULOSE ION EXCHANGER

Cellulose ion exchangers may be purchased from several scientific supply houses. The different preparations can vary in their particle sizes and in their exchange capacities. With preparations of coarse particle sizes, it is usually difficult to pack a smooth column. The varying exchange capacities of different preparations will, of course, influence the total capacity of a packed column, but it can also affect the resolution of a column. This variability in the resolutions of different cellulose preparations is to be borne in mind when attempts are made to duplicate a separation successfully accomplished in other laboratories. The investigator may be required to employ an elution schedule different from that of the original workers in order to achieve the desired resolution.

About 15 gm of the dry cellulose ion exchangers is used to pack a column of 2.5 × 25 cm. The dry cellulose is suspended in about 600 ml of 0.5 N NaOH + 0.5 N NaCl in a 1-liter beaker. The suspension is dispersed with magnetic stirring until free of trapped air bubbles. After settling for 15 to 30 minutes the cloudy supernatant is decanted, and the cellulose is resuspended in 600 ml of 1 N NaCl. After settling and decanting of most of the supernatant, the material is filtered by suction on a Büchner funnel through two pieces of filter paper and washed with several hundred milliliters of 1 N NaCl. The moist cake is suspended in 600 ml of 1 N HCl, immediately filtered by suction, and washed with water until the wash solution is near neutral. The ion exchanger is then brought to the desired pH by three cycles of decantation and resuspended in 600 ml of a concentrated solution of the starting buffer. After decantation of the excess concentrated buffer the cellulose is rinsed once by suspension in 600 ml of the starting buffer and then stored in 400 ml of that buffer.

b. PACKING THE COLUMN

Columns of the dimensions of 25 × 1 cm and 25 × 2.5 cm will satisfy most laboratory needs. The cellulose–buffer mixture is thoroughly dispersed with magnetic stirring. This uniform suspension is poured into the column. After most of the cellulose has settled, an air pressure of 10 psi is applied to pack the cellulose and to drive out the excess buffer. A 3- to 5-cm column of the buffer above the bed is left behind to avoid any disturbance of the packed bed with the next addition of cellulose suspension. The column is packed to a height of about 20 cm; then it is equilibrated with several hundred milliliters of the starting buffer before use.

c. Loading the Column

A mixture of up to about 250 mg of proteins may be fractionated on a 1-cm column, but it is preferable that no single component be much more than 30 mg, otherwise some skewing of that peak may occur. These quantities are for 1-cm columns packed with ion exchangers having capacities of about 0.6 meq/gm. The sample may be applied to the column in a volume of buffer of 10 ml or larger for a load of 250 mg, and less for a smaller load. The exact volume is not critical as the starting buffer is chosen to be one that permits tight binding of the proteins to the top portion of the column. A larger volume is in fact desirable, as this can avoid possible pH drifts during the absorption process. For a 2.5-cm column these quantities may be increased six times.

Before application to a column the sample should be equilibrated properly with the starting buffer by dialysis several times against 10 volumes of that buffer, or the sample may be equilibrated by passage through a Sephadex column which is equilibrated with the starting buffer. After the buffer has been withdrawn on top of the column bed, the sample is 'added with care so as not to disturb the flat surface of the bed. It is driven into the bed by gravity or air pressure. The sides of the column are rinsed two times with a total of 3 to 4 ml of buffer. A sufficient volume of buffer (about 3 to 5 cm above the bed) is added before the column is connected to the gradient device for elution.

d. Elution

In contrast to gel filtration, discussed in Section B,1, the resolution obtainable on a cellulose ion exchange column is less dependent on the ratio of column height to diameter than it is on the elution schedule employed, since the separation is carried out under a condition approaching that of all or none absorption. A 25×1-cm column is eluted at a flow rate of 10 to 15 ml/hour, and 2-ml fractions are collected. Six times these quantities are used for the 2.5-cm column. A small hydrostatic pressure will provide the necessary flow rate.

The concentration of the starting buffer is usually low—about $0.01\ M$. Therefore, it is important to select a buffer whose pK is near the pH to be used so that a maximum buffering capacity is obtainable. The commonly used ones are acetate for pH 4.0 to 5.2, succinate for pH 5.0 to 6.0, phosphate for pH 6.0 to 7.8, and Tris-HCl for pH 7.4 to 8.7 (Appendix II).

For a preliminary survey run, it is perhaps simpler to employ an elution schedule of a linear salt gradient. The gradient is produced by connecting two vessels of identical sizes and shapes. The first vessel, which is connected to the column, contains the starting buffer, and the second vessel contains the limiting buffer. The buffer in the first vessel is gently but thoroughly mixed with a magnetic stirrer to ensure a smooth gradient. The starting buffer has a salt concentration of about 0.01 M, and the limiting buffer has a concentration of 0.20 M. The salt concentration in the limiting buffer can be entirely that of the buffer salts, or, if desired, it can be in part that of any neutral inorganic salt. The volume of each buffer can be 120 ml for the 1-cm column and 700 ml for the 2.5-cm column. Increasing the volumes of the two buffers decreases the slope of the gradient. This may lead to an improved resolution, but it also may lead to the broadening of the peaks. If the protein is not eluted under these conditions, another gradient with a limiting buffer of 2 M salt can be applied next. When the separation obtained by the salt gradient is unsatisfactory, elution by a pH gradient or a combination of pH and salt gradients may be explored.

A linear gradient may not provide sufficient discrimination when the objective is to have inclusive separation of as many components in a mixture as possible. This has been found to be so for the separation of the serum components where a more complex gradient is needed. A gradient of varying slopes in the different regions of the chromatogram can be produced by a device called a Varigrad.[8]

After examination of the collected fractions for the protein distribution, it is useful to determine their pH and conductance.* Measurements of these two physical constants not only serve to check the proper functioning of the gradient device but also help to characterize the chromatographic behavior of a protein. If the protein peak is eluted at a position in the chromatogram where there is a sudden change in the pH or the conductance, the validity of its separation is to be questioned. These sudden changes can occur for several reasons, such as an improperly equilibrated sample or column, poor buffering capacity of the influent, adsorbed carbonate ions on anion exchangers, and possibly other factors. In any event, these sudden changes are to be avoided, as the selectivity of the column is decreased under these conditions. The best condition is one in which the protein separation is carried out with a smooth gradient.

The safest way to determine the authenticity of an observed separation is to rerun the isolated fraction on the same column under identical conditions. The material should emerge at the same effluent volume, with the

[8] H. A. Sober and E. A. Peterson, *Anal. Chem.* **31,** 857 (1959).

* A conductivity bridge (Type RC, Industrial Instruments Inc.) can be used for this purpose. A convenient conductivity cell (cell constant 1.00) is the pipet type. It is modified to have a bottom length of 14.5 cm so that it may be dipped directly into the test tubes containing the fractions.

same pH and conductance as in the initial experiment, and with quantitative recovery of the sample.

When the performance of a packed column is questionable, it can be informative to make a standard run with a known protein. Bovine plasma albumin may be used for a DEAE- or TEAE-cellulose column.[9] Bovine pancreatic ribonuclease may be used for a CM- or SE-cellulose column.[10]

e. REGENERATION OF THE COLUMN

The ion exchange columns can be reused by simply equilibrating with the starting buffer if all the adsorbed components were eluted off. If not, an anion exchange column can be cleaned directly by washing with 1 N NaOH, 1 N NaCl and 1 N HCl, and then equilibrating with the proper buffer. This is not possible with the cation exchange column because of its swelling in strong alkali, and it is necessary to unpack the column and wash the cellulose.

[9] R. W. Hartley, Jr., E. A. Peterson, and H. A. Sober, *Biochemistry* **1**, 60 (1962).
[10] G. Taborsky, *J. Biol. Chem.* **234**, 2652 (1959).

D. Analysis of Column Effluents*

One simple and rapid estimation of the protein concentration of a solution is by ultraviolet spectrophotometry. The absorbance values of most proteins lie in the range of 0.5 to 2.0 at 280 mμ for a concentration of 1 mg/ml and a light path of 1 cm; its exact value depends on the aromatic amino acid content of a protein. However, the method is not specific, as many other aromatic substances also absorb light at 280 mμ. One way to minimize an erroneous identification of the material as a protein is to determine its absorbance at 250 mμ and 320 mμ as well as at 280 mμ. In the absence of a prosthetic group most proteins have an absorbance value of 250 mμ, which is about one half of that at 280 mμ and a value close to zero at 320 mμ (see Chap. 10,A).

Another often used method is the Lowry-Folin-Ciocalteu reaction. The Lowry method[1] has the advantage of being about ten to twenty times as sensitive as that of direct absorbance measurement at 280 mμ, but it also lacks specificity. Phenolic compounds interfere strongly with this method (see Chap. 12,B).

A less often used but more specific procedure is the ninhydrin procedure after alkaline hydrolysis.[2] It is at least fifty times as sensitive as that of

* Section 9,D was contributed by Te Piao King.
[1] O. H. Lowry, N. J. Rosebrough, L. A. Faw, and R. J. Randall, *J. Biol. Chem.* **193**, 265 (1951).
[2] A. M. Crestfield, S. Moore, and W. H. Stein, *J. Biol. Chem.* **238**, 622 (1963).

absorbance at 280 mμ. The only interference will be from nonvolatile amino compounds (see Chap. 12,B).

Specific biologic tests of the effluents should be carried out concurrently with the physicochemical tests of the protein distribution. A combined knowledge of the two distribution profiles can provide valuable leads on the degree of separation obtained. The techniques of immunodiffusion and immunoelectrophoresis are particularly useful in this respect, as they are specific and sensitive (see Chap. 14, Vol. III).

E. Recovery of Proteins*

The proteins in the effluent fractions may be concentrated by a variety of procedures. Perhaps the most simple procedure is by pressure filtration through Visking cellulose tubing.[1,2] It is important to select the proper size of cellulose tubing, as the different size tubings have different permeabilities. According to the studies of Berggård,[2] Visking tubings of 8/32 and 23/32 in diameter are suitable for recovery of proteins having approximate minimal molecular weights of 30,000 and 10,000, respectively. The procedure can be adapted easily to concentrate any volume of solutions, so it will be described in detail here.

The equipment consists of a suction flask, a length of the cellulose tubing, a one-holed rubber stopper, a piece of glass tubing, and a piece of polyethylene tubing. One end of the glass tubing (10 cm in length, 7 mm I.D.) is tapered so that it will fit snugly into the polyethylene tubing (30 cm in length, PE 260 grade). Both ends of the glass tubing are fire-polished, and the tubing is bent into a U shape. The cellulose tubing is soaked in a 0.05 M solution of disodium salt of ethylenediaminetetraacetic acid for several minutes and then washed with distilled water. The exact length of tubing used varies with the amount of solution to be concentrated. After washing, a knot is tied at one end, and the tubing is rolled around the knotted end. The open end is pulled through the hole in the rubber stopper. Inside that open end is placed the bent glass tubing. The glass tubing is pushed gently through the rubber stopper. The rolled-up cellulose tubing is next placed inside a 1-liter suction flask, and the rubber stopper is pushed into the neck of the flask tightly. The polyethylene tubing is connected to the glass tubing and dipped into the solution to be concentrated. When the flask is evacuated to about 50 mm Hg pressure, the solution is pushed into the tubing by the atmospheric

* Section 9,E was contributed by Te Piao King.

[1] P. H. Everall and G. A. Wright, *J. Med. Lab. Technol.* **15**, 209 (1958).
[2] I. Berggård, *Arkiv Kemi* **18**, 291 (1961).

pressure, and the filtration proceeds immediately. A drawing of this filtration apparatus is given in Fig. 5 of Chap. 8.

When 23/32 tubing is used, it is necessary to encase the tubing in an equal length of seamless tubular gauze.* Otherwise, the tubing will burst under the pressure applied.

The filtration rate is about 30 ml/hour per meter of a filled 8/32 tubing under these conditions. A meter of the filled tubing will hold about 100 ml of solution. The following results may be considered as typical. An 80-cm length of 8/32 tubing will concentrate 110 ml to 14 ml in 8 hours at room temperature. A 60-cm length will concentrate 50 ml to 6 ml in 5.5 hours. A 20-cm length will concentrate 18 ml to 2 ml in 7 hours. It is essential that during the concentration no region of the tubing containing solution should be allowed to dry out so as to cause possible irreversible denaturation of the sample.

After concentration, the tubing can be cut and tied for dialysis against the buffer of choice. In some cases, the concentrate may be dialyzed against water, then lyophilized to give a solid sample. However, many proteins cannot withstand the lyophilization process, and irreversible aggregation takes place. Some protein samples tend to aggregate even on prolonged storage in the lyophilized state. Therefore, it is safer to store a protein sample as a concentrated solution in the cold. The formation of aggregates can be detected by the appearance of a new peak by gel filtration chromatography, or by the incomplete recovery of sample on ion exchange chromatography. The aggregates are more tightly adsorbed to the ion exchanger than the monomeric protein.

* Tubegauze No. 01, Scholl Manufacturing Co., New York, New York.

CHAPTER 10

Optical Analysis

A. Applications of Ultraviolet and Visible Spectroscopy[*],[†],[‡]

1. ABSORPTION SPECTRA

The electromagnetic spectrum extends from wavelengths of 1×10^{10} A to 1×10^{-3} A and includes such diverse forms of radiant energy as X-rays, radio waves, sunlight, and microwaves. Regardless of its source, electromagnetic energy from each part of the spectrum travels at the same velocity (in a vacuum) and has both wave and particle properties. The equation

$$E = h\nu \tag{1}$$

defines the relationship of radiant energy (E) to the frequency of radiant emission (ν), when h is Planck's constant. From this relationship it can be seen that atoms or molecules may absorb greater or less energy from a given amount of radiation, depending on the wavelength of the radiation. In the visible and ultraviolet regions of the electromagnetic spectrum, light absorption results in simultaneous changes in rotational, vibrational, and electronic energy levels of the orbital electrons. The close spacing of spectral lines that arise from single electronic transitions results in the generation of spectral bands of absorbance.

The absorption bands produced by organic molecules in the visible and ultraviolet regions of the spectrum result from the excitation of orbital electrons to higher energy states. Unsaturated functional groups such as nitro, carbonyl, and azo groups are capable of electronic transitions in the visible region and often cause a compound to be colored. Such groups are called chromophores, and the relative intensities and spectral positions of absorbance maxima are characteristic for each chromophore, making

* Section 10,A was contributed by J. Russell Little and Helaine Donahue.

† Original research reported in this section has been supported in part by a U.S. Public Health Service research grant (AI-06354-02), by a training grant (5T1-AI-257), both from the National Institute of Allergy and Infectious Diseases, and by a contract with the Research and Development Command, Department of the Army, recommended by the Commission on Immunization of the Armed Forces Epidemiological Board (USDA-49-143-MD-2330).

‡ We wish to express our appreciation to Dr. Herman N. Eisen for his assistance and critical comments in the preparation of the manuscript and tables.

possible its identification in complex molecules. Electron donor groups such as hydroxyl, alkoxyl, or amine groups may shift the absorbance maxima of the chromophore to a longer wavelength (a bathochromic shift) and increase the intensity of absorbance (a hyperchromic effect). Organic functional groups that alone do not absorb in the visible or ultraviolet but augment chromophore absorption are called auxochromes. Electron-withdrawing groups hinder chromophoric excitation and shift absorbance maxima to shorter wavelengths (a hypsochromic shift).

2. EFFECTS OF MOLECULAR ENVIRONMENT ON ABSORPTION

It is important to consider the changes that may occur in the absorption spectrum of a particular compound in different solvents, since the shape and position of the absorption bands will be influenced by the interaction of the solvent with the solute. Close packing of solute and solvent and their interactions may restrict rotational and vibrational movements of the solute molecules, thus decreasing spectral resolution.

Although spectroscopists prefer nonpolar solvents, since they predispose to sharper spectral resolution, immunologists necessarily and almost exclusively utilize aqueous solvent systems. For this reason much of the spectroscopic data in the chemical literature is of limited value to immunologists, since extinction coefficients and the position of absorption bands will be different in aqueous and organic solvents. A corollary problem arises when a solution of hapten is made by dilution from an organic solvent into an aqueous solvent. Under such circumstances as little as 1% organic solvent in the final aqueous solution may shift the hapten absorption peak from its true value in a strictly aqueous environment. Alternatively, the organic solvent may contribute significant absorbance to the final solution unless an absorbance blank of the same aqueous and organic solvent composition is used.

With some compounds, solvent conditions may affect the predominant chemical species in solution. For example, when a chromophore or an auxochrome is an acidic or a basic group, significant spectral shifts can be expected with changes in hydrogen ion activity. For this reason aqueous solvents are usually buffered or spectral measurements are made at an isosbestic point (a wavelength at which the absorbancy is the same for two chemical species that are interconvertible). For detailed discussions of the effects of molecular environment on spectral properties, the monographs by Jaffe and Orchin[1] and Rao[2] are recommended.

[1] H. H. Jaffe and M. Orchin, *in* "Theory and Applications of Ultraviolet Spectroscopy." Wiley, New York, 1962.
[2] C. H. R. Rao, *in* "Ultra-Violet and Visible Spectroscopy." Butterworths, London, 1961.

Occasionally the spectral characteristics of molecular complexes cannot be attributed to the sum of the spectra of the separate components. New absorption bands may arise by the formation of charge-transfer complexes. These are broad intense bands produced by the transfer of an electron from the ground state of one component (donor) to an excited state in the second component (acceptor) of the complex.[3] The significance of charge-transfer complexes in biological systems has been reviewed.[4]

A practical consideration in the interpretation of new or shifting absorption bands derives from the photolability of many of the reagents used as haptens in antibody purification or in binding studies. Although light sensitivity among the 2,4-dinitrophenyl (DNP) amino acids is well known,[5] many aromatic haptens have been less thoroughly studied. Some 2,4,6-trinitrophenyl (TNP) amino acids are so light-sensitive that they must be shielded from incandescent room lighting.[6a, b]

3. ABSORPTION LAWS

Lambert's and Beer's laws are the two principal laws governing the measurement of light absorption. Lambert's law states that the proportion of light absorbed in a transparent medium is independent of the intensity of the incident light and that the intensity of the transmitted energy decreases exponentially as the thickness of the absorbing medium increases arithmetically. Beer's law deals with the effect of the concentration of the solute on absorbance. Since the collision of a photon with a molecule is requisite to the absorption of energy by that molecule, it follows that the probability of such a collision is directly proportional to the number of molecules in the light path. Combining these two laws, one obtains

$$\text{Absorbance or Extinction or Optical density} = \log_{10} I_0/I = abc \quad (2)$$

where I_0 = the radiant energy incident on the sample.

I = the radiant energy transmitted.

a = the absorption coefficient (varies with the wavelength of the incident light).

b = the light path length.

c = the concentration.

If c is expressed in moles per liter and b in centimeters, then a becomes

---

[3] L. J. Andrews and M. Keefer, in "Molecular Complexes in Organic Chemistry." Holden-Day, San Francisco, 1964.

[4] A. Szent-Györgyi, in "Introduction to Submolecular Biology." Academic Press, New York, 1960.

[5] D. W. Russell, Biochem. J. 87, 1 (1963).

[6a] J. R. Little and H. N. Eisen, Biochemistry 5, 3385 (1966).

[6b] M. W. Chase, Intern. Arch. Allergy 5, 163 (1954).

the molar extinction coefficient for which E_M and ϵ are conventional symbols. When the molecular weight of the substance being analyzed is unknown, c may be expressed as a percentage (weight per volume) of solute in a transparent solvent. The notation $E_{1cm}^{1\%}$ is conventional for a 1.0-cm layer of a 1.0% solution.

4. ABSORPTION ERRORS

Apparent deviations from the absorption laws are quite common and arise from chemical and instrumental factors. Light scattering caused by turbidity is a common source of error in spectral measurements of protein solutions. Since light scattering is inversely proportional to the fourth power of the wavelength, this potential source of error becomes especially great in measurements made in the ultraviolet region (see Section B,4). Corrections for turbidity and light scattering in a solution may be made by taking a series of absorbance measurements outside the spectral region of major absorbance (for example, in the visible region for colorless proteins) and by extrapolating these values as a base-line correction for the major spectral band.[7]

A second source of potential error in absorbance measurements is fluorescence. The emission of absorbed light will alter the proportionality between solute concentration and light absorption and may also affect the spectral position of absorption bands. Re-emitted light (for example, fluorescence or phosphorescence) is random in direction, and varying the distance between the photodetector and the sample will alter the intensity of light detected and can be used as a test for fluorescence.[8]

One of the most important factors determining instrumental accuracy is the monochromaticity of the incident light. Commercially available spectrophotometers employ sources of continuous light energy with a monochromator (a prism or grating) for selecting a relatively narrow spectral band. Even a good monochromator will produce a spectral band of appreciable width. Light reaching the photodetector that does not correspond to the wavelength under consideration is called stray light. Since the amount of stray light may vary with the selected wavelength and since stray light may result in spectral shifts, the magnitude of the error will depend on the width of the wavelength band and the change in the absorption coefficient of the sample over this range of wavelengths. Narrowing the exit slit on the monochromator decreases the spectral width of the emergent light and, therefore, increases its monochro-

[7] D. B. Wetlaufer, *Advan. Protein Chem.* **17**, 303 (1962).

[8] M. G. Mellon, *in* "Analytical Absorption Spectroscopy, Absorptimetry and Colorimetry." Wiley, New York, 1950.

maticity. For wide slits and narrow absorption bands the error is maximal; broad bands and narrow slits minimize the error.

Internal sources of error such as inaccuracy of the wavelength or transmission intensity scales of the spectrophotometer may be eliminated by appropriate instrumental adjustments. The National Bureau of Standards recommends the mercury lamp in a quartz envelope as the best single source of radiant energy for the calibration of the wavelength scale of nonrecording spectrophotometers. Spectral transmittancy scales may be calibrated with colored glass filters or standard aqueous solutions of alkaline potassium dichromate, cobalt ammonium sulfate, or copper sulfate.[9]

5. SPECTRAL ANALYSIS OF SPECIFIC ANTIGEN–ANTIBODY REACTIONS

a. GENERAL CONSIDERATIONS

Among the variety of applications of absorbance spectroscopy, it seems likely that the single most important spectral method in immunology laboratories continues to be the analysis of specific precipitates in quantitative precipitin reactions. The importance of spectral methods to the immunologist has become progressively greater, however, with the increasing need for sensitive, quantitative methodology appropriate for the study of antibody structure and specific ligand binding.

In the case of hapten–antibody systems such as phenyl-azo or 2,4-dinitrophenyl specificity, it is possible to determine antigen concentrations by an absorbance measurement at a wavelength of maximum absorption of the covalently bound chromophoric haptenic group. The antigen content of dissolved precipitates is quite unambiguous if such an absorbance measurement can be made in a spectral region where the antibody has negligible optical density. The antibody content of dissolved precipitates can then be estimated by a second measurement at 278 to 280 mμ, and the calculation of antibody mass is possible with the use of the $E^{1\%}$ for antibody or the appropriate immunoglobulin.

b. ALKALI SOLUTIONS OF SPECIFIC PRECIPITATES

The near-ultraviolet absorption spectrum of antibodies (and all other proteins) is related almost exclusively to their content of aromatic amino acids, especially their tryptophan and tyrosine content (Fig. 1). Because antigen–antibody precipitates are dissolved by moderately concentrated

[9] Standards for Checking the Calibration of Spectrophotometers (200 to 1000 mμ). Letter Circular LC-1017, National Bureau of Standards, U.S. Department of Commerce, Washington, D.C., 1955.

alkali solutions, and because antibodies have rather high extinctions in alkali, 0.1 M NaOH has been widely used as the solvent in the spectral analysis of specific precipitates.[10] Figure 2 illustrates several features of the alkaline denaturation of purified 7 S anti-DNP rabbit antibody. Some degree of spectral shift and increase in optical density occurs very promptly after exposure to 0.1 M NaOH. Much of this change is certainly attributable to ionization of the accessible tyrosine phenolic hydroxyl groups. The second feature evident in the spectra is that the changes

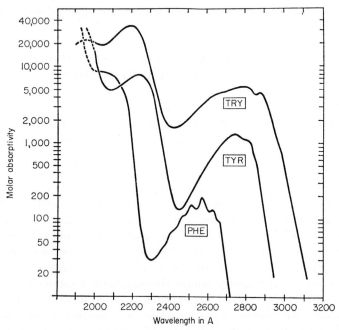

Fig. 1. Absorption spectra of the aromatic amino acids at pH 6. Reprinted with permission from D. B. Wetlaufer, *Advan. Protein Chem.* **17**, 303 (1962).

associated with antibody denaturation in 0.1 M NaOH are slowly progressive. Often 24 to 48 hours is required before the alkaline spectrum reaches a final stable configuration. The process of alkaline denaturation of immunoglobulins has been studied in detail by Steiner and Edelhoch,[11] and others have noted the time dependence of alkaline spectral changes.[12–14]

[10] H. N. Eisen, *J. Immunol.* **60**, 77 (1948).
[11] R. F. Steiner and H. Edelhoch, *J. Am. Chem. Soc.* **84**, 2139 (1962).
[12] G. H. Beaven and E. R. Holiday, *Advan. Protein Chem.* **7**, 320 (1952).
[13] H. N. Eisen, M. E. Carsten, and S. Belman, *J. Immunol.* **73**, 296 (1954).
[14] V. P. Kreiter and D. Pressman, *Biochemistry* **2**, 97 (1963).

An explanation consistent with the available data is that a slow expansion of molecular domain occurs in alkali and that additional tyrosines continue to be ionized for several hours. It has also been noted that the form of the completely developed alkaline spectrum may vary with differences in amino acid composition of the parent molecules (Fig. 3). Spectral features dependent on amino acid composition may become evident in alkali that are inapparent when the ultraviolet absorption spectra of the native antibody molecules are compared.[15] An appreciable

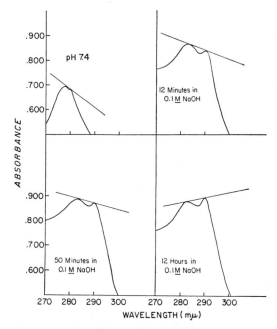

Fig. 2. Time-dependent spectral changes during alkaline denaturation of purified 7 S anti-DNP rabbit antibodies. Spectra were obtained on one antibody sample, first at pH 7.4 and then at successive intervals after the addition of NaOH. Corrections have been made for slight dilution of sample after addition of base. The incubation and recordings were performed at 25°.

limitation to the use of alkaline spectra for the calculation of aromatic amino acid content of antibody molecules is the observation that prolonged exposure to 0.1 M NaOH at room temperature may result in significant tryptophan degradation.[16] The time necessary for alkaline denaturation of immunoglobulins or antibodies may be reduced to minutes if the protein samples are first exposed to concentrated guanidine solu-

[15] W. L. Bencze and K. Schmid, *Anal. Chem.* **29**, 1193 (1957).
[16] J. R. Spies and D. C. Chambers, *Anal. Chem.* **21**, 1249 (1949).

tion for 2 hours and then adjusted to 0.1 M NaOH. Anti-DNP and anti-TNP antibodies treated in this fashion display a spectrum consistent with complete tyrosine ionization within minutes after the addition of alkali (Fig. 3).

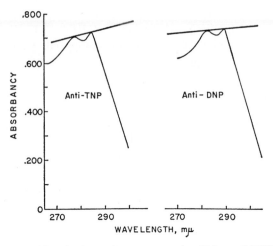

Fig. 3. Fully developed absorption spectra of rabbit anti-DNP and anti-TNP purified antibodies in 0.1 M NaOH and 6.7 M guanidine. The two absorbance maxima correspond to those of tryptophan at about 280 mμ and tyrosine (in phenolate form) at about 290 mμ. Each protein sample was incubated for 2 hours at 4° in 6.7 M guanidine before NaOH was added and the spectrum obtained.

c. ACID AND DETERGENT SOLUTIONS

The occurrence in alkali of a variety of complex and slowly progressive spectral changes has prompted a search for better solvents for the spectrophotometric quantitation of specific precipitates. Both 0.25 M acetic acid[17], and 0.5% sodium dodecylsulfate have been found satisfactory in many laboratories, and either is preferred over sodium hydroxide. At 278 to 280 mμ, 0.25 M acetic acid has negligible absorbance and sodium dodecylsulfate recrystallized from n-butanol should provide 0.5% solutions with an absorbance at 278 mμ of 0.020 or less. Solvents such as acetic or formic acid[18] or the anionic detergents probably result in effective dissociation of protein antigen–antibody precipitates coincident with their solubilization. However, the same solvent conditions that give optically clear solutions of anti-DNP antibody–antigen precipitates probably do not effectively dissociate antigen from antibody molecules.[19]

[17] D. Gitlin, *J. Immunol.* **62**, 437 (1949).
[18] E. Haber, *Proc. Natl. Acad. Sci. U.S.* **52**, 1099 (1964).
[19] H. N. Eisen, personal communication, 1965.

d. Absorbance of Immunoglobulins

The quantitative estimation of antibody concentration by an ultraviolet absorbance measurement is made more convenient by the conversion of optical density to mass units by the use of the extinction coefficient, $E_{278}^{1\%}$. Values reported for the extinction coefficient of rabbit immunoglobulins or purified antibodies vary from 13.5 to 16.8 (see Appendix I). It seems very likely that the entire range of values may be correct. Since purified rabbit antibody samples have been found to differ in their tyrosine and tryptophan content,[20–22], it should be anticipated that antibody samples would differ in ultraviolet absorbance. Extensive studies of various lots of purified rabbit anti-DNP and anti-TNP antibodies from single animals and from groups of animals support the conclusion that there is heterogeneity of antibody extinction coefficients, even for molecules of a given well-defined specificity.[23] An accurately determined extinction coefficient is very important for the calculation of antibody–hapten association constants by fluorescence quenching (see Chap. 18,C, Vol. III). For example, the use of antibody extinction coefficient values of 14.5 or 16.5 may result in the calculation of average intrinsic association constants that differ by more than one decimal order of magnitude.

Ultraviolet absorbance may also provide a useful criterion of antibody or immunoglobulin purity. Rabbit immunoglobulins and purified 7 S anti-DNP antibodies have been found to have a $\lambda_{\max}$ at 278 mμ and a $\lambda_{\min}$ at 251 mμ.[24] The ratio of absorbance ($\lambda_{\max}/\lambda_{\min}$) at these two wavelengths has been found to vary between 2.5 and 2.8 unless the sample is appreciably contaminated with antigen, an aromatic hapten, or a non-immunoglobulin serum protein.[25] Contaminated samples are usually found to have absorbance ratios of less than 2.5. The chemical heterogeneity of antibody populations compels one to acknowledge, however, that antibody or immunoglobulin samples with anomolous tyrosine/tryptophan ratios may be found to have lower absorbance ratios despite freedom from impurities.

e. Spectral Changes of Chromophores Due to Protein Binding

The covalent or noncovalent binding of low-molecular-weight chromophores to protein molecules has often been found to result in a change in

[20] M. E. Koshland, F. M. Englberger, and R. Shapanka, *Science* 143, 1330 (1964).
[21] J. R. Little and H. N. Eisen, *Federation Proc.* 24, 333 (1965).
[22] S. W. Tanenbaum, S. M. Beiser, and E. W. Bassett, *Federation Proc.* 24, 332 (1965).
[23] L. A. Steiner and S. Lowey, *J. Biol. Chem.* 241, 231 (1966).
[24] F. S. Farah, M. Kern, and H. N. Eisen, *J. Exptl. Med.* 112, 1195 (1960).
[25] F. Karush and R. Marks, *J. Immunol.* 78, 296 (1957).

the absorption spectral properties of the chromophore. A major absorbance peak may be shifted to a longer or a shorter wavelength, and the extinction coefficient may be increased or decreased at a given wavelength. The reversible binding of dyes to serum albumins has been extensively studied, and spectral changes have also been found to occur as a consequence of the specific binding of haptens to antibody molecules.[26-28] A particularly novel and interesting spectral change associated with specific ligand binding by antibody has been studied by Wofsy[29] and by Metzger et al.[28] Rabbit antibodies of 2,4-DNP specificity display relatively high affinity for the pH indicator, α-(2,4-dinitrophenylazo)-1-naphthol-3,6-disulfonate (nitrazine yellow). Specific binding of this hapten at pH 7.4 results in a marked spectral change due to a pK_a shift of the naphtholic hydroxyl group of the hapten from 6.5 to 9.0. When the indicator dye is added to an equivalent or excess amount of anti-DNP antibody at neutral pH, a striking change in color from blue to pink occurs instantaneously. Metzger et al. studied antibody–hapten binding by spectrophotometric titration, utilizing the difference in extinction coefficient of the free and bound dye. The value for the average intrinsic association constant obtained by spectrophotometric titration agreed well with the binding constant calculated for the same antibody–hapten interaction by Day et al.,[30] using the method of antibody fluorescence quenching. It is of some interest that reversible binding of the azo dye by albumin at neutral pH results in a spectral shift for the bound ligand to longer wavelengths, in contrast to the shift to shorter wavelengths observed with antibody binding.

Changes in the absorption spectra of ligands that lack ionizing groups or in which ionization per se causes a negligible spectral shift are conspicuous with anti-DNP and anti-TNP antibodies.[6,31] The bathochromic shift and hypochromicity that result when 2,4,6-TNP aminocaproate is bound to purified guinea pig anti-TNP antibody is shown in Fig. 4A. This pattern is similar but not identical to the change in absorbance of TNP-aminocaproate that occurs with binding to the rabbit anti-TNP antibody. No change in spectrum is observed when TNP-aminocaproate is added to nonspecific immunoglobulin or to purified antibody specific for the p-azobenzenearsonate group. Similar bathochromic and hypochromic spectral changes have also been noted with the specific binding of a variety of

[26] A. Froese and A. H. Sehon, Immunochemistry 2, 135 (1965).
[27] F. Karush, J. Am. Chem. Soc. 78, 5519 (1956).
[28] H. Metzger, L. Wofsy, and S. J. Singer, Arch. Biochem. Biophys. 103, 206 (1963).
[29] L. Wofsy, Ph.D. Thesis, Yale University, 1961.
[30] L. Day, J. M. Sturtevant, and S. J. Singer, J. Am. Chem. Soc. 84, 3768 (1962).
[31] H. N. Eisen and G. W. Siskind, Biochemistry 3, 996 (1964).

other DNP and TNP ligands. The possibility that such spectral changes reflect the formation of charge-transfer complexes that result from inter- actions between the bound ligand and certain amino acid residues in the antibody binding site has been suggested.[31] Antibodies specific for TNP and DNP groups have been examined by difference spectroscopy at neutral pH with ligand present at the same final concentration in both the experimental and the reference cell (Fig. 4B). Similar difference spectra were then obtained with the same TNP ligand and mixtures of free amino acids or single amino acid residues in concentrated aqueous solution. Despite the lack of perfect coincidence, it may be seen that the

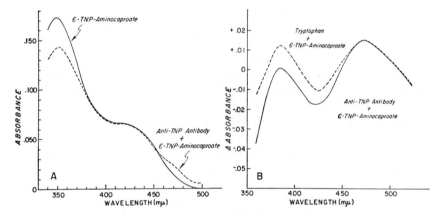

FIG. 4. A, absorption spectra of free ε-TNP-aminocaproate in phosphate buffer at pH 7.4 and of ε-TNP-aminocaproate at the same pH and final concentration in the presence of purified guinea pig anti-TNP antibody at a concentration of 0.5 mg/ml. There is marked hypochromicity and slight bathochromicity at the 350-mμ peak. B, difference spectra of mixtures of ε-TNP-aminocaproate and tryptophan or ε-TNP- aminocaproate and purified guinea pig anti-TNP antibody obtained with ε-TNP aminocaproate in the reference cell.

λ_{max} of the two spectral peaks generated by mixtures of TNP-amino- caproate and antibody or free tryptophan is the same. The position of the difference spectral peaks as well as the orbital electronic properties of tryptophan and TNP-haptens suggest that charge transfer does occur. A similar complex between 2,4,6-trinitrobenzene and indole has been reported by Szent-Györgyi.[4]

Difference spectroscopy is a highly sensitive general method for accentuating relatively minor spectral differences between two solutions. It has not been used extensively by immunologists despite the demonstra- tion of its value to protein chemists and its previous use in ligand binding studies.[32] It seems likely that the expanding interest in the details of antibody and immunoglobulin structure will provide additional opportunities for difference-spectral analyses.

[32] R. A. Plane and T. V. Long, *Acta Chem. Scand.* **17**, *Suppl.* **1**, 174 (1963).

B. Turbidimetric Assay Methods: Application to Antigen–Antibody Reactions*†

1. INTRODUCTION

Quantitative precipitin tests are usually expressed in terms of protein nitrogen found in the antigen–antibody precipitates. Direct determination of the nitrogen is accomplished by means of standard micro-Kjeldahl procedures. Photometric measurements of antigen–antibody precipitates can be used also.[1] Such tests are convenient, and they are usually referred to a nitrogen standard determined by the Kjeldahl method. Spectrophotometers measure the absorbance of light at specific wavelengths by appropriately dissolved or digested antigen–antibody precipitates[2] (see Section A and Chap. 13, Vol. III). Nephelometers are used to measure the light scattered by precipitates that have been appropriately dispersed and suspended.[1,3,4a,4b] Turbidimetric analyses of precipitin tests are used less often than spectrophotometric tests mostly owing to the lesser availability of adequate nephelometers or turbidimeters. To use effectively either spectrophotometric or nephelometric serological data, a clear understanding is needed of the characteristics of the measurements that are made and of the antigen–antibody systems involved. In this section the discussion of turbidimetry is confined to its use as a means of assaying antigen–antibody precipitates. Practical applications are given in Vol. III.

2. THEORETICAL ASPECTS

When a beam of light illuminates a turbid system, a portion of the incident light is absorbed by the suspended particles and the solution, a portion is transmitted through the solution, and a portion of the light is reflected by the particles. Turbidimetry of the system can be accomplished

* Section 10,B was contributed by Charles A. Leone.

† The work reported in this paper was supported, in part, by contract AT(11-1)-1073 with the U.S. Atomic Energy Commission and by grant RH 00063-08 from the U.S. Public Health Service.
[1] R. L. Libby, *J. Immunol.* **34**, 269 (1938); **35**, 289 (1938).
[2] F. C. McDuffie and E. A. Kabat, *J. Immunol.* **77**, 193 (1956).
[3] J. G. Baier, Jr., *Physiol. Zool.* **20**, 172 (1947).
[4a] A. A. Boyden, E. T. Bolton, and D. Gemeroy, *J. Immunol.* **57**, 211 (1947).
[4b] E. T. Bolton, C. A. Leone, and A. A. Boyden, *J. Immunol.* **58**, 169 (1948).

in several ways employing the reflected light and/or the transmitted light. Only the direct measurement of scattered or reflected light will be considered here.

The measurement of turbidity is based on the theory that there is a linear relationship between the amount of suspended particles and the intensity of the light scattered by it. The intensity of the scattered light, according to Rayleigh (see Muller[5a]), is given by the relationship

$$\frac{I}{I_0} = K\,\frac{Nv^2}{\lambda^4}\,\sin^2\alpha \tag{1}$$

where I is the amount of scattered light measured at angle α to the incident beam I_0, N is the number of particles in the volume v, and λ is the wavelength of the light. If colored precipitates are involved, selective absorption of light complicates the measurement. For white precipitates in colorless solutions, the linearity between the amount of reflected light and the amount of suspended matter is good in faintly turbid systems. In densely turbid systems the secondary absorption that occurs destroys the linearity of the response.

3. INSTRUMENTS

Several kinds of turbidimeters and spectrophotometers adapted as turbidimeters have been compared by other workers for their relative capacities to measure amounts of immune precipitates in suspension.[3,5b] Turbidimeters are of two general kinds—those that measure light scattered mainly in a forward direction from the incident beam, and those that measure light scattered at right angles to the incident beam. The first kind (180° instrument) detects light deflected forward, 5° to 25° from the path of the incident beam. The second kind (90° instrument) detects light scattered at angles 63° to 117° from one or both sides of the path of the incident beam. Both kinds of instrument use an arbitrary measuring scale. In the 180° instrument the standard of reference is a small portion of the incident beam that falls directly on the photoelectric cell. In the 90° instrument a fluorescent solution or a suspension of resin or kaolin is the standard of reference. Schematic representations of the two kinds of instrument are shown in Fig. 1.

The effects of various physical factors on the turbidity of a suspension have been treated in detail by Oster.[6] Large spherical particles scatter light preponderantly in a forward direction. The distribution of scattering of small particles (less than 300 mμ) is more uniform. Thus, the two kinds of turbidimeter will respond differently to suspended particles of different

[5a] R. H. Muller, *Indust. Eng. Chem., Anal. Ed.* **11**, 1 (1939).

[5b] J. Y. Macdonald, *Bull. Serol. Museum.* **23**, 1 (1960).

[6] G. Oster, *Chem. Rev.* **43**, 319 (1948).

sizes. Figure 2 shows that a 90° instrument (Fisher photometer) is more efficient in measuring small particles (resin), and the 180° instrument (Libby photronreflectometer[1]) is more efficient in measuring serological precipitates containing particles of many sizes. It is obvious from Fig. 2 that calibration of an instrument in terms of one system of precipitates may give erroneous data if applied to another system. The ratio of the readings given by the 180° instrument to those of the 90° instrument may be used as an indication of the average size of the particles.

The photronreflectometer constructed by Libby[1] measures the light

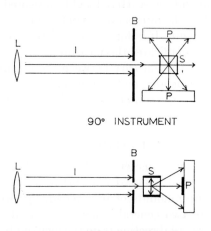

FIG. 1. Schematic representation of the two principal kinds of turbidimeter. L indicates a lens system to produce parallel incident light, I, that passes through a small opening in the barrier, B. Light deflected from the suspended particles in the sample holder, S, impinges upon the photoelectric cell(s) P. The photocell of the 180° instrument has an opaque spot on its sensing surface to absorb light that is transmitted through the sample.

scattered at an oblique angle and has an illumination standard to regulate sensitivity; it is the most useful of all the turbidimeters for analyzing the precipitin test. Unfiltered, white light has proven to be the most useful. The intensities of the incident light beam and the illumination standard can be varied and the sensitivity of the instrument adjusted accordingly. A consequence of this is that the linearity of the response of the machine holds for antigen–antibody precipitates containing as much as 600 μg of particles per milliliter.

Even though nephelometers are sensitive to particle size, the distribution of particle sizes in precipitin systems is such that thoroughly dispersed precipitates exhibit the interesting optical property called *internal compensation*. The curvilinear relations (Fig. 3) found in simple systems of particles such as kaolin tend to be neutralized.[4b] Thus, linear relationships are obtained with antigen–antibody precipitates partly because of their extremely broad distributions of particle sizes.

The photronreflectometer (as is true also for other nephelometers) is readily calibrated to translate turbidity to values of nitrogen precipitated. Once this is done for a particular antigen–antibody system, subsequent

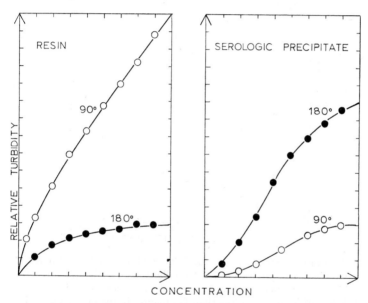

Fig. 2. The relative responses of the 90° and 180° turbidimeters to a suspension of tiny (0.1 to 0.3 micron) resin particles and a suspension of a serological precipitate (serum albumin × antiserum albumin) possessing a broad range of particle sizes (0.1 to 10 microns). The serological precipitate was at equilibrium and appropriately diluted. Curves show that the design of the turbidimeter influences its response.

tests can be carried out rapidly and easily by turbidimetry alone. Bolton and coworkers[4b] examined the performances of several of these machines and proved the validity of the nephelometric method by showing their reliability under a variety of conditions affecting precipitating antisera and antigens.

The responses of all turbidimeters are affected by secondary scattering, in which an initially deflected ray of light subsequently is scattered by other particles so as to not reach the photosensitive cell. Consequently,

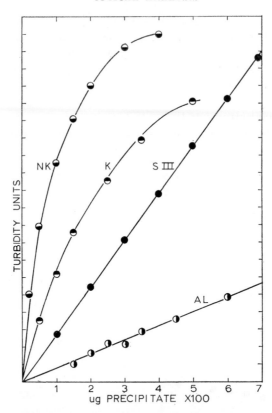

FIG. 3. Effects of particle size on turbidity readings. NK is "No Karb" kaolin having a particle size distribution of 7.2% smaller than 0.5 micron in diameter, 65.3% between 0.5 and 5 microns, and 27% larger than 5 microns. K is "Kamic" kaolin and has 26.6% of its particles less than 0.5 micron in diameter, 44.5% in the 0.5- to 5-micron range, and 28.9% larger than 5 microns. AL is an Al(OH)$_3$ suspension made up of many large flocs and an apparently clear fluid between flocs. SIII is a specific precipitate at optimal proportions between a type III pneumococcus poly- saccharide and its homologous rabbit antiserum.

all turbidimeters become nonlinear at high concentrations of precipitate and give lower readings than would be expected.[7] The extreme situation is when no light at all reaches the sensor because of a great amount of particles in suspension. Each of the two kinds of turbidimeter has a capacity to respond that is dependent on its optical and light-trans- mission design. The maximum or saturation region of an instrument is reached when there is no increase in readings in response to increases in the amounts of suspended particles.

[7] J. H. Yoe, "Photometric Chemical Analysis," Vol. I. Wiley, New York, 1928.

It has been shown by Macdonald[5b] that responses of 90° instruments are sensitive to the amounts of protein in solution in a system. This reduces their value for making serological measurements. Normal practice in precipitin tests is to measure the inherent turbidities of the solution of antigen and the solution of antiserum separately before mixing them and, after mixing and incubation, to subtract their values from that for the serological precipitate. Because the precipitate is formed at the expense of the protein molecules in solution, a "blank" value would have to be determined on the supernatant of each reaction mixture when a 90° instrument is used. Otherwise, the errors may be large, especially in the region of antigen excess. With the 180° instrument, the error will be small because proteins in solution contribute only negligibly to the turbidity readings.

4. EFFECTS OF WAVELENGTH

Very small particles reflect light in inverse proportion to the fourth power of the wavelength. Violet light ($\lambda = 400$ mμ) is scattered sixteen times as strongly as is deep red ($\lambda = 800$ mμ). For larger particles the inverse fourth-power relationship does not hold. In serological precipitates, for example, precipitates give ratios of 2.3:1 or 2.5:1 at the above wavelengths.

Because of the absorptive qualities of the yellow-to-reddish color frequently encountered in serum and solutions of tissue proteins, turbidity measurements of serological precipitates at wavelengths between 350 mμ and 450 mμ should be avoided. To minimize errors due to light absorption, appropriate wavelengths must be selected. In turbidimeters, tungsten-filament lamps are normally used, and the wavelength selection is accomplished by the photoelectric cells that are used.

Selenium barrier-layer photoelectric cells responding to 600 mμ $\pm$ 100 mμ are a reasonable choice. Their use without filters is recommended, since color filters cut down the intensity of the incident light and, therefore, the reflected light. A red filter could be used with advantage because it lengthens the effective wavelength of the photoelectric cells to approximately 670 mμ $\pm$ 50 mμ. Turbidity values will be lowered, but, in 90° instruments especially, errors due to the absorption of light by soluble protein will be reduced to a greater extent. It is worth noting that selenium barrier photoelectric cells have a moderate sensitivity in the near infrared, a region in which unfiltered tungsten light is extremely rich. When instruments whose design would allow a selection of wavelengths are used as turbidimeters, the foregoing precautions concerning the absorption of light by slightly colored solutions of protein are applicable.

5. TURBIDIMETRIC TESTING

Typically, turbidimetric precipitin analysis involves measuring the separate reactions occurring between constant amounts of a precipitating antiserum and constant volumes of serially diluted antigen. The combining proportions extend from extreme antibody excess to extreme antigen excess. The amounts of precipitate are plotted against the amounts of antigen added. Precipitate values are placed on a linear scale. Amounts of antigen can be placed on an arithmetic or a logarithmic scale. The curves obtained are modal, having minimal readings both in the zone of antibody excess and in the zone of antigen excess (Fig. 4). In turbidimetric

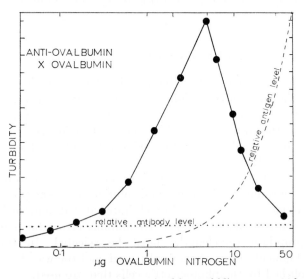

Fig. 4. A typical precipitin curve determined by turbidimetry on 24-hour precipitates read immediately after resuspension as described in the text. The abscissa is plotted logarithmically, the ordinate arithmetically. The relative antigen and antibody concentrations are included to show the antigen-excess and antibody-excess regions found in the individual tubes.

assays the whole curve can usually be obtained with 0.2 ml of antiserum per reaction tube and a serial dilution sequence of 1-ml volumes of antigen ranging downward from 50 μg of protein nitrogen. Thus, the method can represent an economy of materials as well as of time. In most turbidimeters, the intensity of the light can be regulated and the sensitivity adjusted such that 200 to 600 μg of precipitate can be linearly measured.[4a]

Early readings (made between 20 and 30 minutes after mixing antigen and antibody, or made between 30 and 60 minutes at 37°) have been used successfully in certain special applications,[3,5b,9] and have been reported to show correlation with the protein nitrogen in 24-hour precipitates,[4a] but the convention frequently used is to incubate the reaction for 1 hour at 37° (or at 22°–24° for 4–6 hours) and then hold the tubes at 3°–5° for 18 to 24 hours. For most precipitin systems, these conditions yield more than 95% of the equilibrium precipitate, which actually requires 5–10 days at 4°.[10] In the author's laboratory, the 24-hour precipitates are then dispersed and resuspended by holding the end of each tube against a vibrator mixer (such as the Vortex mixer operating at 1750 cpm) for 2–3 seconds and reading turbidity at once after pouring into rectangular narrow turbidimeter cells in which the light transverses 2 mm of the fluid. Single tube comparisons between turbidity and protein nitrogen are subject to more error than "whole-curve" readings, that is, taking readings of the turbidities of precipitate obtained over the entire range of antigen–antibody mixtures from antibody excess to antigen excess.

Time-rate studies on the formation of antigen–antibody precipitates are possible because of the capability of turbidimeters to provide a continuous record of developing precipitates from the moment the reactants are mixed.[11,12] The rate at which the equilibrium precipitate is achieved is a function of the particular combining proportion of antigen and antibody. At and near optimal proportions the rate of precipitate formation is most rapid. The rate in antigen excess is faster than it is in antibody excess.

Ordinarily, physiological saline, buffered to pH 7, is used in the precipitin test. Varying the salinity, buffer, the pH, or the amounts of antigen or antibody introduces factors that influence, in predictable ways,[4a,4b,12] the amounts of precipitate that form and the kinds and amounts of data that are obtained.

[9] A. A. Boyden, *Physiol. Zool.* **15**, 109 (1942).
[10] M. Heidelberger and F. E. Kendall, *J. Exptl. Med.* **65**, 647 (1937).
[11] C. A. Leone, *Trans. Kansas Acad. Sci.* **63**, 147 (1960).
[12] J. G. Baier, Jr., *Bull. Serol. Museum* **17**, 1 (1956).

CHAPTER 11

Radioisotopes and Their Applications*†

A. Labeling of Macromolecules

1. EXTERNAL AND INTERNAL LABELS

The primary application of radioactive tracers in immunochemistry is the labeling of macromolecules that function as antigens and antibodies. Labeling of protein may be achieved either externally by chemical synthesis—namely, by iodination (see Chap. 4,A,2, Vol. I) and diazotization (see Chap. 1,E,1, Vol. I)—or internally by biosynthesis. The latter type of labeling is used in the commercial production of radioactive amino acids, steroids, and nucleosides by algae[1] and by yeast.[2,3] After isolation and characterization, such labeled materials are used as tracers in studies of the metabolism of other species. Serum proteins are usually labeled internally (see Chap. 4,A,1, Vol. I) by either feeding or injecting labeled amino acids into an animal, but labeling can also be demonstrated *in vitro* (see Chap. 14,F,4, Vol. III), with the advantage of delineating the synthetic capacity of particular tissues and isolated cellular components. The labeling of erythrocytes may be achieved by *in vivo* methods[4] when Fe^{59} is injected intravenously into normal and anemic animals. *In vitro* tagging of erythrocytes has generally involved reaction with Cr^{51},[5] and one use of such cells has been to investigate tolerance (Mitchison[6]; see also

* Chapter 11 was contributed by Justine S. Garvey; Section 11G was contributed by Roy E. Ritts, Jr.

† Contribution No. 3382 of the Department of Immunochemistry, California Institute of Technology, Pasadena, California.

[1] J. R. Catch, *in* "Radioisotope Conference 1954 sponsored by the Atomic Energy Research Establishment" (J. E. Johnston, ed.), Vol. 1, Medical and Physiological Applications, Chap. 27. Academic Press, New York, 1954.

[2] J. W. Davis, U. H. Cheldelin, B. E. Christensen, and C. H. Wang, *Biochim. Biophys. Acta* 21, 101 (1956).

[3] A. O. M. Stoppani, L. Conches, S. L. S. de Favelukes, and F. L. Sacerdote, *Biochem. J.* 7, 438 (1958).

[4] L. F Plzak, W. Fried, L. O. Jacobson, and W. F. Bethard, *J. Lab. Chem. Med.* 46, 671 (1955).

[5] M. M. Strumia, L. Taylor, A. B. Sample, L. S. Colewell, and A. Dugan, *Blood* 10, 429 (1955).

[6] N. A. Mitchison, *Immunology* 5, 341 (1962).

Chap. 25,B, Vol. IV). *In vitro* erythropoietic activity resulting in hemoglobin production was observed when Fe^{59} salts or C^{14}-amino acids[7] were incubated *in vitro* with reticulocytes. One of the first immunological investigations with a radioactive label involved use of a nucleoprotein, tobacco mosaic virus (TMV).[8] DNA and RNA syntheses are detected by the incorporation of H^3- and P^{32}-labeled precurors into chromosomal and cytoplasmic constituents of cells. DNA labeling, particularly with H^3-thymidine,[9] is a rather commonly used technique for introducing radioactivity into a wide variety of proliferating cells. Pneumococcal polysaccharide is labeled by addition of glucose, usually labeled with C^{14},[10] to the medium in which the organism is grown. Similarly, other preparations of biological origin may be obtained by either feeding or injecting labeled metabolic precursor substances. An internal label—for example, S^{35}—present with an external label—for example, I^{131}—on the same molecule has particular usefulness in the study of *in vivo* stability of different portions of a heterologous protein[11] and metabolism of dual labels on a homologous protein.[12] An example of double labeling with the same element is the use of I^{125} and I^{131} to determine the specific combining portion of the antibody molecule.[13] Useful combinations of labels are further indicated in Section B,1.

2. STABLE AND RADIOACTIVE ISOTOPES

a. GENERAL DISCUSSION

There is a radioactive species available for most of the elements of immunochemical interest with the exception of oxygen and nitrogen. The radioisotopes of these latter elements are too short-lived for most experiments. Heavy stable isotopes, namely O^{18}, N^{15}, and also H^2, have been used as tracers in immunochemical investigations. The mass spectrometer or nuclear magnetic resonance may be used for measurement of the heavy stable isotopes. A physical property such as density can also be utilized in the assay of H^2 and O^{18}. The analyses for stable isotopes involve more material and technical detail than is common in the assay of radioactive samples.

[7] H. Borsook, E. H. Fischer, and G. Keighley, *J. Biol. Chem.* **229**, 1059 (1957).

[8] R. L. Libby and C. R. Madison, *J. Immunol.* **55**, 15 (1947).

[9] E. P. Cronkite, V. P. Bond, T. M. Fliedner, and J. R. Rubini, *Lab. Invest.* **8**, 263 (1959).

[10] O. K. Stark, *J. Immunol.* **74**, 126 (1955).

[11] W. Friedberg, H. Walter, and F. Haurowitz, *Science* **121**, 871 (1955).

[12] H. Walter, F. Haurowitz, S. Fleischer, A. Lietze, H. F. Cheng, J. E. Turner, and W. Friedberg, *J. Biol. Chem.* **224**, 107 (1957).

[13] D. Pressman and O. Roholt, *Proc. Natl. Acad. Sci. U.S.* **47**, 1606 (1961).

b. Isotope Effects

Stable and radioactive isotopes are capable of yielding the same results when isotope effects can be disregarded, as is usually the case in immuno-chemical investigations. Isotope effects are the differences in the rate and/or equilibria of chemical transformations that depend on the masses of atoms, not on their radioactivity. An extreme case of such effects exists for the different atoms of hydrogen. Since the mass ratio of $H^1 : H^2 : H^3$ is $1 : 2 : 3$, the masses of the compounds corresponding to water are so different that they should not be considered as the same substance. For different isotopes of elements heavier than hydrogen, the ratio of masses of corresponding substances may differ little from unity, and consequently the isotope effects are far less significant than for water. Where the element to be detected contributes a small fractional difference to the molecular weight of a substance—for example, the macromolecules used in immunochemistry—the isotope effects can be ignored, and particularly so if an equilibrium constant or rate of reaction is not involved.

B. Principles in Choice of Radioactive Tracers

1. RADIATION AND HALF-LIFE

In Table I the radioisotopes are listed that have been used in immuno-chemical studies to the present time, and with these are others of use in biochemistry, physiology, and disciplines closely related to immuno-chemistry. Each isotope is identified by columns 1 to 3, where symbols appear in the order used to name an isotope: Z or atomic number (number of protons in nucleus), element symbol, and A or mass number (total number of protons and neutrons in nucleus). For example, tritium is $_1H^3$, but, since the Z number or "1" is common to all the isotopes of hydrogen, tritium may be simply identified as H^3.*

A radioactive isotope has two fundamental properties—its radiation, designated as α, β, γ, or a combination of these (column 5), and its half-life, designated as $T_{1/2}$ (column 4). The type of radiation used in immuno-

---

* In some literature the mass number is placed in the left upper index position around the symbol of an element thus conforming with rules in a 1957 report of the International Union of Pure and Applied Chemistry. The American version of this report, with comments, appears in *J. Am. Chem. Soc.* **82**, 5523 (1960). The purpose of this proposed change was to make the upper right position (where the mass number is generally placed) available for the ionic charge. The commercial suppliers and investigators whose reports are directly related to this manuscript have usually indicated the mass number at the upper right of the symbol. Accordingly the author has been guided by this general practice.

TABLE I
RADIOELEMENTS WITH IMMUNOCHEMICAL OR RELATED APPLICATION

1	2	3	4	5	6	7	8	9
Z	Element	A	$T_{1/2}$	Type of decay	Energy of particles (Mev)	Energy of γ-rays (Mev)	Principal method of production	Chemical form obtainable from ORNL
1	H	3	12.46y	β^-	0.018		$Li^6(n,\alpha)$	Gas containing small amounts of He^3 daughter
6	C	14	5.57×10^3y	β^-	0.155		$N^{14}(n,p)$	Solid $BaCO_3$
11	Na	22	2.6y	β^+, EC, γ	0.54	1.3	$Mg^{24}(d,\alpha)$	$NaCl$ in H_2O soln.
11	Na	24	15.05h	β^-, γ	1.39	1.368, 2.754	$Na^{23}(n,\gamma)$	
12	Mg	28	21.4h	β^-, γ	0.42	1.35	$Li^6(n,t)He$; $Mg^{26}(t,p)$	
15	P	32	14.3d	β^-	1.70		$S^{32}(n,p)$	H_3PO_4 in HCl soln.
16	S	35	89d	β^-	0.167		$Cl^{35}(n,p)$	H_2SO_4 in HCl soln.
17	Cl	36	3.08×10^5y	β^-	0.714		$Cl^{35}(n,\gamma)$	HCl
19	K	42	12.47h	β^-, γ	2.04, 3.58	0.320, 1.51	$K^{41}(n,\gamma)$	KCl in HCl soln.
20	Ca	45	163.1d	β^-	0.254		$Ca^{44}(n,\gamma)$	$CaCl_2$ in HCl soln.
24	Cr	51	27.8d	EC, γ		0.32	$Cr^{50}(n,\gamma)$	$CrCl_3$ in HCl soln.
25	Mn	54	290d	EC, γ		0.84	$Cr^{53}(d,n)$	
26	Fe	55	2.94y	EC		0.006	$Fe^{54}(n,\gamma)$	$FeCl_3$ in HCl soln.
26	Fe	59	44.3d	β^-, γ	0.27, 0.46, 1.56	0.19, 1.10, 1.29	$Fe^{58}(n,\gamma)$	$FeCl_3$ in HCl soln.
27	Co	60	5.24y	β^-, γ	0.31	1.17, 1.33	$Co^{59}(n,\gamma)$	$CoCl_2$ in HCl soln.
28	Ni	63	125y	β^-	0.067		$Ni^{62}(n,\gamma)$	$NiCl_2$ in HCl soln.
29	Cu	64	12.9h	β^-, β^+, EC, γ	0.571 β^-, 0.657 β^+	1.34	$Cu^{63}(n,\gamma)$	$Cu(NO_3)_2$ in HNO_3 soln.
30	Zn	65	246.4d	β^+, EC, γ	0.32	1.1	$Zn^{64}(n,\gamma)$	$ZnCl_2$ in HCl soln.

Z		A	$T_{1/2}$	Type of decay	β	γ	Production	Chemical form
33	As	76	26.8h	β^-,γ	$\begin{cases} 0.36,\ 1.76, \\ 2.4,\ 2.96 \end{cases}$	$\begin{cases} 0.549,\ 0.643, \\ 1.20,\ 1.40, \\ 2.05 \end{cases}$	$As^{75}(n,\gamma)$	$HAsO_2$ in HCl soln.
33	As	77	38.7h	β^-,γ	$\begin{cases} 0.44,\ 0.7, \\ \text{others} \end{cases}$	$\begin{cases} 0.023,\ 0.028, \\ 0.086,\ 0.160, \\ 0.246,\ 0.524 \end{cases}$	$\begin{cases} Ge^{76}(n,\gamma)Ge^{77} \\ Ge^{77} \xrightarrow[12h]{\beta} As^{77} \end{cases}$	$HAsO_2$ in HCl soln.
53	I	125	57.4d	EC,γ		0.035	$Xe^{124}(n,\gamma)Xe^{125} \xrightarrow{EC} I^{125}$ $Xe^{125} \xrightarrow{EC} I^{125}$	NaI in basic sodium sulfite soln.
53	I	131	8.05d	β^-,γ	$\begin{cases} 0.250,\ 0.335, \\ 0.608,\ 0.815 \end{cases}$	$\begin{cases} 0.080,\ 0.163, \\ 0.284,\ 0.364, \\ 0.637,\ 0.722 \end{cases}$	$U^{235}(n,f)$	NaI in basic sodium sulfite soln., also elemental with carrier added

Symbols: Z = atomic number; A = mass number.

Time symbols: $T_{1/2}$ = isotope half-life; y = years; h = hours; d = days.

Type of decay: β^- = β-particle with negative charge (electron); β^+ = β-particle with positive charge (positron); γ = γ-ray; EC = electron capture.

Production terms: n = neutron; α = α-particle (helium nucleus); p = proton; d = deuteron (deuterium nucleus); t = triton (tritium nucleus); γ = γ-radiation; f = fission.

Explanations: The Oak Ridge National Laboratories (ORNL) methods of production are referred to in column 9 except for the radioelements, Na^{22}, Mg^{28}, and Mn^{54}. For these last-mentioned radioisotopes, the reference is E. Broda [in "Radioactive Isotopes in Biochemistry." p. 324. Elsevier, Amsterdam, 1960]. The two-step reaction for Mg^{28} utilizes the uranium pile reactor and Al^{28} is produced as a radioactive daughter; Na^{22} and Mn^{54} are from accelerator reactions.

Both radioisotopes of arsenic are short-lived and have a complex decay. Another radioisotope of arsenic, namely As^{74} has a longer half life, $T_{1/2}$ = 18 d; one source of the arsenic isotopes is The Radiochemical Center, Amersham, Buckinghamshire, England, but there may be other commercial suppliers.

chemical studies is β or γ, since α-emission is chiefly confined to heavier elements, none of which are normally used in biological research. The β-particles emitted from a given isotope have energies ranging from nearly zero up to some maximum that is characteristic of that particular radio-isotope. The value listed in column 6 refers to the maximal energy. As an example, P^{32} is listed with a β-emission of 1.70 Mev, which means that this isotope yields β-particles of all energies up to 1.70 Mev, the average being about one-third of the maximum, or 0.6 Mev. Gamma rays (column 7) are photons, usually of greater energy and penetrating power than the α- or β-particle commonly encountered in biological fields.

Each of the isotopes in Table I can be obtained either carrier-free or with high specific radioactivity. There is no significant contamination of one radioisotope with another during production with the exception of Fe^{55} and Fe^{59}, each of which may contain a considerable amount of the other.

Two of the listed elements, iron and iodine, have two radioisotopes that have been used effectively in double-labeling with the same element. For internal and external labeling of the same protein molecule, two isotopes are usually selected from the following list: P^{32}, S^{35}, I^{131}, I^{125}, C^{14}, and H^3. When there are two radioisotopes to be measured in the same sample, they must differ significantly in half-life, type of radiation, or energy of radiation; for ease and accuracy in the measurement of both, those possessing different types of radiation are the easiest to measure.

Although the information given in column 8 is not pertinent to the present discussion, it may serve as a preliminary introduction to the nuclear reactions that are involved in the production of radioactive isotopes. These reactions are usually written as in column 8, beginning with the naming of the stable atomic nucleus that serves as the target and then identifying, within the parentheses, the high-speed incident particles or rays—that is, the "projectiles"—that bombard the target, and finally the ejected particles or rays. The product nucleus is not written in Table I as it would appear in a nuclear reaction, following the parentheses, because this information has already appeared in columns 2 and 3. For example, the reaction for the production of H^3 would be written as $Li^6(n,\alpha)H^3$.

When an isotope listed in Table I is available from the Oak Ridge National Laboratories (ORNL) the information in columns 4,6,7,8, and 9 pertains to this supplier.*

* ORNL was responsible in large part, not only for development of reactor technology but also in the production and supplying of isotopes for experimental and medical applications. However, as a result of new reactor installations and a change in policy of procurement, most isotopes are no longer obtainable from ORNL unless special consent is obtained from AEC. The latter detailed correspondence is seldom necessary since numerous suppliers are available for most reactor-produced isotopes.

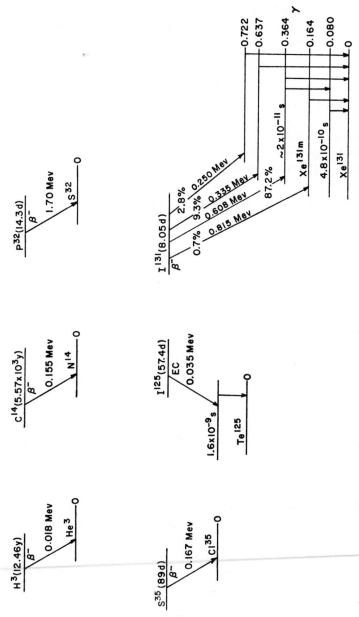

Fig. 1. Decay schemes for radioisotopes of most frequent use in immunological investigations. [Adapted from J. M. Hollander, I. Perlman, and G. T. Seaborg, *Rev. Mod. Phys.* **25**, 469 (1953).]

2. DECAY SCHEMES

The mode of decay is given schematically in Fig. 1 for those radio-isotopes to which special attention should be given because of their very frequent use in immunochemical investigations. Energy levels are indicated by the horizontal lines, the top line for the radioisotope and the bottom line for the stable element or ground state. (The ground-state level is represented by the adjacent "0.") Other energy levels are given between these extremes where more than one means of decay takes place. The percentage figures given for the different levels total 100%; m appears as a superscript following the mass number to indicate a metastable, excited state (see the scheme for I^{131}). A basic reference for disintegration information is Hollander et al.[14]

3. CHEMICAL FORM

a. SPECIFIC RADIOACTIVITY

As was noted in Table I, radioisotopes are obtainable from centers of production in the form of simple inorganic substances. After procurement of these materials one may use them in a synthesis of a radioactive compound that is applicable to an immunochemical investigation; for example, $H_2S^{35}O_4$ may be used to sulfonate aniline, and the resulting sulfanilic acid is then diazotized and coupled to a protein. However, to circumvent tedious steps in synthesis, one usually obtains the radioisotope from a commercial source in a form that one can use more directly in an investigation than would be the case with the material available from the original source of radioisotope production.

The single amino acids used for internal labeling of protein may be obtained from numerous commercial sources and are packaged according to specifications of purity which are not necessarily uniform among suppliers of the same product. Purity of these materials is generally determined by chromatographic methods, combined with microbiological analysis for optical purity of d- and l-amino acids. Chromatography and ultraviolet absorption are used to establish purity of nucleic acids.

Specific radioactivity is usually designated as millicuries per millimole (mCi/mmole). Recently amino acids of "high specific activity" have become available from commercial suppliers; with these, radiation decomposition may be a problem unless special handling is observed, such as storage at low temperature (sometimes deep freeze is preferable) and in an inert atmosphere of nitrogen. A general discussion of self-decomposition

[14] J. M. Hollander, I. Perlman, and G. T. Seaborg, Rev. Mod. Phys. 25, 469 (1953).

is available by Bayly and Weigel,[15] and Evans *et al.*[16] have published a series of papers concerned with stability of various tritium compounds. Unless there are known reasons to the contrary, general storage rules for organic materials are maintenance at the lowest convenient temperature, in a dry solid state (but in as small a quantity as convenient to reduce self-absorption) and freedom from oxygen. An excellent review[16a] contains compiled data pertaining to stability and storage conditions, specified for numerous compounds, for different radioactive labels and for a variety of chemical groups.

It is possible to purchase mixtures of amino acids for more complete labeling of a protein than can be achieved with a single amino acid—for example, protein hydrolyzates of C^{14}-labeled *Chlorella* and S^{35}-labeled yeast cells, the latter if only the labeling of sulfur-containing amino acids is desirable. Protein hydrolyzates may contain impurities or decomposition products, since assays of purity are introduced after additional fractionation procedures. The commercial supplier can usually provide information about the product that can guide the user in performing his own assays for purity. Some suppliers furnish protein labeling mixtures reconstituted from purified radioactive amino acids.

To achieve maximal specific radioactivity, the conditions for biosynthetic labeling should be carefully chosen to favor the incorporation of the isotope into the substance that will eventually be isolated for study (see Chap. 4,A,1, Vol. I). Starvation of the animal of the compound to be administered often increases the rate and degree of incorporation, but this may depend on the biosynthetic product to be labeled. In the case of serum proteins, certain treatments and conditions stimulate or depress serum albumin synthesis, sometimes with the opposite effect on incorporation into serum globulins.[17] It has also been demonstrated that antibody protein has higher specific activity than nonantibody protein if the animal is in a productive phase of antibody synthesis due to recent immunization.[18]

Internally labeled protein may be used for *in vitro* studies (for example, serological tests or cell culture), but in *in vivo* investigations, dilution in the whole animal may reduce the specific activity to a level that is difficult for detection. It is usually possible to obtain a higher specific

[15] R. J. Bayly and H. Weigel, *Nature* **188**, 384 (1960).
[16] E. A. Evans and F. G. Stanford, *Nature* **197**, 551 (1963); E. A. Evans, R. H. Green, J. A. Spanner, and W. R. Waterfield, *ibid.* **198**, 1301 (1963); E. A. Evans and F. G. Stanford, *ibid.* **199**, 762 (1963).
[16a] R. J. Bayly and E. A. Evans, *J. Labelled Compounds* **2**, 1 (1966).
[17] C. A. Williams, M. C. Ganoza, and F. Lipmann, *Proc. Natl. Acad. Sci. U.S.* **53**, 622 (1965); C. A. Williams, *Federation Proc.* **24**, 506 (1965).
[18] J. S. Garvey and D. H. Campbell, *J. Exptl. Med.* **110**, 355 (1959).

radioactivity by an external rather than an internal label. Thus externally labeled preparations are usually employed for *in vivo* studies.

b. *In Vivo* STABILITY OF LABEL

Both means of external labeling, iodination and diazotization, are useful for tracing determinants of antigenic specificity; however, *in vivo* stability of a label is a very important consideration in the evaluation of results, particularly as related to tissue persistence of antigen or antibody. If the animal lacks an enzyme system for breaking down a label—an azolinkage—then this label, unlike the rest of the molecule, will be left undegraded by normal metabolic processes. The degree and type of metabolic change that occur adjacent to this linkage may then be investigated—for example, in studies to characterize antigen material retained intracellularly. On the other hand, where intracellular enzymes exist that do degrade certain labels, such as an iodine label originally present on tyrosine and histidine groups, results based on radioassay cannot be representative of the whole molecule and perhaps not even a portion of it.

4. BIOLOGICAL HALF-LIFE

Health physicists have tried to establish some workable guides for indicating tolerance doses for exposure to external radiation. Types of radiation and levels of energy are determining factors. In the case of internal radiation, other factors must be considered, among which is the tendency of certain elements to accumulate in specific organs—for example, calcium and phosphorus in bone, and iodine in the thyroid tissue. Different tissues vary in their susceptibility to radiation; for example, blood-forming tissue has a very low tolerance for radiation, and nucleic acids are possibly more highly susceptible to radiation than are other intracellular constituents.

Numerous topics concerned with the application of isotopes to hematology are discussed in Szirmai.[18a] In addition to radiation damage, there may be mutagenic effects in cells that have a long life span and several mitotic cycles; because of the latter possibility tritiated nucleic acid precursors are a potential hazard to the investigator if not safely handled.[18b,18c]

Since the thyroid gland has a high affinity for iodine, even though the amounts taken up are small, the specific activity of the isotope is a very important consideration. Although minute doses of I^{131} can be used

[18a] E. Szirmai, ed., "Nuclear Hematology," pp. 1–589. Academic Press, New York, 1965.
[18b] W. R. Guild, *Science* 128, 1308 (1958).
[18c] R. Oliver and L. G. Lajtha, *Nature* 186, 91 (1960).

diagnostically in human medicine, certain precautions must be taken to avoid specific localization in the thyroid when proteins are trace-labeled with I^{131} and injected into experimental animals. In such instances, I^{131}-labeled protein is given after the tissue has first been allowed to become saturated with nonradioactive iodine, which is usually administered in the form of a salt in drinking water. With this procedure, I^{131} degraded from the protein molecule will be excreted rather than localized in the tissues.

Although biological half-life may be defined simply, there is considerable difficulty in determining it. The chemical form of the element influences greatly its biological half-life. As a result, most of the isotopes, even those with a long physical half-life, like C^{14}, have a short biological half-life. Biological half-life, T_b, is defined in the following manner:

$$T_b = 0.693/\lambda_b$$

where λ_b is a constant that indicates biological rate of elimination.

5. EFFECTIVE HALF-LIFE

Another term frequently used by health physicists is effective half-life, T_{eff}, which accounts for both physical half-life and biological half-life. The relation is the following, where T_b represents biological half-life:

$$T_{eff} = \frac{(T_{\frac{1}{2}})(T_b)}{T_{\frac{1}{2}} + T_b}$$

For any term to have significance to the immunologist, consideration must be given to intracellular deposition and the way it may be affected by the chemical form of the element, by its solubility under physiological conditions, and by the injection route. Although it may not be a very practical consideration, it is a definite fact that the actual lifetime of any particular atom of the tracer isotope may be any value from almost zero to the lifetime of the animal. This is obvious from the results obtained following intravenous injection of externally labeled antigen (azoproteins) and probably applies to other antigens.

Rapid equilibration within extravascular spaces occurs for intravenously injected material. Rates of circulatory clearance and excretion depend on foreignness of the material, metabolic factors, etc. As regards the diazo-linked element, it may persist intracellularly with some degree of intactness of the label and at a level that decreases slowly with time. There is fairly strong evidence for some persistence of the original label in an antigenic form for the lifetime of the animal.[19] The external iodine label and internal labels as well may show no persistence intracellularly in the

[19] J. S. Garvey and D. H. Campbell, *J. Exptl. Med.* **105**, 361 (1957).

chemical form that was originally injected, yet the radioactive element may persist intracellularly for a considerable time as a result of metabolic "turnover." The handling of various labels by cellular processes must therefore be considered in the interpretation of experimental findings.

C. The Radioisotope Laboratory and Handling Procedures

The radioisotope laboratory, where only tracer amounts of β- or γ-emitters are handled, may differ little from the immunochemistry laboratory, where other techniques are used. Nevertheless, the organization and type of work areas as well as technical approach are of great importance. The laboratory space should be organized so as to isolate procedures—that is, radioactive from nonradioactive, low-level from high-level radiation, and β- from γ-emitters. If possible, the counting operations should be carried out in an isolated area, preferably in a separate room, away from other operations involving radioactivity. There are a number of references on laboratory design, a very useful one being American Standard Design Guide for a Radioisotope Laboratory (Type B), N5.2-1963, sponsored by American Institute of Chemical Engineers, 345 East 47th Street, New York, New York.

1. LABORATORY SURFACES

a. FLOORS

Well-polished linoleum probably offers the best floor covering, and a cove base installation facilitates cleaning. Liquid does not penetrate easily or spread over such a surface if procedures are begun immediately to remove spilled material. A radioactive spill should be recovered without being diluted; a liquid should be soaked up with a sponge, and solid material should be picked up on an adhesive surface or with a vacuum cleaner, the latter method depending on the size of the area involved. After the gross decontamination has been completed, the surfaces may be scrubbed with a detergent or chelating agent. If it is found to be impossible to reduce the surface count to background, a small area that has become contaminated with a short-lived low-energy β-emitter can be kept covered with an adhesive material until the isotope decays. Replacement of the portion of linoleum may be necessary, but if joins occur in much-used portions of the laboratory these will be particularly accessible spots for the spread of any future spills.

b. WALLS AND CEILING

Precautions should be taken against the possibility of any airborne contamination. For instance, if work with solid material is performed in an isolation box, then walls and ceiling that are smooth and painted with ordinary interior paints should be suitable. Strippable paint offers some additional opportunity for decontamination, but surfaces so painted are also easily defaced.

c. BENCHES

Bench tops should be of nonporous construction. Numerous materials are available, but certain requirements, such as good resistance to chemicals and economy, may dictate the choice. The kind of bench top may not be so important (1) if an absorbent wax-backed paper is used as a surface covering and (2) if all possible operations, particularly those involving transfer of material, are carried out in porcelain or plastic trays. The advantage of the latter is that a spill is confined and recovery of the material for reuse is highly probable.

d. HOODS

Chemical hoods are also available in various materials. A good quality of stainless steel is completely acceptable but is expensive. Transite, the most commonly used material, is adequate when measures are taken to protect the surfaces. Strippable paint is advisable on all surfaces; in addition, the actual working surface should be covered and used as suggested above for benches. Provision must be made for constant air flow at velocities that can be varied for particular operations. The need for exhausting through replaceable high efficiency filters should also be examined. However, for some operations, the positive confinement provided by gloved boxes may be preferable to avoid such hazards as spreading powders or exposing personnel to toxic materials.

e. SINKS

Sinks may be constructed either of stainless steel or of Alberene. Flow of water should be controlled by a foot pedal rather than a hand faucet in order to facilitate sink operations and to avoid spread of any contamination from the hands.

2. MANIPULATIVE EQUIPMENT AND PROCEDURES

a. GLASSWARE

Whenever radioactive material is contained in a glass vessel, the latter should be placed in a tray of such capacity that all the radioactive material can be contained in the tray in the event of a spill.

i. *Washing and Disposal*

Contaminated glassware should be soaked following usage. The soaking solution may be a detergent, a special washing solution such as "Radiacwash" (Atomic Products Corp., Center Moriches, Long Island, New York), or water that contains traces of carrier. Washing of glassware should be confined to one sink regardless of the availability of additional sinks. Ideally, no radioactive material should be discarded into a sink that is connected to the general plumbing of the building. However, from a practical point of view, installation of separate plumbing in the radioactive laboratory may be impossible. Disposal into sink drains may seem appropriate for very dilute radioactivity of short-lived isotopes when present in or followed by large volumes of water. Nevertheless, there should be as little exception as possible to a strict laboratory policy of placing all liquid radioactivity into plastic (for example, polyethylene) containers. (Accordingly, the State or Federal regulations,* whichever are enforced, must be the guide for permissible amounts of radioactivity disposed of into sink drains.) Reduction in liquid volume may be achieved by evaporation, or, alternatively, the liquid may be treated chemically to convert it to a solid for more convenient disposal. Holding of wastes in the laboratory may be feasible for some of the short-lived radiochemical waste, but for the long-lived radioisotopes it is practical to have the waste picked up immediately by a licensed commercial disposal company. Solid wastes should be deposited in metal cans lined with a polyethylene bag; the bag contains the waste so that the metal can is left uncontaminated when the plastic bag of wastes is removed. Before a waste disposal can is reused it should be monitored with a probe of proper sensitivity to establish the absence of radioactivity.

Glassware should be monitored for radioactivity after thorough washing and drying. Draining or oven-drying should be against an aluminum-lined foil surface; the foil is then discarded, and there is little chance for radioactive contamination. Since there may be uncertainty that all radioactivity has been removed, it may be desirable to keep glassware for radioactive use apart from that for nonradioactive use. Moreover, it may

* The registration of organizations that use radioactivity and the provision of regulatory measures for the handling of radioactive materials (licensing) may be under either the Atomic Energy Commission (AEC) or a State agency. The AEC generally licenses Federal-supported projects. The same may be true for other radioisotope projects unless a State has qualified and has given assurance to the AEC that regulatory measures will be satisfactorily enforced by an agency of the State. Accordingly the legislation that a State enforces is essentially that which has been established by AEC, but there may be additional regulations regarding particular operations in that State. A notable exception is the licensing of X-ray machines and the controlling of radium sources that are state-enforced measures and that have never been part of the AEC code of regulations. To date no more than about a dozen states have organized their own agency to legislate all the various phases of handling radioactivity.

be advantageous to use separate sets of glassware, one for each radio-isotope, when several different ones are being handled.

To reduce the number of items stored as either known or potentially contaminated, it may be practical to use inexpensive, expendable items whenever possible. However, too much nonpermanent equipment is usually undesirable, for such practice may lead to some carelessness and a disregard for good technique.

ii. Pipetting

Use of disposable pipets, particularly the Pasteur type, equipped with a dropper bulb for transfer of small volumes, is a definite advantage. There are a variety of devices to avoid mouth pipetting while accurately pipetting; one of these should be used at all times even in an area where radioactivity is just occasionally handled.

b. CAUTION SIGNS

All vessels containing radioactive material should bear the conventional radiation caution symbol (magenta or purple on yellow background), preferably as an adhesive label with quantity, date, and type of isotope indicated—for example, "Time" tape printed in this manner (manufactured by Professional Tape Co., Inc., Riverside, Illinois). Rooms should also be posted with a placard bearing the same radiation caution symbol. Although the extent and type of posting used and the general surveys for laboratory contamination are somewhat arbitrary matters, the State or Federal regulations, whichever may be the licensing agency, must be followed.

c. PERSONNEL PROTECTION

Laboratory coats should be worn in the radioactive laboratory so that street clothing is not exposed to possible contamination. Precautions should be taken to avoid contamination of the hands by application of a silicone water-repellent cream (for example, for wet work Kerodex 71, distributed by Ayerst Laboratories, Inc., New York) and the use of plastic disposable gloves. Disposable clothing such as coats, trousers, foot guards, and caps may be purchased, but they are usually not necessary for low-level tracer work. For personnel, the use of a probe to monitor the hands is a minimal procedure after the handling of radioisotopes. Foot and hand monitoring equipment is useful but not necessary. In addition to intermittent monitoring there should be some form of continuous monitoring—for example, the wearing of film badges by individuals who work with the γ-emitters, and also by those persons who are rather frequently involved in some way with the low β-emitters. Film badges, when processed commercially, constitute an objective and permanent record of personnel exposure. Continuous room monitoring from a permanent location allows the level of radioactivity to be known immediately and may constitute a permanent record if connected with recording equipment. The latter method may be useful for establishing the maximal possible exposure that may have occurred, providing that the sensitivity of the detection system and a representative location are carefully chosen.

d. SHIELDING

For the energy levels of the weak β-emitters, no shielding may be necessary, and even hard β- and γ-emitters, in the amounts encountered in tracer work, may not present any difficult problems in shielding. In many cases adequate shielding may be obtained by simply making the distance between the individual and the source of radiation as great as possible within practical limits. The law governing attenuation of radiation intensity with distance is the familiar inverse square law, expressed as follows for a point source emitting radiation uniformly in all directions:

$$N_p = \frac{N}{4\pi R^2}$$

where N_p = quantity of radiation (expressed in standard units, for example, roentgens) per second per unit area, at point p.

N = quantity of radiation (expressed in standard units, for example, roentgens) emitted per second from the source.

R = distance from source to point p.

It may be recalled from the discussion of Table I that β-particles from the same source have a range of energies. The higher the energy of the particles, the greater is the thickness of an absorbing substance, such as aluminum, required for shielding. Complete absorption by a specified thickness of a substance, expressed as milligrams per square centimeter or the length of an air path (centimeters), to "stop" all radiation may be used to characterize the β-radiation from a particular isotope. Whereas β-particles have definite ranges and can be stopped completely by relatively small amounts of material, γ-ray intensity can only be decreased exponentially. Thus, γ-rays are characterized by the half-value thickness, which is customarily expressed as the mass per unit area required to reduce the initial intensity to one-half its value. Lead is very efficient for attenuating γ-rays. Absorption coefficients for various energies of γ-radiation and for various materials used for attenuation are found in the literature but should serve only as a guide, verification of safe tolerance being obtained by use of a survey meter.

3. EXPERIMENTAL ANIMALS

Since animals are necessary to immunological investigations, their maintenance during tracer experiments, as well as disposal while still bearing radioactive materials, must be carried out under careful control. The usual animal husbandry procedures that are followed with highly infectious materials offer an initial approach but not a complete solution. Adequate attention must be given to shielding, monitoring, decontamination, and handling procedures as discussed above. Although the animal's metabolism of the radioactivity may not be under study, knowledge of this is necessary in order to meet properly all phases of handling. Whereas infectious material may be destroyed by sterilization and incineration it must be remembered that such procedures are not a means of disposal of radioactivity. The practice of disposal of animal excreta into sanitary sewers and the pulverization of animal carcasses in garbage disposal units may take place only if the conditions satisfy the enforced laws dealing with the disposal of radioactivity. Even where animals are commonly destroyed by incineration, this practice may not be assumed arbitrarily for animals containing radioactivity. The Federal code concerning disposal of radioactivity prohibits incineration that may lead to atmospheric contamination with radioactivity and permission for this means of disposal must be obtained by specific request. Burial at sea is practiced in some areas of the world but must be carried out by licensed consent. The International Committee on Radiation Protection (ICRP) has set standards of permissable levels of radioactivity, and these recommendations are the basis for all regulations governing potential contamination of the oceans and the atmosphere. Land burial has also been permitted in some locations. Since there is no uniform procedure of disposal, even for the same investigation, it can only be emphasized that all factors be fully evaluated and final approval be obtained from the licensing organization that legislates over the site of that particular investigation. It will be recalled that this will be either the AEC or a state agency in charge of such matters.

D. Analytical Equipment

When α- and β-particles and γ-rays penetrate matter (for example, air), the molecules in their path are ionized. Electrons are torn away from the atoms of these molecules, whereby the latter are turned into positive ions; the electrons thus set free attach themselves to adjacent atoms, ionizing the latter by collision and turning them into negative ions. Pairs of positive and negative ions are formed as a result of ionization by collision, the number of these pairs of ions varying according to the nature and energy of the ionizing radiation. A single α-particle can produce 20,000 to 40,000 ion pairs per centimeter of its path in air, whereas a fast β-particle will produce 50 to 100 pairs per centimeter, and γ-rays an average of only 1.5 pairs per centimeter. The instrumentation for measuring these ions is discussed briefly with reference to Fig. 2.

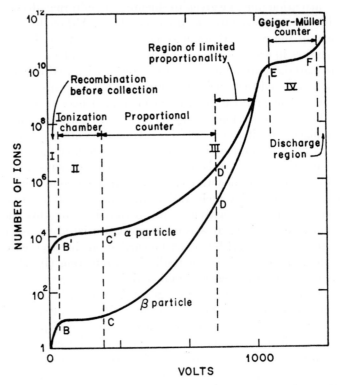

Fig. 2. Ionization as a function of voltage and the relative voltage effective for operation of the various gas counters. The ionization for an alpha particle is indicated along the curve B′C′D′EF and for a beta particle by curve B–F. Broken lines perpendicular to the voltage axis indicate the following: I, region of recombination of ions into neutral molecules resulting in no analytical measurement; the increasing voltage characterizing the operation of different gas counters i.e., II, ionization chamber; III, proportional counter, followed by an intermediate voltage not utilized for measurement and IV, the Geiger-Mueller voltage region and its termination by the region of continuous discharge. (Adapted from R. T. Overman and H. M. Clark. "Radioisotope Techniques," p. 27. McGraw-Hill, New York, 1960.)

1. COUNTING INSTRUMENTS

a. IONIZATION CHAMBER COUNTER

Ionizing radiation may be measured in various ways, one of which is by the ionization chamber counter. This counter consists essentially of an enclosure filled with air or some other gas and containing two oppositely charged electrodes. There is a gas pressure of about 1 atmosphere inside the chamber and a low potential gradient between the anode and the cathode. When the enclosed air or gas is ionized by a radioactive emission, the resulting ions are attracted to the electrodes. The current produced in the ionization chamber may be measured either by the rate-of-charge method (electroscope) or the high-resistance-leak method (electrometer), the former measuring the voltage increase across a small capacitator and the latter the voltage drop across a high resistance. At a very small voltage there is a loss of ions through recombination into neutral molecules as shown in Fig. 2, but for some large increment of voltage above the region of recombination of ion pairs (see Fig. 2), there is a saturation flow of current that is equal to the number of ions produced by the radiation entering the chamber. This is the ionization chamber region or the first of the three operating voltages for gas ionization instruments. Since the specific ionization constant (number of ions formed per unit length of track) is high for α-particles, they give up appreciable energy inside the chamber and are easily measured by this counter. However β- and γ-rays have low specific ionization constants and are not very suitable for measurement in the ionization chamber unless the radiation is considerable or a gaseous compound of the isotope can be used to fill the chamber; C^{14} and H^3 can be measured in the latter way.

b. PROPORTIONAL COUNTER

If the voltage applied to the gas chamber is further increased, a new condition is observed in which the ions produced by radiation possess enough energy to cause additional ionization of the neutral gas molecules on collision. In this voltage region, designated the proportional region, the ratio of ions produced by collision to those produced by the original radiation is usually of the order of 10 to 100 (see Fig. 2). Although the ratio remains essentially constant for a particular voltage, the pulse height delivered by the circuit is proportional to the primary ionization produced. Because of the formation of secondary electrons, it is possible to measure individual β- and γ-emitters with this instrument.

The construction of the proportional counter differs somewhat from that of the ionization chamber counter, since the electrodes of the former are usually constructed so that the potential is applied between a cylindrical metal casing and a thin metal wire along the center of the cylinder, the wire being positively charged. The ionization chamber counter usually has two parallel plates as electrodes.

c. GEIGER-MUELLER COUNTER

As the voltage is still further increased, the discharge produced by each emission increases. The pulses arising from primary events of different ionizing capacities, however, approach one another in magnitude. Finally, a voltage is reached (see Fig. 2) where the size of the pulse is independent of the primary ionization; that is, all discharges are nearly equal in magnitude. This is the Geiger region or voltage range in which a Geiger-Mueller (GM) counter is operated. The necessity of providing a high voltage and the inability to distinguish pulses due to different physical processes may be considered disadvantages, but there are advantages in that the GM counter is simpler and more stable than the proportional counter, and the internal amplification is so great (one primary ion pair can yield 100 million secondary ion pairs) that external (electronic) amplification may be very simple. The background count for most of the lead-shielded GM counters commercially available is less than 25 counts per minute. There are certain "low background" systems in which additional coincidence circuits and shielding have reduced the background count to less than 5 counts per minute.

For a particular GM tube, the pulse height (counts per minute) can be plotted against voltage to show three regions with the Geiger region as the plateau region (see Fig. 3). The operating voltage is usually set at about 100 volts higher than the voltage at the threshold of the plateau, thus ensuring the least fluctuation in counts as a result of slight voltage change. When the voltage is increased beyond the GM region, the gas arcs and goes into a state of continuous discharge.

In both proportional and GM counting the ionization avalanche will continue for extended periods unless quenched. The tube can be restored to normal condition by quenching externally (electronically) or internally by addition of gas (either an organic compound or a halogen) to the tube. Limiting the "dead time" which extends from the beginning of discharge to the end of quenching is important for measurements of high intensity. Although the pulses are registered mechanically, an electronic scaler causes only a fraction of the pulses to trigger the mechanical register; this fraction may be set automatically from a selector switch.

Proportional and GM counters may be either external or internal. In the latter there is no barrier between the sample and the sensitive volume; absorption in the wall or window of the tube is avoided, and there is a greater solid angle over which radiation may be counted. However, self-absorption in the sample remains, and there is the necessity for filling the tube with a gas that has proper characteristics for collecting ions. For routine measurements, the GM end-window counter is probably the most commonly used, although absorption in the air and by the window are among the factors decreasing efficiency. The window is usually constructed of mica, with a weight limit of 1.2 to 1.4 mg/cm^2.

Geiger counters have been developed in various forms and perform a great variety of counting operations, examples being monitoring instru-

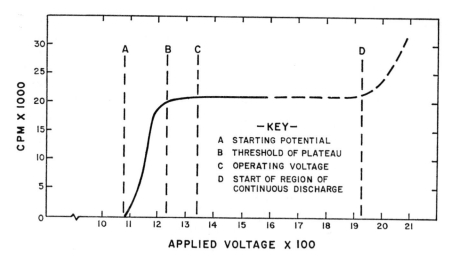

FIG. 3. The effect of increasing voltage on the counting rate of a Geiger-Mueller tube. The curve A–D shows characteristic voltage regions with a plateau, or region of relatively constant count rate, extending from B to D.

ments for checking contamination on hands, clothing, benches, etc., instruments to accommodate liquid samples and to count whole body radioactivity in animal experiments and in clinical studies of patients. Chromatography which is one of the most useful techniques available for separating the components in a mixture and for checking the purity of radioactive compounds depends to a considerable extent on Geiger counting to locate and to measure concentrations of components. Equipment is available commercially for scanning chromatographs prepared on paper and on thin layer plates, and some designs are quite versatile in providing both the efficiency of windowless detection and of end-window counting with one or two detectors in the same basic unit.

d. SCINTILLATION COUNTER

Another type of counter, the scintillation counter, has become very important in the past few years. Its operation is not based on ionization per se as are the gas counters mentioned above, but rather on energy transfer from radiation to a phosphor that responds to this energy transfer by the re-emission of energy in the form of visible or near visible light. This light pulse, when picked up by a photosensitive vacuum tube, is transformed into an electrical pulse, which is preamplified and sent to a scaler; the output signal from the detector is proportional to the energy given up to the detector by the primary particle. Different types of radiation may be detected by changing the phosphor used with the photomultiplier tube so that either α-, γ-, or high-energy β-radiation may be measured. In the "well-type" counter the sample may be either solid, liquid, or gaseous; it is introduced into a tube that is sunk into the depression of a phosphor. Ionizing radiation passes out of the tube and into the phosphor. For low-energy β-radiation, use is made of the liquid scintillation counter in which the radioactive material is put into intimate contact with the phosphor by dissolving, suspending, or immersing it in a liquid solution of the phosphor. The phosphor is in low concentration compared to the solvent molecules so that the β-radiation is transferred primarily to the more abundant solvent molecules of an aromatic hydrocarbon which are ionized, dissociated, or excited. Only a small fraction of the interactions result in excitation. The excitation energy of the solvent can be either emitted as photons in the ultraviolet region or transmitted to molecules of a primary solute (for example, a phosphor such as 2,5-diphenyloxazole, PPO). The excited phosphor molecules return to the ground state by emitting photons with a wavelength in the visible or near ultraviolet region. The wavelength of the fluorescence peak for PPO in toluene is near 380 mμ. The emission peak for this primary solute is below the most sensitive wavelength region of the photocathode which is used to detect photons, and hence a secondary solute, 2-p-phenylenebis-(5-phenyloxazole), known as POPOP, is commonly used as a wavelength shifter to absorb the energy from the primary solute and to re-emit it as light of a longer wavelength, about 420 mμ. With the use of a secondary solute, the efficiency in detection is greatly improved. To determine the extent to which counting efficiency is increased by use of secondary solutes has been the object of recent studies, the findings of which do not lead to a general recommendation for a secondary solute. Rather, it is concluded that the maximal efficiency in counting can be determined only by detailed evaluation of scintillation composition for a particular type of sample and counting system (photomultiplier tubes and optics being critical components). Phosphors that have become available recently were also evaluated. One of these, 2,5-bis-[2(5-tert-butylbenzoxazoly)]-thiophene (BBOT) has been recommended for use as a single solute since it emits at 435 mμ, but in this case also, preference should result from knowledge of sampling and counting conditions.[19a] The photons that are emitted directly and indirectly by this process are transformed into electron pulses that are greatly amplified.

In the liquid scintillation counter, the efficiency with which most β-emitters are detected is high because there is no barrier between the sample and the phosphor solution; for example, C^{14} and S^{35} have detection efficiencies as high as 90%. The detection efficiency for tritium, however, seldom exceeds 40%. In the complicated energy transfer process of scintillation counting, energy losses are of considerable magnitude. This factor, together with an initial failure to detect some of the weaker β-particles, leads to low detection efficiencies for such isotopes as tritium.

e. SEMICONDUCTOR COUNTER

This type of counter is under development and is not commercially available at the time of this writing. The principles and potentialities of the semiconductor detector are available in a book by Dearnaley and Northrop[20] and in a review by Miller et al.[21] The semiconductor detector is an ionization chamber in which the ion pairs produced by radiation move through a solid (silicon or germanium) rather than in a gas as discussed above in the section on the ionization counter. Most difficulties are attributed to an unsatisfactory lattice structure in the solid.

The energy necessary to excite an electron (specific ionization) is lower in a solid than in a gas because of the proximity of atoms in the solid. The value is 3.6 ev in silicon, 30 ev in gas-filled ionization chamber, and 300 ev per photoelectron in a scintillation photomultiplier system. This becomes an important feature of a counting device which depends on the production of an ion pair by impact ionization. The accuracy with which the total energy of low β-particles can be measured is therefore greater for the semiconductor counter than for those counters that are now readily available.

[19a] E. T. Bush and D. L. Hansen, Proceedings of the Symposium on Radioisotope Sample Measurement Techniques in Medicine and Biology held by the International Atomic Energy Agency in Vienna, May 24–28, 1965, pp. 395–408. (Printed by the International Atomic Energy Agency, Vienna, 1965.)

[20] G. Dearnaley and D. C. Northrop, "Semiconductor Counters for Nuclear Radiations," pp. 1–331. Wiley, New York, 1963.

[21] G. L. Miller, W. M. Gibson, and P. F. Donovan, Ann. Rev. Nucl. Sci. 12, 189 (1962).

The outlook is optimistic that suitable lattice structures can be realized. If these can also be shown to withstand the long-term effects of passage of nuclear radiation, then instrumentation utilizing such detectors should become available for low β-particle counting. High-energy resolution and compact structure would constitute advantages over the scintillation system, which is, by comparison, both complex and relatively inefficient in detection of energy.

2. SELECTION OF COUNTER

In Table II are listed the radioisotopes from Table I with their type of radiation, together with suggested counters, and an indication of which radioisotopes may be used in autoradiography to define intracellular localization. Some considerations particularly related to the selection of a counter are the following. The ionization chamber may be used if the

TABLE II
SELECTION OF COUNTER

Isotope	Type of decay	IC	PC	GM	SC	LS	Auto-rad
H^3	β^-	$+^a$				+	+
C^{14}	β^-	$+^a$	+	+		+	+
Na^{22}	β^+, EC, γ	+			+		
Na^{24}	β^-, γ	+			+		
Mg^{28}	β^-, γ	+			+		
P^{32}	β^-	+		+	+		
S^{35}	β^-		+	+		+	+
Cl^{36}	β^-				+		
K^{42}	β^-, γ	+			+		
Ca^{45}	β^-		+	+		+	
Cr^{51}	EC, γ				+		
Mn^{54}	EC, γ				+		
Fe^{55}	EC					+	+
Fe^{59}	β^-, γ	+			+		
Co^{60}	β^-, γ	+			+		
Ni^{63}	β^-		+			+	+
Cu^{64}	β^-, β^+, EC, γ	+			+		
Zn^{65}	β^+, EC, γ	+			+		
As^{76}	β^-, γ	+			+		
As^{77}	β^-, γ	+			+		
I^{125}	EC, γ					+	+
I^{131}	β^-, γ	+			+		

Key: IC, ionization chamber; PC, windowless proportional counter; GM, end-window Geiger-Mueller counter; SC, well-type scintillation counter; LS, Liquid scintillation counter; Auto-rad, autoradiography; EC, electron capture.

[a] Gaseous form of isotope.

radiation energy is considerable (1 Mev or greater) or if the isotope can be easily converted to a gaseous form. The proportional counter, like the ionization chamber, is not used widely, but when an isotope has different types and levels of energy these may be distinguished by this counter. The windowless proportional counter may be used as an alternative instrument to the liquid scintillation counter for some low-energy β-emitters, as indicated in Table II. The Geiger-Mueller end-window counter may be used for γ-particle counting, but, since the efficiency is low for γ-particles, the selection in Table II is confined to the β-emitters that can pass through the window. The scintillation counters are probably the most routinely used wherever they are available, the well-type being used for γ-particles and the liquid-type for β-particles and occasionally for weak γ-particles.

Autoradiography is indicated in Table II only for determining intracellular localization, although every isotope listed is capable of reaction with a photographic emulsion.

Carbon-14 may be counted in different instruments, but the efficiency varies greatly: GM end window, 5 to 25%; GM flow and proportional flow, 50%; gas ionization chamber, 100%, liquid scintillation, $\sim$90%. Sample characteristics may also influence the choice of one instrument rather than another, so that the designation of a single preference of instrument for each isotope is usually impossible.

If one must choose a single instrument that will handle the greatest variety of counting operations that may be encountered, the most likely choice would be the liquid scintillation counter, despite higher initial costs of instrumentation and also the higher costs involved in sample preparation. Versatility in liquid scintillation counting will continue to increase as pitfalls in sample preparation are overcome; when solubility and quenching are not insurmountable difficulties, an acceptable counting efficiency may be realized for all the isotopes listed in Table II. Such a statement is not made without re-emphasizing the fact that the sample preparation may be time-consuming in order to obtain the desired counting efficiency.

E. Sample Preparation

In addition to characteristics of the radioisotope and of the counter, properties of the sample may have a large effect on the measurement of radioactivity. Sample preparation for the ionization chamber will not be discussed, since this counter does not have widespread use among immunochemists. The windowless GM counter is not so widely used as the end-window GM counter for routine sampling because of difficulties inherent with many sample materials. Among these are the physical form of the sample which, if powdery, has a tendency to become dislodged from the sample into the counting chamber, which then presents a decontamination problem. Another difficulty is with trapped solvent so that self-absorption of low-energy β-radiation is increased; counts obtained for consecutive periods of time will show considerable variation if the latter condition exists.

Some samples that contain substances that interfere with the scintillation counting process (because of color or chemical nature), may be counted with greater reproducibility as well as higher efficiency in the GM counter rather than in the scintillation counter. An example of this is the following method of counting low-energy β-radiation in whole tissue. The aim in this and other specific examples will be to give sufficient detail for reproduction. At the same time similar applications will be apparent.

1. SAMPLING TECHNIQUES FOR THE END-WINDOW GEIGER-MUELLER COUNTER

a. S[35]-AZOPROTEIN IN TISSUE

Most of the counting performed by immunochemists is to obtain relative concentrations of radioactivity rather than absolute concentrations. The method described here is such a determination, but it illustrates the calibration with an antigen whose concentration in samples is to be determined by the amount of radioactivity present.[22]

Aluminum pans, 1 mm thick, 6.4 mm deep, and 7.9 cm² in area, such as are marketed for use as milk bottle closures, are weighed to the nearest milligram, the weight being recorded on the bottom of the pan. Markings are made lightly with a brush pen so as not to dent the aluminum. Into each of twenty-one pans is weighed 500 ± 1 mg of wet tissue from a normal rabbit. The residue from this weight of tissue is approximately a linear function of wet weight when a determination of radioactivity is made for different wet weights of radioactive tissue. To triplicate pans containing weighed tissue is added 0.5 ml of a 1% solution of the S[35]-azoprotein. In similar manner doubling dilutions of the same azoprotein are added to pans containing the normal tissue. About seven dilutions in the range 1:100 to 1:6400 are prepared. To each sample is added 2 ml of concentrated HNO_3 for digestion, over the low heat of a hot plate. After digestion, the samples are heated to further dryness, cooled, and weighed for a determination of residue weight. The samples are then counted in an end-window GM counter, the time being determined by

[22] J. S. Garvey and D. H. Campbell, *J. Immunol.* **72,** 131 (1954).

statistics considered under Section F,3. After the samples have been counted they are again weighed so that the mean weights obtained before and after counting can be used for the weight-count relationship that is to be plotted. Time and temperature of heating are varied to obtain several residue weights for each sample. Each reheating to reduce the residue weight is followed by a weighing, counting, and reweighing of the residue. The background count is determined with either an empty sample pan or a pan containing digested normal tissue with no added S^{35}-azoprotein; in either instance the background count is similar. When the log net count is plotted against the residue weight linear curves representing each different concentration of antigen are obtained. Two of these curves are shown in Fig. 4, where each point on a curve represents a different residue weight, or approximately five different residue weights for each of the triplicate samples. A residue weight of 100 mg is arbitrarily chosen as a

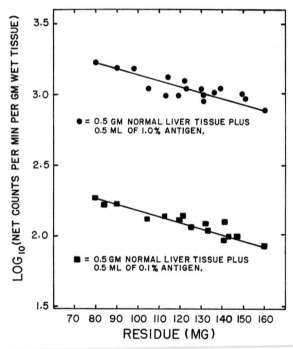

Fig. 4. Count rate obtained in a GM counter as a function of residue weight. The residue weight was obtained by varying the time and temperature of heating a nitric acid digest of a constant wet weight of tissue. Each curve represents a different concentration of antigen (S^{35} azohemocyanin) added in a constant volume to 0.5 gm normal rabbit liver tissue. [From J. S. Garvey and D. H. Campbell, *J. Immunol.* **72**, 131 (1954).]

reference. Then the counts at 100 mg of residue weight on each of the seven different antigen concentration curves are used to construct the log-log plot shown in Fig. 5. By use of the curves in Fig. 4, correction factors are obtained to be applied to residue weights of unknowns that vary from the reference of 100 mg. Although these factors are essentially independent of antigen concentration, each of the curves is used to obtain an average set of correction factors for 5-mg increments between 80 and 160 mg. Inter-

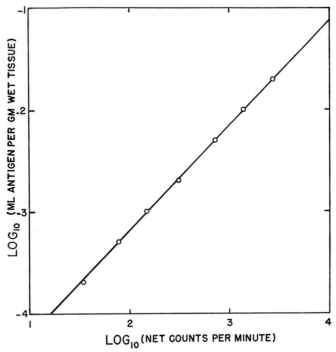

Fig. 5. Standard curve showing relationship of antigen concentration and count rate for a constant wet weight of 0.5 gm tissue and a constant residue weight of 100 mg. The curve represents the count rate obtained for seven different concentrations of S^{35} azohemocyanin, assayed as were the two antigen concentrations in Fig. 4. [From J. S. Garvey and D. H. Campbell, *J. Immunol* **72**, 131 (1954).]

polation between these factors is used for unknowns of intermediate weights.

Tissue removed from a rabbit, injected with the same azoprotein as used for the standardization curve, is sampled in triplicates of 500 mg of wet weight, digested, weighed for residue weight, and counted in the same way as described above. The only deviation from the standardization procedure is that only one residue weight is obtained, to which the proper residue correction factor is applied to determine the count. The count is then referred to a "new" curve, drawn parallel to the one in Fig. 4. The "new" curve corrects for the physical decay (see Section F) of the isotope that has occurred since the standard curve was established. The volume of antigen determined for the sample may be applied to a calculation of the antigen contained in the total weight of tissue.*

b. Antigen–Antibody Precipitates

It is sometimes necessary to determine the specific radioactivity of one of the constituents of a specific precipitate of antigen and antibody. When the specific radioactivity is to be related to antibody nitrogen, the point of equivalence amounts of antigen and antibody is determined by the interfacial ring test made on supernatants removed from quantitative precipitates. It is important that the test antiserum be exposed to an antigen–antibody precipitate of unrelated specificity so that coprecipitating material can be removed prior to the precipitation with the test antigen. Quadruplicate precipitates at the equivalence point are prepared; two are used for a nitrogen determination, and the other two are used for a determination of radioactivity. The precipitates that are to be counted are first dissolved with 2 to 3 drops of 0.1 N NaOH and then transferred quantitatively with 2 ml of water to an aluminum pan (of the type described in the previous procedure). These solutions† are evaporated beneath a heat lamp, and the residues are counted in an end-window GM counter to determine the radioactivity of the antibody. Antibody nitrogen is calculated as the difference obtained when the antigen nitrogen added to form the equivalence precipitate is subtracted from the total nitrogen in the equivalence precipitate. To determine if a correction is necessary for self-absorption, a constant amount of the radioisotope is added to varying amounts of precipitates. These precipitates are dissolved and counted as described above. If the residues in a test series do not exceed a few milligrams, as is the usual case, no correction factor is necessary for self-absorption.

2. SAMPLING TECHNIQUES FOR THE LIQUID SCINTILLATION COUNTER

a. Serum Proteins Labeled with C^{14}-Amino Acids

It was previously mentioned that the sample counted in the liquid scintillation system must be in intimate contact with a solution of scin-

---

* Newer methods of combustion of organic material within scintillation vials [G. N. Gupta, *Analyt. Chem.* 38, 1356 (1966), amounts equivalent to 2 mg dry weight] or larger amounts within Mylar bags [G. N. Gupta, *Microchem. J.* 13, 1 (1968)] avoid the problem of self-absorption in relation to residual tissue weight.

† In case these or other aqueous solutions fail to spread on the aluminum pans, 1 to 2 drops of a 1% aerosol solution (for example, dioctyl sodium sulfosuccinate) is used as a wetting agent.

tillator (fluor). With regard to the latter, one of the most efficient and widely used solvents is toluene, in which the primary fluor, PPO (2,5-diphenyloxazole), has a maximal emission of 380 mμ. A second fluor, dimethyl-POPOP [1,4-bis-2-(4-methyl-5-phenyloxazolyl)benzene], is used that acts as a wavelength shifter, causing the photon emission to occur in the more sensitive region of 430 mμ.* Since biological materials such as serum cannot be dissolved in this solution of fluors, an immersion technique[23] with slight modification (M. B. Rittenberg, unpublished observations) provides the intimate contact that is necessary between sample, fluors, and solvent. Analytical reagent-grade chemicals are used throughout the procedure with the exception of the fluors, which are "scintillation" grade.

Filter paper is cut into strips, 4 × 7.6 cm. A strip of this size, when prepared with sample as described below, can be shaped to form a cylindrical lining of the inside wall of a standard 22-ml low-potassium glass counting vial. Whatman No. 1 chromatography paper purchased in rolls 4 × 200 cm is a satisfactory paper in the procedure and can be cut into strips of the proper size without difficulty. The strips are pencil-marked in one corner for identification with the sample to be applied. Each marked strip is then placed in a plastic grip (a clothes pin is suitable) with a small piece of aluminum foil between the paper strip and the plastic grip to prevent contamination of the latter with radioactivity. The plastic grips have been previously nailed in a desirable number to a board; the latter is held at a convenient height (for applying the samples) by clamps on a ring stand in a chemical hood.

Serum containing C[14]-labeled protein is applied to a strip by means of a Hamilton microsyringe with a needle bent approximately 45 degrees near the tip. The capacity of a strip is about 0.2 ml. of serum when a single application is made and allowed to spread evenly. Duplicate strips are prepared with a varying volume of serum—for example, 0.05, 0.10, 0.15, and 0.20 ml—to demonstrate the linear relationship of counts to volume of serum. The exhaust fan in the hood is turned on to facilitate the drying process (a stream of filtered air may also be used). When the sample strips are dry they are placed in a large beaker (1000 ml) for the precipitation and washing procedure.†

A 10% solution of trichloroacetic acid (TCA) is prepared and main-

---

* 2,5-Bis[2-(5-*tert*-butylbenzoxazolyl]thiophene(BBOT) has become available recently for use as a single solute, thus eliminating a need for primary and secondary solutes. Characteristic absorption maximum is 375 mμ, and the fluorescence maximum is 435 mμ.

† Strips at this point, prepared on glass microfiber, have been counted directly, wetted with scintillation fluid, and sealed within plastic—so-called "solid state" counting [G. N. Gupta, *Analyt. Chem.* 39, 1911 (1967)].

[23] H. Timourian and P. C. Denney, *J. Exptl. Zool.* 155, 57 (1964).

tained ice-cold. This solution should contain a 0.1 M concentration of a nonlabeled amino acid that corresponds to the radioactive amino acid to be measured in the serum protein. The nonlabeled amino acid dilutes the specific activity of the labeled amino acid that was injected into the animal and is present in the serum but not incorporated into the serum protein. The strips are immersed for 10 minutes in the ice-cold TCA solution that contains nonlabeled amino acid. The cold TCA is poured off, and a solution of 5% TCA at boiling temperature is added. After the strips have been swirled in the hot TCA solution, it is poured off. The strips are then washed three times with 95% ethanol, followed by a washing in absolute ethanol. Washing is continued with acetone, in which solution the strips are allowed to stand for 5 minutes. The washing with acetone is repeated with fresh solution for another 5 minutes. A final washing is made in anhydrous ether. The strips are then removed from the beaker, drained on a layer of absorbent paper, and hung by the plastic grips in the hood to dry.

Each strip, when dry, is placed in a counting vial so as to line the inside cylindrical wall of the vial. The vial is then filled to the neck with the scintillator–solvent that has been prepared by dissolving 2.8945 gm of PPO and 0.3483 gm of POPOP in 1 liter of toluene.* (The scintillator–solvent and the vial may be reused, but if this is done, one such vial containing only the scintillator–solvent should be included as a blank.)

The linearity of the method is demonstrated in the accompanying curve (Fig. 6) for serum diluted 1:10; linearity was also maintained with undiluted serum. As is shown by the curve, there is good agreement between the strip method as given here and the disk method of Mans and Novelli,[24] but the advantage of the strip method over the disk method is the ability to apply more sample in one operation.

Any series of samples that are counted should contain the proper complement of blanks, an important one being normal serum that has been precipitated under the same conditions as the serum that contains radioactivity. A convenient measure of reproducibility of the method is to use a C^{14}-labeled serum that has been kept frozen in aliquots, one of which can be used to prepare a reference standard for inclusion with each group of samples. Such a reference serum, when used over a test period of several weeks and with two separate batches of scintillator–solvent, indicated an experimental error of $\pm 6\%$ (ratio of standard error to mean average) for the entire procedure.

Occasionally some serum protein or a substance complexed to it will fluoresce giving signals which are counted very much like scintillations

---

* A 25× concentrate of PPO and POPOP in toluene is available from T. M. Pilot Chemicals Inc., Watertown, Massachusetts.

[24] R. J. Mans and G. D. Novelli, *Arch. Biochem. Biophys.* **94**, 48 (1961).

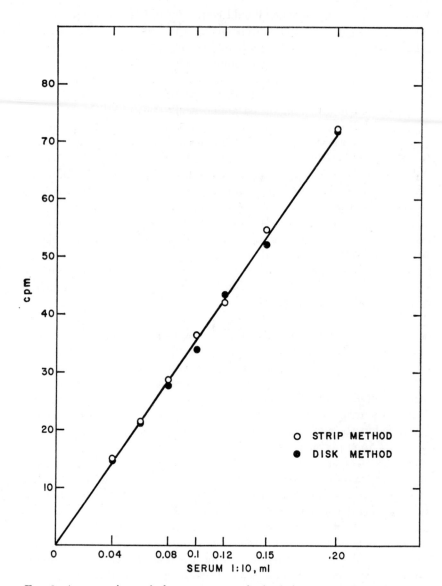

Fig. 6. A comparison of the count rate obtained for a varying volume of a diluted rabbit serum containing C^{14}-labeled protein sampled on either a paper disk [R. J. Mans and G. D. Novelli, *Arch. Biochem. Biophys.* **94**, 48 (1961)] or a strip of paper [H. Timourian and P. C. Denney, *J. Exptl. Zool,* **155**, 57 (1964)]. Count rate was determined in a liquid scintillation counter. From data obtained by M. B. Rittenberg, unpublished observations.

induced by low-energy β-particles emitted by H^3. A certain portion of this artifact is in the higher energy range, characteristic of C^{14} emission. When such a phenomenon is suspected, it can often be completely quenched, with little or no effect on scintillation due to C^{14} radioactivity, by the addition of 5 μl of concentrated HCl to each vial. A control containing the same isotope should be treated in the same manner to determine if the acid quenches the meaningful scintillation (C.A. Williams, unpublished observations).

b. URINE CONTAINING S^{35} FROM SULFANILATE–AZOPROTEIN INJECTION

Specimens of urine present several complications to measurement in a liquid scintillation counter. These became apparent from studies of S^{35} in urine following injection of S^{35}-sulfanilate–azoprotein (J. Garvey, unpublished findings) and are as follows.

(1) Colored materials may absorb or quench photons emitted by the fluor, causing a decrease in measured radioactivity. These may sometimes be removed, but S^{35} derived from sulfanilate–azoprotein is simultaneously removed with the color. (2) Urine is inhomogenous in aqueous as well as in nonaqueous solvent; thus S^{35}-urine is an unstable mixture in the dioxane–naphthalene solvent commonly used as solvent for aqueous samples. As a result, a precipitate settles during counting. (3) Phosphorescence is present to a varying degree; as a result, samples must be equilibrated in the freezer unit of the counter for at least 12 hours.

Because of the nature and magnitude of these factors, it would seem that some method of measurement other than scintillation counting might be preferable, but self-absorption by salts and trapped solvent in the sample make impossible the measurement of extremely low levels of radioactivity with the GM counter. For the latter reasons a method of liquid scintillation counting was developed that involves principally a correction for color, suspension in a thixotropic gel, and handling precautions to reduce phosphorescence.

Rabbits that have been injected with S^{35}-sulfanilate–azoprotein are housed in separate metabolism cages, and urine is collected at 24-hour intervals in a clean beaker containing 5 ml of toluene (analytical reagent grade). The collection of 24-hour samples of urine is begun prior to the injection in order to obtain preinjection urine from the experimental rabbits. In addition, a group of several normal rabbits that are not assigned to the experiment are used for obtaining a series of normal urine samples. The 24-hour collection of urine is measured for volume and poured into a bottle to which is added an additional 5 ml of toluene; the top is covered with plastic wrap and then a screw cap. The urine is refrigerated until sampled for counting, at which time 10 ml is pipetted into a tube and centrifuged at 0 to 2°C and 1400 $\times$ g for 30 minutes (3000 rpm if the rotating radius is 14 cm). The supernatant is decanted, and duplicate 0.5-ml amounts are pipetted into standard counting vials (22 ml, low-potassium glass). To the vials containing sample is added 15 ml of scintillator prepared as follows with a gelling agent: 7.0 gm of PPO (2,5-diphenyloxazole), 0.7 gm of dimethyl-POPOP [1,4-bis-2-(4-methyl-5-phenyloxazolyl)benzene], and 100 gm of naphthalene* (Eastman Distillation Products, Rochester, New York; recrystallized from alcohol) dissolved in 1 liter of p-dioxane (Eastman); the latter solution is added to 40 gm of Cab-O-Sil (silicon dioxide procured as Silicon M-5 from the Cabot Corporation, Texaco Bldg., Los Angeles, California) while being mixed with a stirring rod and finally with a magnetic stirrer to achieve a homogeneous mixture that is slightly gelled.† The beaker used for mixing is 1500 ml in capacity (minimal size for weighing 40 gm of Cab-O-Sil) and is wrapped with aluminum foil around the outside cylindrical wall, to reduce exposure to light. In addition, the gel–scintillator is not exposed to air in order to avoid peroxide formation with the dioxane. A syringe is used to deliver 15 ml of the gel–scintillator to each vial, which is then tightly capped. The vial is given a few quick shakes and placed in the freezer of the scintillation counter for cooling. If counting is started earlier than about 12 hours from the time the samples are placed in the freezer unit, measurements are 25 to 50% higher than thereafter. If at least 12 hours is allowed for cooling in the dark, phosphorescence is no longer a factor, samples remain homogeneous, and a series of measurements over several days gives negligible variation.

Each of several normal urine samples is added in 0.5-ml amounts together with 25, 50, 75, or 100 μl of S^{35}-sulfanilic acid to counting vials. After the vials have been swirled gently to mix the normal urine and the radioactive material, 15 ml of the gel–scintillator is added. The vials are cooled and counted as the samples were. A pool of normal urine, decolorized by treatment with charcoal, is used also in 0.5-ml amounts with the S^{35}-sulfanilic acid to approximate the consistency of urine minus the color.

---

* Naphthalene increases the efficiency of p-dioxane as a scintillation solvent for water, the effect being more appreciable for tritium counting than for C^{14} and S^{35} counting.

† All handling of dioxane in the preparation and likewise the dispensing of the scintillater should be carried out in a vented hood with high air velocity. An additional precaution for personnel safety is the weighing of the Cab-O-Sil in a gloved box or alternately the wearing of a mask to prevent inhalation. The user must not only avoid direct exposure of himself but safeguard other individuals against inhalation of the fine silica particles that are easily airborne.

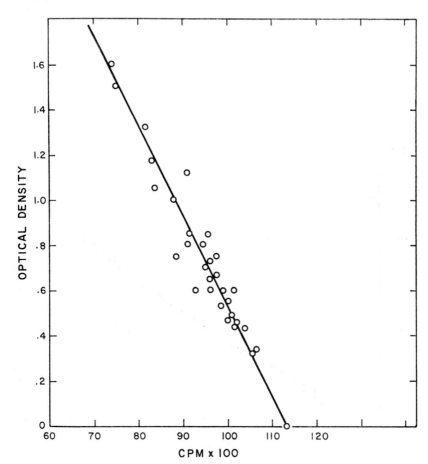

Fig. 7. Count rate as related to a variable O.D. at 440 mμ. A constant amount of radioactivity (S[35] sulfanilic acid) was added to normal rabbit urine after the O.D. of the latter was determined. Count rate in a liquid scintillation system was determined as described in the text.

A curve showing the relationship of counting rate and optical density measurement is given in Fig. 7; the optical density reading is made at 440 mμ, which is near the maximal light emission, considering the scintillators and the sensitivity of the photomultipliers in the scintillation process. There is some sample deviation from a linear relationship, probably due to variable quantities of other quench factors than the one being measured by the absorption. However, any single urine is found to have about the same effect on various counting rates due to radioactivity. As a result of these attempts to assess the effect of urine as a quenching

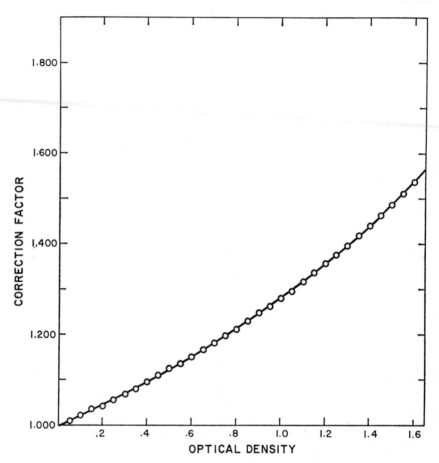

Fɪɢ. 8. Curve of correction factors obtained by dividing the unquenched count of decolorized urine by the quenched count of normal urine in which count rate was found to vary in Fig. 7 as a linear function of O.D. at 440 mμ.

agent, a curve is obtained (Fig. 8) that is used to make an approximate correction.

F. Evaluation of Counting Data

1. DECAY CORRECTION

There is a continuous decrease in the average emission rate of a radioactive sample due to physical decay, the latter being expressed as a half-life which is a specific property of the radioisotope. With the exception of those isotopes with a half-life in years, counting of the same or comparative samples usually requires a correction, with the following equation being used to give the fraction of radioactivity remaining after an interval of time has elapsed.

$$A = A_0 e^{-\lambda t}$$

where A = radioactivity at any time (t).
A_0 = original radioactivity at zero time.
λ, a decay constant with the following relationship to half-life = $0.693/T_{1/2}$.
t = elapsed time in units corresponding to $T_{1/2}$.
Reduced to a $\log_{10}$ expression, the equation becomes

$$\log \frac{A}{A_0} = \frac{-\lambda t}{2.3}$$

$$\log A = \log A_0 \frac{-\lambda t}{2.3}$$

The nomograms shown in Figs. 9 and 10 are useful in the calculation of the radioactivity remaining after 1 to 13 half-lives.

2. SPECIFIC RADIOACTIVITY

When it is necessary to calculate specific radioactivity (A_s), this may be expressed as curies per gram (Ci/gm) from the relationship

$$A_s \text{ in disintegrations/sec/gm} = \lambda N \tag{1}$$

where $\lambda = 0.693/T_{1/2}$, and $N = (6.03 \times 10^{23})/\text{atomic weight}$. Since curies (Ci) = disintegrations/sec/(3.7×10^{10}), the final expression of A_s as curies per gram is

$$
\begin{aligned}
A_s &= \frac{0.693}{T_{1/2}(\text{in sec})} \times \frac{6.03 \times 10^{23}}{\text{atomic wt.}} \times \frac{1}{3.7 \times 10^{10}} \\
&= \frac{1.13 \times 10^{13}}{(T_{1/2})(\text{atomic wt.})}
\end{aligned}
\tag{2}
$$

If the half-life of the radioactive species is expressed in units of time other than seconds, a separate conversion factor replaces the last expression above with

$$
\begin{aligned}
A_s \ (T_{1/2} \text{ in hours}) &= \frac{3.14 \times 10^9}{(T_{1/2})(\text{atomic wt.})} \\
A_s \ (T_{1/2} \text{ in days}) &= \frac{1.308 \times 10^8}{(T_{1/2})(\text{atomic wt.})} \\
A_s \ (T_{1/2} \text{ in years}) &= \frac{3.59 \times 10^5}{(T_{1/2})(\text{atomic wt.})}
\end{aligned}
\tag{3}
$$

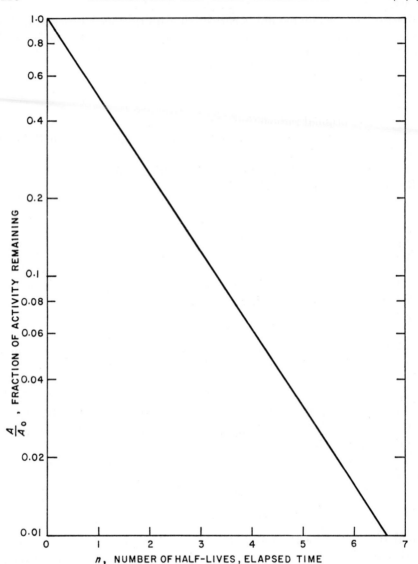

Fig. 9. The fraction of radioactivity remaining after the number of half-lives (elapsed time) has been determined as indicated by the equations that follow and found to vary between 0 and 7 $T_{1/2}$. $A = A_0 2^{-n}$ or $A/A_0 = (\frac{1}{2})^n$, where A_0 = activity at some original or zero time; A = activity at any time, t; A/A_0 = fraction of activity remaining at any time, t; n = number of half-lives in the time interval between the original or zero time and time, t; $n = t/T_{1/2}$. From S. Kinsman (Chairman, Board of Editors), "Radiological Health Handbook, pp. 118–119. U.S. Department of Commerce, Office of Technical Services, Washington, D.C., 1960.

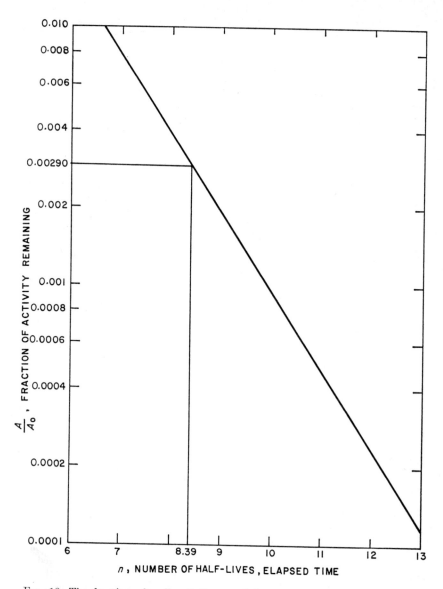

Fig. 10. The fraction of radioactivity remaining after the number of half-lives elapsed time has been determined as indicated in the equations of Fig. 9 and found to vary between 6 and 13 $T_{1/2}$. An illustrated example of a calculation is below.

Example: Given: 10 mCi of a radioisotope like P^{32} with a $T_{1/2}$ of 14.3 days. To find: The activity remaining 120.0 days later. Solution: n = number of half-lives, lapsed time = $t/T_{1/2}$ = 120.0/14.3 = 8.39. Find the position 8.39 half-lives on the abscissa (x-axis) of this graph. The ordinate (y axis) of the point on the graph, whose abscissa is 8.39 is 0.00290. In this case 0.00290 is A/A_0, the fraction of activity remaining. Since the original activity was 10 mCi and the fraction left after 8.39 half-lives is 0.00290, the activity remaining is 0.00290 × 10, or 0.0290 mCi. From S. Kinsman (Chairman, Board of Editors), "Radiological Health Handbook," pp. 118–119. U.S. Department of Commerce, Office of Technical Services, Washington, D.C., 1960.

TABLE III
SUMMARY OF THE ERRORS MOST USED IN STATISTICAL ANALYSIS[a]

Name of error	Probability of observing error as large as or larger than error named in column 1	Limits of error in radiochemical counting[b]	Remarks
Probable error	0.5000	$0.6745(n)^{1/2}$	Quite commonly used in scientific work of all kinds. Becoming obsolete from a statistical standpoint. One half of the values in a series of similar counting determinations will be in error by less than the probable error
Standard deviation	0.3173	$1.000(n)^{1/2}$	Most used statistically, since most statistical tables are computed as functions of the standard deviation. Usually symbolized as the Greek letter sigma
Nine-tenths error	0.1000	$1.645(n)^{1/2}$	Commonly used in radiocounting. Named because there are nine chances out of ten that the error will be smaller. Sometimes abbreviated N.T.E. Statisticians would call this the 0.10 level of significance but would not consider deviations with a probability as high as this very significant
Ninety-five hundredths error	0.0500	$1.96(n)^{1/2}$	Most commonly used by statisticians as the level at which deviations exceed chance variation and thus are considered significant. Called the 0.05 level of significance
Ninety-nine hundredths error	0.0100	$2.576(n)^{1/2}$	Deviations of this magnitude may be considered highly significant. Often used by statisticians and called the 0.01 level of significance

[a] From A. A. Jarrett, "Statistical Methods Used in the Measurement of Radioactivity," AECU 262, Oak Ridge National Lab., Oak Ridge, Tenn., p. 13, available from U.S. Department of Commerce, Office of Technical Services, Washington, D.C., 1946.

[b] n is the total number of observed counts and is preceded by the proportionality constant derived from Gaussian distribution.

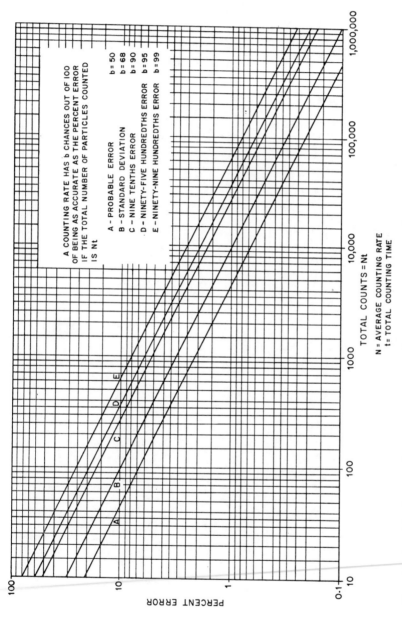

FIG. 11. A series of curves for use in calculating and comparing counting data in terms of common statistical errors. Adapted from A. A. Jarrett, "Statistical Methods Used in the Measurement of Radioactivity," AECU 262, 1946.

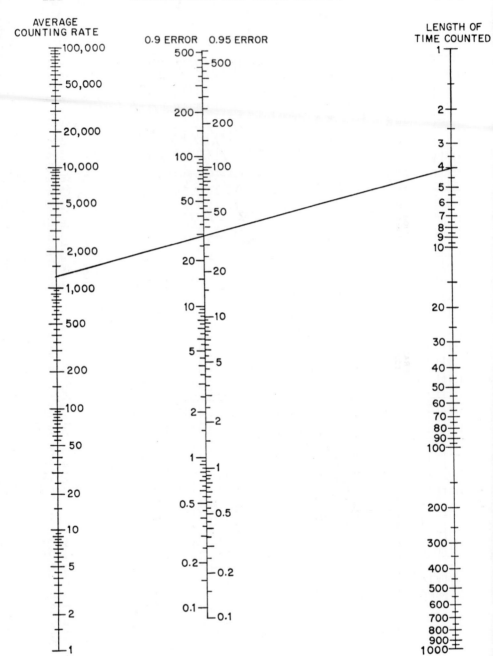

AVERAGE
COUNTING RATE

0.9 ERROR   0.95 ERROR

LENGTH OF
TIME COUNTED

3. STATISTICS

Not only does decay affect counting results, but there is the continuous fluctuation in the counting rate due to the random nature of the disintegration process. As a result of the latter, statistical methods are used to increase the accuracy of counting determinations as well as to interpret counting results. Variations in radioactive counting are represented by a Gaussian distribution, and statistical laws may be used to estimate how well an observed counting determination represents the true average value. It is common practice to determine the actual difference between an observed count and the true average value, this value being referred to as the error of the determination. A limit of error may be arbitrarily selected and the probability calculated that the observed value is in error by at least the amount of the selected error. The probability limit for most statistical problems is set at 0.05 (ninety-five hundredths error) but may be more rigidly set at 0.01 (ninety-nine hundredths error). For general radiochemical data, the probability is commonly set at 0.10, and the resulting error is called the nine-tenths error. Other errors commonly encountered in standard nomenclature are standard deviation, which is numerically equal to the square root of the true average count, and probable error, which has a probability limit of 0.50. These errors are summarized in Table III and used in Fig. 11 as a graphic presentation to facilitate counting calculations. Figure 12 is a nomogram which is useful in the calculation of the 0.9 error and 0.95 error of counting rate determinations from 1 to 100,000 cpm.

To minimize the error introduced by the background count, it is necessary to distribute properly the counting times of sample and background. The purpose of the nomogram in Fig. 13 is to facilitate the calculation of an efficient distribution of sample and background counting times. For further details of statistical methods as applied to counting,

---

Fig. 12. Nomogram with an illustrated example for calculating two of the common statistical errors that result for a counting rate determined for a particular counting time. *Instructions for use:* Draw a straight line from a point on the left scale corresponding to the counting rate of the sample through the point on the right scale corresponding to the length of time the sample was counted. The point where this line crosses the center scale corresponds to the 0.9 error and the 0.95 error of the determination. *Example:* The 0.9 error of a sample which averaged 1250 counts per minute during a 4-minute determination is 29 counts per minute. Adapted from A. A. Jarrett, "Statistical Methods Used in the Measurement of Radioactivity," AECU 262, 1946.

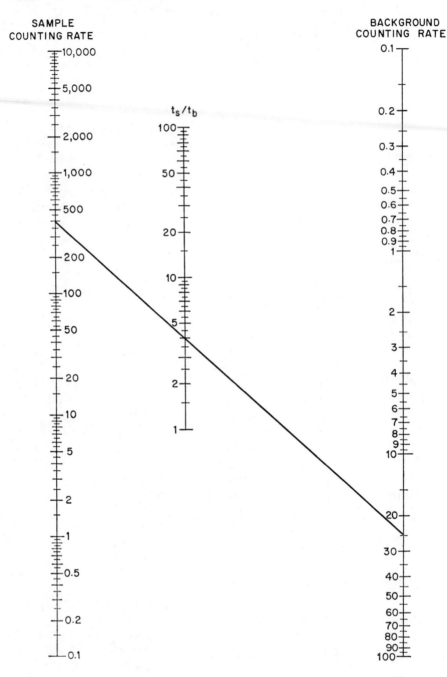

reference should be made to Jarrett[25] and to the discussion in various radiochemical texts.

An excellent compilation of reference material covering many phases of radiochemistry is available in "Source Material for Radiochemistry," 1965 revision, Publication 1351 of National Academy of Sciences–National Research Council, copies being available at a cost of $1.50 from the Printing and Publishing Office, National Academy of Sciences, 2101 Constitution Avenue, Washington, D.C. The main purpose of the latter publication was to cite books, review articles, surveys, and proceedings of symposia rather than individual articles, and there seems to be an excellent achievement of this aim to the publication "cut-off" date of June 1965. An omission was *Journal of Labelled Compounds*, published quarterly by Presses Académiques Européenes, Brussels, which began with Vol. 1, No. 1 in Feb. 1965, and where contained to date are pertinent papers on synthesis, purification, analysis, and storage of radioactive compounds, abstracts of related literature and summaries of papers presented at meetings. In addition to these general reference sources and the individual references, the investigator will find extremely useful a number of excellent technical bulletins, monographs, and instruction manuals that are available from manufacturers of counting equipment and from suppliers of radioisotopes and labeled compounds.

[25] A. A. Jarrett, "Statistical Methods Used in the Measurement of Radioactivity," AECU 262, Oak Ridge National Lab., Oak Ridge, Tenn., available from U.S. Department of Commerce, Office of Technical Services, Washington, D.C. 43 pp., 1946.

FIG. 13. Nomogram with an illustrated example for determining an efficient distribution of sample and background counting times for a range of determined counting rates of sample and background. *Explanation of symbols:* t_s, counting time of the sample; t_b, counting time of the background. *Instructions for use:* Draw a straight line from a point on the left scale corresponding to the counting rate of the sample through the point on the right scale corresponding to the counting rate of the background. The point where this line crosses the center scale corresponds to the ratio of the counting times of the sample and the background necessary for maximum counting efficiency. *Example:* If the approximate counting rate of a sample, including the background, is 400 counts per minute and the background is roughly 25 counts per minute, the sample should be counted four times as long as the background for the maximum counting efficiency. If the total time were to be limited to 20 minutes of counting, the sample should be counted for 16 minutes and the background counted for 4 minutes in order to realize the minimum error in 20 minutes of counting time. Adapted from A. A. Jarrett, "Statistical Methods Used in the Measurement of Radioactivity," AECU 262, 1946.

G. Autoradiography in Immunological Investigation*

1. INTRODUCTION

By means of autoradiography, the presence of isotopically labeled substances may be detected in animal organs, tissues, or single cells and correlated with the existing histological and cytological detail. With proper exposure of tissue sections or cell suspensions to photographic emulsions, and subsequent development of the photographic film, the deposition of the radioactive label will be registered by the silver grains. The resulting preparation is termed an autoradiograph. There are several reviews, editions, and books concerned with these techniques, some of which will be cited in their appropriate content below. The now classic paper of Fitzgerald[26] is recommended for basic theory and many practical considerations.

Interesting applications of autoradiography to immunological problems have included: the localization of labeled antigens or haptens administered to identify tissues and cells involved in the immune response; the localization of labeled antibody to reveal the distribution of antigenic material; the distribution of labeled lymphoid cells in the body; and the specific identification of reactants in gel diffusion or immunoelectrophoresic patterns. (The last-mentioned application is discussed in Chap. 14, Vol. III.) Autoradiography is better suited and more sensitive for certain of these studies than the older method of detecting dye-markers, and, depending on the reagents and level of radioactivity employed, it may be more precise for localization studies than techniques employing fluorescent labels. In unusual circumstances where the site of localization within tissues is not known, preliminary organ screening for radioisotopes can be conducted efficiently by newer methods of tissue combustion and scintillation counting.[27]

2. CHOICE OF ISOTOPES

Labels may be *external* (by adding a radioactive "tag" to a protein by covalent bonds; see Section B and Chap. 4,A, Vol. I), or *internal* (by building the structure by *in vivo* biosynthesis utilizing radioactive precursors of small molecular size, or, in the case of many haptenic substances, by *in vitro* synthesis using smaller radioactive reactants).

External labeling (for example, radioiodination of proteins) must be carried out with due regard to the possibility that too extensive labeling may alter the antigenic specificity of the carrier or lead to an artificially

* Section 11,G was contributed by Roy E. Ritts, Jr.

[26] P. Fitzgerald, E. Simmel, J. Weinstein, and C. Martin, *Lab. Invest.* **2**, 181 (1953).
[27] G. N. Gupta, *Anal. Chem.* **38**, 1356 (1966), **39**, 1911 (1967); *Microchem. J.* **13**, 1 (1968).

shortened half-life of the carrier in the circulation. Also, if the specific activity of the material used as label is high, or if there is extended exposure of the labeled carrier to high radioactivity, denaturation may be caused by radiation damage. In general, where synthesis is possible or convenient, internal labeling is recommended, preferably with C^{14} or H^3 because of their long half-life and relatively low energies of emission; P^{32}, S^{35}, and I^{131} are shorter-lived isotopes, but, since they have greater energies of emission, they will cause much faster registration on photographic film (see Table I of Chap. 11,B).

Whatever the isotope or the method of labeling, however, it is most important to keep in mind that metabolic degradation of labeled substances can occur *in vivo*, resulting perhaps in a number of radioactive fragments that can be localized by mechanisms not under study, possibly leading to unwarranted conclusions. This could be particularly bothersome in tracing potentially immunogenic fragments of macromolecules. Also important to consider is radiation damage to the living system—organism, tissue, cell, or organelle—which may in turn affect the results of the experiment. An example of this effect might be found in the now widespread use of H^3-thymidine to label cells, or, more properly, the newly made DNA during chromosome replication. In tissue culture it has been noted that high concentration of tritiated thymidine of high specific activity (1 μCi/mM) will arrest or abolish all cell division.[28]

In choosing a suitable type and quantity of isotope for a given experiment, one consideration which applies only to H^3 labels is the stability and homogeneity of the compound if produced by the random hydrogen exchange method of Wilzbach.[29] This procedure frequently produces degradation products which must be eliminated before use.* Also, some hydrogen positions randomly exchanged for tritium may readily exchange for hydrogen again under the conditions of the experiment.

The energy of the isotope and the thickness of the tissue section in which it is desired to localize radioactivity are important factors in the efficient utilization of autoradiographic methods. In the case of weak emitters, internal self-absorption of emissions within the tissue and loss of emission in passing to photographic emulsion through a layer of celloidin, Formvar, or other material—used to prevent direct contact with tissue constituents that might sensitize silver bromide grains to undergo later chemical development—are problems that are always present. Only some few among the total emissions register on the photographic emulsion. For example, the geometric efficiency for tritium is

---

* Alternatively, tritium can be added with minimal degradation by means of catalytic exchange methods.

[28] R. B. Painter, R. M. Drew, and W. L. Hughes, *Science* **127**, 1244 (1958).

[29] K. E. Wilzbach, *J. Am. Chem. Soc.* **79**, 1013 (1957).

only 2 to 5% in high-resolution autoradiography with stripping films or painted emulsions.[30]

The β-particle of tritium, having the very weak maximum energy of 18 kev, penetrates only 6 to 7 microns in water, but the average energy of most of the particle (5.7 kev) penetrates only about 1 micron. If such emitting particles are sufficiently concentrated and localized in a tissue section, this low degree of penetration is of obvious advantage for precise determination of the source of radioactivity within a cell, but a sparse and uniform distribution of emitting particles would present a serious drawback to use of tritium.

Carbon-14 labels produce good resolution on autoradiographs. The soft β-particle (0.16 Mev_{max}) is capable of emulsion penetration of 60 microns on the average, and with film preparations of high resolution a geometric efficiency of about 50% can be obtained. It has been estimated that 5×10^5 nonlocalized atoms of C^{14} are necessary to produce an autoradiograph of one cell on stripping film, as contrasted with about 50 atoms of P^{32}.[31]

3. HISTOLOGICAL PREPARATIONS

a. TISSUE FIXATION

Fixed and paraffin-embedded tissues, frozen sections, blood smears, and tissue imprints are all appropriate for autoradiography. Electron microscope sections can also be used for autographs,[32,32a,33] and a combination of autoradiography and fluorescent technique[34] appears to be quite useful in immunology. Nonradioactive normal tissues should be prepared in parallel, as a control for spurious chemophotographic effects of tissue substances on the emulsions.

It is important to avoid extraction and leaching of the labeled substance to be traced in the tissues by the solvents used in fixation, embedding, and clearing. Even in frozen section, microdroplets of water from melting ice may dissolve water-soluble isotope-labeled materials, allowing the knife to smear these irregularly across the section, leading to artifacts or fogged radioautographs.

With careful determination of the factors involved, deliberate extraction of soluble isotope-labeled materials may be desirable if the material under study is bound to tissues.

[30] W. L. Hughes, V. P. Bond, G. Brecher, E. P. Cronkite, R. B. Painter, H. Quastler, and F. G. Sherman, *Proc. Natl. Acad. Sci. U.S.* **44**, 467 (1958).

[31] L. G. Lajtha, and R. Oliver, *Lab. Invest.* **8**, 214 (1959).

[32] L. G. Caro and R. P. van Tubergen, *J. Cell. Biol.* **15**, 173 (1962).

[32a] L. G. Caro, *J. Cell. Biol.* **15**, 189 (1962).

[33] M. M. Salpeter and L. Bachman, *J. Cell Biol.* **22**, 469 (1964).

[34] J. Cairns, *Virology* **11**, 603 (1960).

Fixing by buffered formalin, acetone, or alcohol is satisfactory. Fixatives such as Zenker's, Helly's, and Schaudinn's, however, have been reported to give pseudoautoradiographs.[26] Fixation with cold propylene glycol followed by embedding in Carbowax has shown greater retention of some compounds in tissues compared to other techniques.[35] If leaching of the isotope is not a factor, the tissue may be cleared in water before exposing the tissue to a photographic emulsion.

b. SECTIONING AND MOUNTING

All sections should be cut as thin as practical for increased photographic resolution. Sections 5 to 6 microns thick are satisfactory for high-energy emitters, but sections containing H^3 and C^{14} should be reduced in thickness to the order of 1 micron. Except for tissues containing tritium, improved resolution entails the use of thinner sections and an increased exposure time to register the decreased amount of the labeled substance.

Tissue sections are mounted on chemically clean slides that have been dipped or "subbed" in gelatin solution (gelatin 0.5 gm, chrome alum 0.5 gm, distilled H_2O to 1 liter). These slides are dried by air or by gentle heat from a hair dryer on low speed. Care must be taken that the gelatin-coated slides are not stored longer than several weeks and that they are not exposed to formaldehyde vapor, hardening the gelatin and preventing the emulsion from binding to it. It is suggested that standard 3×1-inch microscope slides be used for all preparations.

As a general rule it is not advisable to prestain tissues before exposure to the radiographic emulsions, since many staining techniques will produce false positive chemophotographic images. Moreover, the assessment of the developed radioautograph by grain counting is quite tedious and imperfect after certain staining procedures, particularly those utilizing most hematoxylins.

c. GENERAL CONTROLS

Control tissues should be prepared in parallel with the tissues under critical study, in order to detect any photochemical effects of normal tissue constituents on the film (particularly from fresh tissues such as kidney sections and leukocyte smears, and also from any fresh material that is contaminated with microorganisms) and to gauge the normal increase in background grain count from cosmic rays accumulated during exposure time. It may be necessary to mount a series of tissues with very thin coatings between the tissue section and the emulsion to serve as barrier to the passage of photochemically active substances in the tissues. Such protective films, however, reduce the penetration of radioemissions—

[35] H. Blank, P. L. McCarthy, and E. D. Delamater, *Stain Technol.* **26,** 193 (1951).

with H³, as much as several hundredfold.[36] Protective barriers can be formed with a variety of materials—for example, a 1% solution of Parlodion in amyl acetate, Perspex (lucite) in chloroform, Formvar in ethyl chloride, or gelatin. Other protective films should always be checked for possible chemophotographic effects.

The required number of replicate slides of every tissue and its control tissue must be planned in advance to allow development at various subsequent dates. Appropriate containers (for example, opaque plastic slide boxes holding 25 slides, sealed with black sealing tape) must be identifiable both at time of loading and at later sampling.

4. APPLICATION OF THE PHOTOGRAPHIC EMULSION

a. General Precautions

There is a wide variety of emulsions obtainable in several forms for different methods. The brief description here of the most frequently encountered techniques may help in selecting an approach, but in general it is wise to compare their suitability in actual practice. Similarly, Table IV may serve as a guide in the choice of emulsion, but several emulsions might be profitably compared for their utility in the experiment at hand.

Careful preparation of the darkroom and its contents is necessary to allow efficient and uninterrupted work. If the darkroom has a fluorescent fixture in it, turn it off ahead of time to avoid afterglow, which may last as long as 30 minutes. So far as possible, it is advisable to work in the dark. Even a safelight recommended for the particular emulsion that has been selected must be used 3 feet or further away with a bulb of 25 watts or less, and only for short periods of time to ensure low background grain counts within the emulsion.

b. Sandwich Technique

A photographic plate may be applied directly over the tissue section, the two glass slides being held tightly together by metal clips or tapes. In this case, "fiduciary marks" must be made on the two slides by scratches or a small dot of radioactive ink in the corner of the slide so that later they may be separated, processed, and realigned exactly for study. This offers the advantage of photographic processing for the film only and allows any stains to be used on the separate tissue section. Further, it is the most simple autoradiographic technique and useful as a pilot method. One disadvantage is that the pressure of holding the slides together may scratch or impress an image in the emulsion. In addition,

[36] J. S. Robertson, V. P. Bond, and E. P. Cronkite, Resolution and image spread in autoradiographs of tritium-labeled cells. *Intern. J. Appl. Radiation Isotopes* **7**, 33 (1959).

TABLE IV
Emulsion Characteristics[a]

Film type[b]	Mean grain diameter (undeveloped) (μ)	Uniformity of grain dispersal	Thickness of emulsion or backing (μ)	Thickness of overcoat (μ)	Sensitivity	Resolution	Application and remarks
Liquid emulsion only							
I K-5	0.18	—	—	—	High	Excellent	Light microscopy.[d]
I L-4	0.12	—	—	—	Very high	Excellent, <1 μ	Electron microscopy.[e]
EK NTE	0.06	—	—	—	Highest	Excellent, <1 μ	Electron microscopy.[e]
Stripping film plates							
EK AR 10	?<0.2	Excellent	5	10	Low, about ½ K-5	Excellent, to 2 μ	Best for autoradiographic and cytologic detail, very slow but best resolution.
EK AR 50	—	Good	12	10	High, about 10× AR 10	Poor, to 15–20 μ	Useful as pilot for AR 10 or G-5 preparations, very grainy.
I G-5	0.32	Excellent	—	—	Moderate	Excellent, to 2–3 μ	Similar to AR 10, but backgrounds have been higher and more rapidly developed.
Autoradiographic plates							
EK no-screen X-ray	1.25	Poor	25	1	Highest for nontrack	Very poor	Useful for determination of minimum quantity or gross localization.
EK medium lantern slide	0.75	Good	—	—	Moderate	Good	Good for histological localization with medium to low concentration.
EK Type A	0.65	Very good	25	1	Moderate to high	Good	Slightly better than above, high contrast of β and α.
Nuclear track plates							
EK NTB3[c]	0.34	Excellent	25, 100	1	Highest	Excellent	Records all charged particles, useful as liquid emulsion.
EK NTB2[c]	0.34	Excellent	10, 25, 100	1	High	Excellent	Records electron tracks up to 0.2 Mev.
EK NTB[c]	0.29	Excellent	10, 25, 100	1	High	Excellent	Records electron tracks up to 30 kev, high-velocity α-particles, protons, deuterons, mesons, and fission fragments.
EK NTA[c]	0.22	Excellent	10, 25, 100	1	High	Excellent	Records low-velocity protons, moderate-energy α-particles, and fission fragments.

[a] A portion of this information was taken from "Kodak Materials for Nuclear Physics and Autoradiography" (Pamphlet No. P-64) with the permission of the Eastman Kodak Company, Rochester, New York.
[b] EK = Eastman Kodak; I = Ilford.
[c] This emulsion also available as gel for dipping, etc.
[d] See Z. Cohn and B. Benson, J. Exptl. Med. 121, 279 (1965).
[e] See L. G. Caro and R. P. van Tubergen, J. Cell Biol. 15, 173, 189 (1962).

the two slides are difficult to align precisely for study and photography. Superimposition of individual photographic negatives from the stained tissues and the developed autograph is frequently the method of choice for examination.

c. STRIPPING FILM

This method, preferred as most uniformly successful by the writer, utilizes gelatin sheets stripped from coated glass slides. In the darkroom, the large stripping film plates ($4\frac{3}{4} \times 6\frac{1}{2}$ inches) are scored with a razor blade longitudinally through the middle of the plate and into eight pieces by three equally spaced horizontal cuts. There is no particular need to discard the peripheral portion unless the film fails to strip easily from the edge of the glass. If the gelatin fails to strip readily, the plate should be discarded.*

As the stripping film is removed from its glass backing, it should be turned so that its emulsion side is down, and be placed gently, floating, on the surface of distilled water in a black-bottomed pan at least 3 to 4 inches in depth. The safelight should be no more than 25 watts and mounted at least 4 feet away, lighting the surface of the water obliquely. As water hydrates the film, the edges and surface become wrinkled. The film should remain about 2 minutes until it is perfectly flat. (It may be necessary to carefully dislodge a bubble or two under the film.) The tissue section, likewise previously hydrated (about 2 minutes), should be submerged under the floating film at about a 30-degree angle. When there is at least a $\frac{1}{4}$-inch overlap on each of three sides of the slide, the slide is raised sideways out of the water. The film will adhere to the slide tightly. It is important that the surface of the water be kept scrupulously clean for the next preparation. The prepared slide is then placed on any rack permitting free circulation of air for drying, for which a small fan or hair dryer proves useful. Moisture remaining in the emulsion will lead to unsatisfactory results. When thoroughly dried, the preparations are placed in alternate slots of a black plastic slide box (25-slide capacity; Clay-Adams). It is recommended that a small gauze or filter paper sack of desiccant be placed inside the box, which is then closed and bound around the closure with black electrical or photographic tape for exposure in the refrigerator. The box should be identified with the date and type of emulsion, number of experiment, etc., written on freezer tape. Prepared

---

* Occasionally the temperature and humidity in some darkrooms will predispose to visible static discharge as the film is stripped from its plate, fogging the emulsion. Other working conditions should be tried. If necessary, the operator may ground himself with copper wire to the plumbing, but strict precautions are needed: all electrical outlets and switches must be out of the operator's reach and be masked. A portable humidifier to produce at least 50% relative humidity has proved successful.

slides should not be stored in the deep-freeze, for ice crystals disrupt the emulsion if the preparations are not completely dried or if condensation develops on the slides. Failure to shield the emulsions, both those unused and those being exposed, from isotopes in the laboratory is a surprising but nonetheless frequent source of error.

d. Liquid Photographic Emulsions

Emulsions of gelatin and AgBr such as nuclear track emulsion can be applied with a No. 6 or 7 camel hair or sable brush, or slides can be dipped directly into emulsions.[37] Total darkness is recommended for both methods, but under such conditions dipping is likely to be more successful. The emulsions are warmed to 40° to 50° in a water bath, and the slides also, to allow as even a coating as possible. The emulsion may be diluted (1 part of 0.05% Duponol "C" to 7 to 8 parts of emulsion) for more uniform flow. The emulsion is gently stirred with a clean glass rod. Even moderate agitation of the melted emulsion may introduce air bubbles. Actual preparation of the autoradiograph should be in complete darkness. Brush strokes should never start or end on the tissue sections.

If the slides are dipped, the slide should be allowed to drain vertically on paper toweling or on gauze pads for a few seconds, and the undersides should be wiped clean. The slides are then placed horizontally on a level rack for 10 to 15 minutes, and the emulsion is allowed to gel. The slides should be stored in lightproof boxes as with the stripping film technique, but with a small container of saturated KNO_2 to maintain the relative humidity at 47%.

In the writer's experience this technique has never been as successful as others primarily because of failure to achieve a uniform thickness of the emulsion over the specimen. In any event, the uneven thickness precludes the use of this method for grain counting. Caro and van Tubergen[32] have minimized the irregularity by casting preformed gelled emulsions. Even with gelatin protective coatings there have been uneven accumulations of emulsion at the periphery of the tissues and frequently within the interspaces of adipose tissues and lungs. The friability of applied emulsion films makes development and staining of the developed emulsion prone to reticulation at temperatures over 19° and simple loss by loosening from the slide. Prestaining with basic fuchsin or metanil yellow is advised in this instance. Development must be carried out under 18° or 19° to avoid reticulation, and all solutions should be of the same temperatures. Extreme gentleness is required in developing, to avoid tearing the emulsions. As soon as the autoradiographs are dried they should be protected with a cover slip or sprayed with one of the acrylic plastics such as Krylon.

[37] B. Messier and C. P. Leblond, *Proc. Soc. Exptl. Biol. Med.* **96**, 7 (1957).

5. EXPOSURE AND PHOTOGRAPHIC PROCESSING

a. EXPOSURE TIME

One of the most critical and vexing problems of radioautography is prediction of the correct exposure time, especially when small amounts of H^3 and C^{14} have been employed. The time for exposure varies with the characteristics of the particular isotope, the manner of preparing the tissue, its thickness, the presence of any barrier film, and the characteristics and thickness of the emulsion. Pelc[38] has suggested formulas that relate the minimal isotope concentrations with exposure times for stripping film and X-ray emulsion images. Most of these and other formulas are based on a uniform distribution of isotope *in vivo*, which is rarely the situation encountered under the experimental conditions. In fact, specific localization is sought, and usually it is the reason for undertaking the autoradiography. Some practical examples will be given. Iodine-131, having a half-life of 8 days, undergoes 75% decay in 15 days; since less than half of the remaining emissions could possibly strike the emulsion, there is little reason to extend the exposure beyond this time. Similarly, exposure times for S^{35} and P^{32} can be based on three-fourths of their half-lives, but generally microcurie amounts give satisfactory autographs in 3 to 7 days. Reference may be made to Boyd[39] in which some sixty examples are cited. With C^{14} and H^3, which exhibit no decay during the time of exposure (that is, within the useful life of the emulsion), exposures can be prolonged but are limited by increasing buildup of background grain counts owing to cosmic radiation.

For C^{14}, 5×10^5 atoms will require about 30 days of exposure; 1 to 20×10^6 atoms will require from 3 to 6 days of exposure for a satisfactory autoradiograph on stripping film. In all smears 6×10^4 atoms of H^3 have to be present to give 10 developed silver grains over a cell when exposed for 25 days with stripping film. Sectioned tissue would require twice this concentration.[31] The specific activity of most available H^3-containing materials is quite high, frequently greater than 1000 $\mu Ci/\mu mole$, so that even small amounts such as 0.1 $\mu Ci/mmole$ will produce satisfactory autographs in 3 to 4 days; but the investigator should appreciate the fact that the radiation dose rate of H^3 is seven times as high as that of C^{14} to achieve the same autographic image. When H^3 is used in living material, the danger of radiation injury to the cell is always present.

[38] S. R. Pelc, *in* "Ciba Foundation Conference on Isotopes in Biochemistry" (G. E. W. Wolstenholme, ed.). Blakiston, Philadelphia, 1951.

[39] G. A. Boyd, "Autoradiography in Biology and Medicine," pp. 124–135. Academic Press, New York, 1955.

While a number of immunological studies utilizing autoradiography have been published in the last several years, they contain little information on the technique used. Two valuable studies employing tritium labels which give complete procedural data are those by Nossal and Mäkelä[40] and Schooley.[41] Both studies employed AR 10 stripping film.

Nossal and Mäkelä used H^3-thymidine in doses of 0.1 to 8.0 μCi/gm of rat in acute 24-hour experiments. Sections of the tissues required 20 to 60 days of exposure, although some were exposed for as long as 130 days. In experiments lasting longer than 24 hours they administered 80 μmoles of H^3-thymidine to minimize reutilization of the tracer. This is an important consideration that is too often overlooked.

Schooley gave 1 μCi of H^3-thymidine and cytidine and 5 μCi of H^3-DL-leucine per gram of mouse. The tissue sections (4 microns) required 30 days for proper exposure.

It is highly useful to set up tissue sections with both fast and slow emulsions. Three or four slides should be set up with a fast emulsion for every slide set up with slow (and more finely resolving) emulsion. The faster, pilot emulsions are developed at various intervals of time such as 1, 2, and 4 weeks, and the time needed to register images allows close estimation of the proper time of exposure on slow emulsions. (See remarks, Table IV.)

b. DEVELOPMENT OF AUTORADIOGRAPH

Development should be carried out in total darkness with time and temperature rigidly controlled. It is convenient to use glass slide staining dishes with glass slide racks to move the slides from solution to solution. Temperature may be maintained by immersing the dishes in large shallow photographic trays with running tap water at 19° to 20°. Specific processing should be performed according to the manufacturer's current guide accompanying the film. Should the stripping film tend to peel away from the slides, a small amount of synthetic mounting medium (for example, Permount, Fisher Scientific Company) on the undersurface of the slide will secure the film through processing.

Slides should be examined for photographic registration before staining. Phase contrast microscopy is recommended at this stage, and grain counting may be performed with high-dry objectives and a reticule in the objective.

c. STAINING

After preliminary examination, staining and mounting should be carried out for histological detail, photography, and preservation. A number of

[40] G. J. V. Nossal and O. Mäkelä, *J. Exptl. Med.* **115**, 209 (1962).
[41] J. C. Schooley, *J. Immunol.* **86**, 331 (1961).

specific stains are noted. Many stains are unsuitable because they penetrate so deeply into the emulsion that they are difficult to differentiate or clear.

i. Neutral Red

For simple contrast with the silver grains and for ease of application, neutral red is the stain of choice. A 1% solution of neutral red in 1% acetic acid applied for 5 minutes and followed by rinsing alternately in distilled water and in 70% alcohol to clear the emulsions has proved to be the simplest method. The water softens the emulsion and permits the alcohol to remove the excess dye.

ii. Ehrlich's Hematoxylin–Eosin Stain

For more extensive histological detail and photography, Ehrlich's hematoxylin–eosin stain is recommended.

1. After development, dry and examine under high-dry objective for silver grains.

2. Soak developed autograph for 30 minutes in water of 18° to 20°, no warmer. All staining dishes are placed in pan in sink and cooled by running water to 18° to 20°.

3. Stain for 1 hour in Ehrlich's hematoxylin* that has been filtered just before use. The standard formula for Ehrlich's hematoxylin is given here, but aging and exposure to air for about a week are needed for best results.

Ehrlich's hematoxylin (acid hematoxylin): 2% hematoxylin in absolute alcohol, 1 volume of water, 1 volume of glycerin, and $\frac{1}{10}$ volume of glacial acetic acid. Add approximately 20 gm of ammonium alum per 50 ml. Stir frequently, and filter before use.

4. Rinse and destain in 0.2% HCl until film is almost transparent and pinkish. Destain each slide by agitating separately. Ten to twenty minutes are required.

5. Wash in running tap water for 30 minutes (slide becomes blue).

6. Stain in eosin for 3 to 5 minutes (1% eosin Y in 20% alcohol, stock solution. Before use, dilute aliquot to 0.25% eosin with distilled water and filter).

7. Destain in running tap water until film is blue and tissue looks pink through film.

8. Dry in air, at least overnight.

9. Mount with Permount and cover slip.

---

* Some hematoxylins are strongly chemophotographic. Harleco, for example, has been found satisfactory in this regard. Bullard's Hematoxylin, on the other hand, should be avoided in autoradiographic studies.

d. PHOTOGRAPHIC RECORDS

Stained slides should be mounted with a synthetic resin rather than balsam, which reduces the developed silver grains. It is best to minimize the stain, particularly the nuclear stains, when photographing autographs for publication. The use of a filter of the same color, or containing the color of the dye, will produce this effect. For example, with tissues stained with neutral red, red or orange filters (Wratten 16, 22, etc.) are used. Several photographs should be taken of each section, varying the focus from the plane of the tissue to that of the silver grains, and the one giving the best detail should be selected. Frequently the best picture is obtained where the focus is set just above the plane that shows the tissue most sharply.

6. EVALUATION OF RADIOAUTOGRAPHS

Gross examination, even by the naked eye, of the specimen may reveal localization of the labeled substance. For low isotope concentrations, however, grain counting under oil immersion with a measured reticule is required. The control-paired nonradioactive preparation is often of great help for background comparison and for alerting to chemophotographic effects. This is particularly inportant when prolonged exposures have been required for low-level emitters or low tissue concentrations. Fresh emulsions having an exposure of a month or two should have a background count of about 1 grain per 1000 square microns. A useful rule is to discard those specimens having more than 1 grain per 50 square microns unless there is unequivocal grain localization over specific histological structures.

Localizing radioactivity to certain specific cells or subcellular structures usually poses no problem when H^3 has been used as the tracer. Its short travel in the emulsion darkens the emulsion immediately above and not more than 1 or 2 microns from the source. Images produced by C^{14} and more especially the β-emitters of higher energy give greater spread of the image from the point of localization. Heavy concentrations localized in a small structure will darken an area considerably larger than the deposit and may even obscure it. Low concentrations of a high-energy emitter may produce a random track or image at some distance from the actual localization. In contrast, α-emissions, having a lower velocity and charge, ionize a considerable path in the emulsion and cause a linear, darker pattern of tracks leading away from the deposit. Understanding of these emission characteristics is important to the interpretation of autoradiographs.

H. Glossary of Symbols, Abbreviations, and Terms

A: The symbol for mass number of an isotope. This is the approximate atomic weight of the isotope and is an integer that indicates the combined number of protons and neutrons in the nucleus of an atom of the isotope, the mass of a proton or a neutron being assumed to equal 1.

Absorption: The process by which radiation imparts some or all of its energy to any material through which it passes. *Self-absorption:* Absorption of radiation emitted by radioactive atoms by the matter in which the atoms are located; in particular, the absorption of radiation within a sample being assayed.

Absorption coefficient: A measure of the rate of decrease in intensity of a beam of photons or particles in its passage through a particular substance. Cause of decrease in intensity is twofold: scattering (reflection in all directions) and absorption (conversion into other forms of energy).

Accelerator of nuclear particles: An apparatus designed to increase the energy of charged particles.

Alpha particle ($\alpha, He^{++}, {}_2He^4$): An elementary particle identified as the nucleus of a helium atom which has lost its two satellite electrons, and is therefore positively charged. Each α-particle consists of two protons and two neutrons. Alpha particles are ejected by certain disintegrating radioactive substances (α-emitters). The velocity, range, energy, and number of α-particles emitted vary according to the emitting substance but are always characteristic of the substance. Their velocities commonly vary between 1.4 and 2.0×10^9 cm./sec, and their energies may be as much as 10.5 Mev, according to the emitting substance. While they are limited in range (up to about 8.6 cm in air), they cause dense ionization in the air along their path. The emission of an α-particle changes the emitting atom into an atom of a different element, reducing its atomic number by 2 and its mass number by 4.

amu: The atomic mass unit is a unit of mass equal to one-sixteenth the mass of oxygen, the latter with a mass number of 16.

$$1 \text{ amu} = 1.657 \times 10^{24} \text{ gm.}$$

In terms of energy,

$$1 \text{ amu} = 931 \text{ Mev} = 1.49 \times 10^{-3} \text{ erg.}$$

Attenuation: The process by which a beam of radiation is reduced in intensity when passing through some material. It is the combination of absorption and scattering processes.

Beta particle (*β-particle*) (*β*, *β⁺*, *β⁻*): An electron (*β⁻*) ejected at high velocity from the nucleus of the atom of a *β*-emitter when one of its neutrons changes into a proton. The inverse process involves the emission of a positively charged electron called the positron (*β⁺*). The energy, velocity, and range of *β*-particles vary widely. One and the same homogeneous radioactive element emits *β*-particles of different energies, velocities, and ranges; the velocity can be very high, up to 99.8% of the speed of light, the energy up to about 3 Mev, and the range is more penetrating than that of *α*-rays but less so than that of *γ*-rays. Their ionizing power, however, is far less than that of the *α*-particle. The mass of the *β*-particle is 0.000548 amu; consequently the emission of a *β*-particle leaves the atomic weight, or mass number, unchanged, but causes the atomic number of the emitting nucleus to increase by 1, since it means the loss of one negative charge—that is, a net increase of the total positive charge by 1.

Carrier-free: A radioisotope is said to be carrier-free if it contains only radioactive atoms of the element.

Curie (Ci): That quantity of a radioactive nuclide disintegrating at the rate of 3.7×10^{10} atoms per second. The following fractions of the curie are in common usage: *Microcurie* (*μ*Ci): One millionth of a curie or 3.7×10^4 disintegrations per second. *Micro-microcurie* (*μμ*Ci), also called a picocurie: One millionth of a microcurie or 3.7×10^{-2} disintegrations per second or 2.22 disintegrations per minute. *Millicurie* (mCi): One thousandth of a curie or 3.7×10^7 disintegrations per second.

Dead time: The time interval of insensitivity in a counter tube and its circuits after the recording of a count.

Electron (*e*, *e⁻*, $_1e^0$, *β⁻*): This is the smallest known particle having a negative charge that is capable of isolation and measurement, and all charges are exact multiples of this "unit of electric charge" which has a magnitude of 4.8025×10^{-10} esu (equal to 1.6023×10^{-20} emu). The electron has an atomic weight of 5.4862×10^{-4} amu, an energy of 0.515 Mev, and a rest mass of about 9.1066×10^{-28} gm; however, its mass increases relativistically with velocity, and therefore *β⁻*-particles, which are electrons emitted by radioactive atoms, and also electrons in high-voltage X-ray tubes, have a mass several times their rest mass. Atoms are composed of a nucleus and a certain number of electrons external to the nucleus. A still useful model of the atom (even though it is oversimplified) envisages the electrons arranged in shells around the nucleus, the individual electrons moving in orbits around the nucleus. The number of these extranuclear orbital electrons equals the number of protons in the nucleus—that is, the atomic number, *Z*, of the element. Disturbances of the electrons close to the nucleus produce X-rays or γ-ray quanta; disturbances of the outer electronic structure produce the optical spectra. Electric currents are produced by mass movements of electrons in electric conductors.

Electron capture: A mode of radioactive decay involving the capture of an orbital electron by its nucleus. Capture from a particular electron shell is designated as K-electron capture, L-electron capture, etc.

Electron volt (ev): The energy received by an electron, or by a particle having the same charge, in falling through a potential difference of 1 volt. One electron volt is equal to 1.60203×10^{12} ergs.

emu: An electromagnetic unit of charge is one of the units used to relate electric and magnetic properties in an absolute system of physical measurement. To define an emu, it is necessary to define first a unit magnetic pole as a pole that, when placed at 1 cm from a like and equal pole, repels with a force of 1 dyne. The unit field (the gauss) is the field at 1 cm from a unit pole. The emu of current is then defined as the current that, flowing in a circular loop, produces 1 gauss of field at the center of the loop for each unit length of the circuit (2 gauss for the loop). The emu of charge is the charge passed through any cross section of a circuit in 1 second when a current of 1 emu is flowing; 1 emu of charge equals 3×10^{10} esu of charge.

esu: An electrostatic unit of charge, a fundamental unit of electricity in the absolute system of physical measurements, is a charge that, when placed at 1 cm from a like and equal charge, repels with a force of 1 dyne.

Fission: The division of a heavy nucleus into two fragments, the process being induced most commonly by the capture of a bombarding neutron. The best-known fissionable elements are uranium, plutonium, protactinium, and thorium. A certain number of neutrons are released with the two fission fragments, and these neutrons can act, under propitious circumstances, as propagators of a fission chain reaction. The fission of the nucleus also liberates considerable amounts of energy, much of this in the kinetic energy of fragments and neutrons, some in the form of neutrinos.

Gamma ray (γ-ray, γ): Electromagnetic radiation of nuclear origin, of very short wavelength, emitted by the nuclei of certain atoms in the course of their radioactive decay. Gamma rays are high-energy photons which may be considered as of wave or of particle nature, depending on experimental conditions. They are quanta of the electromagnetic field, are uncharged, are of zero rest mass, and move at the velocity of light. Their range, both in air and in matter, is much longer than that of either α- or β-particles or rays, but their ionizing capacity is much weaker. In wavelength and penetration power, they occupy an intermediate position between X-rays and cosmic rays. The wavelength of the γ-ray is characteristic of the element emitting it and commonly varies between 0.0466 mμ and 3.9 mμ. Their penetration power is inversely proportional to the density of the substance penetrated and is far higher than that of both α- and β-rays. Although uncharged, they can be detected in a cloud chamber owing to the fact that they impart their energies to dislodged electrons which produce secondary ionization. It is important to note that, while X-rays (and also the photons of visible light) originate in the extra-nuclear structure of the atom, γ-rays are emitted by the atomic nucleus in a state of excitation. The emission of γ-rays usually occurs in close associa-tion with the emission of α- and β-particles. Gamma rays can be a highly dangerous radiation, and because of their long range and high penetration power, the importance of protective measures cannot be overemphasized.

Half-life ($T_{1/2}$): The period of time required for the radioactivity of a substance to drop to one-half its original value—that is, the time it takes for one-half of the atoms of a radioactive substance to disintegrate. The half-life value is a physical constant for each individual isotope and thus far appears to be independent of temperature, pressure, etc.

Ionizing radiation: This term is applied to those radiations or rays of particles that produce wholly visible tracks in the cloud chamber—α-rays, β-rays, protons, nuclei, and electrons. Gamma rays and neutron rays are referred to as *nonionizing radiations*, since they are not detectable in the cloud chamber, except for the tracks of occasional secondary electrons.

Isotope: Isotopes are elements or varieties of the same chemical element, the atoms of which have the same atomic number (the same number of nuclear protons) but different atomic weights or mass numbers (a different number of nuclear neutrons). Since the number of extranuclear electrons (negative charges) must always equal the number of protons (positive charges) in the nucleus, isotopes of the same chemical element have an identical extranuclear electron structure; and since the chemical proper-ties of all elements are determined by the extranuclear electron structure of their atoms, isotopes of the same chemical element have identical chemical properties, and therefore cannot be separated by chemical means. There are many isotopes which for the chemist are varieties of the same element, but can be considered to represent distinct elements for the physicist, due to their different physical properties.

Isotope effect: In spectroscopy, this term is applied to the difference in the position of the lines in the spectra of various isotopes of the same chemical element (also called isotope shift). In chemistry, the term is applied to the effect of the difference in the mass between isotopes of an element on the rate and/or equilibria of chemical transformation. Isotope effects can be observed in such properties as density, rate of diffusion, isotope shift, equilibrium distribution, and rate of reaction; and they are utilized in isotope separation.

Mass spectrometer: A device for the determination of the mass numbers of various isotopes of a given element and their relative abundance in a given sample of material, based on the principle of the dependence of the curvature of the paths of ions in a magnetic field on the masses of the individual particles. A stream of electrically charged atoms (ions) is subjected to the effects of an electric and magnetic field, and those of different masses are brought to a focus at different places. The term is usually restricted to an apparatus so designed that the beam constituents of a given mass-to-charge ratio are focused on an electrode and detected or measured electrically. A similar device, the mass spectrograph, produces a focused mass spectrum of lines on a photographic plate.

Mev: 10^6 electron volts.

Neutron ($_0n^1$, n): One of the fundamental nuclear particles, with mass 1.00894 amu but no electric charge. The nuclei of atoms are considered to consist of neutrons and protons (collectively called nucleons). The number of neutrons in the nucleus is always equal to the mass number minus the atomic number ($N = A - Z$). Capture of free neutrons by atomic nuclei usually leads to the production of a nucleus of a different element or isotope.

Nuclear magnetic resonance (nmr): A form of spectroscopy employing the magnetic properties of nuclei as sensitive probes of their chemical environment. Magnetic properties are always found with nuclei of odd-numbered masses (H^1, C^{13}, N^{15}, and O^{17}) and nuclei of even mass but odd atomic number (H^2, and N^{14}). Nuclei that have both even mass and even atomic numbers (C^{12}, O^{16}, S^{32}), have no magnetic properties and do not give nuclear magnetic resonance signals. In nmr spectroscopy the main matrix of organic molecules produces no spectrum, and the protons show up as spectral peaks giving a clue to their environment and providing excellent landmarks for structure correlation.

Nuclide: A species of atom distinguished by the constitution of its nucleus. To be regarded as a distinct nuclide, the atom must be capable of existing for a measurable time.

Positron (β^+)*:* A particle with mass equal to that of the electron that behaves like a particle of positive charge, hence a positive electron. It is formed in β-decay of many radionuclides.

Proton (p, $_1H^1$)*:* A positively charged elementary particle, with mass about 1847 times the mass of an electron and slightly less than the mass of a neutron—1.00758 amu. The nuclei of atoms are considered to consist of protons and neutrons (collectively called nucleons); the number of the protons in the nucleus always equals the atomic number (Z) of the isotope, and the combined total of all the nucleons is the mass number (A). Since there are as many extranuclear electrons as there are protons in the nucleus of an atom, and since the positive charge of each proton equals numerically the negative charge carried by each individual electron, the atom as a whole is electrically neutral. Protons are strongly ionizing; when accelerated to high velocities or energies they are used as "projectiles" to produce nuclear reactions in the target nuclei at which they are hurled.

Quenching: A phenomenon encountered in liquid scintillation counting which is associated with the sample and solvent and which results in reduction of the average number of light photons emitted per disintegration. Three rather distinct types of quenching occur: (1) *chemical*—in which a molecule absorbs energy that would normally be transferred from the excited solvent molecule to the solute (fluor); (2) *dilution*—as in chemical quenching, solvent excitation is reduced, but in this case, by molecules of a diluent (usually those of the sample, i.e., the solvent for the radioactive substance); and (3) *color*—absorption at a visible wavelength by colored substances in the sample. Unlike chemical and dilution quenching, color quenching occurs as an optical interference with the scintillation process and results in absorption of the photons emitted by the fluors (primary and secondary solutes).

Reactor: An apparatus in which nuclear fission may be sustained in a self-supporting chain reaction. It includes fissionable material (fuel) such as uranium or plutonium, and moderating material, e.g., graphite or beryllium (unless it is a fast reactor), and usually includes a reflector to conserve escaping neutrons, provision for heat removal, and measuring and control elements. There are various classifications for such systems in which the reaction proceeds at a controlled rate—according to fuel arrangement, neutron energy, use, etc.

Roentgen (r): A unit of exposure dose. A quantity of X- or γ-radiation such that the associated ionizing particles produce, in air, ions carrying 1 electrostatic unit (esu) of either sign per 0.001293 gm of air.

Solid angle: An angle made by more than two plane angles meeting in one point, and not lying in the same plane, as the angle of a cube. A solid angle of a cone is measured by the area of the segment cut off by the cone on the surface of the sphere of unit radius, having its center at the vertex of the cone. This geometrical concept is particularly important in the measurement of radioactivity where an increase in the solid angle, Ω, of the sensitive volume of the counter increases counting efficiency. Ω is measured by the ratio of the surface of the portion of the sphere enclosed by the conical surface forming the angle (i.e., the actual counting volume), to the square of the radius of the sphere. It has the following values: $<2\pi$ for a Geiger end window counter, $\sim 2\pi$ for windowless counters of either the Geiger or proportional types and $\sim 4\pi$ for liquid scintillation and internal sample ion chamber counters.

Specific radioactivity: The activity per unit mass of any sample of radioactive material. Specific activity is commonly given in a wide variety of units (millicuries per gram, millicuries per millimole, disintegrations per second per milligram, counts per minute per milligram, etc.).

Stable isotope: A nonradioactive isotope of an element.

Tolerance dose (permissible dose): The amount of radiation that may be received by an individual within a specified period with expectation of no significantly harmful result to himself. It must be emphasized that permissible dose levels are rather arbitrary expressions of the current state of knowledge about the biological effects of radiation exposure. It is good policy to consider any type or amount of radiation as potentially dangerous.

Tracer: The term tracer, without an adjective, is almost universally accepted as meaning a radioactive isotope which can be traced and observed so as to discover the paths, sites, or mechanism of a process under investigation. Radioactive tracer technique consists in adding to a stable element or compound a minute quantity of one of its own radioactive isotopes and subsequently introducing this "labeled" substance into a living organism or into organic or inorganic compounds. The radioisotope used to "label" the substance, being an isotope of the latter, is chemically identical with the rest but can be detected by its characteristic radiation.

Z: The symbol for the atomic number of an element. The atomic number of every element is equal to the total number of positive nuclear charges—that is, to the number of protons contained by the nucleus of its atoms—and also to the total number of the negatively charged extranuclear electrons present in every atom of the element. All atoms of the same element have the same atomic number (the same number of protons in their nuclei, and the same number of extranuclear electrons), but not necessarily the same atomic weight (not necessarily the same number of neutrons in their nuclei). Those atoms of the same element that have different atomic weights are called isotopes of the element in question.

CHAPTER 12

Chemical Analyses

A. Protein Analysis*

1. GENERAL CONSIDERATIONS

a. STANDARDIZATION

Any chemical analysis for the quantitative determination of protein must be considered as a best approximation if it is desired to express data in weight of protein. A weighed amount of a protein preparation will contain a significant amount of moisture, usually increasing with storage, and in many cases a certain quantity of ash will be present. Some commercial preparations of crystalline serum albumin have been found to contain as much as 9% moisture. Ash is typically low, usually less than 0.5%. Fraction II γ-globulins, however, may contain as much as 4% ash. The moisture content of a powder may be appreciably increased on removal from cold storage if the container is opened at room temperature before the material has been allowed to warm. For example, a 15-year-old preparation of human fraction II was found to contain 12.6% moisture. It is good practice, accordingly, to keep storage bottles in plastic bags or evacuated desiccators, preferably with some silica gel or calcium sulfate (Drierite).

Moisture and ash analyses are not difficult, but they are exacting and time-consuming. Consequently, many laboratories prepare standard calibration curves for dry, ash-corrected weights of proteins, using chemical analyses. Once such curves are obtained for a given protein, the graphs permit rapid determination of protein concentrations of prepared solutions. Calibration curves for many chemical assays depart from linearity in the higher levels of their useful ranges. For critical work assays in the linear range are advised.

If a protein is not pure or if the investigation concerns the assay of total generic protein in crude biological fluids or extracts, moisture and ash corrections on dried preparation have little meaning. Especial concern is needed with mixed proteins if assays such as the biuret and Folin-

* Section 12,A was contributed by Merrill W. Chase and Curtis A. Williams.

Ciocalteu reaction or ultraviolet absorbancy are employed. The behavior of individual proteins varies considerably in these assays—usually by less than 20% with biuret, but often by 100% or more with Folin reagent. In the case of absorbancy at 278 to 280 mμ, variability is even more striking; for example, a 1% solution of human serum albumin in a 1-cm path may show absorbancy of about 5.3, and γG-immunoglobulin gives about 15 units. (See Appendix I for selected data on ultraviolet extinction by proteins.) Since the content of tyrosine and tryptophan is largely responsible for the activity of a protein in ultraviolet extinction and in Folin-Ciocalteu tests, these tests show wide variations among common protein types and significant variations even among protein homologs from different species. For example, 1% bovine serum albumin gives an absorbancy of 6.3 to 6.5 at 280 mμ. More recently the Folin reagent has been used with alkaline-copper solution (See Section 7), thereby including a measurement of peptide bonds as in the biuret test. This reduces the variability due to relative content of specific amino acids.

The nitrogen content most consistently represents the amount of protein present in a sample when ammonium sulfate, azide, and other such chemicals are known to be absent; hence nitrogen determinations are routinely used as standard reference for protein analysis. Nearly all proteins of immunological interest contain between 15.5 and 16.5 (w/w) Kjeldahl nitrogen, with the majority yielding close to 16%. For purified proteins, standard curves can be prepared in terms of nitrogen by several methods, each dilution of the sample being assayed for nitrogen and also evaluated by other methods. Determinations of the nitrogen content of a protein corrected to a dry, ash-corrected weight basis permits estimation of protein concentrations by any assay from a standard calibration curve.

b. Analysis of Protein in Crude Biological Mixtures

Meaningful estimation of protein in tissue extracts, culture media, or biological fluids by any method depends on the removal from the sample of reactive materials not associated with protein. These would include free amino acids and small peptides, nucleotides and nucleic acids, amino sugars and other amines, and certain other soluble substances, depending on the assay to be employed. For example, any significant concentration of reducing sugars (often employed in tissue extractions and culture media) excludes the use of biuret reagent because of its cupric ion.

Since protein is precipitated by 5 to 10% trichloroacetic acid (TCA) or 0.25 to 0.5M perchloric acid (PCA), these reagents are frequently employed to separate the protein from interfering small molecules. Nucleoproteins, nucleic acids, and protein-bound polysaccharides are also precipitated, but they are hydrolyzed by heating the mixture to a temperature above 90°. Protein remains precipitated and is washed with fresh TCA. Nucleic acids are particularly troublesome in assays by direct absorbancy of ultraviolet light, and in some cases (notably in extracts of certain microorganisms) they are completely hydrolyzed only after prolonged heating. It is important to continue heating until there is no further release of material absorbing maximally at 260 mμ into the digestion supernatant. The protein precipitate can be dissolved in acid or alkali, but if alkali is employed (for example, 0.1 N NaOH), the absorption maximum usually shifts to a higher wavelength (Chap. 10,A,5,b).

If chemical analyses are to be performed on the supernatant, PCA is often employed. Perchlorate can be reduced to about 0.05 M at 0° by adding an equivalent amount of KOH and removing the precipitate.

It is useful at times to precipitate peptides which remain soluble in TCA and PCA. Phosphotungstic acid is used for this purpose; indeed the smaller proteins of plant pollens are commonly measured as "phosphotungstic acid-precipitable nitrogen" in standardizing allergenic extracts.*

Proteins may also be separated for assay by salting-out procedures. Protein-associated nucleic acids and polysaccharides will be precipitated in addition. Depending on the assay method final dialysis may be required. If dialysis presents a special problem, salt and low molecular weight peptides, amino acids, and other such contaminants can be removed by proper application of gel filtration (See Chapter 9). Salting-out procedures are highly useful in securing bulk preparative yields prior to purification procedures. As in all techniques, certain tissue and microbial proteins may be rendered insoluble, particularly if salting out is carried out at low pH.

The most versatile precipitant is ammonium sulfate:† serum globulins

---

* Two solutions, 0.5% and 10%, are prepared in 10% hydrochloric acid and stored in doubly glass-stoppered "ether" bottles: (a) Dissolve 2.5 grams of phosphotungstic acid in 100 ml of distilled water; add 112 ml of 38% hydrochloric acid (d 1.18) and dilute with distilled water to 500 ml. (b) Dissolve 25.0 grams of phosphotungstic acid in distilled water (100 ml), add 56 ml of concentrated hydrochloric acid and dilute with distilled water to 250 ml.

Acidify the solution with one-tenth its volume of concentrated hydrochloric acid and add one-quarter volume of the 10% phosphotungstic reagent. Collect the precipitate after 30 minutes and check completeness of precipitation. Wash twice with the 0.5% phosphotungstic reagent. Dissolve the washed precipitate with NaOH.

† Saturated ammonium sulfate solution is conveniently stored at room temperature (4.1 M) and at 0° (3.75 M). At 25°, 767 gm of dry ammonium sulfate dissolve in 1 liter of H$_2$O to yield a volume of ca. 1.4 liters. Heat the water, dissolve the salt plus 5% excess, and allow to cool. Filter, add to the bottle a layer of well-formed clean crystals, lightly vaseline the neck of the bottle, and close with a Teflon stopper. The pH is acidic, ca. 5.5.

Proteins should be brought to a concentration of ca. 2% (as, serum diluted with

are precipitated at "one-half saturation" (one volume plus one volume of saturated ammonium sulfate solution, 25°) and serum albumin is precipitated by "three-quarters saturation" (addition of 17–20 gm of solid ammonium sulfate per 100 ml of half-saturated filtrate). Complete removal is mandatory prior to determination of protein nitrogen. The presence of sulfate in dialysate or chromatographic effluent can be determined by adding a drop of 1% barium acetate and two drops of N HCl per milliliter.

Sodium sulfate is less versatile than ammonium sulfate as precipitant because its solubility limits the classes of proteins that precipitate, but its solutions are neutral.* When it is used to precipitate serum globulins, Kjeldahl nitrogen values can be determined directly on both precipitate and supernatant. Total globulins are precipitated at 37° by 21.5% Na_2SO_4, with subclasses precipitable by 14.8% and 17.7% solutions.[1]

c. Choice of Method

The choice of methods for protein assay will depend on several factors. In addition to the general considerations already mentioned, other notes are presented briefly.

i. Sensitivity

The amount of material available for an assay will determine the sensitivity required of the method. The most sensitive modifications of the general methods will be indicated in the following sections along with

---

an equal volume of water), saturated salt solution added to the extent desired, and several hours allowed for precipitation. For concentrations greater than "two thirds saturation," add solid ammonium sulfate. Tables for the addition of solid $(NH_4)_2SO_4$ are given by M. Kunitz, *J. Gen. Physiol.* **35**, 423 (1952); R. W. McGilvery *in* "Manometric Techniques," 3rd ed. (W. W. Umbreit, R. H. Burris and J. F. Stauffer, eds.) pp. 306 and 307, Burgess, Minneapolis, 1957; and by A. A. Green and W. L. Hughes *in* "Methods in Enzymology," (S. P. Colowick and N. O. Kaplan, eds.) Vol. I, pp. 72–78, Academic Press, New York (1955). The pH of the ammonium sulfate-protein mixture can be adjusted by adding NH_4OH; above pH 7, the container should be kept sealed to avoid pH shift by loss of ammonia.

* Anhydrous sodium sulfate dissolves in water to form a decahydrate but abruptly becomes anhydrous at 33° where it is most soluble, 100 ml water dissolving 50 gm. It is usual to work at 37°, sodium sulfate solution being mixed with the warmed protein solution. One or more hours at 37° is allowed for precipitation, and precipitate is separated at 33–37°. It is customary to add, for example, about 10 volumes of sodium sulfate concentration; for 10 volumes, the salt is dissolved to 110% of the desired final concentration. Globulins have been removed from serum at 30° by dissolving anhydrous Na_2SO_4 directly, 20 gm per 100 ml [R. A. Kekwick, *Biochem. J.,* **32**, 552 (1938)].

[1] P. E. Howe, *J. Biol. Chem.* **49**, 93, 109, 1921.

their useful ranges. The Folin-Ciocalteu, ninhydrin, and Nessler are the most sensitive methods, roughly in that order. Biuret and semimicro-Kjeldahl assays are significantly less sensitive but have the advantage of being precise and applicable to concentrated solutions. There is no special virtue to great sensitivity except as required for use with solutions of very low concentrations, or to conserve material; the normal range of dilution errors is, of course, multiplied. Unless there are compelling reasons, it is never recommended to dilute concentrated solutions or to employ micropipets (or microbalances) merely to work in the range of the more sensitive methods.

ii. Precision

Reproducibility of assays is largely a function of the care employed by the investigator. Some of the other factors that affect precision, and instances in which special care or decision is important, might include the size or volumes of samples or reagents to be weighed or pipetted, the number of independent operations, the number of pieces of apparatus to clean and monitor, the stability of reagents and standards, and the nature of possible contaminants in samples, diluents, and reagents (one of the commonest sources of error in all assays is microbial contamination, yet few take care to control this by a simple culture method—one capillary drop spread over a nutrient agar slant, incubation at 20° for 2 days). Certain reagents have limited shelf-life; others must be prepared fresh each time; and still others that are obtained commercially may vary from lot to lot. It is always good practice to employ a known standard solution in each series of assays as a control of technique.

iii. Speed and Simplicity of Assay

The most rapid and the least complicated method should be chosen, but the choice must be weighed against other considerations. For example, ultraviolet absorbancy is the most rapid and the simplest of all assays that depend on the chemical nature of the protein, but it is also the most susceptible to errors due to contamination with nonprotein material, to preparative methods, and to adsorption of proteins on cuvette surfaces. It may also be remarked that many readings are taken at only one wavelength, whereas demonstration of a *maximum* (λ_{max}) at the chosen wavelength should be checked in each series of unknowns. With proteins of cellular origin, the 260/280 ratio should be determined as a presumptive test for nucleic acids. Turbidity is an important consideration in all spectrophotometric assays, but it is of particular significance at shorter wavelengths, since its effect varies inversely as the fourth power of the wavelength (see Chap. 10,A,4; 10,B,2; and 10,B,4).

iv. State of Sample

Solutions are easily transferred with accuracy and precision by the use of pipets standardized "to deliver." The quantitative transfer of precipitate to reaction vessels requires extreme care, and when samples are numerous, as is often the case with specific immune precipitates, this procedure can be quite laborious. Recommendations for methods of dealing with immune precipitates are given in Chap. 13, Vol. III.

The reader is referred to "Kabat and Mayer's Experimental Immunochemistry"[2] for bibliography and discussion of applications of various analytical methods concerned with the estimation of proteins. Other general approaches are discussed in Vol. 13 of "Methods in Biochemical Analysis".[3]

2. DETERMINATION OF MOISTURE AND ASH CONTENT

a. Volatile Weight (Moisture)

Drying is achieved by holding the sample in vacuum over a desiccant, such as phosphorus pentoxide (P_2O_5), calcium sulfate (Drierite), silica gel, or other agent. The attainment of constant weight must be demonstrated, not assumed. When it is desired to dry and subsequently to use the same specimen for immunological procedures or immunochemical analysis, drying is conducted at room temperature or at a somewhat elevated temperature, say 45°, in a vacuum oven. In practice, moisture and ash are often determined on a single side portion, which is sacrificed. Very efficient drying occurs over desiccant at 100° or *in vacuo* at 63° (b.p. methanol), and 3 to 4 hours may suffice. The dried sample is then subjected to ashing.

Since the moisture of dry powders will fluctuate with the humidity of the air, a moisture determination is considered valid only for the particular time at which it is performed. Its purpose, therefore, along with determination of ash, is to permit standardization of the protein on the basis of some parameter (for example, nitrogen) other than sample weight.

Another important point is that "dry weight" is an *operational concept*. The hydration properties of proteins may vary considerably, depending on their structure, their dry state, and the methods employed in their preparation. Water (and other solvents) may be present free (absorbed) or bound (hydration). If analysis concerns a crystalline protein, water or

[2] E. A. Kabat, "Kabat and Mayer's Experimental Immunochemistry," 2nd ed., Chaps. 13, 26, 27, 28. Thomas, Springfield, Illinois, 1961.
[3] S. Jacobs, *in* "Methods of Biochemical Analysis" (D. Glick, ed.), Vol. 13, pp. 241–265. Wiley Interscience, New York, 1965.

solvent of crystallization will usually be removed on heating if there is reversion from the crystalline to the amorphous state. Without heating, however, it is likely that only absorbed solvent will be lost, irrespective of the physical state of the material. Consequently, one should speak only of weight loss under defined drying conditions, and one should not consider the material moisture-free, or to have lost only water if organic solvents were used in its preparation.

After drying under high vacuum at 100°, the protein residue should be used *only* for ash determination. Variable amounts of amido nitrogen may be lost in the procedure, and while this may not amount to more than a few tenths percent of the starting weight, the error in nitrogen determinations on such material would be significantly greater. The amounts of material required for determining moisture and ash depend on the method to be used. A microanalyst can secure wholly reliable figures from the use of 5 to 10 mg of starting solid with ash as little as 1.5%. If microbalances are not available, amounts of 25 mg or more are needed. An excellent apparatus for drying many types of compounds is the Abderhalden drying pistol (Kimble Glass Company, Vineland, New Jersey).[4] Its particular advantage is that the drying temperatures may be selected and accurately controlled at the boiling point of an appropriate solvent, the vapor being used to heat the drying chamber. P_2O_5 is the recommended desiccant. The apparatus is attached to a high vacuum pump, although for some tasks a house vacuum can be used. Care must be given to placement of this equipment in the laboratory in order to exclude vapors and fire hazards.

In general, volatile weight loss is best determined by drying to constant weight at 100° *in vacuo* over desiccant. In an Abderhalden apparatus with high vacuum (0.2 mm of mercury) drying may be complete in 3 hours at 100°.

b. Ash

Volatilization of the organic substance of proteins is readily achieved at 700°. Basically, the ash value is a correction factor for metals and non-volatile salts which may be present in the sample.

There are several commercially available combustion ovens or muffles which are adaptable to a wide variety of uses. If the primary use of such apparatus is to be microanalysis, however, a simple micromuffle can be purchased or constructed[4a] from standard combustion glass tubing. Heat

[4] A. Steyermark, "Quantitative Organic Microanalysis," 2nd ed., pp. 88–90. Academic Press, New York, 1961.
[4a] A. Steyermark, "Quantitative Organic Microanalysis," 2nd ed., pp. 134–136. Academic Press, New York, 1961.

may be applied through Nichrome windings and regulated by a rheostat, or by the simple application of a Meker burner.

The Pregl-type muffle is basically an L-shaped tube with one leg horizontal, into which the sample container is inserted, and the other leg directed downward, which is heated to create a chimney effect and a flow of air over the sample. The air is superheated before passing over the sample by the application of another burner under the horizontal leg of the tube. Combustion, therefore, is effected by a flow of dry heated air passing over the sample container. Ten minutes at 700° to 750° is sufficient to ash most samples in a micromuffle of this type.

Generally no other treatment is required for ashing. If the ash has a charred appearance, however, or if it is known that certain metals are present, then it may be advisable to add one or two drops of concentrated H_2SO_4. The ash is then reported as sulfates. If the metals are known along with their relative proportions, a correction can be made for the added sulfate and the true ash content determined.

Lightweight, platinum combustion boats (micro-Pregl), 39 mm long, equipped with platinum cylinder sleeves (Coombs-Albers platinum cylinder), are best suited as sample holders and will contain from 5 to 25 mg of protein. Drying for volatile weight determination may be performed in the same platinum boat in the Abderhalden drying pistol, and the ashing process carried out subsequently. Boats and sleeves are cleaned in hot dilute nitric acid, rinsed with distilled water, burned in a gas flame, and stored in a desiccator.

c. CALCULATIONS

After drying, the volatile fraction, v, of the sample weight, w is obtained from

$$v = \text{Weight loss}/w \tag{1}$$

After combustion of the dry sample, w_d, the ash fraction, a, is calculated:

$$a = \text{Residue weight}/w_d \tag{2}$$

The dry, ash-corrected sample weight, w_c, can be determined from w, v, and a by $w_c = w - vw - a(w - vw)$ which rationalizes to

$$w_c = w(1 - v)(1 - a) \tag{3}$$

In eqs. (1) and (2), v and a are usually multiplied by 100 and expressed as percent if they are employed as individual data. If percent ash is to be referred to the original sample weight, w must be employed in Eq (2), rather than w_d.

3. DETERMINATION OF NITROGEN BY
THE KJELDAHL METHOD

a. GENERAL CONSIDERATIONS

The digestion of nitrogenous material with quantitative recovery of nitrogen in the form of ammonium sulfate was introduced by Kjeldahl. Measurement of the ammonia after its liberation within a closed system by excess NaOH was greatly simplified when boric acid was introduced[5] in 1934 for trapping the ammonia. This permitted HCl to be used for titrating ammonia directly from ammonium borate in the form of NH_4Cl. Alternatively, potassium acid iodate can be employed as described below under Section f.

For the chemist, the varieties in organic nitrogen pose problems in choice of catalyst ($CuSO_4$, selenium oxide, mercury oxide or mercuric acetate, zinc dust, etc.) and in decision to reduce nitro groups before undertaking digestion, for assuring quantitative recovery of structural nitrogen. For the immunochemist, the determination of protein nitrogen is often the principal goal; standardized conditions are given by Kabat.[6] When the problem at hand offers more complexity, conditions require careful re-examination. An excellent discussion is given in "Kabat and Mayer's Experimental Immunochemistry."[6]

Quantitative recovery requires elevation of the boiling point of sulfuric acid to about 360° by adding a proper amount of K_2SO_4, but to no higher than about 400°, lest ammonia be lost.

Kjeldahl determinations are usually run at the semimicro level (250 to 800 μg of nitrogen, or in practice a range of 2 to 5 mg of protein per digestion) or at the micro level (10 to 100 μg of nitrogen), although specialized methods are available for lesser amounts.[6]

Sizes of stills, digestion racks, digestion flasks, and burets differ in the semimicro and the micro techniques; therefore a double set of equipment will be needed if both techniques are to be run.

While the semimicro method is apt to give more uniform results, owing to its relatively larger readings of sample versus reagent blanks, the required sample sizes can be costly. In the following discussion the micro method will be described in detail, in the belief that most workers will find the required sample sizes to be more suitable for routine work. It is not difficult to adapt to the larger apparatus; apart from scaled-up quantities, the chief difference is immersion of the condenser tip under fluid in

[5] A. Eisner and E. C. Wagner, *Ind. Eng. Chem. Anal. Ed.* **6**, 473 (1934).
[6] E. A. Kabat, "Kabat and Mayer's Experimental Immunochemistry," 2nd ed., Chap. 13. Thomas, Springfield, Illinois, 1961.

the receiving flask, for which purpose the volume of indicator mixture is increased initially by adding 1 volume of carbonate-free water. A mercury-type buret of 10-ml capacity is suitable for determinations in the range of 250 to 800 μg of nitrogen.

b. EQUIPMENT AND REAGENTS FOR MICRO METHOD
     (10 TO 100 μG OF NITROGEN)

i. Kjeldahl Distillation Apparatus, Markham (Fig. 1)*

In the author's (M.W.C.) laboratory, the narrow side arm of the usual 2-liter distillation flask is replaced by a wide-bore Pyrex tube, 160 × 13 mm o.d., elevated to an angle of 15 degrees, extended within the flask with mouth turned downward. This device serves as an efficient return for water condensing along the steam pathway. The water in the boiler is acidified with 2 ml of concentrated H_2SO_4. Boiling stones (Hengar granules, plain) are added.

ii. Digestion Rack

Positive and fast control of the boiling rate in individual flasks is best achieved by using individually controlled gas burners, not electric heat. Such a rack is supplied by Microchemical Specialties Company, Berkeley, California, No. 4700 (six-place) or No. 4710 (twelve-place), micro-Kjeldahl model with transite plates for digestion flasks of 10-ml capacity.

iii. Kjeldahl Flasks*

Pyrex 10-ml micro-Kjeldahl flasks are used, with 6½ inch neck and a lip for pouring.

iv. Receiving Flasks

Extraction flasks (50-ml size, Corning No. 5160) serve as convenient receptacles to receive distillate for titration. Alternatively, micro-Fernbach flasks, 50 ml, such as Kimble No. 26502, can be used. These should be marked at the 35-ml level.*

---

* Apparatus is supplied with the specifications of E. A. Kabat ("Kabat and Mayer's Experimental Immunochemistry," 2nd ed., Chap. 13. Thomas, Springfield, Illinois, 1961) by Mr. Frederick F. Anderson, 239 Greenwood Avenue, Madison, New Jersey, who also supplies the 10-ml size Pyrex micro-Kjeldahl flasks. Permanent markings can be applied easily with an S. S. White dental abrasive point No. 5 mounted in a hand-held tool such as Moto-tool No. 1, Dremel Manufacturing Co., Racine, Wisconsin.

v. Microburet

A convenient instrument is the Manostat mercury-type direct-reading Digi-pet 1.0-ml buret (Manostat Corporation, New York, New York). For proper stability, a plate of lead or iron should be bolted inside the front panel. Readings are made to the fourth decimal. The counter can be reset to zero at any position of travel of the screw through the mercury chamber. Calibration is made as usual, by weighing mercury discharged between chosen numbers on the dial; final hanging droplets of mercury

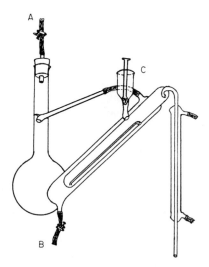

FIG. 1. Micro-Kjeldahl apparatus according to Markham. The modified 2-liter distilling flask that serves as boiler is described in the text; it is supported over a Fisher high-temperature gas burner. Short lengths of heat-resistant rubber tubing (A. H. Thomas Co., No. 8836, ¼-inch bore × 5⁄64-inch wall) are attached as shown and steamed out thoroughly. Operation of clamps at *A* and *B* and of the ground-glass plunger in cup *C* is described in the text. Dimensions of the still are: outer jacket 31 cm, diameter 6 cm; inner jacket diameter 4 cm, containing a siphon tube 19 × 8 mm; condenser 40 cm; condenser tube diameter, 11 mm.

are cut with a razor blade. The weight of mercury is divided by its density (13.546) to obtain aqueous equivalents.

vi. Nitrogen Bubbler

Nitrogen bubbles serve to stir the titration flasks during titration. The tank gas is passed into the bottom of a 16-ounce wide-mouth bottle two-thirds filled with saturated boric acid to remove any ammonia. Nitrogen washed by the boric acid is led through a long-tipped capillary pipet, clamped parallel to and extending slightly below the delivery tip of the Manostat buret. The receiving flasks are raised into position during the titration so that nitrogen bubbles arise in the bottom of the flask. The flow rate, set by a needle valve on the tank, is just sufficient to cause mixing.

vii. Sulfuric Acid–CuSO₄ Reagent

To 1 pound of analytical reagent H_2SO_4 designated as "low nitrogen," add 4.5 ml of saturated aqueous $CuSO_4$ slowly in portions, and blend well. (Saturated $CuSO_4$ is prepared from 19 gm of finely divided $CuSO_4 \cdot 5H_2O$ + 50 ml of hot distilled water.) Let stand for several days until excess anhydrous $CuSO_4$ crystallizes out and settles. The supernatant solution is withdrawn as needed.

viii. Potassium Sulfate

Potassium sulfate of analytical reagent quality, low in nitrogen, is added to raise the boiling point of the reaction mixture to about 350° to 400°. The proper ratio is 0.25 gm per 0.5 ml of concentrated H_2SO_4.

ix. Concentrated NaOH Solution

Commercially available saturated (50%) NaOH solution is available in plastic bottles. The container of concentrate must be kept well stoppered *at all times* to avoid formation of carbonate. The solution is best handled by pouring portions of about 25 ml into culture tubes, closed by a rubber stopper, withdrawals being made by means of a coarse-bored capillary tube fitted to a 5-ml all-glass syringe.*

x. Standardized HCl

Constant-boiling HCl is held in a doubly glass-stoppered "ether bottle." Direct weighings of this product, which is not very volatile, are made and diluted in volumetric flasks. To prepare constant-boiling HCl, equal parts (500 ml) of high-grade HCl and water are distilled, the desired distillate being the secondary fraction (approximately 650 ml) collected between 0.75 volume and a residual, discarded portion of 60 to 80 ml.[7] The barometric pressure on the day of distillation, which determines the acidity, should be recorded.

HCl ($N/70$) made up *exactly* permits simple calculations, since nitrogen (mg) = 0.2 × ml $N/70$ HCl. For 1 liter of $N/70$ HCl, weigh and dilute

---

* The Pyrex model of the Baketel glass adapter No. 421B (Becton, Dickinson and Company, Rutherford, New Jersey) which fits Luer-type syringes can be drawn out to give a capillary of suitable length.

[7] W. D. Bonner and B. F. Branting, *J. Am. Chem. Soc.* **48**, 3093 (1926); cf. W. D. Bonner and R. E. Wallace, *ibid.* **52**, 1747 (1930).

to volume as follows: 2.565 gm of constant-boiling acid distilled at 730 mm, 2.568 gm at 740 mm, 2.571 gm at 750 mm, 2.574 gm at 760 mm, and 2.577 gm at 770 mm.

xi. Indicator Dyes

(a) Methyl red is twice recrystallized from 95% alcohol. A saturated solution in 95% alcohol is prepared (500 mg per 130 ml of alcohol, equilibrate, filter). (b) Methylene blue, 1% aqueous solution. (c) The combined indicator is prepared by mixing these stocks in the proportion of 125 ml of methyl red solution to 15 ml of methylene blue solution. On the day of titration, add 0.1 ml of combined indicator (c) to 30 ml of saturated boric acid. Place 2.1 ml of boric acid indicator mixture (for 35 ml of distillate) in the receiving flasks just before distilling the samples, and cap with Parafilm. A commercially available indicator, methyl purple indicator solution (Fleischer Chemical Corp., Washington, D.C.), can be employed alternatively.

xii. Ammonium Sulfate Nitrogen Standard

Dry to constant weight a product such as Fisher's certified primary standard No. A-938. It is kept in a desiccator. Weigh out 140.83 mg, and dissolve with distilled water to 500 ml, including 0.7 ml of concentrated H_2SO_4 as preservative (60 μg of nitrogen per milliliter).

xiii. Protein Standard Solution

Nitrogen-standardized crystalline bovine albumin (about 10 mg of protein nitrogen per milliliter) is available from the Armour Laboratories in 3-ml portions. The precise value is supplied with each vial of Protein Standard Solution.

c. DIGESTION

Step 1. Introduce samples in duplicate into the special 10-ml Pyrex digestion flasks: (i) Unknowns to contain 10 to 100 μg of nitrogen. (ii) Reagents only, and same solvent and volume as were used for unknowns. (iii) Ammonium sulfate (60 μg of nitrogen) plus reagents. (iv) Protein of known nitrogen value to check digestion. Antigen–antibody precipitates, washed, are suspended in a few drops of water and dissolved by adding 1 drop of 0.5 N NaOH. When completely dissolved, quantitative transfer is made to Kjeldahl flasks (Chap. 13, Vol. III). With rinsings, volumes should not exceed 3 ml.

Step 2. Add to each flask: 1 boiling stone (Hengar granules, plain); about ¼ gm of K_2SO_4 by porcelain spatula; 0.5 ml of concentrated H_2SO_4 saturated with $CuSO_4$.

Step 3. Digest over gas flame at 45-degree angle in a micro-Kjeldahl digestion apparatus connected to a water pump in a chemical hood. Use medium flame to bring to gentle continuous boil, and *keep boiling.* Increase flame as possible. Watch continuously during early stages of digestion. (If foam appears, boil as gently as possible! Octyl alcohol may be added sparingly if foaming persists.)

Step 4. After water boils off, SO_3 fumes appear. Continue until char disappears and solution becomes colorless. (Inspect neck of flask for remaining char. If char is present, cool, wash down, reheat with constant shaking, *not* in digestion stand, to boiling point.) Continue boiling for 30 minutes after solution is clear and colorless. Time for steps 3 and 4 is 2 to $2\frac{1}{2}$ hours.

Step 5. Cool to room temperature. Add about 2.5 ml of carbonate-free water. Cap tightly with prestretched Parafilm until distillation can be undertaken.

d. Distillation

Step 1. Boil 1 liter of distilled water, and let cool. A calcium chloride tube with soda lime is used to protect the water from uptake of CO_2. Use carbonate-free rinse water in two plastic wash bottles, one used for rinsings at inlet C (Fig. 1) the other reserved for rinsing the distilling tip only.

Step 2. Steam out apparatus for 5 minutes with hosecocks A (top) and B (rinse) closed. Place several Hengar granules (plain) and 2 ml of H_2SO_4 in boiler. Remove flame to create a partial vacuum, sucking contents of inner distilling flask into the outer steam jacket. Introduce several rinses of distilled water through C by back suction (avoiding loss of vacuum); finally, drain off the rinsings.

Step 3. Ascertain "distillation blank" value on NaOH and water. (*i*) Open A and B, and position burner below boiler. (*ii*) Run 3 ml of saturated NaOH from all-glass apparatus into C and run it past C, avoiding emergence of steam. Add, in portions, about 20 ml of water similarly to clean NaOH from C. (*iii*) Distill the same volume portion(s) that are planned for step 5 below, into the same type of container. For 35-ml portions, use 2.1 ml of dilute indicator mixture (made freshly for the day by adding 0.1 ml of indicator mixture to 30 ml of saturated boric acid). Do not immerse condenser tip into distillate: ammonia is so dilute that gaseous loss does not occur.[8] Distillation takes 4 minutes for 35 ml. (*iv*) Wash tip of condenser into distillate with water from plastic wash bottle reserved for this purpose. (*v*) Clean apparatus as in step 2 above by removing flame. Rinse repeatedly, and finally drain rinsings. (*vi*) Cap "distillation blank" firmly with Parafilm. It will be titrated subsequently

[8] R. Markham, *Biochem. J.* **36**, 790 (1942).

(the amount of titrant measures cleanliness of saturated boric acid, ammonia in room air, etc.). Its adjusted color will be used as the reference standard in titrating unknown samples. The atmosphere of the distillation area must be as nitrogen-free as possible. Nitric acid and NH_4OH bottles must be kept in distant chemical hoods; smoking of tobacco can not be permitted.

Step 4. Have A and B opened and flame set at side of boiler to prevent its cooling. Proceed with step 5.

Step 5. Distillation of actual sample: (*i*) Place another receiving flask with 2.1 ml of indicator mixture per 35 ml of total distillate. Meanwhile keep apparatus on verge of boiling (see step 4 above). (*ii*) Remove plunger at C, and fix it in a clamp. Transfer quantitatively through C a diluted, digested sample warmed to about 55° with rinses of carbonate-free water from plastic wash bottle. (Grease outer rim of pouring spout of digestion flask very lightly with Lubriseal to assist in quantitative transfer.) Insert plunger C. (*iii*) Run 3 ml of saturated NaOH from a pipet through C by lifting plunger slightly without admitting air, as in step 3(*ii*), followed by several portions of water. (*iv*) Close pinch-clamps A and B. Start distillation, repeating steps 3(*iii*) and 3(*iv*). After a few milliliters have been distilled, mix indicator solution. (*v*) Wash tip of condenser into distillate, using specially reserved plastic wash bottle. (*iv*) Clean apparatus as in step 2.

e. TITRATION

The Manostat 1.0-ml buret is kept filled with mercury; either the tip is kept immersed in mercury, the tip passing through a suitable closure that prevents mercury vapor from entering the laboratory air, or it is closed with a narrow "rubber policeman." Just prior to titration, about 0.9 ml of mercury is discharged, and $N/70$ HCl is drawn up slowly until the Monostat is again filled. (Avoid trapping air bubbles in the capillary bore.) The tip of the nitrogen bubbler is clamped firmly into position, as described, and at once the tips of the microburet and the bubbler are immersed under the surface of the distillate, by raising the receiver flask on a support placed on the table of the Manostat. The support should afford space not only for the flask being titrated but for the titration standard flask. Start and control the nitrogen stream, and then titrate the "distillation blank" from its gray or faintly purple cast to a first faint pink color (with brief experience, this point is easily learned). At this point, cap the titrated "distillation blank" tightly with Parafilm to serve as a standard color for the remaining titrations.

Since very little acid will be used for the "distillation blank," the buret tip, once a small extra droplet of acid has been expelled and discarded, is introduced into the next sample, the counter is reset to zero, and titration is continued. The formation of ammonium borate, providing an alkaline reaction, turns the indicator green (yellow color of methyl red plus methylene blue color), and so likewise do combustion products of a cigarette, or expiratory air from the lungs. The objective of titration is conversion of ammonium borate to ammonium chloride and boric acid; hence titrating is independent of the concentration of boric acid present in the system.

Each distillate is titrated to the color of the titrated "distillation blank." From the values so secured, one must subtract the value secured on titrating the "digestion blanks," which measures the acid needed to titrate both the "distillation blank" and the ammonia arising from the reagents used in the Kjeldahl digestion. The value attributable to the "reagent blank" should not exceed 3 to 4 μg of nitrogen—a reading of 0.0150 to 0.0200 on the Manostat buret. Error in measuring 10 to 100 μg of nitrogen is about ± 2 μg of nitrogen.

Calculation when the HCl is *exactly* $N/70$, and the Manostat readings are corrected to milliliters of titrant, is: nitrogen (mg) = 0.2 × ml $N/70$ HCl. Samples of 10 μg of nitrogen, accordingly, would require a net addition, over the reagent blank, of 0.0500 ml of $N/70$ HCl, and samples of 100 μg of nitrogen would require 0.5000 ml of $N/70$ HCl.

f. ALTERNATIVE TITRATION FOR SEMIMICROMETHOD
(250 TO 1000 μG OF NITROGEN)

A titration method using simply prepared reagents has proved quite satisfactory in the author's (C.A.W.) laboratory for the determination of ammonia distilled from digests of larger samples of protein. The method is based on the back-titration of potassium acid iodate* with NaOH after the collection of ammonia in the acid. The procedure is applicable to the micromethod if smaller volumes of more dilute potassium acid iodate are used, and if dilute NaOH is discharged from a Manostat 1.0-ml buret as described in Section e above.

i. Equipment and Reagents

Burets: 10-ml burets graduated in 0.05-ml intervals are most suitable. These burets will be used for the dilute NaOH titrant, so if automatic burets are to be employed and the titrant is to be stored as such, the apparatus should be equipped with CO_2 traps at all permanent openings to the atmosphere. These are standard, commercially available items.

---

* KH(IO$_3$)$_2$, c.p. (Amend Drug and Chemical, New York), is used as a titrant for standardization of alkalis. [J. B. Niederl and V. Niederl, "Micromethods of Quantitative Organic Analysis," 2nd ed., Wiley, New York, 1948; F. C. Koch and T. L. McMeekin, *J. Am. Chem. Soc.* **46**, 2066 (1924).]

Pipets: 10-ml volumetric pipets accurately standardized to deliver are required.

Receiving Flasks: 125-ml Erlenmeyer flasks are suitable. They may be marked at 60 ml.

Standard Acid: 0.01 N HCl may be used, but a standard 0.01 N acid is obtained conveniently by dissolving 3.8994 gm of potassium acid iodate, $KH(IO_3)_2$, in 1 liter of CO_2-free water in a volumetric flask.

NaOH Titrant: A solution of NaOH is diluted to approximately 0.011 N. It is titrated against exactly 10 ml of the standard acid before each use.

Indicator Dye: The dye mixture described above (Section A,3,b,xi) is suitable, but so are many others that change color sharply in a narrow pH range or give an easily reproducible end point. Methyl purple indicator solution (Fleischer Chemical Corp., Washington, D.C.) changes from purple at pH 4.8, passes through a neutral gray, and changes to bright green at pH 5.4.

ii. Procedure

(a) *Titration of NaOH* Ten milliliters (or standardized volume delivered) of 0.01 N $KH(IO_3)_2$ is accurately pipetted to a 125-ml Erlenmeyer flask to which is added 0.1 ml of methyl purple solution. CO_2-free water is added to the 60-ml mark, and NaOH is added from the buret until a recognizable green is achieved. Since the acid is the standard, NaOH concentration is determined empirically by each operator according to the most convenient color end point and his own pipetting and buretting techniques.

(b) *Collection of Distillates* Erlenmeyer flasks are used as receivers; they contain 10 ml (or standardized delivery of pipet) of 0.01 N $KH(IO_3)_2$. The receiver is secured to the still with the condenser tip at the surface of the acid solution in the receiver. After about 50 ml of condensate has been collected, the flame is removed from the boiling flask.

(c) *Titration of Distillate* Methyl purple solution (0.1 ml) is added, and, if necessary, water to the 60-ml mark on the flask. NaOH is buretted to the color of the NaOH titration flasks which are used as reference.

(d) *Calculations* Calculations are based on the difference in the amount of NaOH required to neutralize a known amount of standard acid and the amount required to neutralize the residual acid after an unknown quantity of ammonia has been added. The difference between the volumes of NaOH (Δ ml NaOH) multiplied by the concentration of NaOH ([NaOH]) is the ammonia equivalence. Micrograms of nitrogen in the sample is calculated thus:

$$\text{Nitrogen } (\mu g) = \Delta \text{ ml NaOH} \times [\text{NaOH}] \times (14 \times 10^3)$$

4. DETERMINATION OF NITROGEN BY THE NESSLER REACTION

a. GENERAL CONSIDERATIONS

Nitrogen is converted to ammonium sulfate on digestion of protein with sulfuric acid, as in Kjeldahl digestion. The assisting oxidant is 30% hydrogen peroxide. Instead of conversion to NH_4OH and steam distillation into boric acid, a colored complex, $NH_2Hg_2I_3$, is formed and read as absorbancy at 440 mμ. The color is developed by reaction with Nessler's reagent, a solution of $HgI_2 + KI$ in NaOH, as described by Koch and McMeekin.[9] The colored complex develops in 30 minutes and is stable for several hours when containers are covered (for example, by Parafilm) to prevent entry of contaminating nitrogen present in the laboratory air.

Also in parallel to Kjeldahl techniques, two test procedures are available, one for nitrogen values in the range of 20 to 300 μg,[10] the other in the range of 2 to 50 μg.[11] The first method has a sensitivity of 5 μg of nitrogen and is reproducible to $\pm 2\%$; it is recommended for routine work.[11] The second, more sensitive procedure requires experience and attention in detail: it can attain a sensitivity of 1 μg of nitrogen in its useful range, but careful pipetting of small samples is required. Further, with some sera, adsorption of protein to glass can cause the control tubes to yield rather large blank values.

b. EQUIPMENT

Digestion tubes: Straight-walled Folin-Wu tubes, 25 × 200 mm, are used, such as Corning No. 1920 or Kimble No. 47125 with etched marks at 35 and 50 ml.

Digestion Racks: Two types of special racks are recommended[10,11] for handling tubes in groups; these are not commercially available. A rack holding forty-two tubes, 13 × 100 mm, is shown in Fig. 2. Another similar rack to hold ten Folin-Wu digestion tubes contains ten holes $1\frac{1}{32}$ inches in diameter, with plates spaced $2\frac{3}{4}$ inches apart and a center rod 9 inches high. Holes in the bottom plate are countersunk to correspond to the curvature of the Folin-Wu tubes.

[9] F. C. Koch and T. L. McMeekin, *J. Am. Chem. Soc.* **46**, 2066 (1924).

[10] D. H. Campbell, J. S. Garvey, N. E. Cremer, and D. H. Sussdorf, "Methods in Immunology," pp. 53–57. Benjamin, New York, 1963.

[11] F. Lanni, M. L. Dillon, and J. W. Beard, *Proc. Soc. Exptl. Biol. Med.* **74**, 4 (1950).

Stirring Rods: Rods 25 cm long, mushroomed on one end, one for each digestion tube.

Tripod: having an inside diameter of 6 inches.

Ammonium Sulfate Nitrogen Standard: This is prepared by drying to constant weight a product such as Fisher's certified primary standard, No. A-938. It should be maintained in a desiccator. The standard is weighed out (234.72 mg) and dissolved with distilled water to 500 ml, including 0.7 ml of concentrated H_2SO_4 as preservative (100 μg of nitrogen per millilter). A standard solution of ammonium sulfate (5 mg/ml) is

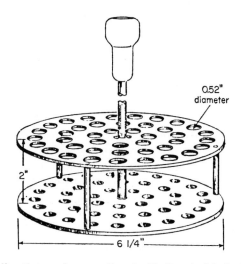

0.52" diameter

2"

6 1/4"

Fig. 2. Brass digestion rack, according to F. Lanni, M. L. Dillon, and J. W. Beard [*Proc. Soc. Exptl. Biol. Med.* **74,** 4 (1950)]. The upper plate is $\frac{3}{32}$ inch thick. The lower plate is $\frac{1}{8}$-inch and is milled out with a ball-shaped mill to increase the area of contact with the tubes. Handle is an 8-inch brass rod with a Bakelite cap.

commercially available (A. H. Thomas Company). It is diluted with boiled, freshly distilled water to the nitrogen value desired.

Sulfuric Acid: Concentrated, analytical reagent grade, specified low in nitrogen.

Hydrogen Peroxide: 30%, available in 4-ounce bottles.

Nessler Solution, "Koch and McMeekin": Available commercially in pints and quarts. Large-scale preparation is described by Campbell *et al.*[10]

Buret: For dispensing Nessler's reagent, to be filled by gravity through glass. Gum rubber tubing can be used in short length at the tip, but a Teflon stopcock is desirable.

c. PROCEDURE FOR 20 TO 300 μg OF NITROGEN

Step 1. Introduce into separate Folin-Wu digestion tubes: (*a*) *unknowns* calculated to contain 20 to 300 μg of nitrogen in 1- to 2-ml volume; (*b*) *Reference* standard of ammonium sulfate (100 μg of nitrogen); (*c*) *diluent* used in unknowns and in corresponding volume. It is helpful to include (*d*) a *known* protein standard to check the digestion procedure. Determinations in duplicate are advisable.

Step 2. Add to each digestion tube, by means of an all-glass dispenser, 0.5 ml of concentrated sulfuric acid.

Step 3. Place the special rack containing the digestion tubes on a tripod in a chemical hood having adequate exhaust.

Step 4. Heat the tubes over a Fisher high-temperature burner, at first under low heat to evaporate water (which condenses on the side walls and may be expelled by cautiously applied free flame). Digest under higher heat, turning the rack occasionally to heat uniformly. After the digestion tubes are filled with dense fumes, digest for another 10 minutes. Step 4 requires about 1 hour.

Step 5. Remove the rack, and allow it to cool for 1 minute. Let 1 drop of 30% H_2O_2 fall directly from a dropper bottle into the digest. Replace the rack, and heat for 5 minutes over a low flame. If color should persist beyond 2 minutes, remove the rack, cool, and add a second drop of 30% H_2O_2. Apply higher heat, and digest for 15 minutes. Dense fumes must fill the tubes and acid must be observed to reflux to ensure digestion, destroy H_2O_2, and reduce the sulfuric acid content.

Step 6. Cool the tubes, and add distilled water to the 35-ml mark. Place in each tube a stirring rod, and, beginning with the standards and blanks, add 15 ml of Nessler's reagent followed by immediate stirring. (If a short connection of gum rubber is employed in the siphoning system, discard the reagent within the rubber tubing and draw fresh reagent). It is advisable to cap the tubes tightly with Parafilm.

Step 7. Allow the tubes to stand at room temperature for 30 minutes, and then read the samples from each tube in a spectrophotometer at 440 mμ (tungsten light); round cuvette tubes 22 mm in diameter are often used. Read in the order in which the Nessler's reagent was introduced.

Step 8. Subtract the reading of the reagent blank from the readings of the standard and the unknown. The corrected absorbancy of the unknown is divided by the corrected absorbancy of the standard, and the quotient is multiplied by the nitrogen of the reference standard in milligrams and by the factor 6.25 to convert to milligrams of protein. For the ammonium sulfate standard given, the factor is 0.1. It is convenient to construct a straight-line plot relating absorbancy observed through the selected type of cuvette to nitrogen as determined on graded amounts of standard ammonium sulfate.

d. PROCEDURE FOR 5 TO 30 μG OF NITROGEN IN 0.5 ML [12,13]

Digestion of proteins is conducted in micro-Kjeldahl flasks. Samples of 0.5 ml are treated with 0.4 ml of 1:1 sulfuric acid (diluted with 1 volume of carbonate-free water), allowed to run down the side of the flask. Steps c1 through c4 are carried out in a Kjeldahl digestion rack. Step c5 consists in adding 2 drops of 30% H_2O_2, allowed to run down the side of the flask (hold on a slant, away from the face), digesting for 2½ minutes, and adding another 2 drops of 30% H_2O_2. Digest for a further 5 minutes, or until colorless and a ring of acid is seen in the neck of the flask.

For Nesslerization, add 7.3 ml of freshly boiled and cooled distilled water, then 1.5 ml of a 1:4 dilution of 50% NaOH made in carbonate-free water, and cool to 12° in a pan of water. Add 1 ml of Nessler's reagent from a volumetric pipet, shake, and return to the 12° pan. Transfer one at a time to colorimeter tubes for reading.

e. NITROGEN DETERMINATIONS ON ANTIGEN–ANTIBODY PRECIPITATES

i. Precipitates calculated to contain 20 to 300 μg of nitrogen are formed and washed in 13 × 100-mm tubes. After step c5, contents are diluted and rinsed quantitatively into Folin-Wu tubes, the volumes being brought to 35 ml. Continue with step c6.

ii. Precipitates calculated to yield 5 to 80 μg of nitrogen, perferably 15 to 60 μg,[11] are formed, washed, and digested in 13 × 100-mm tubes (Fig. 2) as in (*i*), with appropriate blanks and with 0.5 ml (50 μg of nitrogen) of the ammonium sulfate standard. For digestion 0.16 ml of special H_2SO_4 (1 volume of concentrated acid plus 1.2 volumes of distilled water) is added, and the tubes are heated as in steps c3 through c5 above. The heating is conducted so as to allow refluxing of the acid about one-half to two-thirds of the way up the tubes. (Water condensing initially on the upper portions of the tubes may be driven off by carefully applying a small flame.) Spattering during each peroxide treatment can lose 1% of the digest. Add 5 ml of distilled water from a buret, and mix with a footed stirring rod. Add 2 ml of Nessler's reagent with a pipet rapidly, and again

[12] G. L. Miller and E. E. Miller, *Anal. Chem.* **20,** 481 (1948).

[13] F. L. Seibert and L. F. Affronti, *in* "Methodology Manual for Investigation of Mycobacterial and Fungal Antigens," American Thoracic Society, New York, N.Y. 1963.

mix. Transfer to a colorimeter tube for readings of absorbancy at a fixed time, such as 60 seconds after adding Nessler reagent.

5. DETERMINATION OF NITROGEN BY THE MICRO-DUMAS METHOD

a. GENERAL CONSIDERATIONS

Nitrogen is released totally from organic compounds by combustion with copper oxide at red heat in an atmosphere of CO_2 followed by passage over reduced copper to reduce oxides of nitrogen. The gaseous nitrogen is washed through the tube with CO_2, the latter being removed by KOH, and the nitrogen is collected and measured in a metal syringe. The volume, pressure, and temperature of the nitrogen gas released permit precise calculation of the weight of nitrogen. Under conditions usually employed, 1 mg of nitrogen will occupy about 1000 μl in the apparatus; sample sizes that give 500 to 700 μl (5 to 6 mg of protein) are most convenient, but up to 2 mg of N_2 can be measured.

b. APPARATUS AND REAGENTS

Micro-Dumas analysis is most simply performed in the automated Coleman Model 29 nitrogen analyzer, which allows five to six complete nitrogen determinations per hour. Special preparations, Causticon (KOH) and Cuprox, are sold with the instrument. Highly purified CO_2 (99.99% CO_2 by volume) is provided by the Matheson Co. as Coleman grade. A mercury barometer and a microbalance are needed.

c. SAMPLE SIZE

Precisely weighed protein (1 to 10 mg to provide 0.5 mg of nitrogen) is introduced into the combustion boat. The instrument is best adapted to solid samples. Concentrated liquid samples can be weighed in tare-weighed capillaries, which are delivered to the combustion tube, or liquid samples can be weighed as a slurry made with copper oxide that has been introduced beforehand into the boat and weighed with it. Dilute solutions are not practical to handle.

d. SENSITIVITY

Nitrogen determinations are possible to 0.01% nitrogen content, and routine recovery is $\pm 0.2\%$ of theoretical nitrogen.

6. DETERMINATION OF PROTEIN BY
THE BIURET METHOD*

a. GENERAL CONSIDERATIONS

The characteristic "biuret color" is produced from α-amino nitrogens in peptide linkage when these complex with copper in alkaline solution. In the copper complex, one copper is bound to four peptide nitrogens, yet secondary effects cause the biuret values of various proteins to differ slightly from one another. Consequently, curves showing biuret values versus protein concentration are established for each protein on the basis of protein nitrogen—determined, for example, by the Kjeldahl method. The straight-line portions of such concentration curves serve for quantitative estimation of the particular proteins.

The methods in chief use are the Weichselbaum-Dittebrandt procedure[14,15] cited by Kabat[16] and the procedure of Gornall *et al.*[17] The writer (M.W.C.) prefers the Weichselbaum-Dittebrandt method, which is given here in detail. The procedure of Gornall *et al.* uses reagents altered in proportion, develops color at room temperature for 30 minutes, and determines absorbance of light at 540 mμ.

b. REAGENTS

Prepare 1 liter of carbonate-free 0.2 N NaOH in freshly boiled and cooled water. In 400 ml of this alkali, dissolve 9.0 gm of sodium potassium tartrate, then 3.0 gm of finely ground $CuSO_4 \cdot 5H_2O$, added in small amounts; finally add 5.0 gm of KI dissolved beforehand in a small volume of 0.2 N NaOH; bring volume to 1000 ml with 0.2 N NaOH. It is best to keep the bulk of this reagent tightly stoppered, and to pour out into another stoppered polyethylene container the "working volume" for the task at hand.

c. PROCEDURE

For minimal assay volumes, place accurately measured 1-ml portions of sample, protein nitrogen standard, and the solvent(s) used for the

---

* This section is based largely on the procedure described by E. A. Kabat ("Kabat and Mayer's Experimental Immunochemistry," 2nd ed., pp. 559–561. Thomas, Springfield, Illinois, 1961).

[14] T. E. Weichselbaum, *Amer. J. Clin. Pathol. Technol. Suppl.* **10**, 40 (1946).

[15] M. Dittebrandt, *Am. Clin. Pathol.* **18**, 439 (1948).

[16] E. A. Kabat, *in* "Kabat and Mayer's Experimental Immunochemistry," 2nd ed., pp. 559–561. Thomas, Springfield, Illinois, 1961.

[17] A. G. Gornall, C. J. Bardawill, and M. M. David, *J. Biol. Chem.* **177**, 751 (1949).

sample(s) into 100 × 13-mm tubes, all in duplicate. Since desirable samples should contain 1 to 5 mg of protein per milliliter (160 to 800 μg of protein nitrogen per milliliter), two or three dilutions of the unknown (prepared in the original solvent) are tested. To each tube add 1.5 ml of biuret reagent prepared as described above, mix, cap tightly with Parafilm, and incubate in a water bath at 37° for 30 minutes. Transfer into 1-cm Beckman cuvettes, and read at a wavelength of 555 mμ. Since the minimal volume to fill the cuvette is nearly 2.5 ml, check visually and adjust the cuvettes in the holder so that no fluid-air menisci show in the optical pathway.

If available volumes permit, use 1.2-ml portions of the unknown plus 1.8 ml of biuret reagent, or 1.4-ml portions of test fluids plus 2.1 ml of biuret reagent. Conversely, smaller volumes can be employed by using micropipets and microcuvettes—for example, 0.2 ml of sample and 0.3 ml of biuret reagent.

d. Calculation

Because standard curves are determined under similar conditions, no correction is made for the volume of biuret reagent added in the test system. The concentration-biuret color curves are straight up to 0.62 mg of protein nitrogen per milliliter for γ-globulin and up to 1.0 mg/ml for bovine serum albumin. Dialyzed guinea pig serum shows the same curve as bovine serum albumin.

The absorbancy reading for biuret color developed by 1.0 mg of BSA nitrogen per milliliter is close to 0.650 at wavelength 555 mμ, and that given by 0.62 mg of RGG nitrogen per milliliter is close to 0.540.

Unknowns are read at 555 mμ in a spectrophotometer against the blank taken as zero absorbancy. Two blanks should be included. Standard protein read similarly gives assurance of fully developed biuret color. Stability of the color decreases with time.

e. Application to Antigen–Antigen Precipitates

The amount of antiserum employed should provide about 200 μg of antibody nitrogen per tube. Specific precipitates are formed in special 8-ml conical test tubes marked at the 2.5-ml level. The conditions and washing are those described elsewhere for quantitative precipitation determinations. (The original supernatant fluids are retained for determination of excess antigen or antibody.) The washed precipitate is broken up by gentle tapping and dissolved by adding 1.5 ml of biuret reagent, and the volume is brought to 2.5 ml with distilled water. Duplicate reagent blanks are set up with 1 ml of distilled water. Development of color and reading are carried out as above.

7. ESTIMATION OF PROTEIN BY THE FOLIN-CIOCALTEU REACTION

a. General Considerations

The reaction of proteins with the Folin-Ciocalteu phenol reagent is among the more widely used assays for the estimation of protein. The modifications of Lowry et al.[18] have become standard procedures in biochemistry laboratories and are most satisfactory for solutions containing 50 to 500 μg of protein per milliliter (10 to 100 μl of nitrogen per milliliter). The sensitivity of the method in terms of absolute quantities of protein to be assayed depends on the minimum volume of reaction solution which can be accommodated in the colorimeter or spectrophotometer at hand. For convenience it is generally desirable to have approximately 3 ml of an assay for a $1 \times 1 \times 4$-cm cuvette. Such a system, which employs 0.1 to 0.3 ml of protein solution, is described below; it detects 10 μg of protein with adequate precision. Lowry et al.,[18] using a spectrophotometer adapted to read extremely small final volumes, were able to assay as little as 0.3 μg of protein with errors of the order of 5%.

As in all chemical procedures, it is good practice to include a known protein standard routinely and also a reagent control in each experimental series. This has a further utility in the case of the Folin reaction, since the color absorption curve is rather broad. The λ_{max} is 750 mμ, but, with a known standard, proportionality can be established at wavelengths as low as 500 mμ with adequate precision. If the absorbancy at 750 mμ is very high, a sample and several concentrations of the standard can be compared at 500 mμ, where readings of about 60% of those at 750 mμ are obtained.

A characteristic of the Folin reaction and other tests giving colors absorbing at longer wavelengths is that turbidity contributes minimal errors. In spite of the advantages of sensitivity, precision, and rapidity of the assay, however, there are serious drawbacks to its application to certain types of problem. The color varies significantly from protein to protein, and absorbancy is not linear with respect to the amount of protein in higher concentration, nor is the color strictly proportional to concentration if the assay is scaled down to the ultramicro range. Thus a separate calibration curve is required for each protein or protein mixture (such as serum or tissue extract), and for each modification of technique.

b. Reagents

Solution 1: 2% Na_2CO_3 in 0.1 N NaOH.

[18] O. H. Lowry, N. J. Rosebrough, A. L. Farr, and R. J. Randall, *J. Biol. Chem.* **193**, 265 (1951).

Solution 2: 0.5% $CuSO_4 \cdot 5H_2O$ in 1% sodium tartrate, prepared freshly each day by mixing equal volumes of double-strength reagents.

Solution 3: Alkaline copper solution—50 parts of solution 1 plus 1 part of solution 2. The mixture is not stable and should be prepared fresh on the day of use.

Solution 4: Carbonate copper solution, prepared as solution 3 using 2% Na_2CO_3 in water. This reagent is employed in place of solution 3 when protein precipitates are not readily soluble in solution 3, as is sometimes the case with heated TCA or PCA precipitates. The precipitate is first dissolved in 1 N NaOH before solution 4 is added.

Phenol Reagent: Commercially available phenol reagent,* according to Folin and Ciocalteu (see Kabat[19] for formulation), is approximately 2 N in acid and must be diluted to 1 N for use in the test proportions given below. For precise dilution, the phenol reagent is first titrated to phenolphthalein. Usually 5 parts of commercial reagent mixed with 4.7 parts of water gives a solution close to the required acidity.

c. PROCEDURE

The critical volumes in the reaction mixture are the alkaline copper (solution 3) and the phenol reagent. The sample volume can vary slightly, provided a correction for color dilution is made. If accurately graduated reaction tubes are available, the final volumes of a test series can be equalized before the color is read.

Step 1. To 0.1 to 0.3 ml of sample containing 50 to 500 μg of protein per milliliter, add 2.5 ml of solution 3. Mix thoroughly, and allow to stand for 12 to 15 minutes at room temperature for reaction of protein with copper. Test tubes of 13 × 100 mm are suitable for this reaction volume.

Step 2. Rapidly add 0.25 ml of diluted phenol reagent, and mix thoroughly within seconds. Allow 30 minutes for color development.

Step 3. Read the color at a suitable wavelength between 500 and 750 mμ. Make necessary corrections to standard reaction volume, and determine protein from calibration curve.

d. APPLICATIONS

No problems are presented by proteins in solution, and immune precipitates generally dissolve readily in the alkaline copper solution. The application to the assay of immune precipitates is discussed in Chap. 13, Vol. III. Use a merthiolate blank if the sample is so preserved.

Estimation of protein in tissue or cell homogenates or in subcellular

* Fisher Scientific Co., New York; Amend Drug and Chemical Co., New York.
[19] E. A. Kabat, *in* "Kabat and Mayer's Experimental Immunochemistry," 2nd ed., pp. 556–558. Thomas, Springfield, Illinois, 1961.

components is usually performed on material insoluble in hot TCA or PCA. This step removes large amounts of nonprotein material, some of which produces color in the test, and others which may inhibit it. In such circumstances it is sometimes necessary to dissolve the precipitate, particularly if it is copious, by heating at 100° in 1 N NaOH for 10 minutes. This may reduce the color, but it should be a reproducible error. Often heating is not required if sufficient time is allowed for solution, in which case there is little if any effect on the reaction.

Whenever it is necessary to use 1 N NaOH to solubilize the precipitate, solution 4 is used in place of solution 3 in ten times the volume of 1 N NaOH employed. To conform to the reaction volumes given in the procedures above, 0.25 ml of 1 N NaOH should be used to dissolve the precipitate, and 2.5 ml of solution 4 is added. The volume of phenol reagent is the same. The 10:1 ratio of alkaline copper to phenol reagent is critical for providing the proper pH of the final reaction mixture.

8. NINHYDRIN METHOD FOR ESTIMATION OF PROTEIN

a. GENERAL CONSIDERATIONS

The ninhydrin method detects protein sensitively (30 to 90 μg of protein, containing 5 to 15 μg of nitrogen), but various proteins may yield different extinction values. It is advisable always to run an appropriate protein standard solution in each series of tests.

For increased sensitivity—about ninefold—in determining protein, preliminary alkaline hydrolysis has been introduced (1) to increase the number of primary amino groups available for reaction and (2) to effectively remove all ammonia including amide ammonia.[20] This procedure, studied particularly in determining the concentration of dilute ribonuclease,[21] is capable of general application. Thus pancreatic ribonuclease hydrolyzed as shown below yields 131 O.D. units per milligram at 570 mμ in a 1-cm path.

The sensitivity of the method, even without alkaline hydrolysis, allowed Kunkel and Ward[22] to determine the concentration of albumin in whole human serum by measuring the amount of specific precipitate produced by the addition of 0.2 ml of a rabbit anti-human serum albumin. Standard curves were prepared with 0.5-ml portions of albumin at several concentrations (0.01, 0.02, and 0.03 mg/ml), and the unknown (whole human serum) was diluted to give precipitates in this range.

In principle, ninhydrin partially reduced to hydrindantin (a bimolecular complex) reacts at 100° in mild acidity with primary amino groups of

[20] S. Moore and W. H. Stein, *J. Biol. Chem.* **211,** 907 (1954).
[21] R. G. Fruchter and A. M. Crestfield, *J. Biol. Chem.* **240,** 3868 (1965).
[22] H. G. Kunkel and S. M. Ward, *J. Biol. Chem.* **182,** 597 (1950).

amino acids to deaminate and decompose the amino acid to CO_2 and α-carbon aldehyde, and to condense with the nitrogen, producing the violet product diketohydrindylidene-diketohydrindamine. Free ammonia, if present, reacts also. With proteins, ninhydrin reacts to deaminate ϵ-amino groups of lysine residues and terminal α-amino groups, but the reaction does not liberate CO_2 concomitantly. The greater contribution comes from the lysine residues.

Ninhydrin
triketohydrindene hydrate
(1, 2, 3-indantrione hydrate)

Diketohydrindylidene-
diketohydrindamine

The method described here utilizes a modified ninhydrin-hydrindantin reagent.[*,20]

b. REAGENTS

Ninhydrin and Anhydrous Hydrindantin, crystallized: Stored in dark glass (obtainable from Pierce Chemical Company, Rockford, Illinois).

Methyl Cellosolve (Pierce), ethylene glycol monomethyl ether, peroxide-free grade (peroxide content less than 3 ppm): Test for peroxide by adding 2 ml of the Cellosolve to 1 ml of freshly prepared 4% aqueous KI, after which the solution should be colorless or lightly straw-yellow. The solvent should give no haze on mixing with 1 volume of water. If it is necessary to redistill, add 1 gm of stannous chloride per liter, and work in a hood with good exhaust. The vapors are toxic.

Sodium Acetate Buffer, 4 N, pH 5.5: Dissolve 136 gm of sodium acetate·$3H_2O$ (reagent grade) in 100 ml of water by warming on steam bath. Cool. Add 25 ml of glacial acetic acid, and bring the volume to 250 ml with distilled water. The reaction of the concentrated buffer should be pH 5.51 ± 0.03. If adjustment is necessary, 0.25 gm of NaOH corresponds to about 0.04 pH unit. Store at 4° without preservative.

Ninhydrin–Hydrindantin Reagent: Dissolve 4 gm of ninhydrin and 0.6 gm of hydrindantin in 150 ml of methyl Cellosolve. Avoid vigorous (oxidative) stirring. Add 50 ml of 4 N NaAc buffer, pH 5.5, transfer to a dark glass bottle, and store under nitrogen at room temperature. Make fresh each week. (Reagent can be checked by color developed with 1mM standard amino acid solution.)

---

* The details are provided through the courtesy of Dr. Stanford Moore and Dr. Arthur M. Crestfield.

Acetic Acid (free of ammonia), 30% aqueous (v/v): If a device such as the Cornwall continuous pipetting outfit is to be used, the solution should first be deaerated with a water pump and the metal sinker replaced with glass.

Ethanol–Water: Mix equal volumes of ethanol and water.

c. PROCEDURE FOR PROTEINS (NONHYDROLYZED)

i. Soluble Proteins

Into suitable tubes (10 × 75-mm round cuvettes as used in the Coleman junior spectrophotometer) dispense accurately, in duplicate, 0.1-ml portions of sample, sample solvent, and several dilutions of standard protein solution. Sample should contain 1 to 20 μg of nitrogen. Add 0.4 ml of water and 0.5 ml of ninhydrin reagent to each flask. Mix well, and place flasks in boiling water for 20 minutes. Dilute with 2.0 ml of ethanol–water, mix, and clarify by centrifugation if required. Shake well, and read against the blank in a spectrophotometer at 570 mμ. Readings of the standard protein can vary somewhat from one test to another, and the particular readings will serve as a reference curve for the material under test.

ii. Immune Precipitates[20,22]

Antigen–antibody precipitates are formed directly in 10 × 75-mm round cuvettes as used in the Coleman junior spectrophotometer to yield 30 to 90 μg of protein (5 to 15 μg of protein nitrogen). The precipitates are washed in the cuvettes with 2 ml of saline three times. The precipitate is dissolved in 0.1 ml of 0.1 N NaOH, and 0.4 ml of H_2O and 0.5 ml of ninhydrin–hyrindantin reagent are added. The cuvettes are heated for 20 minutes in the boiling water bath, cooled, and diluted with 2 ml of 50% ethanol prior to reading at 570 mμ. The "blank" is a saline–antiserum mixture carried through the entire procedure.

d. PROCEDURE FOR HYDROLYZATES OF PROTEINS

i. Equipment

Hot air oven at 110° with forced draft (for example, Model OV-510, Blue M Electric Company, Blue Island, Illinois).

Polypropylene Centrifuge Tubes, 115 × 19 mm. (Nalge): The use of temperature-resistant plastic tubes has been introduced since Pyrex tubes etch and absorb ammonia. If blue color is retained after use, the plastic tubes should be extracted with 10 ml of 50% alcohol and dried at 110°.

Polyethylene Caps: Size 4 to fit 19-mm plastic centrifuge tubes.

ii. Alkaline Hydrolysis

Deliver the samples, the sample solvent, and the standard protein solution in triplicate into individual 115×19-mm polypropylene centrifuge tubes (Nalge). Samples of 0.01 to 3 ml are calculated to deliver 2 to 3 μg of nitrogen. Add 1 ml of 1.0 N NaOH to each tube (may be added by syringe devoid of metal parts). Place the carrier racks on wooden blocks in the oven at 110°, with the tubes uncovered. The water largely evaporates after 3 to 5 hours, and hydrolysis is complete in 5 hours. (If tubes are left at 110° overnight for convenience, the same values will be found *providing* the Na_2CO_3 which forms is dissolved completely before ninhydrin is added.) Not only is adventitious ammonia removed, but even samples containing up to 0.2 M NH_4^+ may be used. Cool the tubes for 5 minutes, and neutralize the samples by adding 1 ml of 30% acetic acid; place the tubes in boiling water for 6 minutes to dissolve Na_2CO_3. The reaction should be pH 5.2 ± 0.1.

iii. Reaction with Ninhydrin

Add 1 ml of ninhydrin–hydrindantin reagent. Check the reaction (pH 5.2 ± 0.2) in an appropriate tube. Cover with inverted No. 4 polyethylene stoppers. Heat for exactly 15 minutes in a vigorously boiling water bath. Let 5 ml of 50% aqueous ethanol flow down the wall; then mix well by hand. Cool rapidly; avoid sunlight. Let the sample sit at room temperature for 15 minutes, then shake well for about 30 seconds to oxidize most of the residual hydrindantin. Pour into spectrophotometer cuvettes, and read at 570 mμ. If cuvettes of 0.5-cm light path are used, the 5 ml of diluent can be omitted. The color of the blank should be observed closely, since it may point to errors: light yellow, normal; brown, pH too high; colorless, pH too low; blue, extraneous ammonia in the acetic acid; red, incomplete oxidation of hydrindantin. Following alkaline hydrolysis, variations in the blank are larger than in the ordinary ninhydrin procedure.

iv. Reading

Read the blanks against the diluent (50% aqueous ethanol) at 570 mμ, and ascertain the average blank. Read the hydrolyzed unknowns and standard proteins against this blank. The readings of the standard protein should correspond to the calibration curve used for determining protein in the unknown.

9. ULTRAVIOLET SPECTROSCOPY FOR PROTEIN DETERMINATION

The general principles of light absorption are treated at length in Chap. 10,A, along with discussion of applications, common errors, and

If the nucleic acid (DNA or RNA) is of high molecular weight and not denatured, an estimate of its concentration can be obtained by the increase (about 33%) in absorption at 260 mμ upon alkaline denaturation.[26] In 1-cm cuvettes an exact amount of solution (10 to 50 μg of nucleic acid per milliliter of 0.1 M NaCl) is made alkaline (pH > 11.5) by the addition of 0.05 ml of 6 N NaOH. The difference in absorption (corrected for volume changes) multiplied by 3 gives the absorbancy of the native, high-molecular-weight DNA and RNA in the solution ($A_{260} = 1.0$ for about 45 μg of nucleic acid per milliliter). It is important to remember, however, that in most extracts cleared by ultracentrifugation, the bulk of the nucleic acid present is low-molecular-weight RNA which does not give absorption increment.

[26] R. D. Hotchkiss, in "Methods in Enzymology" (S. P. Colowick and N. O. Kaplan, eds.), Vol. III, p. 708. Academic Press, New York, 1957.

B. Carbohydrate Analysis*†

In recent years, a large number of color reactions have been developed for the estimation of relatively minute quantities of carbohydrates in the presence of relatively large amounts of protein.[1a-c] Certain of these methods are reactions for carbohydrates in general, while others detect specific kinds of carbohydrates, such as hexoses, heptoses, ketoses, methylpentoses, amino sugars, and uronic acids. Some methods even have applicability for the identification and estimation of individual sugars. When the sugars present in a biological material are not known, it is customary to express results in terms of a specified sugar arbitrarily chosen as a standard. Furthermore, in many of the reactions for carbohydrates, individual sugars may not give the same color value per unit weight so

* Section 12,B was contributed by Curtis A. Williams and Merrill W. Chase.

† The editors are grateful to Dr. Elvin A. Kabat and Charles C. Thomas, Publisher, for permission to excerpt sections of Chapters 18 through 23 of "Kabat and Mayer's Experimental Immunochemistry," 2nd ed., to compile this abbreviated guide to carbohydrate analysis. The advice of Dr. Kenneth O. Lloyd in updating the final copy is also gratefully acknowledged.

   It would have been futile for any other author to attempt an improvement on Dr. Kabat's handling of this material. With his advice we have selected a few of the more widely used and most reliable procedures; and in the interest of our limitations on space, we have omitted parts of the discussions and many of the bibliographic references. Investigators who feel the need of a more complete review of the literature with respect to applications, modifications, and interpretations are urged to consult the original text.

[1a] Z. Dische, in "Methods of Biochemical Analysis" (D. Glick, ed.), Vol. 2, p. 313. Interscience, New York, 1955.

[1b] R. L. Whistler and M. L. Wolfrom (eds.), "Methods in Carbohydrate Chemistry. Vol. I: Analysis and Preparation of Sugars," Academic Press, New York (1962).

[1c] E. F. Neufeld and V. Ginsberg, "Methods in Enzymology, Vol. VIII: Complex Carbohydrates" (S. P. Colowick and N. O. Kaplan, eds.), Academic Press, New York (1966).

special techniques. Absorption coefficients and absorbing wavelengths (λ_{max}) of common proteins, haptens, amino acids, and components of nucleic acids are tabulated in Appendix I. The application of ultraviolet spectroscopy to analysis of specific immune precipitates is discussed in Chap. 10,A and in Chap. 13, Vol. III.

Here we shall discuss only a few considerations in the application of ultraviolet spectroscopy to special problems.

a. GENERAL CONSIDERATIONS

i. Measurements at λ_{max}

Proteins will vary somewhat in their λ_{max}, between 277 and 280 mμ, depending on their relative content of tyrosine ($\lambda_{max} = 275$ mμ, $E_M = 1340$) and tryptophan ($\lambda_{max} = 278$, $E_M = 5550$) and certain as yet undefined characteristics of the three-dimensional conformation. There is a significant shift in λ_{max} in alkaline solution (for example, 0.1 N NaOH) used to solubilize protein precipitates, due in part to loss of native structure and in part to the shift of the λ_{max} of tyrosine to 293 mμ ($E_M = 2330$). With some proteins the absorption will not remain constant at the high pH, necessitating the arbitrary selection of a time for reading after addition of alkali. Reading in 0.25 M acetic acid or in 0.5% sodium dodecyl sulfate is also recommended (p. 170).

Calibration curves or extinction coefficients for each protein employed should be determined at its λ_{max} in solutions most likely to be measured.

ii. Effect of Small Molecules

There are two categories of interference by small molecules to be considered: those in free solution and those bound to protein. The former present no serious problem if dialysis or gel filtration is feasible. Reading a solution at several wavelengths is advisable. The λ_{min} for most proteins is in the vicinity of 250 mμ. If the A_{280}/A_{260} ratio is sufficiently high (approaching 2.0, sometimes higher) and if there is no reading at 320 to 340 mμ, the 280-mμ reading may usually be considered to be due entirely to protein.

Any significant amount of compounds with aromatic nuclei, bile pigments, small nucleotides, nucleoside phosphates, cofactors, etc., which are present will make ultraviolet determinations meaningless. Preservatives containing aromatic rings cannot be used. For example, merthiolate in the concentration ordinarily employed as a preservative (0.01%) would give a reading at 280 mμ equivalent to that of some proteins at 1 mg/ml.

iii. Effect of Nucleic Acids

DNA and RNA have absorption maxima around 260 mμ (individual nucleotides vary in λ_{max}—see Appendix I). Solutions such as tissue or cell extracts that contain nucleic acid in addition to protein obviously cannot be assayed quantitatively by direct spectroscopy in the ultra-violet range. Under some conditions, however, crude estimates can be obtained by methods described in Section A,9,b,*ii* below.

b. SPECIAL APPLICATIONS

i. Monitoring Chromatographic Effluents

Many spectrophotometers can be adapted with a flow cell to receive column effluents, and to deliver a signal proportioned to the absorbancy to a recording device. The fractions are collected in the usual fashion after being monitored spectrophotometrically. Monitors of fixed wavelength are commercially available for this purpose (for example, Gilford Instru-ment Laboratories, Inc., Oberlin, Ohio; Instrumentation Specialties Co., Inc., Lincoln, Nebraska; LKB Instruments, Inc., Rockville, Maryland; LKB Produkter, Stockholm, Sweden).

It is particularly useful in such a procedure to have an "event" record superimposed on the absorption record by signals from the fraction collector each time it shifts tubes. If such refinements are desirable, and time-saving devices sometimes are critical in fractionation procedures, all components of the monitoring system should be selected for the best compromise between compatibility and versatility.

ii. Nucleic Acid and Protein Content of Crude Solutions

There is always a certain amount of nucleic acid in crude extracts of tissues and cells. It is often important to gain rapidly and conveniently a rough estimate of this quantity as well as the amount of protein present. Several empirical schemes utilizing the readings at 280 mμ and 260 mμ have been devised for this purpose, but they can serve only for prelimin-ary estimations. Further, crude extracts will contain small molecules (oligopeptides or nucleotides) which must be removed, as by dialysis, if A_{280}/A_{260} ratios are to provide an adequate basis for assay.

For protein, the A_{280}/A_{260} ratio tends toward a value of 2.0 and for nucleic acid toward 0.5. Nucleic acids, however, have a much greater absorbancy at 260 mμ than do proteins at their λ_{max} of 280 mμ. Conse-quently, the A_{280}/A_{260} ratio is useful only in mixtures where, as in most tissues, nucleic acid comprises less than 20% of the ultraviolet-absorbing material.

From absorbancy ratios on mixtures of yeast enolase ($E_{280}^{1\%} = 20.6$) and yeast nucleic acid ($E_{260}^{1\%} = 500.8$), Warburg and Christian calculated factors by which the absorbancy at 280 mμ could serve to estimate the protein concentration of the solution.[23] Kalckar estimated the protein in

[23] O. Warburg and W. Christian, *Biochem. Z.* **310**, 384 (1942).

solutions of enzymes[24] by using the equation, mg protein/ml = 1 − 0.74 A_{260}. The latter method is somewhat handier since ta factors or graphs are not required. Neither method is valid for a tions. The proteins from crude extracts of liver, for example, ha average absorbancy of 1.1 to 1.3 O.D. units/mg/ml. Clearly, f based on a special protein absorbing 2.06 O.D. units/mg/ml[23] shoul be used to estimate protein in liver extracts. The average absorban serum proteins is about 1 O.D. unit/mg/ml, although the serum albu of some species may absorb only 0.5 O.D./mg/ml. Immunoglob absorbancies have been reported to be as high as 1.6.

A method recently described by Groves *et al.*[25] for estimating protein the presence of nucleic acids is based on the difference in optical densiti at wavelengths on either side of the λ_{min} for nucleic acids. If wavelength are chosen so that the absorbancies for nucleic acid alone would be equal the difference (Δ O.D.) between the measurements would be due to the protein. Appropriate calibration curves could be drawn. The principle is illustrated in Fig. 3. As with other methods, this one requires preliminary analysis to accommodate to special properties of the system. For exam-ple, if the lower wavelength is fixed, the higher isoabsorbant wavelength will vary somewhat depending on the buffer system and the type of nucleic acid. The Δ O.D./mg protein/ml will still vary with the content of aromatic amino acids in the proteins, a characteristic for all methods based on ultraviolet absorbancy.

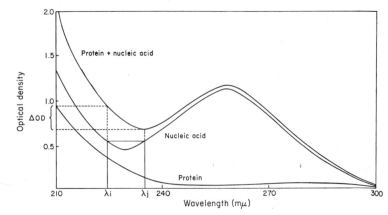

FIG. 3. The contribution of nucleic acid to optical density of protein is eliminated by measuring solution at two isoabsorbance wavelengths, λ_i and λ_j, on either side of the λ_{min} for nucleic acids. The Δ O.D. at these wavelengths is assumed to be proportional to the protein concentration. [W. E. Groves, F. C. Davis, Jr., and B. H. Sells, *Anal. Biochem.* **22**, 195 (1968).]

[24] H. M. Kalckar, *J. Biol. Chem.* **167**, 461 (1947).

[25] W. E. Groves, F. C. Davis, Jr. and B. H. Sells, *Anal. Biochem.* **22**, 195 (1968).

that the results obtained with polysaccharides or mixtures may vary substantially from the true value. Also, in the presence of proteins, methods of sugar analysis based on reduction are not applicable, since proteins possess reducing power. In all studies special attention should be paid to the cleanliness of the glassware, and lint should be avoided. Otherwise the preparation of solutions for carbohydrate assay requires no special attention other than that routinely recommended for quantitative chemistry on biological materials. If a preservative is desirable, a drop of chloroform will generally suffice and will not interfere with carbohydrate reactions.

Most methods described below may be carried out with solutions at 1 to 2 mg of carbohydrate per milliliter. In general, smaller absolute quantities of a sample can be employed if smaller test volumes can accurately be manipulated and assayed. If accurate weights are required, as when percentage content of a given sugar is to be determined, the sample should be dried to constant weight over P_2O_5 at room temperature. Sometimes ashing is necessary to obtain correction factors for weighed samples (see Section A,2).

For identification and assay of specific sugars and their derivatives, the reader should refer also to newer chromatographic methods[1d-1f] and the highly sensitive separation of trimethylsilyl derivatives of carbohydrates by gas chromatography.[1g]

1. DETERMINATION OF REDUCING SUGARS ON HYDROLYSIS

The estimation of the quantity of reducing sugar liberated on hydrolysis is of substantial importance in characterizing polysaccharides. A variety of reagents have been used for this purpose, including alkaline copper and alkaline ferricyanide solutions, 3,4-dinitrobenzoic acid, and tetrazolium salts. (For a review see ref. 2.) The stoichiometry of these reactions is not clearly understood, since the numerous oxidation products of the sugars have not been defined. The methods, however, are quite reproducible, and results are generally expressed in terms of the reducing power of glucose, which is used as a standard.

In studying unknown polysaccharides, it is necessary to establish con-

[1d] R. W. Bailey and J. B. Pridham, in "Chromatographic Reviews" (E. Lederer, ed.), Vol. 4, p. 114, Elsevier, Amsterdam, 1962.

[1e] K. C. B. Wilkie, in "Laboratory Handbook of Chromatographic Methods" (O. Mikes, ed.), p. 70, Van Nostrand, London, 1966.

[1f] E. Stahl and U. Kaltenbach, in "Thin Layer Chromatography" (E. Stahl, ed.), p. 461, Academic Press, New York, 1965.

[1g] C. C. Sweeley and B. Walker, Analyt. Chem. 36, 1461, 1964.

[2] E. Borel, "Uber die quantitative Zuckerbestimmung mit Hilfe von 3, 4 Dinitrobenzosaure," Doctoral Thesis, Pr. No. 2212 Eidgenossene Technische Hochschule, Zurich, Switzerland, 1953.

ditions for the maximum liberation of reducing sugar. Samples of polysaccharide are usually hydrolyzed in 1 to 2 ml of 1 to 4 N HCl or H_2SO_4 for 2, 4, 6, or more hours in sealed tubes placed in a boiling water bath. After cooling, the contents of the tubes are carefully neutralized to phenolphthalein in the cold by the cautious addition of N NaOH or 4 N NaOH, and the red color is just discharged by the dropwise addition of HCl. Care should be taken to avoid local excesses of alkali by rapid mixing during neutralization. If the amount of reducing sugar expected is in the correct range the entire neutralized sample may be used; otherwise it should be transferred quantitatively to a volumetric flask made up to the mark, and a suitable aliquot portion taken for analysis. In the determination of reducing sugars by hydrolysis low results are obtained if the acid used in hydrolysis is removed by evaporation as is recommended for hexosamine determination (see Section B,7 below).

a. Submicro Method[3]

This procedure is suitable for quantities ranging from 1 to 9 μg of reducing sugar as glucose. It is based on the formation of Prussian blue (ferric ferrocyanide) from the ferrocyanide formed by the reducing action of the sugar. The Prussian blue is estimated quantitatively at 690 mμ. Increased sensitivity is obtained by carrying out the ferricyanide reduction in the presence of cyanide which increases about threefold the amount of ferricyanide reduction by a given quantity of sugar. The method as given is stated[3] to give results to within 0.2 μg of the expected result with over 90% of the samples, and even greater precision was reported in a second laboratory.[4]

Reagents

1. Ferricyanide Solution: 0.5 gm of potassium ferricyanide per liter.

2. Carbonate–Cyanide Solution: 5.3 gm of sodium carbonate + 0.65 gm of KCN per liter.

3. Ferric Iron Solution: 1.5 gm of ferric ammonium sulfate + 1 gm of Duponol "ME dry" in 1 liter of 0.05 N H_2SO_4.

Procedure. The determinations are best performed in 5-ml Pyrex volumetric flasks to which 1 ml of sample, 0.50 ml of solution 1, and 0.50 ml of solution 2 are added. Heat in a boiling water bath for 15 minutes. Cool rapidly, and add 2.5 ml of solution 3. Make up to volume, mix, and read after 15 minutes at room temperature at 690 mμ in a spectrophotometer. A standard solution of glucose is run in parallel.

The relative reducing powers of various sugars are: glucose 1.00, maltose

[3] J. T. Park and M. J. Johnson, *J. Biol. Chem.* **181**, 149 (1949).

[4] M. M. Rapport, K. Meyer, and A. Linker, *J. Biol. Chem.* **186**, 615 (1950).

0.53, isomaltose 0.74, panose 0.44, isomaltotriose 0.62, maltotetraose 0.27, N-acetylglucosamine 0.79, and glucosamine 0.99.

Notes: 1. It is possible to work satisfactorily in a range from 0.5 to 4.5 μg by reducing ferricyanide concentration to one-half and doubling the cyanide concentration without changing the carbonate concentration.

2. Any turbidity developing in the final reaction mixture may be avoided by a slight increase in the acid concentration.

3. The procedure presents some difficulties in the determination of reducing sugar after hydrolysis, since chloride ions interfere to some extent. It is especially useful, however, for analysis of substances with reducing groups and for following chromatography of sugars on columns, etc.

2. REACTIONS FOR CARBOHYDRATES IN GENERAL

These reactions include reactions of the sugar solution in sulfuric acid with reagents such as α-naphthol, orcinol, indole, and tryptophan. The reactions of carbohydrates in strong sulfuric acid have been studied. Each individual sugar reacted with sulfuric acid at a different rate. The ether-extractable, ultraviolet-absorbing chromogens have been identified as furfuraldehyde and some crotonaldehyde from pentoses, and 5-(hydroxymethyl)-2-furfuraldehyde and propionaldehyde from hexoses; formaldehyde and acetaldehyde are also formed with each type of sugar.

a. α-NAPHTHOL REACTION[1a]

This reaction serves as a measure of the hexose, pentose, and methylpentose present, since uronic acids and amino sugars give no color.

Reagents

1. Sulfuric Acid: 89% by volume.

2. α-Naphthol: 2% alcoholic solution freshly prepared. The α-naphthol may be purified by steam distillation and crystallization from toluol.

Procedure. To 0.5 ml of solution (5 to 25 μg of sugar) is added, with mixing, 4.5 ml of reagent 1 with cooling in ice water. Standards and water blanks are run simultaneously. The tubes are transferred to tap water and then to a boiling water bath for 3 minutes. Cool in tap water. Add 0.2 ml of reagent 2 and mix. Read at 560 mμ after 6 hours.

Notes: 1. Absorption maxima: pentose 550 mμ, hexose 570 mμ, heptose and methylpentose 560 mμ. At 560 mμ, ribose, arabinose, rhamnose, and fructose have molar extinction coefficients within 5% that of glucose; galactose and mannose give 50% and 60%, and xylose gives 145% of the color of glucose. Sugars with at least one pair of cis-hydroxyls on carbons 2, 3, or 4 give about one-half of the color of sugars lacking this configuration.

2. In the analysis of proteins two additional blanks are needed: (1) protein plus sulfuric acid; (2) sulfuric acid plus water. Blank 1 is read against blank 2, and the difference in optical density is subtracted from the density of the unknown read against the blank containing α-naphthol plus sulfuric acid.

b. ORCINOL REACTION

Reagents

1. *Sulfuric Acid Solution:* 60 ml of concentrated H_2SO_4 + 40 ml of water.

2. *Orcinol:* 1.6 gm of orcinol (recrystallized from benzene) in 100 ml of water.

3. *Orcinol–Sulfuric Mixture:* 1 volume of reagent 2 plus 7.5 volumes of reagent 1 prepared before use.

Procedure. Place 1 ml of sample (0.10 to 0.50 mg of sugar) and 8.5 ml of reagent 3 in glass-stoppered test tubes; mix by inversion. Heat in a water bath at 80° for exactly 15 minutes along with similarly prepared water blanks and standards. Cool in tap water, and read at 540 mμ.

Notes: 1. For determination of protein-bound hexose in serum, Winzler[5a] recommends mixing 5 ml of 95% ethanol with 0.1 ml of serum in a 15 × 150-mm test tube. Centrifuge precipitated proteins for 15 minutes, decant, wash with 5 ml of 95% ethanol, centrifuge, dissolve the precipitate in 1.0 ml of 0.1 N NaOH, and carry out the procedure as above. Trichloroacetic acid precipitation has also been used for the determination of protein-bound carbohydrate in cerebrospinal fluid[6]; 0.25 ml of 50% trichloroacetic acid to 5.0 ml of cerebrospinal fluid is used. For serum glycoproteins a galactose–mannose mixture containing 0.1 mg of each sugar per milliliter is used, since these are the proportions generally thought to be present in serum glycoproteins.[5a]

2. Hexosamines and sialic acid do not give the orcinol reaction; methylpentoses give 80% of the hexose color. Hexoses and pentoses may be determined in the presence of fucose by correcting for the amount of fucose present (as determined by the Dische and Shettles method described in Section 6,a, below).[5b] Other sugars vary in the color given per mole, and choice of a standard should be determined by the material under study. Several investigators have used different heating times and concentrations of H_2SO_4 and orcinol to identify and estimate individual sugars, and in the determination of protein-bound hexose.

[5a] R. J. Winzler, *in* "Methods of Biochemical Analysis" (D. Glick, ed.), Vol. 2, p. 279. Interscience, New York, 1955.

[5b] C. Nolan and E. L. Smith, *J. Biol. Chem.* **237**, 453 (1963).

[6] Z. Stary, H. Bodru, and S. G. Lisie, *Klin. Wochschr.* **31**, 339 (1953).

special techniques. Absorption coefficients and absorbing wavelengths (λ_{max}) of common proteins, haptens, amino acids, and components of nucleic acids are tabulated in Appendix I. The application of ultraviolet spectroscopy to analysis of specific immune precipitates is discussed in Chap. 10,A and in Chap. 13, Vol. III.

Here we shall discuss only a few considerations in the application of ultraviolet spectroscopy to special problems.

a. GENERAL CONSIDERATIONS

i. Measurements at λ_{max}

Proteins will vary somewhat in their λ_{max}, between 277 and 280 mμ, depending on their relative content of tyrosine ($\lambda_{max} = 275$ mμ, $E_M = 1340$) and tryptophan ($\lambda_{max} = 278$, $E_M = 5550$) and certain as yet undefined characteristics of the three-dimensional conformation. There is a significant shift in λ_{max} in alkaline solution (for example, 0.1 N NaOH) used to solubilize protein precipitates, due in part to loss of native structure and in part to the shift of the λ_{max} of tyrosine to 293 mμ ($E_M = 2330$). With some proteins the absorption will not remain constant at the high pH, necessitating the arbitrary selection of a time for reading after addition of alkali. Reading in 0.25 M acetic acid or in 0.5% sodium dodecyl sulfate is also recommended (p. 170).

Calibration curves or extinction coefficients for each protein employed should be determined at its λ_{max} in solutions most likely to be measured.

ii. Effect of Small Molecules

There are two categories of interference by small molecules to be considered: those in free solution and those bound to protein. The former present no serious problem if dialysis or gel filtration is feasible. Reading a solution at several wavelengths is advisable. The λ_{min} for most proteins is in the vicinity of 250 mμ. If the A_{280}/A_{260} ratio is sufficiently high (approaching 2.0, sometimes higher) and if there is no reading at 320 to 340 mμ, the 280-mμ reading may usually be considered to be due entirely to protein.

Any significant amount of compounds with aromatic nuclei, bile pigments, small nucleotides, nucleoside phosphates, cofactors, etc., which are present will make ultraviolet determinations meaningless. Preservatives containing aromatic rings cannot be used. For example, merthiolate in the concentration ordinarily employed as a preservative (0.01%) would give a reading at 280 mμ equivalent to that of some proteins at 1 mg/ml.

iii. Effect of Nucleic Acids

DNA and RNA have absorption maxima around 260 mμ (individual nucleotides vary in λ_{max}—see Appendix I). Solutions such as tissue or cell extracts that contain nucleic acid in addition to protein obviously cannot be assayed quantitatively by direct spectroscopy in the ultraviolet range. Under some conditions, however, crude estimates can be obtained by methods described in Section A,9,b,*ii* below.

b. SPECIAL APPLICATIONS

i. Monitoring Chromatographic Effluents

Many spectrophotometers can be adapted with a flow cell to receive column effluents, and to deliver a signal proportioned to the absorbancy to a recording device. The fractions are collected in the usual fashion after being monitored spectrophotometrically. Monitors of fixed wavelength are commercially available for this purpose (for example, Gilford Instrument Laboratories, Inc., Oberlin, Ohio; Instrumentation Specialties Co., Inc., Lincoln, Nebraska; LKB Instruments, Inc., Rockville, Maryland; LKB Produkter, Stockholm, Sweden).

It is particularly useful in such a procedure to have an "event" record superimposed on the absorption record by signals from the fraction collector each time it shifts tubes. If such refinements are desirable, and time-saving devices sometimes are critical in fractionation procedures, all components of the monitoring system should be selected for the best compromise between compatibility and versatility.

ii. Nucleic Acid and Protein Content of Crude Solutions

There is always a certain amount of nucleic acid in crude extracts of tissues and cells. It is often important to gain rapidly and conveniently a rough estimate of this quantity as well as the amount of protein present. Several empirical schemes utilizing the readings at 280 mμ and 260 mμ have been devised for this purpose, but they can serve only for preliminary estimations. Further, crude extracts will contain small molecules (oligopeptides or nucleotides) which must be removed, as by dialysis, if A_{280}/A_{260} ratios are to provide an adequate basis for assay.

For protein, the A_{280}/A_{260} ratio tends toward a value of 2.0 and for nucleic acid toward 0.5. Nucleic acids, however, have a much greater absorbancy at 260 mμ than do proteins at their λ_{max} of 280 mμ. Consequently, the A_{280}/A_{260} ratio is useful only in mixtures where, as in most tissues, nucleic acid comprises less than 20% of the ultraviolet-absorbing material.

From absorbancy ratios on mixtures of yeast enolase ($E_{280}^{1\%} = 20.6$) and yeast nucleic acid ($E_{260}^{1\%} = 500.8$), Warburg and Christian calculated factors by which the absorbancy at 280 mμ could serve to estimate the protein concentration of the solution.[23] Kalckar estimated the protein in

[23] O. Warburg and W. Christian, *Biochem. Z.* **310, 384** (1942).

solutions of enzymes[24] by using the equation, mg protein/ml $= 1.45\,A_{280}$ $- 0.74\,A_{260}$. The latter method is somewhat handier since tables of factors or graphs are not required. Neither method is valid for all solutions. The proteins from crude extracts of liver, for example, have an average absorbancy of 1.1 to 1.3 O.D. units/mg/ml. Clearly, factors based on a special protein absorbing 2.06 O.D. units/mg/ml[23] should not be used to estimate protein in liver extracts. The average absorbancy of serum proteins is about 1 O.D. unit/mg/ml, although the serum albumin of some species may absorb only 0.5 O.D./mg/ml. Immunoglobulin absorbancies have been reported to be as high as 1.6.

A method recently described by Groves $et\ al.$[25] for estimating protein in the presence of nucleic acids is based on the difference in optical densities at wavelengths on either side of the λ_{min} for nucleic acids. If wavelengths are chosen so that the absorbancies for nucleic acid alone would be equal, the difference (Δ O.D.) between the measurements would be due to the protein. Appropriate calibration curves could be drawn. The principle is illustrated in Fig. 3. As with other methods, this one requires preliminary analysis to accommodate to special properties of the system. For example, if the lower wavelength is fixed, the higher isoabsorbant wavelength will vary somewhat depending on the buffer system and the type of nucleic acid. The Δ O.D./mg protein/ml will still vary with the content of aromatic amino acids in the proteins, a characteristic for all methods based on ultraviolet absorbancy.

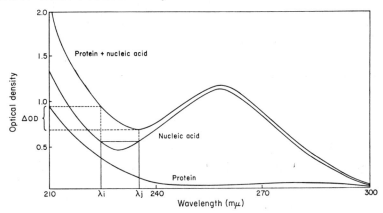

FIG. 3. The contribution of nucleic acid to optical density of protein is eliminated by measuring solution at two isoabsorbance wavelengths, λ_i and λ_j, on either side of the λ_{min} for nucleic acids. The Δ O.D. at these wavelengths is assumed to be proportional to the protein concentration. [W. E. Groves, F. C. Davis, Jr., and B. H. Sells, $Anal.\ Biochem.$ **22**, 195 (1968).]

[24] H. M. Kalckar, $J.\ Biol.\ Chem.$ **167**, 461 (1947).
[25] W. E. Groves, F. C. Davis, Jr. and B. H. Sells, $Anal.\ Biochem.$ **22**, 195 (1968).

If the nucleic acid (DNA or RNA) is of high molecular weight and not denatured, an estimate of its concentration can be obtained by the increase (about 33%) in absorption at 260 mμ upon alkaline denaturation.[26] In 1-cm cuvettes an exact amount of solution (10 to 50 μg of nucleic acid per milliliter of 0.1 M NaCl) is made alkaline (pH > 11.5) by the addition of 0.05 ml of 6 N NaOH. The difference in absorption (corrected for volume changes) multiplied by 3 gives the absorbancy of the native, high-molecular-weight DNA and RNA in the solution ($A_{260} = 1.0$ for about 45 μg of nucleic acid per milliliter). It is important to remember, however, that in most extracts cleared by ultracentrifugation, the bulk of the nucleic acid present is low-molecular-weight RNA which does not give absorption increment.

[26] R. D. Hotchkiss, *in* "Methods in Enzymology" (S. P. Colowick and N. O. Kaplan, eds.), Vol. III, p. 708. Academic Press, New York, 1957.

B. Carbohydrate Analysis*†

In recent years, a large number of color reactions have been developed for the estimation of relatively minute quantities of carbohydrates in the presence of relatively large amounts of protein.[1a–c] Certain of these methods are reactions for carbohydrates in general, while others detect specific kinds of carbohydrates, such as hexoses, heptoses, ketoses, methylpentoses, amino sugars, and uronic acids. Some methods even have applicability for the identification and estimation of individual sugars. When the sugars present in a biological material are not known, it is customary to express results in terms of a specified sugar arbitrarily chosen as a standard. Furthermore, in many of the reactions for carbohydrates, individual sugars may not give the same color value per unit weight so

* Section 12,B was contributed by Curtis A. Williams and Merrill W. Chase.

† The editors are grateful to Dr. Elvin A. Kabat and Charles C. Thomas, Publisher, for permission to excerpt sections of Chapters 18 through 23 of "Kabat and Mayer's Experimental Immunochemistry," 2nd ed., to compile this abbreviated guide to carbohydrate analysis. The advice of Dr. Kenneth O. Lloyd in updating the final copy is also gratefully acknowledged.

It would have been futile for any other author to attempt an improvement on Dr. Kabat's handling of this material. With his advice we have selected a few of the more widely used and most reliable procedures; and in the interest of our limitations on space, we have omitted parts of the discussions and many of the bibliographic references. Investigators who feel the need of a more complete review of the literature with respect to applications, modifications, and interpretations are urged to consult the original text.

[1a] Z. Dische, *in* "Methods of Biochemical Analysis" (D. Glick, ed.), Vol. 2, p. 313. Interscience, New York, 1955.

[1b] R. L. Whistler and M. L. Wolfrom (eds.), "Methods in Carbohydrate Chemistry. Vol. I: Analysis and Preparation of Sugars," Academic Press, New York (1962).

[1c] E. F. Neufeld and V. Ginsberg, "Methods in Enzymology, Vol. VIII: Complex Carbohydrates" (S. P. Colowick and N. O. Kaplan, eds.), Academic Press, New York (1966).

c. Indole Reaction

Reagents

1. *Sulfuric Acid:* 75% by volume.
2. *Indole:* 1% indole in ethanol, freshly prepared.

Procedure. One-half milliliter (5 to 25 μg) of sugar is mixed with 5.0 ml of reagent 1. Add 0.2 ml of reagent 2, mix thoroughly, and heat for 10 minutes in a boiling water bath. Blanks and standards are treated similarly. Cool in tap water, and read at 470mμ.

Notes: 1. All carbohydrates except amino sugars produce a brownish color. Blanks turn yellow on addition of indole, but this color disappears on heating.

2. At 470mμ the extinction coefficients of hexoses, pentoses, and hexuronic acids are within ±50% that of glucose. Fucose and galactose give 1.25 and mannose gives 1.5 times the glucose absorption.

d. Tryptophan Reaction

Reagents

1. *Sulfuric Acid:* 77% by volume.
2. *Tryptophan:* 1% aqueous solution.

Procedure. Mix 7.5-ml portions of reagent 1 with 1 ml of sample (5 to 50 μg of sugar), blanks, and standards in a water bath at 10° to 15°. Add 1 ml of reagent 2, mix, and heat for 20 minutes in a boiling water bath. Cool to room temperature. Read violet brownish color after 30 minutes at 500 mμ in a spectrophotometer.

Notes: 1. At 500 mμ, the optical density of glucose, galactose, mannose, fucose, ribose, and arabinose is about the same; that of xylose is about 20% higher, and that of rhamnose very much higher. Absorption maxima: glucose 480 mμ, pentoses 485 mμ, and methylpentoses 495 mμ

2. For serum carbohydrate 0.2 ml of serum is treated as in note 1 under the orcinol reaction.

3. By including 50 gm of boric acid per liter in reagent 1, and reading at 520 mμ, an increase of about 20 to 30% in optical density per unit weight[7a] was obtained, but the absorption of various monosaccharides was not the same.

e.   Phenol–Sulfuric Acid Reaction[7b]

This reaction is used widely as it is sensitive, rapid and convenient. No separate heating step is required and the reagents are inexpensive and the color is stable for several hours.

[7a] J. Badin, C. Jackson, and M. Schubert, *Proc. Soc. Exptl. Biol. Med.* **84,** 288 (1953).
[7b] M. Dubois, K. A. Gilles, J. K. Hamilton, P. A. Rebers and F. Smith, *Anal. Chem.* **28,** 350 (1956).

Reagents

1. *Sulfuric Acid:* Concentrated analytical reagent grade.

2. *Phenol:* 80% by weight in water.

Procedure. To 400 μl of sugar solution (1–15 μg sugar) is added 20 μl of 80% phenol reagent. Then 1.0 ml of sulfuric acid is added rapidly using a fast-delivery pipet (this pipet may be prepared by cutting off a portion of the tip from a standard 1.0 ml pipet). The stream of acid is directed onto the surface of the liquid in order to obtain rapid mixing. The tubes are allowed to stand at room temperature for at least 30 minutes. The absorbance of the solution is then measured at 490 mμ for hexoses and 480 mμ for methylpentoses, pentoses, and uronic acids.

Notes: 1. Tubes must be scrupulously free of dirt.

2. The intensity of the color is a function of the amount of phenol added. The amount of phenol used may be modified to give maximum sensitivity for the particular sugar being determined.

3. Various classes of compounds such as amino acids, keto acids, aldehydes, and ketones may interfere.[7c]

3. REACTIONS FOR TOTAL HEXOSES

a. ANTHRONE REACTION

Numerous modifications of this reaction have been developed since its introduction by Dreywood. They depend on the formation of furfural derivatives. The procedure of Scott and Melvin[8] is given but with lesser volumes.

Reagents. Anthrone, 0.4 gm in 200 ml of concentrated sulfuric acid (reagent grade) with the lowest possible nitrate content should be used. Keeping the reagent in the refrigerator reduces rate of oxidation by nitrate and discoloration.

Procedure. Two milliliters of anthrone reagent is pipetted into the bottom of 16 $\times$ 150-mm test tubes in a water bath at 10° to 15°. The sample, 1 ml (10 to 50 μg of carbohydrate), is then carefully layered above the reagent. Blanks and standards of glucose or dextran are also included. Each tube is then vigorously shaken while immersed in the cold water bath until thoroughly mixed. The tubes are then brought to about room temperature and heated at 90° for 16 minutes, cooled, and the blue color read at 625 mμ in 10-mm I.D. round cuvettes, such as Coleman "Perfect Round" cuvettes, in the appropriate cuvette holder.

[7c] R. Montgomery, *Biochim. Biophys. Acta,* **48,** 591 (1961).

[8] T. A. Scott and E. H. Melvin, *Anal. Chem.* **25,** 1656 (1953).

Notes: 1. In this method substantial errors may be caused by cellulose fibers, lint, and other sources of carbohydrate.

2. An additional absorption band at 530 mμ has been shown to be due to the formation of a complex of sugar with tryptophan in excess anthrone and sulfuric acid. This may cause an error of 5 to 15%. Tuller and Keiding[9] have corrected for this by a nomogram. Graff *et al.*[10] have shown that lipids may also react with anthrone reagent to produce absorption in this region.

3. The method as given above has been used to determine total hexose in dextran, glycogen, cellulose, etc.[1a] These materials behave identically like glucose. Fructose gives 94% of the color value of glucose.[8] The precision of the method is about 0.5%.

4. Fructose reacts with anthrone more rapidly and under milder conditions than glucose, and the anthrone reaction has been used under different conditions to determine fructose in dextran[11] or in the presence of aldohexoses when pentoses and methylpentoses are absent.[12] Johanson[13] reports that, while pentoses alone give no color with anthrone, a mixture of arabinose and glucose gives substantially higher recoveries than would be expected. If pentose is present, it should be determined independently and a suitable correction made.

b. PRIMARY CYSTEINE–SULFURIC ACID REACTION[1a]

The reaction with cysteine and sulfuric acid using 3 minutes of heating is carried out as described for methylpentoses in Section B,6. For the estimation of total hexose, however, the yellow color that develops is estimated within the first hour after the reaction. Total hexose is proportional to the difference in optical density at 414 and 380 mμ (D_{414} − D_{380}). This second reading at 380 mμ corrects for the absorption due to heptoses and methylpentoses. If greater accuracy is required, a simultaneous analysis of a methylpentose solution is carried out and the exact wavelength around 414 mμ is found at which the absorption is equal to that at 380 mμ; this wavelength is then used for all readings. Under these conditions of temperature and acid concentration pentoses do not interfere.[14] Masamune and co-workers[15] have employed thionalide, $C_{10}H_7NH\cdot$

[9] E. F. Tuller and N. R. Keiding, *Anal. Chem.* **26**, 875 (1954).

[10] M. M. Graff, J. T. McElroy, and A. L. Mooney, *J. Biol. Chem.* **195**, 351 (1952).

[11] C. S. Wise, R. J. Dimler, H. A. Davis, and C. E. Rist, *Anal. Chem.* **27**, 33 (1955).

[12] M. A. Jermyn, *Nature* **177**, 38 (1956).

[13] R. Johanson, *Nature* **171**, 176 (1953).

[14] Z. Dische, *J. Biol. Chem.* **181**, 379 (1949).

[15] H. Masamune and K. Ogawa, *Tohoku J. Exptl. Med.* **60**, 1, 23, 33 (1954). H. Masamune and M. Sakumoto, *ibid.* **63**, 345, 357, 363 (1956).

COCH$_2$SH, in place of cysteine for estimating hexoses, pentoses and methylpentoses under conditions similar to those of Dische.

4. REACTIONS FOR KETO SUGARS

Three procedures are generally available (see ref. 1a): reactions with diphenylamine, with resorcinol and HCl (Seliwanoff's reaction), and with carbazole, cysteine, and sulfuric acid. The latter is the most sensitive and will be described here. It has proved useful for the analysis of fructose in levan-antilevan specific precipitates.

a. DISCHE-BORENFREUND METHOD[16]

Reagents

1. *Cysteine Hydrochloride:* 1.5% aqueous solution.
2. *Sulfuric Acid:* 190 ml of H$_2$O + 450 ml of concentrated sulfuric acid.
3. *Carbazole Solution:* 0.12% carbazole in 95% ethanol.

Procedure. To 1 ml of sample (1 to 10 μg of keto sugar) + 0.2 ml of cysteine solution add 6 ml of sulfuric acid in the cold with shaking, and 0.2 ml of carbazole solution. Mix thoroughly, and let stand for 24 hours at room temperature. The violet color is read at 560 mμ for ketohexoses.

Notes: 1. Maximum absorption for ketopentoses is 540 mμ, and heptuloses vary from 565 to 580 mμ. The extinction coefficient for ketopentoses is less than one-half that of fructose at 18 hours.

2. Color development is much more rapid with ketopentoses; with ribulose optimum color is reached after 15 minutes, and with xylulose after 1 hour.

3. Trioses give a color with an absorption maximum at 650 mμ. In mixtures of fructose and trioses, the former may be determined after 24 hours as $D_{560} - D_{750}$ and the latter as $D_{650} - D_{470}$ at concentrations of up to 10 and 5 μg, respectively.

4. Fructosans like levan and inulin may be determined without hydrolysis.

5. Gamma globulin and antibody give no color with the reagents, so that no correction is necessary in analysis of specific precipitates for keto sugars.[17]

5. PENTOSE DETERMINATION

Two reactions for the determination of pentoses in polysaccharides are given: the Bial reaction with orcinol and ferric chloride in HCl, and

[16] Z. Dische and E. Borenfreund, *J. Biol. Chem.* **192**, 583 (1951).
[17] P. Z. Allen and E. A. Kabat, *J. Exptl. Med.* **105**, 383 (1957).

the cysteine–sulfuric acid method introduced by Dische. A variety of modifications of the Bial reaction have been used. Many of these employed long times of heating to ensure hydrolysis of nucleotides in studies on ribonucleic acid, conditions under which substantial colors due to hexoses appear and must be corrected for by a variety of procedures such as dichromatic readings. A number of these methods have been compared directly.[18] For use with polysaccharides the original procedures of Dische and Schwarz,[19] which employ a short heating time (3 minutes), under which interferences due to hexoses and aldoheptoses are negligible, are given.

a. BIAL REACTION FOR PENTOSES[19]

Two procedures are described.

1. Two-milliliter samples of unknown and standard are each mixed with 2 ml of concentrated HCl containing 0.5 ml of 10% $FeCl_3$ solution per 100 ml. After addition of 0.2 ml of 10% alcoholic orcinol solution, the mixtures are heated for 3 minutes in boiling water.

2. Mix 1 ml of sample and standard with 5 ml of the HCl–$FeCl_3$ reagent, and 0.4 ml of 10% orcinol solution. Heat for 3 minutes in a water bath at 80°. With both procedures, chill the mixtures in ice water and keep in ice water during the entire period necessary for photometry.

Pentoses give a green color with both procedures, as do nucleotides containing a pentose. Trioses also give this reaction but only at concentrations that do not normally occur in animal tissue. Hexoses give a yellow color. The color intensities are measured at 670 mμ. A 0.1% solution of glucose gives no absorption, while a 0.01% solution of fructose has about $\frac{1}{20}$ the absorption of an equivalent amount of adenylic acid in reaction 1, and about $\frac{1}{50}$ the absorption in reaction 2.

Efforts should always be made to evaluate possible interferences due to other materials known to be present in the polysaccharide. Individual pentoses give very different extinction coefficients by this procedure, and the relative extinctions vary with procedures 1 and 2. Dische and Schwarz have taken advantage of this to determine individual pentoses in binary mixtures. This reaction has been used by Svennerholm[20] for the determination of sialic acids which give a red-violet color with an absorption maximum at 570 mμ; the colored compound is extracted with amyl alcohol. Heating time is prolonged to 15 minutes.

[18] G. L. Miller, R. H. Golder, and E. E. Miller, *Anal. Chem.* **23**, 903 (1951).

[19] Z. Dische and K. Schwartz, *Mikrochim. Acta* **2**, 13 (1937).

[20] L. Svennerholm, *Arkiv Kemi* **10**, 577 (1957).

b. CYSTEINE–SULFURIC ACID METHOD[14]

This procedure (called PCyR) permits the determination of pentoses in the presence of hexoses and methylpentoses. Hexuronic acids, heptoses, and 2-deoxypentoses may interfere. By varying conditions, these other substances may also be determined, but the modifications given in the sections on these constituents are more satisfactory.

Reagents

1. Concentrated Sulfuric Acid.

2. Cysteine–HCl: 3% aqueous solution.

Procedure. To 1 ml of sample (10 to 50 μg of pentose) add 4 ml of concentrated sulfuric acid with cooling in tap water. The reaction mixture is then kept at room temperature for 1 hour with shaking to avoid formation of air bubbles. Add 0.1 ml of cysteine solution and mix. Pentoses are determined by the difference $D_{390} - D_{424}$ between 10 and 30 minutes after addition of the cysteine solution.

Notes: 1. Extinction coefficients for ribose, yeast adenylic acid, and arabinose are about the same per mole; xylose gives values about twice that of ribose. Adenosine 3-phosphate absorbs about sixteen times as strongly as adenosine 5-phosphate.

2. With increasing times beyond 30 minutes, the $D_{390} - D_{424}$ decreases for pentoses and increases for methylpentoses. If large amounts of methylpentose are present some interference may result even in 10 to 30 minutes. Hexoses may be detected by the yellow color which they produce. Heptoses interfere in this reaction, but they may be detected by the slowly developing purple color with an absorption at 510 mμ.

3. Polysaccharides require no previous hydrolysis.

4. With crude materials additional blanks without cysteine should be run.

6. METHYLPENTOSE DETERMINATION

Methylpentoses such as rhamnose (6-deoxy-D-mannose) and fucose (6-deoxy-L-galactose) occur in a number of polysaccharides of immunologic interest. Rhamnose has been found in the type II pneumococcal capsular polysaccharides, the cell wall of the hemolytic streptococcus, consisting largely of the somatic "C" carbohydrate, and the somatic polysaccharides of *Shigella*, *Salmonella*, and *Escherichia coli*; fucose has been found in animal tissues, notably in the blood group substances, the serum glycoproteins, and various neutral mucopolysaccharides. The 3,6-dideoxyhexoses are present in *Salmonella* somatic polysaccharides, and a series of fucose–containing oligosaccharides have been isolated from human milk and from blood group substances. Fucose and rhamnose may be separated from one another, from the dideoxyhexoses, and from other monosaccharides on paper chromatograms.[21,22]

a. DISCHE AND SHETTLES METHOD[23]

Reagents

1. *Sulfuric Acid:* 6 parts of concentrated H_2SO_4 + 1 part water by volume.

2. *Cysteine Hydrochloride:* 3% solution prepared weekly and stored in the refrigerator.

Procedure. To 1 ml of an ice-cold solution containing 3 to 10 μg of methylpentose, 4.5 ml of chilled sulfuric acid solution is added slowly and with constant shaking in an ice bath to prevent a rise in temperature. The tubes are transferred to a water bath at room temperature for a few minutes, then to a vigorously boiling water bath, which should not cease boiling when the tubes are inserted. After being heated for exactly 3 minutes, the tubes are placed in a water bath at room temperature; 0.1 ml of cysteine hydrochloride solution is added, and the contents of each tube are thoroughly mixed. After 2 hours the absorption is measured in a suitable spectrophotometer at 396 mμ and at 430 mμ, the difference being directly proportional to methylpentose content of the solutions.

Notes: 1. The principle of the method depends on the absence of methylpentose absorption at 430 mμ and the finding of Dische and Shettles that the hexoses, pentoses, and glucuronic and galacturonic acids have symmetrical absorption curves such that their absorption at 396 mμ and at 430 mμ is the same, and hence subtraction of the latter value from the former corrects for all absorptions except that due to methylpentose. In some instances the absorption at 427 mμ rather than at 430 mμ for the hexoses equaled that at 396 mμ. This may be checked by running a known hexose solution along with the methylpentose determinations.

2. The method may also be carried out by using a 10-minute period of heating rather than 3 minutes. Dische and Shettles consider this 10-minute reaction somewhat more specific, but the 3-minute reaction permits simultaneous determination of hexoses. Ikawa and Niemann[24] have studied the reaction of methylpentoses and hexoses on heating for 15 minutes in 79% by weight sulfuric acid (1.0 ml of sample + 9 ml of

[21] J. T. Edward and D. M. Waldron, *J. Chem. Soc.* Part III, 3631 (1952).

[22] E. A. Kabat, "Kabat and Mayer's Experimental Immunochemistry," 2nd ed., p. 540. Thomas, Springfield, Illinois, 1961.

[23] Z. Dische and L. B. Shettles, *J. Biol. Chem.* **175**, 595 (1948).

[24] M. Ikawa and C. Niemann, *J. Biol. Chem.* **180**, 923 (1949); *Arch. Biochem. Biophys.* **31**, 62 (1951).

84% by weight H_2SO_4). Methylpentoses showed a characteristic absorption at 327 mμ not given by the other sugars. Ketohexoses showed a unique absorption with a maximum at about 315 mμ after 2 hours in 79% H_2SO_4 at room temperature.

3. With substances of biological origin which give colors on heating with sulfuric acid alone, additional samples of the standard, the unknown solution, and a water blank without addition of cysteine are carried out to evaluate the extent of this interference. With this type of correction, 0.05% serum albumin, which gave a brownish color in sulfuric acid, did not affect the $E_{396} - E_{430}$ for 0.001% fucose.

4. Confirmatory evidence for the presence of methylpentose may be obtained[25a] after carrying out the procedure as outlined above if 0.8 or 1.2 ml of water are added to each determination and to the standards with mixing. After 4 hours at room temperature $E_{390} - E_{430}$ is again determined. Dilution with 0.8 ml or 1.2 ml of water causes a decrease of about 40% and 60%, respectively, in the absorption. If galactose is present in the unknown, the change in absorption for a galactose standard on dilution should be used to correct the methylpentose readings.

5. Fucose and rhamnose give equal color intensities. On a molar basis D-glucomethylose gave 165%, D-gulomethylose 115%, L-thevetose (3-O-methyl-D-glucomethylose) 150%, and 3-O-methyl-D-fucose 94% of the fucose color. 2-Deoxy-6-methylpentoses (dideoxyhexoses) gave no specific colors by this method. 2-Deoxyglucose reacted differently with cysteine and with thioglycolic acid; only with the former reagent could methylpentose be satisfactorily determined in the presence of 2-deoxyglucose.

6. The determination of 3-deoxy-hexoses and their derivatives, such as 3,6-dideoxyhexoses, may be accomplished by a specific method involving periodate oxidation of the sugar followed by assay of the malonaldehyde product with 2-thiobarbituric acid.[25b]

7. Heidelberger et al.[26,27] have used precipitation with antibody to isolate the antigenic moiety from mixed polysaccharides for carbohydrate analysis. Washed specific precipitates were dissociated with a measured volume of 5% TCA at room temperature for 15 minutes, immunoglobulin remaining insoluble. Carbohydrate analysis was conducted as above on the supernatant: the procedure was applicable to galactan, glucuronic acid, and galactose. In such work, antibody standards were made up with comparable quantities of 5% TCA.

[25a] Z. Dische and L. B. Shettles, J. Biol. Chem. 192, 579 (1951).

[25b] M. A. Cynkin and G. Ashwell, Nature, 186, 155 (1960).

[26] M. Heidelberger, Z. Dische, W. Brock Neely, and M. L. Wolfrom, J. Am. Chem. Soc. 77, 3511 (1955).

[27] M. Heidelberger and J. Adams, J. Exptl. Med. 103, 189 (1956); M. Heidelberger, J. Adams, and Z. Dische, J. Am. Chem. Soc. 78, 2853 (1956).

7. HEXOSAMINE AND N-ACETYLHEXOSAMINE ESTIMATION

Many immunologically active polysaccharides, including some of the pneumococcal polysaccharides and the blood group substances, have been found to contain hexosamines generally present as the N-acetyl derivatives. The two most frequently encountered are glucosamine (2-amino-2-deoxy-D-glucose) and galactosamine or chondrosamine (2-amino-2-deoxy-D-galactose), so that the total hexosamine content is an important analytical datum in characterizing preparations of these materials (for a review of the chemistry of amino sugars, see Baer[28]).

The term hexosamine originally was employed in studies on glucosamine and galactosamine and their derivatives when identification was uncertain, and this term will be retained for the 2-amino-2-deoxy-hexoses and their derivatives. In instances in which identification has only been made chromatographically, some doubt may exist as to the identity of a given hexosamine. Crumpton[29] has reported chromatographic and electrophoretic data which should prove very useful in identifying unknown amino sugars or their N-acetyl derivatives; a detailed summary of the data may be found in Kabat.[30a] Amino acid analyzers, when available, afford a convenient method for the determination of hexosamines, particularly in mixtures.[30a]

a. HEXOSAMINE DETERMINATION

The earliest and most widely used method of hexosamine (2-amino-2-deoxyhexose) determination was developed by Elson and Morgan.[31] It involves the condensation of the amino sugar with alkaline acetylacetone; Ehrlich's reagent, p-dimethylaminobenzaldehyde, is then added to give a reddish pink color. Two and possibly three chromogens are formed in the reaction. One of these, 2-methylpyrrole, is the principal chromogen absorbing maximally at 550 mμ, while the other chromogen shows an absorption maximum at 512 mμ. These findings may explain the erratic results encountered with the reaction which have led to numerous modifications and which emphasize the importance of adhering carefully to a rigid technique, since slight variations in procedure, especially those affecting pH during the condensation with acetylacetone, markedly influence the

[28] H. H. Baer, *Fortschr. Chem. Forschung.* **3**, 822 (1958).

[29] M. J. Crumpton, *Biochem. J.* **72**, 479 (1959).

[30a] E. A. Kabat, "Kabat and Mayer's Experimental Immunochemistry," 2nd ed., pp. 514–519. Thomas, Springfield, Illinois, 1961.

[30b] R. Montgomery and Y. C. Wu, *J. Biol. Chem.* **238**, 3547 (1963).

[31] L. A. Elson and W. T. J. Morgan, *Biochem. J.* **27**, 1824 (1933).

color.[32] In addition, similar colors are developed owing to interactions between sugars and amino acids under these conditions. Boas[33] and Blix[34] eliminated such interference, the former by separating the hexosamines by absorption on an ion exchange resin, and the latter by modifying the acetylacetone reagent.

In hexosamine analysis of polysaccharides considerable difficulty has been caused by the need for the removal or neutralization of the acid used for hydrolysis before proceeding with the analyses. Neutralization procedures are difficult to perform because of the ease with which amino sugars may be destroyed by local excesses of alkali. A variety of neutralization procedures have been examined recently in some detail.[35a] One satisfactory procedure consists in removal of the hydrochloric acid used for hydrolysis by evaporation to dryness in a vacuum desiccator over solid NaOH and P_2O_5 with a hyvac pump.[35b] Since not all polysaccharides are completely hydrolyzed under a given set of conditions, it is important to run hydrolysis curves for each sugar to determine conditions for maximum liberation of hexosamine.

With a view toward completely standardizing the Elson-Morgan method described here, an automated procedure has been recently introduced.[35c]

ELSON-MORGAN METHOD (MODIFIED)

Reagents

1. Acetylacetone Solution: Prepared immediately before use by dissolving 0.2 ml of acetylacetone in 10 ml of 0.5 N Na_2CO_3. The acetylacetone (Eastman Kodak No. 1088), which should be colorless, is kept cold.

2. Aldehyde-Free Absolute Alcohol: U. S. Industrial Chemicals.

3. Ehrlich's Reagent: Dissolve 0.8 gm of *p*-dimethylaminobenzaldehyde in 30 ml of absolute ethanol and add 30 ml of concentrated HCl (specific gravity 1.18). This solution can be kept in the refrigerator for a few days. *p*-Dimethylaminobenzaldehyde of satisfactory purity can be obtained from Pfanstiehl.

[32] C. J. M. Rondle and W. T. J. Morgan, *Biochem. J.* **61**, 586 (1955).

[33] N. F. Boas, *J. Biol. Chem.* **204**, 553 (1953).

[34] G. Blix, *Acta Chem. Scand.* **2**, 467 (1948).

[35a] E. F. Hartree, *Anal. Biochem.* **7**, 203 (1964).

[35b] J. P. Johnston, A. G. Ogston, and J. E. Stanier, *Analyst* **76**, 88 (1951).

[35c] E. A. Balazs, K. O. Bernstsen, J. Karossa, and D. A. Swann, *Anal. Biochem.* **12**, 559 (1965).

Procedure (Modified from Rondle and Morgan[32] and Belcher *et al.*[36]).
A solution of polysaccharide containing a suitable quantity of hexosamine
(10 to 100 μg) is pipetted into a Pyrex test tube (100 × 13 mm), and
concentrated HCl (12 *N*) is added to give the concentration determined for maximum liberation of hexosamine. The tubes are sealed
and placed in a vigorously boiling water bath and hydrolyzed for an
interval to yield maximum liberation of hexosamine. With the blood
group substances this has been found to be 2 hours in 2 *N* HCl.[37] The
tubes are cooled, centrifuged to remove traces of solution from the
upper end, opened, and evaporated to dryness in a vacuum desiccator
with an oil pump. The desiccator should contain copious amounts
of NaOH pellets and phosphorus pentoxide, each in separate small
beakers. Care should be taken to guard against spattering. This may
be accomplished by not evacuating below about 10 to 20 mm of mercury at first and resuming evacuation after an hour or two until the
pressure is below 1 mm of mercury. It is not necessary to run the pump
continuously. (Protect the pump with a soda-lime trap.) If the volumes of
solution are not large, tubes may be dry overnight. Care should be taken
to be sure the tubes are completely dry. The contents of each tube are
dissolved in a small amount of water and quantitatively transferred to a
10-ml Pyrex volumetric flask. The amounts of water used should be
measured; the total volume used for each transfer is 4 ml. Blanks and
standard solutions containing 10 to 100 μg of glucosamine hydrochloride
are also set up. One milliliter of acetylacetone reagent is added from a
1.0-ml analytical pipet. Mix by rotation. Stopper flasks securely, and
immerse in boiling water to a depth sufficient to cover the solution. After
30 minutes, cool the flasks to room temperature. Add 3 ml of absolute
ethanol, and mix by rotation. Add 1.0 ml of Ehrlich's reagent with stirring.
Make up to mark with absolute ethanol. Stopper and mix thoroughly and
vigorously, taking care to allow release of CO_2 by loosening the stopper
carefully several times while mixing. Place in a 37° water bath for 30
minutes to allow maximum color development. Cool to room temperature.
Read in a spectrophotometer at 540 mμ. The amount of hexosamine is
calculated from a calibration curve.

Notes: 1. In analyzing specific precipitates for hexosamine the washed
precipitate in the conical centrifuge tube should be dissolved completely
in 0.2 ml of concentrated HCl; then 1.0 ml of water is added to make the
final concentration 2 *N* (or appropriate volumes for other desired concentrations), the tube is sealed, and the solution is hydrolyzed.[37]

2. It is desirable to run one or two known solutions of glucosamine

[36] R. Belcher, A. J. Nutten, and C. M. Sambrook, *Analyst* **79**, 201 (1954).
[37] E. A. Kabat, A. Bendich, and A. E. Bezer, *J. Exptl. Med.* **83**, 477 (1946).

hydrochloride which have been hydrolyzed and dried just like the samples and to compare these with standards which are pipetted directly into the volumetric flasks.

3. The final colors developed by glucosamine and galactosamine hydrochloride are identical spectrophotometrically and are of equal intensity for equal weights of the sugars. Crumpton,[29] reading at 530 mμ and developing the final color at 65° to 70°, reported the following color equivalents ($\pm 3\%$) relative to glucosamine as 100; mannosamine 69, gulosamine 81, allosamine 83, galactosamine 92, fucosamine 92, galactosaminuronic acid 100, talosamine 112, and xylosamine 156. Values will vary somewhat with the various techniques.

b. N-Acetylhexosamine Determination

N-acetylhexosamines have been determined by the formation of a chromogen which reacts with Ehrlich's reagent on heating in sodium carbonate solution in the absence of acetylacetone. The reaction has been used extensively in studies on the blood group substances, since these materials yield a substantial amount of chromogen on treatment with sodium carbonate.[38] Sialic acids react with Ehrlich's reagent on heating,[39] and the substituted N-acetylglucosamine from group O(H) substance reacts with Ehrlich's reagent in the cold[40]; with these substances sodium carbonate treatment is unnecessary.

Three chromogens may be detected by paper chromatography after reaction of N-acetylglucosamine in 0.05 N Na$_2$CO$_3$ at 100°, of which chromogen I predominates; by boiling N-acetylglucosamine in pyridine, chromogen III is formed in largest quantity. Chromogen III was crystallized and its structure determined as 3 acetamino-5-(α,β-dihydroxyethylfuran).

Two procedures are given, one based on the reaction in sodium carbonate and the other on the reaction in borate buffer. The latter has been found to give about twice the color intensity of the former. The latter method has also been adapted to very small volumes by use of micropipets.

AMINOFF, MORGAN, AND WATKINS METHOD[38]

Reagents

1. *0.5 N Na$_2$CO$_3$ Solution.*

2. *Ehrlich's Reagent:* Dissolve 2 gm of p-dimethylaminobenzaldehyde in 100 ml of glacial acetic acid (analytical reagent) which contains 2.5% (v/v) of 10 N HCl. The solution should be prepared just before use.

[38] D. Aminoff, W. T. J. Morgan, and W. M. Watkins, *Biochem. J.* **51**, 379 (1952).

[39] I. Werner and L. Odin, *Acta Soc. Med. Upsaliensis* **57**, 230 (1952).

[40] G. Schiffman, C. Howe, and E. A. Kabat, *J. Am. Chem. Soc.* **80**, 6662 (1958).

3. Glacial Acetic Acid: Analytical reagent.

Procedure. To 1 ml of a neutral solution of the sample in a 10-ml Pyrex volumetric flask, add 0.1 ml of 0.5 N Na_2CO_3 solution, and mix the contents of the flask by rotation. Set up known samples of 10, 20, and 30 μg of N-acetylglucosamine or 50, 100, and 150 μg of N-acetylgalactosamine, and a blank of distilled water. Then heat the flasks for exactly 4 minutes in a vigorously boiling water bath, and cool in ice water. Add 7 ml of glacial acetic acid to each flask from a fast flowing buret, and then add 1.0 ml of Ehrlich's reagent. Adjust to 10 ml with glacial acetic acid. Stopper and mix thoroughly. Set in the dark for 1.5 hours to allow maximum color development. Read in a spectrophotometer at 550 mμ.

Notes: 1. N-Acetylgalactosamine gives but 23% [38] and talosamine 20% [41] of the color of N-acetylglucosamine. Results are generally expressed as equivalent N-acetylglucosamine.

2. In examining unknown polysaccharides for equivalent N-acetylglucosamine content, it is desirable to heat in Na_2CO_3 solution for various intervals to determine the time for optimum color development and compare this with the 4-minute heating period for N-acetylglucosamine.

3. Derivatives of N-acetylglucosamine linked in position 4 have been shown[42] not to give a color for N-acetylhexosamine. Further studies[43] using the Aminoff, Morgan, and Watkins method have given the following color equivalents relative to N-acetyl-D-glucosamine for its substituted derivatives: 3-methyl 160%; 4-methyl 3%; 6-methyl 100%; 3,4-dimethyl 3%; 3,6-dimethyl 140%; 4,6-dimethyl 8%; 3,4,6-trimethyl 1%; for N-acetyl-D-galactosamine 25%; for derivatives of N-acetyl-D-galactosamine: 4-methyl 4%; 3,4-dimethyl 2%; 4,6-dimethyl 3%; 2,4,6-trimethyl 2%; N-acetyl-D-allosamine 50%.

REISSIG, STROMINGER, AND LELOIR METHOD[44]

Reagents

1. Potassium Tetraborate (Fisher Scientific): 24.7 gm of H_3BO_3 + 9 gm of KOH adjusted with KOH to pH 9.1 and made up to 1 liter (pH 8.9 when diluted six fold).

2. p-Dimethylaminobenzaldehyde: 10 gm dissolved in 100 ml of glacial acetic acid and containing 12.5% (v/v) 10 N HCl. The reagent may be stored for a month at 2°, or small quantities may be made up fresh. Before use dilute with 9 volumes of glacial acetic acid.

[41] M. J. Crumpton, *Nature* **180**, 605 (1957).
[42] R. Kuhn, A. Gauhe, and H. H. Baer, *Chem. Ber.* **87**, 1138 (1954).
[43] R. W. Jeanloz and M. Tremege, *Federation Proc.* **15**, 282 (1956).
[44] J. L. Reissig, J. L. Strominger, and L. F. Leloir, *J. Biol. Chem.* **217**, 959 (1955).

Procedures.[40,44] To the samples, blanks, and standards containing about 5 to 10 μg of *N*-acetylglucosamine in a volume of 0.25 ml is added 0.05 ml of potassium tetraborate solution. Samples and potassium tetraborate are measured with micropipets into 75 × 13-mm test tubes. After thorough mixing, the tubes are heated for exactly 3 minutes in a boiling water bath and cooled in tap water. Then 1.5 ml of *p*-dimethylamino-benzaldehyde solution is added to each tube; the contents are mixed, placed for exactly 20 minutes in a water bath at 37°, cooled in tap water, and read without delay in the spectrophotometer at 544 mμ or at 585 mμ with cells of 1-cm light path holding about 0.8 to 1.0 ml.

Notes: 1. *N*-Acetylgalactosamine has been found to give 31% and 35% of the color value of *N*-acetylglucosamine. Values for the other amino sugars are not available.

2. Hexosamine × 1.238 = *N*-acetylhexosamine.

8. ESTIMATION OF URONIC ACID

A number of immunologically active polysaccharides contain uronic acids, so that their determination is frequently of importance to the immunochemist. A variety of reactions for uronic acid are available. One widely used procedure is based on the reaction of uronic acids with 12% HCl by weight to liberate one molecule of carbon dioxide and to form furfural and water.

Ogston and Stanier[45] have introduced a convenient micro method based on diffusion of the CO_2 which requires of the order of 100 μg of free or combined uronic acid.

In addition, qualitative and quantitative methods for uronic acids based on the Tollens color reaction with naphthoresorcinol[46] have been proposed, and the Bial reaction for pentoses[46] has also been used when pentoses were absent. Dische,[47] however, has introduced a very convenient colorimetric method for the determination of uronic acids applicable to the analysis of specific precipitates,[48] as well as methods for the differentiation of galacturonic from glucuronic acids.[49] Separation of these two uronic acids has also been accomplished by ion exchange[50] and by paper chromatography.[51] Two modifications of the Dische colorimetric carbazole method are given below.

[45] A. G. Ogston and J. E. Stanier, *Biochem. J.* **49**, 591 (1951).

[46] A. H. Brown, *Arch. Biochem.* **11**, 269 (1946).

[47] Z. Dische, *J. Biol. Chem.* **167**, 189 (1947).

[48] E. A. Kabat, "Kabat and Mayer's Experimental Immunochemistry," 2nd ed., pp. 384–404. Thomas, Springfield, Illinois, 1961.

[49] Z. Dische, *J. Biol. Chem.* **183**, 489 (1950).

[50] J. X. Khym and D. G. Doherty, *J. Am. Chem. Soc.* **74**, 3199 (1952).

[51] H. Masamune and M. Maki, *Tohoku J. Exptl. Med.* **55**, 299 (1951).

a. METHOD A: REACTION AT 100° [47]

This procedure is essentially a method for determining total uronic acid, since free uronic acids and polyuronides react with almost equal intensity. 5-Formylfuroic acid appears to be the chief substance responsible for the color formation in this reaction.[52]

Procedure. To 1 ml of solution containing 5 to 100 μg of uronic acid, 6 ml of concentrated sulfuric acid (analytical reagent grade) is added with cooling and thorough mixing. The tubes are then heated for 20 minutes in a boiling water bath. The mixture is cooled to room temperature, and 0.2 ml of a 0.1% solution of carbazole in ethanol is added with shaking. After about 10 minutes a pink color appears which increases in intensity for about 2 hours and remains practically unchanged for at least an hour. The color later decreases in intensity by about one-third in 24 hours. Read in a spectrophotometer at 530 mμ against blank using water.

Notes: 1. The pink color shows a very characteristic sensitivity toward water. If 3.8 ml of water is added to the reaction mixture with cooling, the color fades rapidly and disappears in about 3 minutes. On further prolonged standing at room temperature a weak violet color characteristic of all sugars appears. Bowness[53] has used this for the quantitative estimation of glucuronolactone, glucose, and xylose in mixtures.

2. At a concentration of 100 μg/ml, at which uronic acids give a deep violet color, no visible reaction is given by true sugars. Higher concentrations give rise to colors that differ from those given by uronic acids. If the quantity and nature of other sugars is known, as for instance in purified polysaccharides, their contribution to the color may be estimated on a known sample and the uronic acid value corrected accordingly.

3. Per unit weight, galacturonic acid gave only about 88%, heparin 162%, hyaluronic acid 113%, and alginic acid 20% of the color of glucuronic acid.[47]

4. Sulfhydryl compounds interfere with the determination by increasing the rate of color development and its intensity.

5. Serum proteins do not interfere appreciably up to a concentration of 200 μg/ml. At higher levels they exert a depressing effect on the uronic acid color. If the depressing effect of the protein is determined by addition to known amounts of uronic acid, the protein contribution may be estimated.

b. METHOD B: REACTION AT 60° [49]

This modification in which the acid concentration and time and temperature of heating are decreased gives different color values with

[52] J. M. Bowness, *Biochem. J.* **70**, 107 (1958).
[53] J. M. Bowness, *Biochem. J.* **67**, 295 (1957).

different hexuronic acids; the color depends also on the mode of linkage of the various polyuronides. Galacturonic acid gives a color thirty times as intense as does glucuronic acid.

Procedure. 5.4 ml of a mixture of 1 part of water plus 6 parts of concentrated H_2SO_4 are pipetted into test tubes. The acid is cooled to 0°, and 0.4 ml of a solution containing 20 to 100 μg of hexuronic acid is added. The contents of the tubes are mixed in ice water. When the reaction mixture has cooled to 0°, it is held for 3 minutes in tap water at room temperature, and then immersed immediately in a 60° water bath for 90 seconds The mixture is cooled in tap water, and 0.2 ml of a 0.1% solution of carbazole in ethanol is added with vigorous mixing. Read after 1 hour at room temperature against a blank containing 0.4 ml of distilled water in the spectrophotometer at 527 mμ.

Notes: 1. Carbazole (Eastman-Kodak) should be recrystallized twice from benzene.

2. Amounts as high as 200 μg of hexoses, pentoses, methylpentoses, and deoxyribosenucleic acid do not give an appreciable color.

3. Two types of behavior of polyuronides have been noted. One group including pectic acid and Types I and III pneumococcal polysaccharide, gives no color whatever, nor does β-menthol glucuronide. The second group, including hyaluronic acid, chondroitin sulfuric acid, heparin, and alginic acid, shows a considerable increase in color, and hyaluronic acid shows twenty times the color expected from its content of glucuronic acid. Accordingly certain polymers of uronic acids are linked in a manner reducing color development, while others have linkages which give enhanced color.

4. Dische[49] suggests characterization of polyuronides by combined determination of their uronic acid content by the LeFevre-Tollens reaction and their color value by method B as compared with equal amounts of glucuronic or galacturonic acid. He also proposes the use of methods A and B relative to galacturonic acid as a standard at equal concentrations as a way of characterizing different polyuronides. Thus at concentrations of 0.8 mg/ml the ratio of the 60°:100° reactions (i.e., optical density developed at 60° to that at 100°) relative to galacturonic acid was 0.53 for hyaluronic acid and 0.17 for chondroitin sulfuric acid.

9. DETERMINATION OF SIALIC ACIDS

This group of substances refers to derivatives of an amino sugar, termed neuraminic acid, which has never been isolated except as its methylglycoside. The sialic acids include the *N*-acetyl, the *N,O*-diacetyl, and the *N*-glycolyl derivatives. They are present in erythrocytes, in various serum proteins, in mucolipids and mucoproteins, and in various bacteria, notably *E. coli* K235 and the group C meningococcus (for a survey and references, see ref. 54).

Numerous colorimetric reactions for the sialic acids have been developed, including the Bial orcinol (see Section B,5,a and ref. 20), resorcinol, diphenylamine[55] (see also Section D,1,b), direct Ehrlich,[56] and tryptophan–perchloric acid reactions, and a method involving periodate oxidation and coupling with 2-thiobarbituric acid which has been used for the detection of 2-deoxyribose and 2-keto-3-deoxysugar acids.[57-60] Most of the reactions are used for the determination of other carbohydrates as well and cannot be applied directly to tissues. The Bial orcinol reaction gives identical colors with ketohexoses and sialic acids and can be used only when these substances are present in minimal quantity.

Three methods are described below.

a. Resorcinol–HCl Method[61]

Use of dichromatic readings permits determination of the sialic acids in the presence of other carbohydrates and ketohexoses.

Reagents

1. Hydrochloric Acid: Analytical reagent, density 1.19, containing at least 36.4% HCl and not more than 0.0001% iron.

2. 0.1 M Copper Sulfate: 24.97 gm of $CuSO_4 \cdot 5H_2O$ made up to 1 liter with water.

3. Resorcinol: 2 gm of resorcinol in 100 ml of distilled water (stable for months in refrigerator).

4. Resorcinol Reagent: 10 ml of reagent 3 + 80 ml of reagent 1 containing 0.25 ml of reagent 2. Prepare at least 4 hours before use; stable for 1 week in refrigerator.

5. Blank Reagent: Identical with reagent 4 but without resorcinol.

6. Isoamyl Alcohol: Mix 1 liter of isoamyl alcohol with 200 ml of concentrated HCl; allow to stand for 1 week. Separate and wash alcohol phase ten times with 200 ml of water. Dry over anhydrous K_2CO_3. Distill, taking fraction boiling between 130° and 133°.

Procedure. Three 2-ml samples of unknowns and standards containing 10 to 30 μg of any of the sialic acids are pipetted into test tubes. Add

[54] G. F. Springer (ed.), "Fifth Macy Conference on Polysaccharides in Biology," June 1–3, 1959, Josiah Macy Jr. Foundation, New York.

[55] A. Saifer and H. A. Siegel, *J. Lab. Clin. Med.* **53**, 474 (1959).

[56] I. Werner and L. Odin, *Acta Soc. Med. Upsaliensis* **57**, 230 (1952).

[57] V. S. Waravdekar and L. D. Saslaw, *Biochim. Biophys. Acta* **24**, 439 (1957).

[58] A. Weissbach and J. Hurwitz, *J. Biol. Chem.* **234**, 705 (1959).

[59] D. Aminoff, *Virology* **7**, 355 (1959).

[60] L. Warren, *J. Biol. Chem.* **234**, 1971 (1959).

[61] L. Svennerholm, *Biochim. Biophys. Acta* **24**, 604 (1957).

2 ml of reagent 4 to two tubes and 2 ml of reagent 5 to the third. If the unknowns contain other carbohydrates, a known mixture of these is also set up. Heat at 110° in an oil bath for 15 minutes or in a boiling water bath. Cool in running water, and add 5 ml of reagent 6 to each tube. Shake vigorously, and place in ice water for 15 minutes. Centrifuge at 1000 to 1500 rpm for 1 minute. The tubes are replaced in ice water, and the amyl alcohol phase is read at 450 mμ and at 580 mμ against pure amyl alcohol within 1 hour after heating. The difference $D_{580} - D_{450}$ is a measure of the sialic acid content.

b. THIOBARBITURIC ACID METHOD[60]

This procedure has been reported to be the most specific.
Reagents
1. *Sodium Metaperiodate:* 0.2 M in 9 M H_3PO_4.
2. *Sodium Arsenite:* 10% solution in 0.5 M sodium sulfate and 0.1 N H_2SO_4.
3. *Thiobarbituric Acid:* 0.6% in 5 M sodium sulfate.
4. *Cyclohexanone.*
All solutions are stable for at least 1 month at room temperature.
Procedure. To a sample containing up to about 15 μg (0.05 μmole) of N-acetylneuraminic acid or the other sialic acids in a volume of 0.2 ml, add 0.1 ml of reagent 1. Mix and allow to stand for 20 minutes. Add 1 ml of reagent 2, and mix until the yellow color disappears. Add 3 ml of reagent 3, mix, and heat in a boiling water bath for 15 minutes while covered with a glass marble. Place in cold water for 5 minutes. The red color that develops may fade, and the solution may become cloudy without affecting the results. Add 4.3 ml of cyclohexanone, shake to extract color, centrifuge, and read at 549 mμ against a blank using water instead of the sample. The color developed is linear up to 0.06 μmole.

Notes: 1. In tissues, a correction for 2-deoxyribose is necessary. This may be detected by the presence of a second peak at 532 mμ. The formula μmole N-acetylneuraminic acid = 0.09 OD_{549} − 0.033 OD_{532} has been used to correct for the 2-deoxyribose when small amounts are present with large amounts of sialic acid. The color due to the sialic acid is destroyed by strong base, while that due to 2-deoxyribose is stable.

2. A large number of sugars and amino sugars give no interference except for L-fucose, which causes a 35% decrease in optical density attributable to the acetaldehyde formed on periodate oxidation.

3. The procedure as described measures only free sialic acid. For determination of bound sialic acid, the tissue is heated in 0.1 N H_2SO_4 at 80° for 1 hour to release the sialic acid.[61]

4. Paper chromatographic separation of N-acetyl and N-glycolyl neur-

aminic acids has been accomplished on Whatman No. 1 paper using
n-butanol, n-propanol, 0.1 N HCl mixtures in ratios of $1:2:1$. The R_f
values are: N-acetyl $= 0.45$; N-glycolyl $= 0.34$.[62] Spots were located with
Ehrlich's reagent (see below).

c. DIRECT EHRLICH'S REACTION

Reagent.[56] Five percent solution of p-dimethylaminobenzaldehyde in
equal parts of concentrated HCl and distilled water.

Procedure. To 10 to 25 mg of protein in 5 ml in glass-stoppered tubes,
add 1 ml of Ehrlich's reagent. Mix. Heat for 30 minutes in a boiling water
bath. Cool in ice water to room temperature. Centrifuge at 2000 rpm for
20 minutes. Read the purple color at 565 mμ against standards similarly
treated containing 50 to 100 μg of sialic acid. The linearity of the color
with varying amounts of unknown and standards should be checked.

[62] L. Svennerholm and E. Svennerholm, *Nature* **181**, 755 (1959).

C. Preparation of Lipoproteins and Analysis of Lipids*

1. GENERAL CONSIDERATIONS

The lipoproteins are a large group of conjugated proteins characterized
by their high content of lipid. They occur in the organism either as
soluble complexes (for example, in serum) or as insoluble complexes, such
as are present in nervous tissue or in subcellular components of cells.
Lipids are ubiquitous in the animal organism and are probably always
associated with protein; it is doubtful that any lipid exists in the completely free state. Cholesterol, cholesterol esters, phosphatides, and
triglycerides are either insoluble or only slightly soluble in aqueous
solutions, although in serum they are present in solution in relatively
high concentration. It is the association of the lipids with protein that
enables these water-insoluble materials to exist in a soluble form.

The soluble lipoproteins in serum constitute the most widely studied
group of this class of conjugated proteins. The methods described below
have been devised for serum lipoproteins, but with minor modifications
they should be adaptable to tissue components as well.† Normal human
serum contains 0.5 to 0.7% lipid. Serum lipoproteins have been isolated
and fractionated by a number of methods: moving boundary and zone
electrophoresis, precipitation of low-density lipoprotein by sulfated poly-

* Section 12,C was contributed by Lewis I. Gidez.

† The preparation of lipopolysaccharides of bacterial cell walls is described in Chap.
1,F, Vol. I. The preparation and analysis of tissue lipids are considered in Chap.
1,B,2, Vol. I.

saccharides, ultracentrifugation, and techniques that take advantage of the differential solubility of lipoprotein classes.

The most useful and specific method for lipoprotein separation is ultracentrifugal flotation. Because of their relatively high lipid content, lipoproteins have hydrated densities which are considerably lower than those of the other serum proteins. If the density of serum is adjusted to 1.21 (accomplished by the addition of appropriate amounts of solid KBr), and the resultant serum is ultracentrifuged at 100,000 g for 20 to 24 hours, all the lipoproteins will float to the top of the tube. By adjusting the original serum to densities intermediate between 1.006 (native density) and 1.21, lipoproteins can be separated from one another. Since the lipoproteins float, the centripetal movement is denoted as a rate of flotation rather than negative sedimentation. The units are expressed as Svedberg units of flotation, S_f, when measured at 26° in a solution of NaCl whose density is 1.063 gm/ml. One S_f unit is a flotation rate of 1×10^{-13} cm/sec/dyne/gm at 26°. The density of 1.063 marks the division point between the dense α_1-lipoproteins ($d > 1.063$) and the low-density β- and α_2-lipoproteins ($d < 1.063$).

Individual classes of lipoproteins are isolated by ultracentrifugation of serum at different densities. Chylomicrons ($S_f > 400$) are prepared by centrifuging serum at its native density at 26,000 g for 30 to 40 minutes. It is the product of g times minutes which is important in the isolation of the chylomicrons, and ultracentrifugation for 10^6 "g-minutes" will result in separation of the chylomicrons from the other lipoproteins. If serum is centrifuged at its native density at 100,000 g for 20 to 24 hours, lipoproteins from S_f 20 to 10^5 will float up. Ultracentrifugation of serum at $d = 1.019$ after removal of S_f 20 to 10^5 lipoproteins will result in the isolation of a fraction with S_f 10 to 20. If the infranatant is then adjusted to $d = 1.063$ and spun at 100,000 g for 20 to 24 hours, the S_f 0 to 10 lipoproteins will float up, and the infranatant layer will contain the high-density lipoproteins. These latter lipoproteins may then be ultracentrifuged at $d = 1.21$, or at an intermediate density between 1.063 and 1.21, to obtain two subfractions of high-density lipoproteins.[*]

A number of investigators have described the formation of insoluble complexes of sulfated polysaccharides and certain serum lipoproteins.[1]

---

[*] The designation of lipoproteins is somewhat arbitrary; for example, some investigators refer to lipoproteins of S_f 10 to 20 as very low density, while others define very low density lipoproteins as having S_f values of 10 to 400. Similarly, fractions S_f 0 to 20 and S_f 0 to 10 have each been designated as low-density lipoproteins. It is thus important that S_f values or, more commonly, densities or density limits be used to define a given lipoprotein fraction. For large particles the designation should be "g-minutes" in the ultracentrifuge.

[1] D. G. Cornwell and F. A. Kruger, *J. Lipid Res.* **2**, 110 (1961).

The polysaccharide–lipoprotein complex is formed at neutral pH and is readily dissociated by increasing the ionic strength of the medium, or by chelation of metal ions which appear to be necessary for the formation of the complex. Several polysaccharides, including heparin, dextran sulfate, the sodium salt of sulfated polygalacturonic acid, methyl ester methyl glucoside, and corn amylopectin sulfate, have been utilized for such isolation of low-density lipoproteins. The interaction of the polysaccharide with the lipoproteins appears to involve the charged groups on the phospholipids. The specificity for low-density lipoproteins may be related to the relative amounts of phospholipid and protein in this lipoprotein class. This technique, in conjunction with ultracentrifugal separation, constitutes an extremely useful method for the isolation of relatively large amounts of pure low-density lipoproteins.

2. ULTRACENTRIFUGAL SEPARATION OF LIPOPROTEINS[2]

Serum (or plasma) is ultracentrifuged at its native density (1.006), or the density is increased by addition of concentrated salt solution. The stock salt solution consists of 153.0 gm of NaCl and 354.0 gm of KBr per liter. The KBr should be dry and as fine as possible. The density of this solution should be 1.346. Solutions of lower density are prepared by dilution of the stock solution with 0.15 M NaCl (density = 1.005) according to the equation

$$(A \times 1.005) + (B \times 1.346) = (A + B)(X) \tag{1}$$

where A = volume of 0.15 M saline, B = volume of stock solution, and X = desired density.

In a similar fashion, the density of serum or of infranatant solutions after ultracentrifugation can be adjusted as follows:

$$(A \times Y) + (B \times Z) = (A + B)(X) \tag{2}$$

where A = volume of serum or serum infranatant, B = volume of salt solution, Y = nonprotein solvent density of sample whose density is to be raised (1.006 for serum), Z = density of the salt solution, and X = nonprotein solvent density of the mixture.

Samples are centrifuged at 105,000 g for 20 to 24 hours at 12 to 15° in the 40 or 40.3 rotor of a Spinco ultracentrifuge (Model L or L2). Lipoproteins of a density less than the solvent density are concentrated in a

[2] R. J. Havel, H. A. Eder, and J. H. Bragdon, *J. Clin. Invest.* **34,** 1345 (1955).

layer at the top of the tube. Beneath is a clear colorless layer, and further below is the remainder of the serum. The tube is placed in a tube-slicing device (Beckman Instruments, Inc., Spinco Division) and divided in the middle of the clear layer below the lipoproteins. The infranatant is transferred to a volumetric flask with washings of salt solution of the same density. If desired, the density of the infranatant can be adjusted and centrifugation repeated in order to obtain other lipoprotein fractions.

The lipoproteins can be washed by recentrifugation in salt solution of the same density as in the original centrifugation. This washing is necessary in some instances to obtain distinct lipoprotein fractions (free of other lipoproteins or proteins).

Certain serum lipoproteins interact with sulfated polysaccharides to form insoluble complexes. This reaction provides the basis of preparing relatively pure lipoprotein fractions. One procedure is outlined below. The reader is referred to a review article for a more extensive treatment of the subject.[2] The procedure outlined is essentially that of Burstein and Samaille.[3]

To 100 ml of serum are added 2 ml 10% dextran sulfate (Dextranine, from Equilibre Biologique, France) and 10 ml of 1 M $CaCl_2$. The solution is centrifuged at 5450 g for 10 minutes at 5°, and the supernatant is discarded. The precipitate (β-lipoprotein–dextran sulfate complex) is dissolved in 10 ml of 5% NaCl, reprecipitated by addition of 90 ml of distilled water and 10 ml of 1 M $CaCl_2$, and recentrifuged at 5450 g for 10 minutes. The precipitate should be redissolved and reprecipitated twice as outlined. The final precipitate is dissolved in 5 ml of 0.1 M sodium oxalate. Two grams of NaCl and 2.5 ml of 2% protamine sulfate are added, and the sample is centrifuged. The high ionic strength prevents formation of a protamine-lipoprotein complex. The precipitate (dextran sulfate–protamine complex) is discarded, and the supernatant is dialyzed against 0.15 M NaCl to eliminate the excess NaCl and protamine.

Instead of using dextran sulfate as a precipitant, the sodium salt of sulfated polygalacturonic acid methyl ester methyl glycoside (Mepesulfate, from Hoffmann-LaRoche) can be used (10% solution) following the same procedure as described above. The final product may be freed of Mepesulfate as described, or by one of two other methods: (1) The final precipitate of β-lipoprotein is dissolved in KBr ($d = 1.063$) and ultracentrifuged (the β-lipoprotein goes to the top of the tube while the Mepesulfate remains at the bottom); or (2) the lipoprotein is dissolved in a minimum volume of 5% NaCl, the solution is brought to 0.9% NaCl by dilution or dialysis, Mepesulfate is precipitated by addition of $BaCl_2$ (10 mg/ml of solution), and the sample is centrifuged for 1 hour at 4°.

[3] M. Burstein and J. Samaille, *J. Physiol. (Paris)* **49**, 83 (1957).

3. ANALYSIS OF SERUM LIPIDS

a. TOTAL CHOLESTEROL

In this procedure,[4] serum, plasma, lipoprotein, or a lipid extract is treated with alcoholic KOH which saponifies the lipids, including cholesterol esters. The cholesterol is then extracted into petroleum ether.

Reagents

1. 33% KOH: 50 gm of KOH in water, diluted to 100 ml.

2. Alcoholic KOH: 6 ml of 33% KOH plus 94 ml of absolute ethanol.

3. Petroleum Ether (boiling range 30° to 60°).

4. Standard: Recrystallized cholesterol in absolute ethanol, 0.4 mg/ml.

Procedure. 1. Saponification. Plasma or serum (0.5 ml or an amount equivalent to 0.8 to 3.0 mg of cholesterol not exceeding 1 ml in volume) is added to a 50-ml round-bottomed glass-stoppered centrifuge tube. To the sample is added 5 ml of freshly prepared alcoholic KOH. The samples are heated in an oven at 40° for 55 minutes and then allowed to come to room temperature.

2. Extraction of Cholesterol. Exactly 10 ml of petroleum ether is added to each tube. This is followed by addition of 5 ml of water. The glass stoppers are moistened with water, and the tubes are sealed and shaken vigorously to extract the cholesterol into the petroleum ether phase. The samples are then centrifuged for 5 minutes at 1000 rpm. Aliquots (3 ml, or portions equivalent to 0.2 to 0.6 mg of cholesterol) are carefully taken from the ether layer (in duplicate) and transferred to 25-ml bottles or Erlenmeyer flasks. The petroleum ether is allowed to evaporate (in a vacuum oven, under a stream of nitrogen, or by standing overnight at room temperature).

3. Color Development. The color reagent is prepared by addition of 1 volume of concentrated H_2SO_4 to 20 volumes of chilled acetic anhydride (in an ice bath). After cooling for 10 minutes, 10 volumes of glacial acetic acid are added, and the mixture is vigorously swirled. To each Erlenmeyer flask or bottle containing the cholesterol is added 6 ml of freshly prepared color reagent. The additions are made at 30-second intervals, and after swirling the flasks are placed in a water bath at 25°. After 30 to 32 minutes, optical density measurements are made at 625 mμ at 30-second intervals.

4. Blanks and Standard. The blank consists of 6 ml of color reagent. To 5 ml of the standard solution is added 0.3 ml of 33% KOH. After saponification and extraction (steps 1 and 2 above), 1-, 2-, and 3-ml aliquots

[4] L. L. Abell, B. B. Levy, B. B. Brodie, and F. E. Kendall, *J. Biol. Chem.* **195**, 357 (1952).

of the petroleum ether solution are taken for subsequent solvent evaporation and color development. For analyses of 40 to 240 μg of cholesterol,
the following modifications can be carried out.

1. Five milliliters of alcoholic KOH is added to 0.3 to 1.0 ml of serum,
or plasma, or lipoprotein solution. The aliquot of plasma should correspond to 0.12 to 1.0 mg of cholesterol. Subsequently, 2 to 4 ml of petroleum
ether solution is taken for analysis. Two milliliters of color reagent is
added instead of 6 ml, and optical density measurements are made at
625 mμ.

2. The standard consists of 2 ml of the standard solution (see Reagents
above) plus 3 ml of absolute ethanol. Petroleum ether aliquots of 0.5,
1.0, 2.0, and 3.0 ml are used for analysis. Two milliliters of color reagent
is added as above.

b. DETERMINATION OF FREE AND ESTERIFIED CHOLESTEROL

In the modified Schoenheimer-Sperry procedure,[5] free cholesterol is
isolated and analyzed on one aliquot of a lipid extract, while on a second
aliquot total cholesterol is determined. Esterified cholesterol can then
be estimated by difference.

Reagents
1. *Absolute Ethanol–Acetone (1:1).*
2. *Acetone–Ether (1:2).*
3. *Ether.*
4. *0.5% Digitonin:* Dissolve 500 mg of digitonin in 100 ml of 50%
ethanol at 60°.
5. *33% KOH:* Dissolve 50 gm of KOH in water, and dilute to 100 ml.
6. *20% Acetic Acid.*
7. *Color Reagent:* Immediately before use add 1 volume of concentrated
H_2SO_4 to 20 volumes of chilled acetic anhydride in an ice bath.
8. *Stock Standard:* 1 mg of recrystallized cholesterol per milliliter of
glacial acetic acid.
9. *Working Standard:* 40 ml of stock standard diluted to 100 ml with
glacial acetic acid.

Procedure. 1. Extraction of Lipid. To a 25-ml volumetric flask approximately half filled with 1:1 acetone–alcohol is added 1 ml of serum (or an
amount of serum or lipoprotein solution containing 2 to 3 mg of cholesterol). The mixture is swirled, allowed to stand for 10 minutes, and then
diluted to volume and shaken thoroughly. The mixture is filtered into a
50-ml Erlenmeyer flask through S&S Sharkskin filter paper.

2. Precipitation of Free Cholesterol. Duplicate aliquots (equivalent to
0.2 to 0.6 mg of free cholesterol) of the clear filtrate are pipetted into

[5] W. M. Sperry and M. Webb, *J. Biol. Chem.* **187**, 97 (1950).

12 ml of conical centrifuge tubes, and 1 drop of 20% acetic acid is added. One milliliter of digitonin solution per 2 ml of filtrate is added, and the contents of the centrifuge tube are mixed on a Vortex (or similar type) tube mixer. The centrifuge tubes are capped (with marbles) or put in a Mason-type jar, and allowed to stand overnight.

3. Precipitation of Total Cholesterol. Duplicate aliquots (equivalent to 0.2 to 0.6 mg of *total* cholesterol) of the clear filtrate are pipetted into 12-ml conical centrifuge tubes. One drop of 33% KOH is added for each milliliter of filtrate. The contents of the tube are mixed thoroughly (on a tube mixer). The centrifuge tubes are capped (with marbles) and heated at 40° to 50° for 30 minutes in an oven or sand bath. The tubes are cooled, and 1 drop of phenolphthalein is added. The contents of each tube are neutralized with 20% acetic acid. This is followed by 1 drop of acetic acid and 1 ml of digitonin solution for every 2 ml of solution. The samples are thoroughly mixed and allowed to stand overnight as above.

4. Treatment of Digitonides. The contents of each tube are stirred and centrifuged for 20 minutes at 2000 rpm. The supernatant solution is carefully decanted and discarded. The precipitated free cholesterol digitonides are washed once with 5 ml of acetone–ether and twice with 5 ml of ether. After final centrifugation, traces of ether are removed by placing the tubes in a warm water bath or by allowing them to stand overnight. If a vacuum oven is to be used, care should be taken that portions of the precipitate do not "bump" out of the tube. The ether-free digitonides are then heated at 80° in a vacuum oven. While the tubes are still hot, 2 ml of glacial acetic acid is added. The samples are mixed and placed in a gently boiling water bath for about 2 minutes. The precipitate should dissolve. Finally 4 ml of the color reagent (ice cold) is added at 0.5- or 1-minute intervals. The samples are mixed and kept at 25° for 30 minutes. The optical densities are read at 625 mμ at 0.5- or 1-minute intervals.

5. Blank and Standards. The blank consists of 2 ml of glacial acetic acid and 4 ml of color reagent. Standards of 0.2, 0.4, and 0.6 mg of cholesterol (0.5, 1.0, and 1.5 ml of working standard) are prepared in duplicate, and the volumes are adjusted to 2 ml. Color reagent is added directly to the standards.

c. DETERMINATION OF TRIGLYCERIDES

This method is a modification of the procedure of Van Handel and Zilversmit[6] and Van Handel.[7] The method is a determination of formaldehyde derived from periodate oxidation of triglyceride glycerol.

[6] E. Van Handel and D. B. Zilversmit, *J. Lab. Clin. Med.* **50**, 152 (1957).
[7] E. Van Handel, *Clin. Chem.* **7**, 249 (1961).

Reagents

1. *Redistilled CHCl₃.*

2. *Redistilled 95% Ethanol.*

3. *0.4% Alcoholic KOH:* Stock solution—2 gm of KOH dissolved in 5 ml of water and diluted to 100 ml with absolute ethanol. Working solution—stock solution diluted 1:5 with redistilled 95% ethanol.

4. *0.2 N Sulfuric Acid.*

5. *0.25 M Sodium Metaperiodate, NaIO₄.*

6. *5% Sodium Bisulfite, NaHSO₃.*

7. *Chromatropic Acid:* 600 ml of concentrated H_2SO_4 is added very slowly to 300 ml of cold water. In a separate flask 2 gm of chromatropic acid (or 2.24 gm of the sodium salt) is dissolved in 200 ml of water. This solution is filtered through Whatman No. 1 filter paper into a brown bottle. Chilled 0.2 N H_2SO_4 is added to the chromatropic acid solution, and it is stored away from excessive light. The reagent is stable for about 30 days.

8. *Standard Triglyceride Solution:* A stock solution of a purified triglyceride in redistilled CHCl₃ should be prepared at 1.5 to 3.0 mg/ml. A working standard is prepared by dilution of the stock solution with redistilled CHCl₃. The final concentration of the triglyceride should be approximately 0.03 mg/ml.

9. *Silicic Acid:* 100 to 200 mesh (Unisil, Clarkson Chemical Co., Williamsport, Pennsylvania).

Procedure. 1. *Extraction of Lipid.* One volume of plasma (1 ml, or an amount equivalent to approximately 0.5 mg of triglyceride) is added to 20 volumes of $CHCl_3$–CH_3OH (2:1) in a 50-ml round-bottomed centrifuge tube or small Erlenmeyer flask. After standing for a short while the sample is evaporated to dryness under nitrogen or in a vacuum oven at 40°.

2. *Separation of Glycerides from Phosphatide.* Two grams of Unisil and 5.0 ml of CHCl₃ are added to the dried residue. The tube is swirled gently, and 20.0 ml of additional CHCl₃ is added. The tube is stoppered and shaken vigorously, and the contents are filtered into 50-ml Erlenmeyer flasks through S&S Sharkskin filter paper. Aliquots (equivalent to 0.03 to 0.09 mg of triglyceride, usually 3 ml when 1-ml samples of plasma are used) are transferred into a test tube, and the CHCl₃ is removed in a vacuum oven or by heating the tube in a boiling water bath.

3. *Saponification and Neutralization.* To each tube containing the triglyceride is added 0.5 ml of alcoholic KOH. The tubes are heated in a water bath at 60° to 70° for 15 minutes. After the saponification, 0.5 ml of 0.2 N H_2SO_4 is added to each tube, and all the tubes are then heated in a boiling water bath for 15 minutes. Care must be taken to avoid condensation of water in the necks of the tubes.

4. Oxidation. After cooling, 1 drop of 0.25 M periodate solution is added to each tube. After 10 minutes (tubes should be shaken intermittently) 3 drops of 5% bisulfite solution are added, and the contents of the tubes are shaken thoroughly and allowed to stand for at least 10 minutes.

5. Color Development. Five milliliters of chromotropic acid solution is added to each tube away from excessive light. The tubes are mixed on a tube mixer, covered with marbles, and heated at 100° for 30 minutes in the absence of light. After cooling, the optical density is measured at 570 mμ.

6. Blanks and Standards. Blanks containing $CHCl_3$ and aliquots of the working standard corresponding to 0.03, 0.06, and 0.09 mg of triglyceride are treated in the same manner as the samples.

If it is desired to carry out analyses on unsaponified samples, aliquots of sample (in $CHCl_3$) are treated with 0.5 ml of 95% ethanol instead of 0.5 ml of alcoholic KOH, and then treated in the same manner as the experimental sample. The optical densities of such samples are then subtracted from the readings of the saponified samples.

d. Titration of Free Fatty Acids[8,9]

Reagents

1. Stock Solution of Nile Blue, 0.1% in water.

2. Extracted Nile Blue, 0.02% in water: The diluted stock indicator is extracted with successive volumes of heptane in a separatory funnel until the heptane is colorless.

3. Titration Mixture: Extracted Nile Blue diluted 1:10 with absolute methanol.

4. Extraction Mixture: 100 parts of redistilled heptane, 400 parts of redistilled isopropyl alcohol, and 10 parts of 1 N H_2SO_4.

5. 0.018 N H_2SO_4.

6. 0.02 N $NaOH$.

7. Standard: 0.5 μmole of recrystallized palmitic acid per milliliter of heptane.

Procedure. To 2 ml of plasma in a glass-stoppered test tube is added, with shaking, 10 ml of extraction mixture. This is followed by addition of 6 ml of redistilled heptane and 4 ml of water. The mixture is shaken for at least 2 minutes. A 4- or 5-ml aliquot of the upper layer is transferred to a glass-stoppered centrifuge tube and shaken with an equal volume of 0.018 N H_2SO_4. The tube is then centrifuged at about 300 g for 5 to 10 minutes. Three milliliters of the upper heptane layer is transferred into a centrifuge tube containing 1 ml of the titration mixture. The sample is

[8] V. P. Dole, *J. Clin. Invest.* **35,** 150 (1956).

[9] D. L. Trout, E. H. Estes, Jr., and S. J. Friedberg, *J. Lipid Res.* **1,** 199 (1960).

titrated with 0.02 N NaOH while being agitated with a stream of nitrogen. Heptane layers from blank samples and palmitic acid standards are similarly washed with the 0.05% H_2SO_4 before titration.

e. LIPID PHOSPHORUS

The determination of the lipid phosphorus content of serum or lipoproteins involves the preparation of a lipid extract, oxidation of an aliquot of this extract to convert organic phosphorus to phosphate, and, finally, colorimetric determination of the phosphate. The procedure described below[10] is a modification based on several previously published methods.

Reagents

1. 7.1 to 7.2 N H_2SO_4.

2. 2.5% Ammonium Molybdate: 5 gm of $(NH_4)_6Mo_7O_{24}\cdot4H_2O$ dissolved in 200 ml of water. This solution should be made up every 2 weeks.

3. 0.125% Hydrazine Sulfate.

4. Stock Standard: 877.6 mg of KH_2PO_4 dissolved in 500 ml of water. This solution is equivalent to 400 μg of phosphorus per milliliter.

5. Working Standard: 25.0 ml of stock solution diluted to 1 liter. This solution is equivalent to 10.0 μg of phosphorus per milliliter.

Procedure. One milliliter of serum is added to approximately 10 ml of ethanol–ether (3:1) in a 25-ml volumetric flask. Lipoprotein solutions can be extracted in a similar manner. The mixture is allowed to stand for 10 minutes and is then made up to volume with ethanol–ether. After shaking, the solution is filtered through S&S Sharkskin filter paper. Aliquots are transferred into Pyrex digestion tubes with 25-ml calibration marks. For standards, transfer aliquots of 1.0, 2.0, and 3.0 of the working standard into digestion tubes. The blank tube should be empty.

To each tube is added 2 ml of 7.1 N H_2SO_4 and a boiling chip. After mixing, the tubes are placed in preheated digestion rack (about 215°) for 30 minutes. The tubes are removed from the heat, and about 15 drops of concentrated HNO_3 are added to each tube. Digestion is resumed for an additional 15 minutes. After cooling for 5 or 6 minutes the sides of the tubes are washed with 2 ml of water, and the tubes are returned to the digestion rack for an additional 15 minutes. If digestion is still incomplete more HNO_3 must be added, followed by heating, washing, and reheating. Finally the tubes are cooled to room temperature.

Approximately 10 ml of distilled water is added to each tube; after mixing, 1 ml of ammonium molybdate and 5 ml of water are added. The contents are mixed, and 1 ml of hydrazine sulfate and 5 ml of water are added. The contents are mixed, and the tubes are placed in a boiling water bath for 10 minutes, and then in cold water. When cool the

[10] J. M. R. Beveridge and S. E. Johnson, *Can. J. Res.* **27E**, 159 (1949).

volume is adjusted to 25 ml in the digestion tube. After mixing again, the optical density is read at 600 mμ.

f. EXTRACTION AND FRACTIONATION OF LIPIDS

There are numerous methods by which lipids can be extracted from serum, plasma, or solution of lipoproteins. The reader is referred to an article by de Iongh and van Pelt[11] for a thorough treatment of this subject. One commonly used procedure employing chloroform–methanol (2:1) is described below. This is the method of Folch et al.,[12] slightly modified for the extraction of aqueous solutions.

i. Extraction Procedure

One volume of plasma is pipetted into 20 volumes of $CHCl_3$–CH_3OH (2:1) in an Erlenmeyer flask. The mixture is swirled and allowed to stand for at least 10 to 20 minutes to ensure complete extraction. The suspension is then filtered through fat-free filter paper or glass wool into a beaker which should hold two to four times the volume filtered. For quantitative work glass wool is preferable. The beaker is placed into a very large beaker (ten to twenty times the volume of the beaker containing the lipid extract). Distilled water is carefully layered to brimming above the lipid extract. When the upper (aqueous) layer is clear, the larger beaker is carefully filled with water. The beakers are left overnight. The small beaker is then removed from the larger one, and the aqueous layer is drawn off. (After the interface separates, no further water should be removed. The whitish material at the interface should not be removed.) Methanol is added to the remaining solution, with stirring, until the solution is clear. The washing procedure may be repeated if necessary. After the final wash, the solution is clarified with methanol, and the sample is evaporated in vacuo at a temperature no higher than 40° to 45°. The dry lipid is then dissolved in $CHCl_3$. This solution should be filtered to remove any insoluble material.

If a solution of lipoprotein is to be extracted, several washes (as described above) may be necessary unless the solution is dialyzed initially to remove the salts.

ii. Thin-Layer Chromatography

Once a lipid extract is obtained, there is a wide variety of techniques by which total lipids may be subfractionated into individual classes.

[11] H. de Iongh and J. G. van Pelt, J. Lipid Res. 3, 385 (1962).
[12] J. Folch, I. Ascoli, M. Lees, J. A. Meath, and F. N. de Baron, J. Biol. Chem. 191, 833 (1951).

Probably the most convenient method and the one that gives the most satisfactory separations is thin-layer chromatography.

In this chromatographic technique a thin layer of adsorbent such as silica gel or alumina is formed on glass plates. After the thin-layer plate is dried, a solution of the lipids to be separated is introduced with a micro-pipet about 1 to 1.5 cm from the lower edge of the plate. The plate is then developed in a chromatography tank with a suitable developing solvent. The most commonly used method is that of ascending one-dimensional chromatography. The solvent rises past the origin, and the individual substances from the solution move up the plate at varying rates, depending on the particular adsorbent, the solvent system, and the nature of the compounds being separated. After the solvent has moved 100 mm or more (30 to 60 minutes), the plate is dried and the individual spots or bands of lipids can be identified by a variety of methods, some of them similar to the visualization techniques of paper chromatography. The purified lipids can be eluted from the plates by scraping off the area that contains the compound, or the relative amounts of individual compounds can be estimated by charring the plates with 50% H_2SO_4 and measuring the degree of blackening photometrically.

Not only can lipid classes be separated from each other—for example, cholesterol esters, triglycerides, free fatty acids, mono- and diglycerides, free sterols, and phosphatides—but by selection of appropriate solvent systems and adsorbents, the classes can be subfractioned. Thus, there are methods for separating individual phosphatides; phosphatidyl choline, phosphatidyl ethanolamine, sphingomyelin, etc. By using silica gel impregnated with $AgNO_3$, separations can be made on the basis of the degree of unsaturation of the fatty acid moieties of a given lipid. Thus, cholesterol esters, fatty acids, triglycerides, and even phosphatides can be subfractionated. Separations based on fatty acid composition can also be made by preparing mercuric acetate adducts of lipids. Finally, reversed phase partition thin-layer chromatography can be carried out: The thin-layer plate is impregnated with a nonpolar material such as mineral oil or silicone oil, and polar solvents are used to develop the chromatogram. By this technique, separations can be made on the basis of chain length of the fatty acids—for example, methyl esters or cholesterol esters.

It is beyond the scope of this chapter to detail specific methods used in thin-layer chromatography.

The reader may refer to a number of publications[13-15] as well as to

[13] K. Randerath, "Thin-Layer Chromatography." Academic Press, New York, 1963.
[14] E. V. Truter, "Thin Film Chromatography." Interscience, New York, 1963.
[15] E. Stahl, "Thin Layer Chromatography—A Laboratory Handbook." Academic Press, New York, 1965.

numerous papers in the *Journal of Lipid Research* and the *Journal of the American Oil Chemists' Society* (see, for example, Mangold[16]) for specific instructions regarding equipment, adsorbents, solvent systems, etc.

[16] H. K. Mangold, *J. Am. Oil Chemists' Soc.* **38**, 709 (1961).

D. Nucleic Acid Analysis

1. METHODS FOR CHARACTERIZING DEOXYRIBONUCLEIC ACID IMMUNE SYSTEMS*

a. INTRODUCTION

The biological, physical, and chemical properties of the nucleic acids have been studied extensively.[1] Their immunologic properties, however, have, until recently, received little attention because of the failure to demonstrate their serologic activity unequivocally. Undoubtedly, one must consider the high charge density of the nucleic acid polymers when characterizing their serologic properties. During isolation, it is difficult to remove all extraneous proteins and polysaccharides that have associated with the nucleic acids during the purification procedures. Also, addition of DNA or RNA to serum may lead to protein–nucleic acid interactions and can result in nonspecific serologic activity unless the concentration, pH, and ionic strength in the reaction mixtures are carefully controlled. Such factors may possibly account for some of the immunogenic and serologic properties of pneumococcal,[2] calf thymus,[3] *Brucella,*[4–6] and *Salmonella typhimurium*[7] DNA. Synthetic immunogens are described in Chap. 1,E,8, Vol. I.

Although the nature of the immunogen remains unknown, antibodies reacting with DNA have been detected in sera of patients with lupus

* Section 12,D,1 was contributed by Lawrence Levine and William T. Murakami.

[1] J. N. Davidson, and W. E. Cohn (eds.), "Progress in Nucleic Acid Research," Vol. 1, Academic Press, New York, 1963.

[2] D. Lackman, S. Mudd, M. G. Sevag, J. Smolens, and M. Weiner, *J. Immunol.* **40**, 1 (1941).

[3] U. Blix, C. N. Iland, and M. Stacey, *Brit. J. Exptl. Pathol.* **35**, 241 (1954).

[4] J. H. Phillips, W. Braun, and O. J. Plescia, *J. Am. Chem. Soc.* **80**, 2710 (1958).

[5] O. J. Plescia, J. J. Noval, N. C. Palczuk, and W. Braun, *Proc. Soc. Exptl. Biol. Med.* **106**, 748 (1961).

[6] N. C. Palczuk, O. J. Plescia, and W. Braun, *Proc. Soc. Exptl. Biol. Med.* **107**, 982 (1961).

[7] V. D. Timakov, A. G. Skavronskaya, N. B. Borisova, and L. A. Zamchvk, 70. *Zh. Mikrobiol., Epidemiol. i Immunobiol.* **40**, 5 (1963) [cf. *Federation Proc. Transl. Suppl.* **22**, T 128 (1963)].

erythematosus. Various serologic techniques, including precipitin,[8,9] complement (C') fixation,[10-12] passive cutaneous anaphylaxis,[13] and fluorescent antibody staining,[14,15] have implicated the DNA as the serologically active molecule. Loss of serologic activity after incubation of DNA with DNase has frequently been used as evidence that DNA was the antigen. In the study of Deicher et al.,[8] DNA was identified as the antigen by the complete recovery of the added DNA in the washed immune precipitates.

A number of criteria are now available for identifying DNA as the serologically active molecule. When neutral solutions of DNA are heated, changes in a number of properties (extinction coefficient, buoyant density, viscosity, optical rotation, light scattering, and transforming ability) are observed.[16] These changes occur at the temperature at which the native double-strand structure collapses to give a denatured molecule. When partially denatured, the DNA molecule may possess both double-strand and single-strand areas. When completely denatured, the two strands of DNA may be completely separable. Irrespective of the model of denatured DNA that one visualizes, it is generally agreed that the bases are now exposed to the solvent, whereas in the native state they were oriented toward the center of the double-strand helix.

Furthermore, studies on fractionation and identification of oligonucleotides resulting from enzymatic hydrolysis and specific chemical degradation of DNA have progressed to a point where identification of the antigenic determinant is feasible. Thus, it is possible to identify the active antigen as DNA by a number of criteria, including (1) characterization of the nucleic acids, (2) conformation of the active antigen, (3) susceptibility to enzymatic digestion, and (4) isolation and identification of the antigenic determinant.

Some procedures employed in our laboratory for the chemical and

[8] H. R. G. Deicher, H. R. Holman, and H. G. Kunkel, J. Exptl. Med. **109**, 97 (1959).

[9] M. Seligmann, Compt. Rend. **245**, 243 (1957).

[10] M. Seligmann, and F. Milgrom, Compt. Rend. **245**, 1472 (1957).

[11] W. C. Robbins, R. H. Holman, H. R. G. Deicher, and H. G. Kunkel, Proc. Soc. Exptl. Biol. Med. **96**, 575 (1957).

[12] R. Ceppellini, E. Polli, and F. Celada, Proc. Soc. Exptl. Biol. Med. **96**, 572 (1957).

[13] H. R. G. Deicher, H. R. Holman, H. G. Kunkel, and Z. Ovary, J. Immunol. **84**, 106 (1960).

[14] G. S. Friou, S. C. Finch, and K. D. Detre, J. Immunol. **80**, 324 (1958).

[15] H. R. Holman, and H. G. Kunkel, Science **126**, 162 (1957).

[16] J. Marmur, R. Rownd, and C. L. Schildkraut, Progr. Nucleic Acid Res. **1**, 231 (1963).

physical characterization of the antigen and identification of the antigenic determinants are presented.

b. General Methods for Identification and Analyses of DNA

i. Extraction and Purification

The most generally used procedure for the isolation of DNA from microorganisms is that described by Marmur.[17]

Bacteria are lysed with lysozyme followed by the addition of detergent (sodium lauryl sulfate), or with detergent alone. Nucleolytic enzymes are inactivated by heating the lysed cells at 60° for 10 minutes. The lysate is then deproteinized by repeated extractions with chloroform–isoamyl alcohol, treated with ribonuclease, and precipitated with ethanol. This procedure yields DNA with molecular weight of the order of 10 million. The basic steps of the Marmur procedure have been used successfully for the isolation of DNA from vertebrate tissues.[18]

For isolation of DNA from viruses, various modifications of the phenol method have been most successful.[19] Some phages can be lysed directly with phenol, whereas others have to be subjected to osmotic shock prior to the phenol deproteinization. The phenol extraction procedure, when performed carefully without vigorous agitation or alcohol precipitation, yields DNA with molecular weight of the order of 100 million.

ii. Base Ratio Analysis—Method of Wyatt[20]

One-half to one milligram of DNA is precipitated with 2 volumes of cold acetone in a 12.0-ml conical centrifuge tube, and the precipitate is dried in a stream of cold air. To the dried DNA pellet is added 0.015 ml of concentrated (70%) perchloric acid, and hydrolysis is allowed to proceed at 100° for 1 hour. After the hydrolyzates have cooled at room temperature, they are neutralized with 0.04 ml of 4 N KOH. The heavy potassium perchlorate precipitate is sedimented by centrifugation, and the supernatant (to contain the equivalent of 500 μg of DNA) is spotted on Whatman No. 1 paper. A control mixture containing the bases is also put on the chromatogram.

The chromatogram is run by the descending technique for 18 hours in isopropanol—HCl–H$_2$O (170:41:39). After the chromatogram has dried in air, it is scanned with an ultraviolet lamp, and the absorbing spots are cut out. Elution is carried out with 1.5 ml of 0.1 N HCl at room tem-

[17] J. Marmur, *J. Mol. Biol.* **3**, 208 (1961).
[18] K. S. Kirby, *Progr. Nucleic Acid Res.* **3**, 1 (1964).
[19] J. D. Mandell and A. D. Hershey, *Anal. Biochem.* **1**, 66 (1960).
[20] G. R. Wyatt, *Biochem. J.* **48**, 584 (1951).

perature overnight. The amount of each base is determined from its absorption as measured with a Beckman or Cary spectrophotometer using the following constants: adenine, $\lambda_{max} = 260$, $E_M = 13{,}000$; thymine, $\lambda_{max} = 262$, $E_M = 7950$; guanine, $\lambda_{max} = 250$, $E_M = 11{,}000$; cytosine, $\lambda_{max} = 275$, $E_M = 10{,}500$.

iii. Diphenylamine Reaction of DNA—Method of Burton[21]

Reagents. The diphenylamine reagent is prepared by dissolving 1.5 gm of diphenylamine in 100 ml of glacial acetic acid and adding 1.5 ml of concentrated H_2SO_4. On the day it is to be used, 0.1 ml of aqueous acetaldehyde (16 mg/ml) is added for each 20 ml of reagent required.

Commercial diphenylamine should be purified by recrystallization from 70% alcohol or petroleum ether or by steam distillation before use. Acetaldehyde is redistilled and stored at 4° as an aqueous solution containing 16 mg/ml.

Procedure. The test solution is diluted with 0.5 N $HClO_4$ so that the final solution contains between 5 and 80 μg of DNA per milliliter. A measured volume (1 or 2 ml) is mixed with 2 volumes of diphenylamine reagent containing acetaldehyde. The color is developed by incubation at 30° for 16 to 20 hours. The optical density at 600 mμ is measured against a similarly treated blank containing 0.5 N $HClO_4$ but no DNA.

Purified DNA or deoxyribose solutions are used in constructing a standard curve. As with the orcinol reaction, only deoxyribose associated with the purine bases is hydrolyzed and measured under the test conditions.

iv. Determination of Chain Length

The numerical average chain length of polynucleotide preparations which are homogeneous or nearly homogeneous with respect to length can be obtained by determining the ratio of total phosphorus to terminal phosphorus in the preparation.

To measure terminal phosphorus, the test sample is incubated at 37° with *Escherichia coli* alkaline phosphatase (chromatographically purified, Worthington Biochemical Corp., Freehold, New Jersey) in 0.5 to 1.0 M Tris buffer, pH 8, until dephosphorylation is complete. The protein is precipitated with cold 0.4 N perchloric acid, and inorganic phosphorus is estimated on the solution.

Total phosphorus is determined by first converting the organically bound phosphorus to inorganic phosphorus by ashing and then estimating inorganic phosphorus.

[21] K. Burton, *Biochem. J.* **62**, 315 (1956).

(a) *Phosphorus Determination—Method of Chen et al.*[22] Reagent C is prepared fresh each day by mixing 1 volume of 6 N H_2SO_4 with 2 volumes of distilled water and 1 volume of 2.5% ammonium molybdate $((NH_4)_6$-$Mo_7O_{24} \cdot 4H_2O)$. One volume of 10% ascorbic acid is added, and the solution is mixed well.

(b) *Inorganic Phosphorus Determination* The volume of the test solution, containing up to 8 μg of phosphorus, is adjusted to 4 ml with distilled water. Samples containing protein must be deproteinized first by precipitation with trichloroacetic or perchloric acid, and an aliquot of the acid supernatant taken for analysis. Four milliliters of reagent C is added; the tubes are capped with parafilm, mixed, and incubated at 37° for 1 to 5.2 hours. The optical density at 820 mμ is measured against a similarly treated blank.

A convenient modification, through the use of 1.5 ml of test sample and 1.5 ml of reagent C, allows 0.15 μg of phosphorus to be determined accurately.

(c) *Total Phosphorus Determination* Total phosphorus is determined by ashing the test sample prior to measurement of inorganic phosphorus. The sample to be ashed is placed in a test tube and evaporated to dryness. Four drops of concentrated H_2SO_4 are added, and the sample is heated until the white fume of sulfur trioxide appears. Two drops of 70% perchloric acid are added, and the sample is heated until the liquid becomes clear. After cooling, the volume is adjusted to 25 ml in a volumetric flask with distilled water. Aliquots are taken for analysis.

c. IMMUNOCHEMICAL METHODS FOR DETERMINING CONFORMATION OF THE ANTIGEN

i. Denaturation of DNA.[23]

Native DNA—10 μg/ml in 0.01 M Tris–HCl (pH 7.4), 0.14 M NaCl—is incubated at varying temperatures for 10 minutes and diluted into chilled buffer—0.01 M Tris–HCl (pH 7.4), 0.14 M NaCl, 1.5 × 10^{-4} M CaCl$_2$, 5.0 × 10^{-4} M MgCl$_2$, and 0.1% bovine serum albumin—to a concentration of 0.3 μg/ml. The serologic activity of the DNA is then determined by micro-complement (C') fixation.[24]

The C' fixation assays for denatured DNA in a series of *E. coli* and *Proteus vulgaris* DNA samples which had been incubated for 10 minutes at varying temperatures are shown in Fig. 1.[25] The C' fixation for the

[22] P. S. Chen, Jr., T. Y. Toribara, and H. Warner, *Anal. Chem.* **28**, 1756 (1956).
[23] L. Levine, W. T. Murakami, H. Van Vunakis, and L. Grossman, *Proc. Natl. Acad. Sci. U.S.* **46**, 1038 (1960).
[24] E. Wasserman and L. Levine, *J. Immunol.* **87**, 290 (1960).
[25] E. Seaman, H. Van Vunakis, and L. Levine, *Biochemistry* **4**, 1312 (1965).

samples of DNA which had been completely denatured by heating at 100°
for 10 minutes is used as a calibration curve to estimate the amount of
denatured DNA present after incubation at any given temperature. The
ratio of the amounts of completely denatured DNA to partially denatured
DNA which gives 50% C′ fixation in the region of antibody excess is
equal to the fraction of denatured DNA in the test sample. For example, the
data in Fig. 1 show that 50% C′ fixation is obtained with 20 mμg of *P.
vulgaris* DNA after incubation at 100° for 10 minutes. The same amount of
C′ fixation is obtained with 40 mμg and 115 mμg of DNA incubated at 91°

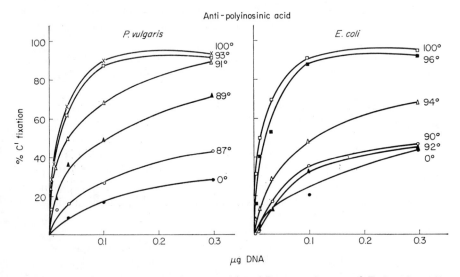

FIG. 1. Fixation of C′ by varying quantities of *Proteus vulgaris* and *Escherichia coli*
DNA after incubation of the DNA samples (3 μg/ml) for 10 minutes at the designated
temperatures in 0.15 *M* NaCl–Tris buffer followed by fast cooling and appropriate
dilution. Antipoly I was used at a 1/80 dilution. From E. Seaman, H. Van Vunakis,
and L. Levine, *Biochemistry* **4**, 1312 (1965).

and 89° for 10 minutes, indicating that 50% and 16% of the DNA,
respectively, have been denatured in these samples. The immunologic
temperature melting curves of *P. vulgaris* and *E. coli* DNA as measured
by antipolyinosinic, antipolycytidylic, and antipolyadenylic acids are
shown in Fig. 2.[25]

It has been shown by Marmur and Doty[26] that the base composition
of DNA can be determined from its T_m (temperature after 50% of the
total increase in relative absorbance). By use of the immunologic pro-

[26] J. Marmur and P. Doty, *J. Mol. Biol.* **5**, 109 (1962).

cedure, temperature melting curves for various DNA's have been obtained with many of the antibodies to DNA available in our laboratory. The temperature at which 50% denaturation occurs as measured immunologically is in good agreement with the T_m obtained by hyperchromicity measurements at ambient temperatures; the immunologically determined value is slightly higher. The immunologic assay requires that the DNA samples be quenched by quick cooling prior to analysis and thus measures only irreversibly denatured DNA. With suitable antisera, the thermally induced helix to random coil transition for any DNA can be obtained with extremely small amounts of sample—for example, about 2 μg of DNA.

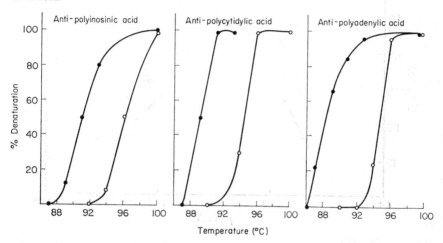

Fig. 2. Temperature melting curves of *Proteus vulgaris* (●) and *Escherichia coli* (○) DNA as measured immunologically. From E. Seaman, H. Van Vunakis, and L. Levine, *Biochemistry* **4**, 1312 (1965).

ii. Renaturation of DNA

The extent of renaturation of DNA can be determined by measuring the loss of serologic activity caused by base-pairing.[27] Before the immunologic procedure can be used to measure renaturation, however, the serologic identity of the original thermally denatured DNA and the denatured DNA remaining after incomplete renaturation has to be demonstrated. Only after demonstration of serologic identity can it be stated that the structure of the renatured DNA, like native DNA, does not interfere with the quantitative estimation of denatured DNA.

Renaturation is measured as follows: Bacterial or viral DNA (250 μg/ml) in 0.15 M NaCl is thermally denatured by heating at 100° for

[27] L. Levine, E. Wasserman, and W. T. Murakami, *Immunochemistry* **3**, 41 (1966).

10 minutes. Appropriate dilutions of the thermally denatured DNA into the desired salt solution which has been preheated at the desired temperature are then made. Prior to the dilution of the thermally denatured DNA, the pipets should be rinsed a few times with 0.15 M NaCl at 100°. After varying times of incubation at the desired temperature, aliquots are removed and rapidly diluted into the cold Tris–HCl buffer used for C' fixation. The serologic activity of the DNA is then determined by C' fixation.[28]

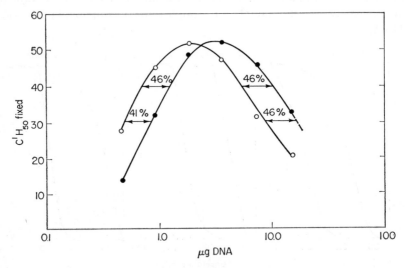

FIG. 3. Complement fixation of thermally denatured T_4 DNA before and after 60 minutes of incubation at 55° in 0.15 M NaCl. T_4 DNA (250 μg/ml) was heated to 100° for 10 minutes and then diluted in 0.15 M NaCl preheated to 55° to contain 15 μg/ml. At the time of dilution and after 60 minutes of incubation, aliquots of the reaction mixtures were chilled in an ice bath and assayed for thermally denatured DNA by C' fixation. From L. Levine, E. Wasserman, and W. T. Murakami, *Immunochemistry* **3,** 41 (1966).

The results of C' fixation assays for thermally denatured T_4 DNA (15 μg/ml) before and after 60 minutes of incubation in 0.15 M NaCl at 55° are shown in Fig. 3. The C' fixation curve after incubation displays a lateral displacement which is equal in the regions of antibody excess, equivalence, and antigen excess. Thus, although there is a decrease in the quantity of denatured DNA in the renatured sample, the shapes of the curves are identical. The ratio of the amount of DNA required to give

[28] M. M. Mayer, A. G. Osler, O. G. Bier, and M. Heidelberger, *J. Immunol.* **59,** 195 (1948).

equivalent C′ fixation in the thermally denatured control to that in the renatured sample is equal to the proportion of DNA remaining. This value is 46% in the example under discussion (Fig. 3).

The serologic identity of denatured DNA and denatured DNA remaining in the renatured sample is found only up to 70% renaturation. Presumably the renatured DNA after 70% renaturation is competing with the remaining thermally denatured DNA for the antibody.

In most renaturation experiments entire C′ fixation curves are not obtained. Instead, two amounts of DNA, calculated to be in the region of antibody excess, are determined. The C′ fixation data obtained when thermally denatured T_4 DNA (10 μg/ml) is incubated at 55° in 0.2 M NaCl for varying periods of time is shown in Fig. 4. The ratio of the amounts of thermally denatured DNA initially present to thermally denatured DNA after varying times of incubation required to fix $30C′H_{50}$ in the region of antibody excess is equal to the fraction of thermally denatured DNA in the renatured sample. The calculations shown in Table I were obtained from the C′ fixation data of Fig. 4.

TABLE I

RENATURATION OF THERMALLY DENATURED T_4 DNA (10 μG/ML) AT
55° IN 0.2 M NaCl

Time (minutes)	Total DNA required for fixation of $30C′H_{50}$ (μg)	Thermally denatured DNA remaining (%)
00.00	0.41	100
15.02	0.47	87
31.29	0.51	80
45.00	0.55	75
59.87	0.63	65
74.60	0.71	58
91.38	0.75	55
106.06	0.78	53
122.63	0.83	49
236.37	0.97	42
370.24	1.26	33
527.19	1.48	28

d. METHODS FOR IDENTIFICATION OF THE ANTIGENIC DETERMINANTS

Identification of the antigenic determinants in DNA involves degradation of the nucleic acids by either chemical or enzymatic methods followed by separation and identification of the oligonucleotides. The oligonucleotides of known base composition can then be assayed for specific inhibition of the DNA–anti-DNA C′ fixation.

DNA can be modified to give a product that lacks purine or pyrimidine residues, or guanine. Such modified DNA preparations are easily prepared and are useful for the qualitative identification of the antigenic determinants. Procedures for preparation of such products are presented here.

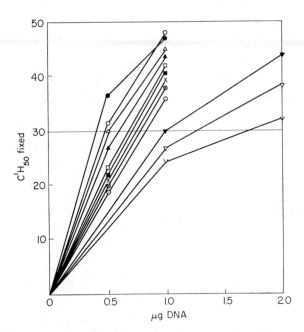

FIG. 4. Complement fixation of thermally denatured T_4 DNA before and after incubation for varying periods of time at 55° in 0.2 M NaCl. After thermal denaturation at 100° for 10 minutes, the DNA (250 μg/ml) was diluted in 0.2 M NaCl preheated at 55° to contain 10 μg/ml. At the time of dilution and after varying periods of time, aliquots were removed and diluted to either 1.0 or 2.0 μg of DNA per milliliter in chilled buffer in which the final NaCl concentration was 0.15 M NaCl, and assayed for thermally denatured DNA by C′ fixation. From L. Levine, E. Wasserman, and W. T. Murakami, *Immunochemistry* **3**, 41 (1966).

It may also be possible to isolate and identify the entire oligonucleotide antigenic determinant such as has been done by Stollar *et al.*[29] For example, cytidine, thymidine, or cytidine–thymidine tracts can be prepared by chain scission at the site of purine degradation in apurinic acids,[30–32] while purine tracts can be obtained by chain scission at the

[29] D. Stollar, L. Levine, H. I. Lehrer, and H. Van Vunakis, *Proc. Natl. Acad. Sci. U.S.* **48**, 874 (1962).
[30] H. S. Shapiro and E. Chargaff, *Biochim. Biophys. Acta* **39**, 62, 68 (1960).
[31] K. Burton, and G. B. Petersen, *Biochem. J.* **75**, 17 (1960).
[32] J. B. Hall and R. L. Sinsheimer, *J. Mol. Biol.* **6**, 115 (1963).

site of pyrimidine degradation in apyrimidinic acid.[33,34] In addition, oligonucleotides prepared by the synthetic and biosynthetic routes are becoming available and may be used for specific inhibition studies. These latter procedures have only special application and will not be presented here.

i. Preparation of Apurinic Acid—Method of Tamm et al.[35]

Apurinic acid is a nondialyzable preparation in which the DNA has been deprived of its purine constituents without impairment of its original pyrimidine ratios. The derivative possesses a lower molecular weight than the original DNA, owing to some rupture of phosphodiester bonds.

To prepare apurinic acid: 0.1 N HCl is added to a DNA solution (usually containing 1 to 2 mg of DNA per milliliter of water) until the pH is adjusted to 1.6. The reaction mixture is then transferred to a dialysis bag and dialyzed against 20 volumes of dilute HCl at pH 1.6 for 26 hours at 37°. Alternatively, the reaction mixture need not undergo simultaneous dialysis with this solvent but may be allowed to incubate at 37° for 26 hours if precautions are taken to see that the pH is maintained at 1.6. When apurinization is complete, the reaction mixture is dialyzed overnight in the cold room against 15 volumes of 0.2 M borate buffer (pH 7.3), and then against frequent changes of distilled water until it is essentially salt-free. The retentate is then lyophilized. The apurinic acid forms a white hydroscopic material which is readily soluble in water.

ii. Preparation of Apyrimidinic Acid—Method of Sedat and Sinsheimer[33]

Apyrimidinic acid is a nondialyzable preparation in which the pyrimidine residues of the DNA have been destroyed, leaving the purine constituents essentially intact.

To prepare apyrimidinic acid: The DNA preparation is exhaustively dehydrated by drying over P_2O_5 *in vacuo* for 3 to 4 hours at room temperature, 3 hours at 60°, and 3 hours at 110°. To approximately 350 mg of the dry nucleic acid in a glass-stoppered flask is added 20 ml of anhydrous hydrazine (97%+), and the vessel is heated at 60° for 20 hours. The purine polymer is precipitated by addition of 0.1 volume of 3 M sodium acetate and 2 volumes of cold isopropanol. After standing overnight at 4°, the resulting precipitate is redissolved in 1 to 2 ml of H_2O

[33] J. Sedat and R. L. Sinsheimer, *J. Mol. Biol.* **9,** 489 (1964).
[34] E. Chargaff, P. Rust, A. Temperli, A. S. Morison, and A. Danon, *Biochim. Biophys. Acta* **76,** 149 (1963).
[35] C. Tamm, M. E. Hodes, and E. Chargaff, *J. Biol. Chem.* **195,** 49 (1952).

and reprecipitated by addition of 0.1 ml of 3 M sodium acetate plus 2 to 4 ml of cold isopropanol. The centrifuged precipitate is washed with anhydrous ether.

iii. Preparation of DNA Lacking Guanine—Method of Simon and Van Vunakis[36,37]

If DNA is irradiated with visible light in the presence of methylene blue (MB), the guanine residues are selectively destroyed to yield a product which has yet to be identified. This derivative then differs from apurinic and apyrimidinic acids in that the susceptible base has not been eliminated from the phosphodiester backbone, and no means of specifically rupturing the chain at the point of guanine destruction has yet been found.

To each milliliter of solution containing 35 to 500 μg of DNA in 0.1 M Tris buffer, pH 8.5, is added 0.01 to 0.2 ml of a MB solution which has been made up by dissolving 2.5 mg of MB in 10 ml of the same buffer. The reaction mixtures are irradiated by two 150-watt Sylvania flood lamps in a glass-wall temperature bath (at 20° to 30°) at 2500 to 3700 foot-candles. Air or O_2 is bubbled through the mixture during the course of the reaction. At the end of the illumination period, the sample is treated with Dowex 50 (Na$^+$) to remove the MB.

MB acts in a catalytic fashion but can be bleached during the photo-oxidation reaction. Therefore, sufficient MB should be added to keep the solution visibly blue at all times. Excessive amounts of dye (above 50 μg/ml) should not be added initially, however, since it diminishes the effective light and in great excess may even precipitate the DNA.

Depending on the conditions of the experiment, 20 to 50 hours may be required to completely destroy the guanine. Base analysis on the photo-oxidized DNA should be done to determine the extent of guanine destruction until the system is standardized. The reaction is more rapid with denatured than with native DNA.

[36] M. Simon and H. Van Vunakis, *J. Mol. Biol.* **4**, 488 (1962).
[37] M. Simon and H. Van Vunakis, *Arch. Biochem. Biophys.* **105**, 197 (1964).

2. ISOLATION AND CHARACTERIZATION OF RIBONUCLEIC ACID*

a. INTRODUCTION

In the light of current understanding of the control of protein synthesis and protein structures, one of the crucial questions concerning the control of antibody specificity can be formulated as follows: To what degree are

* Section 12,D,2 was contributed by Bernard Mach.

the structures of immunoglobulin molecules responsible for the unique fit of an antibody to the inducing antigen determined by the genetic material of the antibody-producing cell? A corollary question of current interest is whether this specificity is encoded in the sequence of nucleotides of certain RNA molecules. An experimental approach to the latter question is to test for the production of immunoglobulin molecules or chains with a specific affinity toward a particular antigen, induced in an antigen-free environment by purified antigen-free nucleic acid preparations from an immunized animal. Progress along these lines requires the use of methods for the extraction, purification, and analysis of RNA from antibody-producing tissues and, in particular, for the preparation of fractions rich in RNA with defined properties.

Recent investigations have often been hampered by failure to obtain, from either spleen or lymph nodes, RNA in undegraded form, despite various efforts to inhibit nuclease activity. Another difficulty in interpreting the results of this type of experiment has come from the frequent contamination of so-called "RNA-rich preparations" by significant amounts of antigen.[1-3]

A method will be described below for the isolation of RNA in an undegraded and uncontaminated form from tissues such as spleen, lymph nodes, and plasma-cell tumor (Section D,2,b,ii). A procedure will also be described for the purification of a small RNA fraction with strong stimulatory activity on cell-free protein synthesis (Section D,2,b,*iii*). Alternative procedures will be briefly discussed. Methods for the estimation of RNA will be given in detail, and procedures for the characterization of RNA, with respect to size, nucleotide composition, or template activity, will be outlined and appropriate literature references cited.

b. Extraction and Purification of RNA

i. *General Considerations*

The basic method for the isolation of RNA[4] consists in the extraction of crude tissue homogenates with phenol, followed by the separation of the two phases by centrifugation, and precipitation of RNA from the aqueous phase with cold ethanol. If the isolation of RNA from spleen or lymph nodes is attempted with such a procedure, the RNA obtained (1) is to a large extent degraded and consists mainly of low-molecular-weight fragments, (2) is grossly contaminated by as much as 1% of the tissue proteins, and (3) does not represent the totality of cellular RNA.

[1] M. Fishman and F. L. Adler, *J. Exptl. Med.* **117**, 595 (1963).
[2] H. Friedman, A. B. Stavitsky, and J. M. Solomon, *Science* **149**, 1106 (1965).
[3] B. A. Askonas and J. M. Rhodes, *Nature*, **205**, 470 (1965).
[4] A. Gierer and G. Schramm, *Nature* **177**, 702 (1956).

Because of these three problems—degradation, contamination, and incomplete extraction—it has been necessary to introduce several modifications to the basic procedure.

1. It is important, particularly in a tissue rich in ribonuclease, to minimize enzymatic hydrolysis of RNA during all steps of the purification procedure. This can often be achieved by the use of inhibitors of ribonuclease such as bentonite (1 mg/ml), polyvinylsulfate (3 to $4 \times 10^{-4}\%$), or detergents, and especially by avoiding any preliminary homogenization of the tissue in buffer prior to the extraction with phenol.

2. To avoid important contamination of RNA with proteins, it is necessary, following the initial phenol extraction, to further deproteinize the aqueous phase by at least two additional phenol extractions. It has also been shown that, following an initial precipitation of RNA from $0.1\ M$ NaCl with ethanol, repeated precipitations of RNA from high-concentration salt solutions (2 M KCl and $\frac{1}{3}$ volume of ethanol) were required to free the preparation from contaminating oligonucleotides.[5] If the procedure used also extracts DNA, as is the case for the method involving phenol extraction at pH 9,[6] it is necessary to treat the RNA with DNase (5 μg/ml for 10 minutes at 0°) and then to eliminate DNase by an additional phenol extraction.

3. In the case of animal cells, an important portion of newly synthesized RNA does not appear in the aqueous phase after phenol extraction at 0° to 20°. It has been found, however, that the use of higher temperatures,[7] of detergents,[8] or of higher pH[6] permits the extraction of the totality of RNA.

Several methods pertaining to liver and to animal cells in culture have been described in the literature; these include some of the modifications and additions just outlined. They permit the isolation of relatively pure, undegraded RNA, including the rapidly labeled RNA fraction. These methods are characterized by the use of sodium dodecyl sulfate (SDS),[5] SDS and heating,[9] heating,[7] or pH 9 buffers.[6]

ii. Hot Phenol–SDS Method for Total Cellular RNA

A method that permits the isolation of the totality of RNA, from either spleen, lymph node, or plasma-cell tumor, in an undegraded and

[5] A. DiGirolamo, E. C. Henshaw, and H. H. Hiatt, *J. Mol. Biol.* **8**, 479 (1964).

[6] B. Braverman, L. Gold, and J. Eisenstadt, *Proc. Natl. Acad. Sci. U.S.* **50**, 630 (1963).

[7] G. P. Georgiev, O. P. Samarina, M. I. Lerman, M. N. Smirnov, and A. N. Severtzov, *Nature* **200**, 1291 (1963).

[8] H. H. Hiatt, *J. Mol. Biol.* **5**, 217 (1962).

[9] K. Scherrer and J. E. Darnell, *Biochem. Biophys. Res. Commun.* **7**, 486 (1962).

uncontaminated form has been described by Mach and Vassalli.[10] All operations, unless otherwise specified, are performed at 0° to 4°. The organs are excised within seconds following the killing of the animal and are immediately frozen at −70°. Frozen tissues are homogenized at 4° in a mixture of equal volumes of buffer (0.5% SDS, 0.5% 1,5-naphthalenedisulfonate, 0.1 M Tris or acetate buffer, pH 5) and of fresh phenol (Commercial preparations of 88% phenol, analytical reagent grade, without preservative, from Mallinckrodt can be used, stored in small bottles at 4°, and only as long as the solution is colorless.) For each gram of tissue, 6 ml of buffer and 6 ml of phenol are used, and no more than 15 to 20 gm is processed at a time. Homogenization is performed first in a Waring blender at full speed for 1 to 2 minutes, then in a Teflon/glass Potter homogenizer kept refrigerated in ice.

The homogenate is heated at 65° for 6 minutes with constant gentle shaking and quickly cooled in an acetone–dry ice bath. The mixture is centrifuged at 4000 rpm at 4° in a swinging-bucket centrifuge, and the aqueous phase is collected. An equivalent amount of fresh buffer is added to the remaining interphase and phenol; after shaking at 20° for 10 minutes, the mixture is centrifuged and the aqueous phase is again collected. The pooled aqueous phases are then extracted twice more, at 20° for 10 minutes each time, with only ½ volume of phenol.

The aqueous phase obtained after the last centrifugation is brought to 0.1 M NaCl, and 2½ volumes of cold ethanol (−30°) is added. After 2 to 3 hours at 0° the RNA precipitate is centrifuged at 10,000 g for 15 minutes and dissolved in water. RNA is reprecipitated by the addition of 1 volume of 4 M potassium acetate, and 1 volume of chilled ethanol; after 2 hours at −30° and centrifugation, the RNA pellet is dissolved in water with a small Potter homogenizer. The same potassium acetate precipitation is performed twice more, and the final RNA solution is stored frozen. RNA obtained by this procedure represents 98 to 100% of cellular RNA, gives a negative diphenylamine reaction for DNA (see Section D,1), and contains less than 0.01% of the tissue proteins; its sedimentation profile shows three peaks at 30S, 18S, and 4S (Fig. 1).

iii. Successive Fractional Extraction of RNA

It is possible to apply to the case of immunoglobulin-producing tissues an observation made by Georgiev with rat liver[7]; successive extractions at increasing temperatures yield distinct RNA fractions in a stepwise manner.[11] The three fractions extracted successively at 20°, 45°, and 65°

[10] B. Mach and P. Vassalli, *Proc. Natl. Acad. Sci. U.S.* **54**, 975 (1965).
[11] B. Mach and P. Vassalli, *Science* **150**, 622 (1965).

possess distinct chemical and biological properties and may correspond to distinct species of cellular RNA. The procedure is diagrammed in Fig. 2.

Homogenization of frozen tissues is performed as described above (Section D,2,b,*ii*), except that the buffer contains *no* SDS. The initial phenol extraction is performed at 20° for 6 minutes; as before, phenol and interphase are re-extracted with fresh buffer (*minus* SDS) at 20°, and the pooled aqueous phases are subjected to repeated deproteinizations with phenol and precipitations with ethanol. The RNA obtained is fraction I (20°).

The phenol below the remaining interphase is aspirated and discarded, and the interphase is extracted with one volume of phenol and one volume

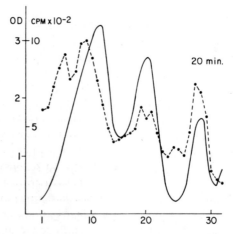

Fig. 1. Sucrose density gradient analysis of spleen RNA from immunized rats, (after 20 minutes of *in vivo* labeling with uridine-C[14]). RNA was isolated as described in Section D,2,b,*ii*. The solid line is the 260-mμ absorbancy profile and shows the characteristic 30S, 18S, and 4S peaks; the dotted line indicates the sedimentation pattern of rapidly labeled RNA. See B. Mach and P. Vassalli, *Science* **150**, 622 (1965).

of buffer (*containing* 0.5% SDS) at 45° for 6 minutes. Following removal of the aqueous phase and a repeated extraction of the phenol and interphase at 20°, the pooled aqueous phases are treated as in Section D,2,b,*ii*. The resulting RNA constitutes fraction II (45°).

The remaining interphase, after removal of the underlying phenol, is extracted with phenol and SDS buffer at 65° for 6 minutes as in Section D,2,b,ii, and again a second phenol extraction is performed at 20°. The pooled aqueous phases are treated as before, and the resulting RNA constitutes fraction III (65°). Table I gives the yield of each of the three fractions and some of their characteristics.

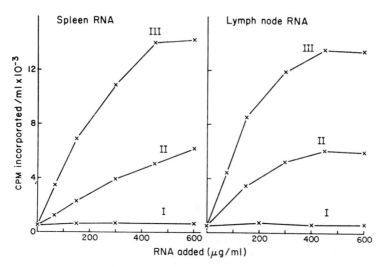

Fig. 2. Diagram of the RNA isolation procedure involving successive phenol extractions at increasing temperature. See text for details (Section D,2,b,*iii*).

TABLE I

Some Properties of RNA from Fractions I, II, and III from Either Spleen or Lymph Node of the Immunized Rat[a]

RNA fraction	Yield	Relative specific activity	Template activity
I	70–80%	1	0–5
II	10–20%	2–3	10–15
III	5–10%	6–8	30–35

[a] See B. Mach and P. Vassalli, *Science* **150**, 622 (1965). The yield is in percent of total RNA; the relative specific activity was measured after 20 minutes of *in vivo* labeling; the template activity is expressed as the stimulation of protein synthesis resulting from the addition of RNA to an *Escherichia coli* cell-free system.

iv. Isolation of RNA from Subcellular Components

RNA preparations from nuclei, cytoplasm, or microsomes can also be achieved with the methods described in Sections D,2,b,ii and D,2,b,iii. In such cases the risk of ribonuclease digestion is greater, and polyvinyl-sulfate (3 to 4 × 10^{-4}%) should be included in the medium used for homogenization and fractionation of the tissues. Classical methods of differential centrifugation (see Chap. 7) can be applied to obtain subcellular fractions from spleen or lymph nodes, and RNA can then be extracted from these fractions in undegraded form.[10]

c. ANALYSIS AND ESTIMATION OF RNA

i. Spectrophotometric Analysis

The absorbancy of nucleotides at 260 mμ can be used for a quantitative estimation of either the amount of RNA in a pure RNA preparation or the amount of ribonucleotides (resulting from hydrolysis of RNA) extracted from crude tissues extracts. The problem of the spectrophotometric analysis of nucleotides and nucleic acids has been extensively reviewed.[12]

a. To estimate the amount of RNA in a relatively pure RNA preparation, free from oligonucleotides and from protein or DNA contamination, measure of absorbancy at 260 mμ is the method of choice. The exact molar extinction coefficient (E_M) for a given RNA preparation depends (1) on the different E_M values of the four bases present, (2) on the relative amount of these four bases in the RNA, and (3) on the hyperchromic effect, which causes a given number of free nucleotides to give ultraviolet absorption readings about 30% higher than would the same amount of nucleotides linked in a polymeric form. For any RNA a "theoretical" E_M can be estimated from its nucleotide composition and its chain length as indicated from the phosphorus content of the preparation (determined by the method of Fiske-Subbarow, as described by Hurlbert *et al.*[13]). There are no great variations, however, in the E_M of different RNA's, and the values for RNA's of mammalian tissues are around 8000; thus for mouse liver RNA, E_M is 8190, while the nucleotide product of the alkaline hydrolysis of the same RNA has an E_M value of 10,700, an increase of 31%.[14] From the average molecular weight of the four nucleotides (325) and an E_M value of 8000, the absorbancy at 260 mμ for each milligram of RNA can be calculated to be 25 O.D. units.

b. To estimate the amount of total and/or isotope-labeled RNA in a tissue, it is best to take advantage of the Schmidt-Tannhauser procedure,[15] which consists in the hydrolysis of RNA, and not of DNA, in dilute alkali, following the removal of free nucleotides and other small molecules by acid precipitation. The optimal concentration of cold perchloric acid

[12] G. H. Beaven, E. R. Holiday, and E. A. Johnson, *in* "The Nucleic Acids" (E. Chargaff and J. N. Davidson, eds.), Vol. I, pp. 439–554. Academic Press, New York, 1955.

[13] R. B. Hurlbert, H. Schitz, A. F. Brumm, and V. R. Potter, *J. Biol. Chem.* **209**, 23 (1954).

[14] B. Magasanik, *in* "The Nucleic Acids" (E. Chargaff and J. N. Davidson, eds.), Vol. 1, pp. 373–408. Academic Press, New York, 1955.

[15] G. Schmidt and S. J. Tannhauser, *J. Biol. Chem.* **161**, 83 (1945).

(PCA) for the preliminary precipitations and washings is 0.2 N, and subsequent lipid extractions should be avoided, since they can result in losses of RNA.[16] Hydrolysis for prolonged periods of time as originally proposed (18 hours at 37° in 0.3 N KOH) results in extensive extraction of non-RNA material, which can account for 30% or more of the 260-mμ absorbing material. For most animal tissues and bacteria, a period of 1 hour of alkaline hydrolysis is sufficient to render acid-soluble the totality of RNA.[17] It must be kept in mind, however, that in certain tissues, such as the thyroid, extraction of some peptide material in the acid-soluble fraction occurs even with a brief hydrolysis time.

The following procedure[17] can be recommended: Tissue extracts ($\frac{1}{30}$, w/v) are precipitated in 0.2 N PCA at 0° for 15 minutes. The precipitate is washed twice in the cold in 0.2 N PCA, and the excess acid is drained off. KOH (0.3 N) is added (about one-half the original volume of 0.2 N PCA mixture), and incubation is carried out at 37° for 1 hour. After cooling of the sample in ice, KOH is neutralized with excess cold PCA to a final concentration of 0.3 N PCA. The precipitate is collected, washed twice with 0.2 N PCA, and the pooled supernatants are made 0.1 N PCA in a volume suitable for absorbancy measurements.

ii. Orcinol Reaction

The orcinol reaction, or Bial reaction, as described in Section B,5 (see also Dische[18]), is specific for ribose (pyrimidine nucleotides are not hydrolyzed under the conditions of the reaction, and consequently only purine-bound ribose reacts with orcinol). When the reaction is applied to crude tissue extracts, there is interference from various substances, mainly from polysaccharides. The following modification[13] is recommended: To a sample (0.2-ml aliquot) in 1.0 ml of water is added 2.0 ml of freshly prepared reagent containing 0.4% orcinol in 12 N HCl–0.04% $FeCl_3$. The tubes are mixed, capped, heated for 15 minutes in a boiling water bath, and cooled; the optical density is read at 660 mμ within minutes, since the color fades at a rate of 13% per hour. Samples from standard RNA solutions are measured for reference. This procedure gives a higher color yield than the standard method (as described in ref. 18), and maximum color development occurs between 5 and 10 minutes. With readings over an optical density range from 0.1 to 1.0, the molar extinction values vary less than 5%.

[16] T. P. Hallinan, A. Fleck, and H. N. Munro, *Biochim. Biophys. Acta* **68**, 131 (1963).

[17] A. Fleck and D. Berg, *Biochim. Biophys. Acta* **108**, 333 (1965).

[18] Z. Dische, *in* "The Nucleic Acids" (E. Chargaff and J. N. Davidson, eds.), Vol. I, pp. 285–306. Academic Press, New York, 1955.

iii. Contamination

The extent of contamination of RNA by DNA can be measured by the diphenylamine reaction (see Section D,1); in the case of RNA prepared by phenol extraction at 65° as described above (Section D,2,b,ii), the reaction is negative.[19]

Contamination by protein is an important problem, particularly for the study of the possible transfer of antibody specificity by antigen-free RNA preparations. Protein in RNA can be estimated by the reaction of Lowry (see Section A,6), but when protein contamination is less than 1% (as in RNA obtained by the procedure described above, Section D,2,b,ii) a more sensitive technique is required. After a short pulse of radioactive labeling in vivo with an amino acid, the radioactivity of purified RNA is measured and compared with the radioactivity of proteins extracted from the same tissue; it could thus be shown that RNA extracted as described in Sections D,2,b,ii and D,2,b,iii contains less than 0.01% of the radioactive proteins of the spleen,[11] whereas RNA obtained by usual extraction procedures[20] can be contaminated by as much as 1% of the radioactive proteins of the spleen.

d. Characterization of RNA

The usual methods for the characterization of RNA involve the study of such properties as size, nucleotide composition, kinetics of synthesis (by radioactive labeling), and "template" activity (defined as the ability to stimulate cell-free protein synthesis). According to these criteria one can characterize the various RNA fractions obtained either from different subcellular components or by fractionation of isolated RNA; one can thus identify different types of RNA which are thought to represent the different types of RNA existing in the cell. These techniques and methods are briefly outlined below with references to detailed descriptions in the literature.

i. Identification on the Basis of Size

(a) *Fractionation Procedures* A practical method for the fractionation of RNA according to its size, and one that also permits a sedimentation analysis, is sucrose gradient centrifugation (see Chap. 7,C). A gradient from 5 to 20% sucrose is commonly used,[21] and good fractionation of spleen and lymph node RNA has been achieved[10] with SDS (0.5%) in the

[19] A. V. Rake, and A. F. Graham, *Biophys. J.* **4**, 267 (1964).
[20] H. Friedman, *Biochem. Biophys. Res. Commun.* **17**, 272 (1964).
[21] R. J. Britten and R. B. Roberts, *Science* **131**, 32 (1960).

gradient at 15°, as described by Gilbert[22] for bacterial RNA. The three RNA peaks, corresponding to 30S, 18S, and 4S, must be well resolved, and any accumulation of ultraviolet-absorbing material in the lighter part of the gradient strongly suggests artifactual degradation of RNA. After collection, each fraction is assayed for absorption at 260 mμ and for acid-precipitable radioactivity; sedimentation profiles are thus obtained for both total RNA and labeled RNA (as in Fig. 1). RNA can also be fractionated on methylated albumin columns (MAK), where separation is achieved on the basis of size, hydrogen bonding, and nucleotide composition.[23,24] Gel filtration on Sephadex has also been used, especially for the fine resolution of some species of soluble-RNA (S-RNA).[25] Finally, analytical ultracentrifugation (see Chap. 7,B) is particularly useful for the characterization (sedimentation coefficient) of homogeneous species of RNA molecules, such as ribosomal RNA.

(b) *Determination of Chain Length* A precise chemical method has recently been proposed for the estimation of polynucleotide chain length which is applicable to the various types of RNA.[26] When RNA is reacted with periodate ($NaIO_4$), only the terminal ribose molecule with unsubstituted hydroxyl groups is oxidized. RNA can then be reacted with radioactive isonicotinic acid hydrazide (INH), which reacts only with oxidized ribose, thus in a one-to-one stoichiometry with RNA chains. The radioactive RNA–isonicotinic acid hydrazone can then be precipitated and counted. This method has been applied to the determination of both chain length and molecular weight of 4S, 16S, and 28S RNA from *Escherichia coli*.

Another method of determining chain length takes advantage of the fact that, during alkaline hydrolysis of RNA, one ribonucleoside and one ribonucleoside diphosphate are released from each chain of RNA. Either nucleosides or (2′, 3′)-5′-nucleoside diphosphate can then be identified and measured.[27]

ii. Analysis of Nucleotide Composition

(a) *Principle* Various types of RNA have characteristic ratios of their four nucleotides; ribosomal RNA has typically a high G + C/A + U ratio while messenger RNA is characterized by a lower G + C/A + U ratio, closer to the low ratios observed in DNA. (G, C, A, and U signify

[22] W. Gilbert, *J. Mol. Biol.* **6**, 374 (1963).

[23] J. D. Mandell and A. D. Hershey, *Anal. Biochem.* **1**, 66 (1960).

[24] N. Sueoka and T. Yamane, *Proc. Natl. Acad. Sci. U.S.* **48**, 1454 (1962).

[25] T. Schleich and J. Goldstein, *Proc. Natl. Acad. Sci. U.S.* **52**, 744 (1964).

[26] J. E. M. Midgley, *Biochim. Biophys. Acta* **108**, 340 (1965).

[27] B. G. Lane, *Biochemistry* **4**, 212 (1965).

guanylic, cytidylic, adenylic, and uridylic acid, respectively.) The nucleotide composition can be measured after hydrolysis of RNA in alkali, which specifically yields 2'(3')-ribonucleotides. Hydrolysis must take place in dilute alkali (0.3 N KOH), since a higher molarity results in some deamination of cytidylic acid, which is then counted as uridylic acid. To ensure a complete digestion to the mononucleotide level, hydrolysis is continued for 18 hours at 37°. The solution is neutralized in the cold with PCA, and the precipitate of potassium perchlorate is removed by centrifugation. When RNA labeled with P^{32} is hydrolyzed under these conditions, each atom of P^{32} introduced during biosynthesis in one nucleotide is transferred to the 2'(3') position of the adjacent nucleotide. If labeling is sufficiently random throughout the RNA chain, this transfer does not affect the determination of the nucleotide ratio in the chain. 2'(3')-Ribonucleotides can be separated and identified by paper electrophoresis or by ion exchange column chromatography.

(b) *Paper Electrophoresis of Ribonucleotides* Complete separation of the four nucleotides is achieved in 18 hours at 11 volts/cm in 0.02 M citrate buffer, pH 3.5.* This procedure[28,29] requires concentrated neutral solutions for spotting on the paper, and the low solubility of some of the nucleotides can interfere with their separation. Furthermore, the spectrophotometric readings are complicated by the necessity of eluting the nucleotides and of subtracting "paper blanks" of comparable size.

(c) *Ion Exchange Chromatography of Ribonucleotides* Complete separation of the four nucleotides on anion exchange resins, such as Dowex I in the formate form, can be achieved either by stepwise elution[30] or by a gradient elution.[13] A recommended procedure for gradient elution is that of Osawa *et al.*[31] A mixture of 5 to 7 mg of mononucleotides is separated on a 0.6 × 20-cm Dowex I (formate) column. In a 50-ml mixing flask, first containing water, the concentration of the eluant is continuously increased, first with 30 ml of 1 N formic acid, then with 200 ml of 4 N formic acid. Three-milliliter samples are collected every 15 minutes. In contrast to paper electrophoresis, anion exchange chromatography is not limited to small aliquots, neither in volume nor in quantity of material. However, the large elution volumes often must be concentrated by lyophili-

---

* Formic acid–ammonium formate, pH 3.5, at 0.02 M has also been used as a volatile buffer, allowing drying and examination of the strip under ultraviolet illumination after electrophoresis for 3 hours [K. K. Reddi, *Proc. Natl. Acad. Sci. U. S.* **50**, 419 (1963)]. Three parts of 1 M formic acid and 2 parts of 1 M ammonium formate are mixed and diluted to 0.02 M.

[28] J. N. Davidson and R. M. S. Smellie, *Biochem. J.* **52**, 594 (1952).
[29] J. D. Smith, *in* "The Nucleic Acids" (E. Chargaff and J. N. Davidson, eds.), Vol. I, pp. 267–284. Academic Press, New York, 1955.
[30] W. Cohn *in* "The Nucleic Acids" (E. Chargaff and J. N. Davidson, eds.), Vol. I, pp. 211–245. Academic Press, New York, 1955.
[31] S. Osawa, K. Takata, and Y. Hotta, *Biochim. Biophys. Acta* **28**, 271 (1958).

zation or flash evaporation for ultraviolet absorbancy and radioactivity measurements.

A recent method,[32] which is rapid and requires only small amounts of nucleotide mixture, involves the use of a small column of cation exchange resin, Dowex 50-H$^+$. Below pH 2, GMP, AMP, and CMP have charged amino groups and are thus exchanged on the column, while UMP passes through; elution with water first releases GMP alone and then CMP and AMP together. The absorbancy due to each of these two nucleotides can be calculated from the extinction values of the mixture at 257 mμ and 279 mμ in 0.05 N HCl from the equations

$$x = \frac{2.32\,(A_{257}) - A_{279}}{2.08} \tag{1}$$

and

$$y = A_{279} - 0.238x \tag{2}$$

where x is the absorbancy at 257 mμ due to AMP alone, y is the absorbancy at 279 mμ due to CMP alone, and A is the absorbancy of the mixture. Alternatively CMP and AMP can be separated on a short anion exchange column (Dowex I, formate) as described above.

The cation exchange method has a disadvantage if the radioactivity of P^{32}-labeled nucleotides is to be measured. Since UMP is never exchanged in this procedure, it can be contaminated with inorganic P^{32} which also passes through in first column volume. UMP must then be adsorbed on charcoal to correct these excessively high radioactivity values for UMP.

iii. Chromatographic Separation

Several procedures have been described for the separation of RNA by column chromatography; these methods are mainly used to separate the various amino-acid specific species of S-RNA, either for analytic or for preparative purposes. In view of the recent report[33] that, in certain plasmocytoma tumors of the mice, specific leucyl-S-RNA and threonine-S-RNA species are absent, these fractionation procedures will be applied with interest to S-RNA of immunoglobulin producing tissues.

a. As mentioned earlier (Section D,2,d,*i*,*a*) chromatography of RNA on methylated albumin kieselguhr (MAK) has been described.[23,24] This method however, even with some modifications,[33] can only separate certain S-RNA peaks and has a lower resolution than the procedures to be mentioned next.

b. Reverse phase chromatography is a method combining both ion-exchange and differential solubility phenomena and which can re-

[32] S. Katz and D. G. Comb, *J. Biol. Chem.* **238**, 3065 (1963).

[33] Mach, B., H. Koblet and D. Gros, *Cold Spring Harbor* Symp. *Quant. Biol.* **32**, 1967 (in press).

solve well the various S-RNA species of *E. coli*.[34] This method is now being applied successfully to the separation of S-RNA from mouse plasmocytoma.[35]

c. Other methods of S-RNA separation, used mainly for preparative purposes, include partition chromatography on Sephadex G 25,[36] chromatography on DEAE columns with gradient elution at elevated temperatures[37] and countercurrent distribution.[38]

iv. *Measurement of Template Activity*

One of the characteristics of a certain type of RNA (messenger RNA) is its ability to function as a template in protein synthesis and to stimulate

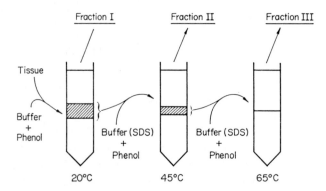

Fig. 3. Template activity of RNA from fractions I, II, and III tested in a cell-free system derived from *Escherichia coli*. See B. Mach and P. Vassalli, *Science* **150,** 622 (1965).

the incorporation of amino acids into hot TCA-insoluble material (protein) in cell-free extracts. The template activity of RNA can be best demonstrated and measured by using a cell-free system derived from *E. coli*,[39] which responds particularly well to the addition of either synthetic polynucleotides or messenger RNA. The two important phases of the experiment, the preparation of the bacterial extracts and the assay for amino acid incorporation, are described in detail in the papers of

[34] Kelmers, A. D., G. D. Novelli, and M. P. Stulberg. *J. Biol. Chem.* **240,** 3979 (1965).
[35] Mach, B. and H. Koblet. To be published.
[36] Tanaka, K., H. H. Richards, and G. L. Cantoni. *Biochim. Biophys. Acta* **61,** 846 (1962).
[37] Baguley, B. C., P. L. Bergquist, and R. K. Ralph. *Biochim. Biophys. Acta* **95,** 510 (1965).
[38] Apgar, J. R., W. Holley, and S. H. Marill. *J. Biol. Chem.* **237,** 796 (1962).
[39] M. Nirenberg and J. H. Matthei, *Proc. Natl. Acad. Sci. U.S.* **47,** 1588 (1961).

Nirenberg and Matthei[39] and of Nathans *et al.*[40] It must be noted that there are often unexplained variations in the activity of different *E. coli* S30 preparations obtained by identical procedures. It should be noted that by comparison cell-free amino acid incorporation systems prepared from animal tissues respond poorly to the addition of messenger RNA.

Except in the case of RNA from f₂ bacteriophage,[40] it has not as yet been shown that the protein synthesized *in vitro* under the influence of a particular messenger RNA is indeed the specific protein coded by that RNA in the living cell. Nevertheless, the response of the *E. coli* cell-free system is a convenient and reproducible assay for the characteristic template activity of generalized messenger RNA, and in the case of RNA from antibody-producing tissues it has permitted the identification of a small RNA fraction which strongly stimulates cell-free protein synthesis[11] (see Fig. 3).

[40] D. Nathans, G. Notani, J. H. Schwartz, and N. D. Zinder, *Proc. Natl. Acad. Sci. U.S.* **48**, 1424 (1962).

APPENDIX I

Spectral Properties of Proteins and Small Molecules of Immunological Interest*

The following table was assembled in the hope that it might prove to be useful in a variety of immunological techniques. The format and organization have been selected to facilitate its use in the laboratory. The material included was arbitrarily selected through the use of the Immunochemistry Section of *Chemical Abstracts* from 1962 to 1965. Earlier papers were consulted and material was reproduced where it seemed likely to be of current interest. No figures have been reproduced, and we have not quoted data calculated from figures in the reference sources. Only when explicit numerical values for extinction coefficients and wavelengths were given in the cited publication have they been included in the tables. When spectral data have been explicitly stated for wavelength maximum or wavelength minimum values, this notation has been indicated in the table by the terms (λ_{max}) or (λ_{min}). References to "text" refer to Chapter 10. In the table, "antibody" is used for simplicity, even though within any given immunoglobulin class hetereogeneous molecules constitute the specific antibodies.

Nomenclature for immunoglobulins used in the table conforms, insofar as possible, to the World Health Organization guidelines discussed in Chap. 3,A,1, Vol. I. Therefore the terms employed may differ from those used in the cited reference, but the changes were made only when they could be justified by operational equivalence.

* Appendix I was contributed by J. Russell Little and Helaine Donahue.

PROTEINS

Protein[a]	λ (mμ)	$E_{1cm}^{1\%}$	Solvent	Comments	Ref.
Bovine insulin	278	10.60	0.025 M phosphate, pH 7.0	$E_M = 6080$ M.W. = 5734	1
Bovine pancreatic ribonuclease (Armour, lot #381–059)	277.5	7.2	Water	$E_M = 9800$ M.W. = 13,683	2
Carboxypeptidase A	280	19.4			3
α-Chymotrypsinogen (Worthington Biochemical Corporation)	282	20.0		$E_M = 50, 200$; 16.5% N by dry weight and Kjeldahl N	4
β-Lactoglobulin	280	9.5		Kjeldahl N	64
Pepsinogen	280	12.5		$E_M = 51,220$	67
Pepsin	280	14.3	Water	Dry weight	66
Egg white lysozyme	280	26.5	0.2 M sodium phosphate, pH 7.0	Dry weight, salt-free	5
Trypsin (Worthington Biochemical Corporation)	280	14.4		Kjeldahl N	6
Trypsinogen	280	13.9		Kjeldahl N	7
Papain	278(λ_{max})	25.0		$E_M = 51,800$	8
Hen egg albumin	277		0.25 M acetic acid	Extinction coefficient given as 0.0046 O.D./ μg N/ml (Kjeldahl)	9
Hen egg albumin	280	7.35			65
Bovine serum albumin	279	6.67	Water		63
Bovine serum mercaptalbumin	280(λ_{max})	6.6		$E_M = 43,600$	8
Human serum mercaptalbumin	279(λ_{max})	5.3		$E_M = 35,000$	8
Human serum albumin	277		0.25 M acetic acid	Kjeldahl N: 0.0043 O.D./μg N/ml	10
Hemocyanin from *L. polyphemus*	278	11.2	Water	Dry weight	61

Protein					Ref.
Apomyoglobin (sperm whale)	280		0.1 M phosphate pH 6.8	$E_M = 15,800$ M.W. = 17,000	70
Apohemoglobin (human)	280		0.1 M phosphate pH 6.8	$E_M = 49,600$ M.W. = 68,000	70
Bence-Jones Proteins					
B.T. (kappa)	278	14.0	0.04 M potassium phosphate, pH 7.4	Kjeldahl N	11
Gi (kappa)	278	14.1	0.04 M potassium phosphate, pH 7.4	Kjeldahl N	11
Vi (lambda)	278	14.2	0.04 M potassium phosphate, pH 7.4	Kjeldahl N	11
Nonspecific Immunoglobulins					
Human γ-globulin (II$_{1,2}$ Cohn Fr.)	277		0.25 M acetic acid	Kjeldahl N: 0.0090 O.D./μg N/ml	10
Human γ-globulin (II$_3$ Cohn Fr.)	277		0.25 M acetic acid	Kjeldahl N: 0.0091 O.D./μg N/ml	10
Human γG-immunoglobulins	280	14.3 ± 0.2	pH 7.5, 0.2 M NaCl	Kjeldahl N	13
Human 3 S γ_1-globulin	280(λ_{max})	14.7	0.1 M NaCl, pH 6.0	Kjeldahl N	14
Human pathological γM-immuno-globulin	280	11.85 ± 0.02	pH 7.5, 0.2 M NaCl	Kjeldahl N	13
Human pathological γM-immuno-globulin subunit	280	12.0 ± 0.2	pH 7.5, 0.2 M NaCl	Kjeldahl N	13
Horse γG-immunoglobulins	280	13.8	0.0175 M Na phosphate buffer, pH 6.5	Dry weight	15
	280	13.6	8 M urea, neutral buffer	Dry weight	15
Heavy chains, horse γG-immuno-globulins	280	15.4	0.04 M Na decyl sulfate	Kjeldahl N	76
		15.2	1 N propionic acid	Kjeldahl N	76

Proteins (*Continued*)

Protein[a]	λ (mμ)	$E^{1\%}_{1cm}$	Solvent	Comments	Ref.
Light chains, horse γG-immunoglobulins	280	14.0	0.04 M Na decyl sulfate	Kjeldahl N	76
Rabbit γG-immunoglobulins		13.6	1 N propionic acid	Kjeldahl N	76
	280	14.6		Protein concentration determined by digestion and nesslerization	16
Rabbit γG-immunoglobulins	278	15.0	0.04 M K phosphate, pH 7.4	Kjeldahl N	11
γG-Immunoglobulins from Aa 3-3 Ab 4-4 single rabbits	278	15.4, 14.5	0.04 M K phosphate, pH 7.4	Kjeldahl N	11
γG-Immunoglobulins from Aa 1-1 Ab 4-4 single rabbits	278	15.1, 14.7	0.04 M K phosphate, pH 7.4	Kjeldahl N	11
γG-Immunoglobulins from Aa 1-1 Ab 5-5 single rabbit	278	14.9	0.04 M K phosphate, pH 7.4	Kjeldahl N	11
Rabbit γG-immunoglobulins	278	14.6 $\pm$ 0.4	0.15 M NaCl, 0.02 M phosphate, pH 7.4	Kjeldahl N	17
Rabbit γG-immunoglobulins	280	13.5	0.01 N HCl	Dry weight	18
Heavy chains, rabbit γG-immunoglobulins	280	13.7	0.01 N HCl	Dry weight	18
Light chains, rabbit γG-immunoglobulins	280	11.8	0.01 N HCl	Dry weight	18
Fd fragment, rabbit γG-immunoglobulins	280	14.4	0.01 N HCl	Dry weight	18
Heavy chains, rabbit γG-immunoglobulins (mildly reduced and alkylated)	280	14.5	0.04 M decylsulfate, 0.01 M phosphate, pH 7.2	Kjeldahl N	19
Light chains, rabbit γG-immunoglobulins (mildly reduced and alkylated)	280	13.2	0.04 M decylsulfate, 0.01 M phosphate, pH 7.2	Kjeldahl N	19

Protein	λ (nm)	Absorptivity	Solvent	Basis	Ref.
Rabbit γG-immunoglobulins	280	13.6 ± 0.1	5 M guanidine hydrochloride, pH 7	Dry weight	60
Heavy chains, rabbit γG-immunoglobulins	280	13.7 ± 0.1	5 M guanidine hydrochloride, pH 7	Dry Weight	60
Light chains, rabbit γG-immunoglobulins	280	11.4 ± 0.1	5 M guanidine hydrochloride, pH 7	Dry weight	60
Fab fragment, rabbit γG-immunoglobulins	278	15.0	5 M guanidine hydrochloride, pH 7	Molar absorptivity = 7.5×10^4 M^{-1} cm^{-1} at λ 278, assuming M.W. = 50,000 (dry weight)	20
Rabbit γG-immunoglobulins	278	13.8	"Dilute buffer solution"	Dry weight	72
Fab fragment, rabbit γG-immunoglobulins	278	15.3	"Dilute buffer solution"	Dry weight	72
Fc fragment, rabbit γG-immunoglobulins	278	12.2	"Dilute buffer solution"	Dry weight	72
Fab fragment, rabbit γG-immunoglobulins	280	15.0	0.1 M phosphate, pH 7.5		21
5 S pepsin fragment, rabbit γG-immunoglobulins	280	14.8	0.1 M phosphate, pH 7.5		21
Rabbit γA-immunoglobulins from colostrum	280	13.5	0.1 N NaOH		59
Rabbit γA-immunoglobulins from colostrum	280	12.8	5 M guanidine hydrochloride		62
α chains from rabbit colostral γA-immunoglobulins	280	10.6	5 M guanidine hydrochloride	Dry weight	62
Guinea pig γ1-immunoglobulins	278	15.0	"Neutral solution"	Kjeldahl N 0.0094 O.D./μg N/ml	73, 74
Guinea pig γ2-immunoglobulins	278	13.2	"Neutral solution"	Kjeldahl N 0.0083 O.D./μg N/ml	73, 74
Chicken γ-globulin fraction	280	13.5		N content 14.8%	68

PROTEINS *(Continued)*

Protein[a]	λ (mμ)	$E_{1\,cm}^{1\%}$	Solvent	Comments	Ref.
Lemon shark γG-immunoglobulins	280	13.85 ± 0.23	0.3 M KCl	Dry weight	77
		14.04 ± 0.26	0.1 N NaOH	Dry weight	
		12.82 ± 0.18	5 M guanidine	Dry weight	
Lemon shark γM-immunoglobulins	280	13.39 ± 0.67	0.3 M KCl	Dry weight	77
		13.75 ± 0.03	0.1 N NaOH	Dry weight	
		12.79 ± 0.01	5 M guanidine	Dry weight	
Heavy chains, lemon shark γG-immunoglobulins	280	11.74 ± 0.05	5 M guanidine	Dry weight	77
Light chains, lemon shark γG-immunoglobulins	280	13.1 ± 0.7	5 M guanidine	Dry weight	77
Purified Antibodies and Their Fragments and Polypeptide Chains					
Rabbit antibody to human γ-globulin	279(λmax)	14.4	0.25 M acetic acid	Kjeldahl N	12
Rabbit antibody to bovine serum albumin	279(λmax)	15.0	0.25 M acetic acid	Kjeldahl N	12
Rabbit antibody to hen egg albumin	277		0.25 M acetic acid	Kjeldahl N: 0.0102 O.D./μg N/ml	10
Rabbit antibody to human γ-globulin (II₃, Cohn Fr.)	277		0.25 M acetic acid	Kjeldahl N: 0.0097 O.D./μg N/ml	10
Rabbit γG-anti-SUp antibodies	279	14.3-14.6	0.15 M NaCl 0.002 M Na phosphate buffer, pH 7.8	Kjeldahl N	78
Rabbit γG-anti-SUp pepsin fragment	280	15.0		Kjeladhl N	78
Rabbit antibody to pneumococcal polysaccharide type XIV	277		0.25 M acetic acid	Kjeldahl N: 0.0098 O.D./μg N/ml	10
Rabbit γG-anti-DNP antibodies DN-23 (intact molecules)	278	15.8	0.15 M NaCl, 0.02 M	Kjeldahl N, low-	22

Sample	(nm)	Value	Solvent	Notes	Ref
5 S pepsin fragment, DN-23	278	16.9	0.15 M NaCl, 0.02 M K phosphate, pH 7.4	affinity antibody	22
DN-22 (intact molecules)	278	16.8 ± 0.2	0.15 M NaCl, 0.02 M K phosphate, pH 7.4	Kjeldahl N, low-affinity antibody	17
Fab fragment, DN-22	278	16.5	0.15 M NaCl, 0.02 M K phosphate, pH 7.4	Kjeldahl N, high-affinity antibody	17
Fc fragment, DN-22	278	13.5 ± 0.4	0.15 M NaCl, 0.02 M K phosphate, pH 7.4	Kjeldahl N, high-affinity antibody	22
5 S pepsin fragment, DN-22	278	18.1	0.15 M NaCl, 0.02 M K phosphate, pH 7.4	Kjeldahl N, high-affinity antibody	22
DN37-1	278	15.4	0.04 M K phosphate, pH 7.4	Kjeldahl N, high-affinity antibody	11
DN37-2	278	15.7	0.04 M K phosphate, pH 7.4	Series of purified antibodies from bleedings at different times in the immune response from 10 days to 12½ weeks	
DN37-3	278	15.5	0.04 M K phosphate, pH 7.4		
DN37-4	278	15.6	0.04 M K phosphate, pH 7.4		
DN37-5	278	16.4	0.04 M K phosphate, pH 7.4		
Anti-DNP antibodies from serum pool	278	13.6	0.15 M NaCl, 0.01 M phosphate, pH 7.4	Kjeldahl N	23
	251	5.3	0.15 M NaCl, 0.01 M phosphate, pH 7.4	Kjeldahl N	

PROTEINS (*Continued*)

Protein[a]	λ (mμ)	$E^{1\%}_{1\text{cm}}$	Solvent	Comment	Ref.
γG-anti-DNP antibodies from single rabbits					
Aa3-3, Ab4-4	278	16.2	0.04 M K phosphate, pH 7.4	Kjeldahl N	11
Aa1-1, Ab4-4	278	16.0	0.04 M K phosphate, pH 7.4	Kjeldahl N	11
Aa3-3, Ab4-4	278	16.2 ± 0.5	0.02 M K phosphate, pH 7.4, 0.15 M NaCl	Kjeldahl N, intermediate-affinity antibody	17
Aa3-3, Ab4-4	278	15.9 ± 0.5	0.02 M K phosphate, pH 7.4, 0.15 M NaCl	Kjeldahl N, high-affinity antibody	17
Rabbit γG-anti-TNP antibodies					
TN-9	278	15.8 ± 0.2	0.02 M K phosphate, pH 7.4, 0.15 M NaCl	Kjeldahl N, high-affinity, boosted antibody	17
TN-8	278	14.9 ± 0.1	0.02 M K phosphate, pH 7.4, 0.15 M NaCl	Kjeldahl N, low-affinity antibody	17
γG-anti-TNP antibodies from single rabbits					
Aa3-3, Ab4-4	278	15.3	0.15 M NaCl, 0.02 M K phosphate, pH 7.4	Kjeldahl N, low-affinity antibody	17
Anti-*p*-azobenzenearsonate rabbit antibodies	278	14.8	0.04 M K phosphate, pH 7.4	Kjeldahl N	11

Anti-p-azobenzenearsonate rabbit γG antibody	278	14.8 ± 0.3	0.02 M phosphate, pH 7.2	Kjeldahl N, O.D. 278/250 = 2.82 ± 0.05	24
Light chains of rabbit anti-p-azoben-zenearsonate antibody	278	12.8	0.05 M Na decyl-sulfate, pH 8.0		25
Rabbit γG-antiphenyl (p-aminoben-zoylamino) acetate antibody (anti-D-I$_p$ antibody)	279(λ_{max})	13.9	0.15 M NaCl, 0.02 M phosphate, pH 7.4	Kjeldahl N, O.D. 279/251 = 2.54	26
Horse antipneumococcal polysac-charide type XIV	277		0.25 M acetic acid	Kjeldahl N: 0.0085 O.D./μg N/ml	10
Horse γG-anti-lac antibodies, unfractionated	280	14.7	"Neutral solvent"	Kjeldahl N	76
Horse γA-anti-lac antibody	280	14.7	"Neutral solvent"	Kjeldahl N	76
Horse γA-anti-lac pepsin 5S fragment	280	14.6	"Neutral solvent"	Kjeldahl N	76
Human anti-A (blood group) antibodies, unfractionated	280	—	"Isotonic buffer"	Kjeldahl N 0.00987 O.D./μg N/ml	75
Human γG-anti-A antibody	280	—	"Isotonic buffer"	Kjeldahl N 0.00953 O.D./μg N/ml	75
Human γM-anti-A antibody	280	—	"Isotonic buffer"	Kjeldahl N 0.00829 O.D./μg N/ml	75
Mouse anti-hen egg albumin antibody	277		0.25 M acetic acid	Average extinction co-efficient given as 0.0100 O.D./μg N/ml	9

[a] SUp designates a synthetic hapten of f.wt. 540; DN indicates anti-dinitrophenyl antibodies.

SMALL MOLECULES

Chemical compound	λ (mμ)	E_M^{1cm}	Solvent	Comment	Ref.
Azo Compounds					
Mono(p-azobenzenearsonic acid)-N-chloroacetyltyrosine	460	9,600	0.1 M NaOH	Relative amounts of azotyrosine and azo-histidine in azopro-tein can be calculated by simultaneous equations presented by authors	27
	500	10,500	0.1 M NaOH		
Mono(p-azobenzenearsonic acid)-N-acetylhistidine	460	16,500	0.1 M NaOH		27
	500	2,650	0.1 M NaOH		
Bis(p-azobenzenearsonic acid diazo)-e-aminocaproic acid	460	1,650	0.1 M NaOH		27
	500	130	0.1 M NaOH		
Mono(p-azobenzenesulfonic acid)-N-chloroacetyltyrosine	460	9,800	0.1 M NaOH		27
	500	10,900	0.1 M NaOH		
Mono(p-azobenzenesulfonic acid)-N-acetylhistidine	460	18,700	0.1 M NaOH		27
	500	4,000	0.1 M NaOH		
Mono(p-azobenzoic acid)-N-chloro-acetyltyrosine	460	9,200	0.1 M NaOH		27
	500	10,200	0.1 M NaOH		
Mono(p-azobenzoic acid)-N-acetyl-histidine	460	17,700	0.1 M NaOH		27
	500	3,550	0.1 M NaOH		
Mono(p-azobenzenecarboxylic acid)-L-tyrosine	330	17,700	0.1 M phosphate, pH 6	Elemental analysis in text	28
	330	14,900	0.1 M NaOH		
	485	9,700	0.1 M NaOH		
Mono(p-azobenzenecarboxylic acid)-L-histidine	375	21,000	0.1 M phosphate, pH 6	Elemental analysis in text	28
p-Dimethylaminoazobenzene-arsonic acid	440	22,500	0.1 M NaOH		29
	455	21,200	Γ/2 = 0.1, borate, pH 9.5		
p-(p-Hydroxyphenylazo)-phenyl-arsonic acid	435.5 (λmax)	25,400	0.1 M NaOH		30
p-Iodobenzenearsonic acid	238	16,400			16

Compound	λ_{max}	E	Conditions	Remarks	Ref.
(2-Methoxy-6-chloro-9-acridinyl)-N-p-aminobenzenearsonic acid	425	7,700	$\Gamma/2 = 0.1$, borate, pH 9.5	Binding of hapten by antibodies measured by fluorescent changes on binding	29
1-Naphthol-4-(4-(4'-azobenzene azo) phenylarsonic acid)	610	5,800	Borate–KNO$_3$, pH 8.0, $\Gamma/2 = 0.1$	E_M at 610 mμ when bound to bovine serum albumin = 28,000 λ_{max} at 510 mμ for free dye	31
1-Naphthol-2-sulfonic acid-4-(4'-azobenzeneazo) phenylarsonic acid)	610	21,000	Phosphate, pH 7.0, $\Gamma/2 = 0.1$	E_M at 610 mμ when bound to bovine serum albumin = 10,400	31
p-(p-Dimethylaminobenzeneazo)-phenyl β-lactoside	455 (λ_{max})	24,800	0.15 M NaCl, 0.02 M phosphate, pH 7.4	E_M = 5200 at λ_{min} 340 mμ	32
d-Phenyl [p-(p-dimethylaminobenzeneazo) benzoylamino] acetate	470 (λ_{max})	29,000	0.15 M NaCl, 0.02 M phosphate, pH 7.4 0.05 M phosphate, pH 7	E_M = 33,600 for dye bound to antibodies at λ_{max} = 475 mμ E_M = 24,500 for dye bound to serum albumin at λ_{max} = 325 mμ	33
4,5-Dihydroxy-3-(p-nitrophenylazo)-2,7-naphthalene disulfonic acid disodium salt	515 (λ_{max})		Borate, pH 8.0, $\Gamma/2 = 0.1$	λ_{max} when bound to antibody = 530 mμ E_M at 530 mμ for free dye = 23,600 E_M at 530 mμ for antibody-bound dye = 32,000	34

SMALL MOLECULES (*Continued*)

Chemical compound	λ (mμ)	$E_M^{1\text{cm}}$	Solvent	Comment	Ref.
Nitrophenyl Compounds					
p-Nitroaniline	370	12,600	0.1 M Tris-chloride, pH 7.6		35
p-Nitrophenol	403	16,000	pH 7.6, $\Gamma/2 = 0.2$		36
o-Nitroaniline	410	4,640	0.1 M Tris-chloride, pH 7.6		35
m-Nitrophenol	350	14,520	pH 7.6, $\Gamma/2 = 0.2$		36
o-Nitrophenol	410	15,120	pH 7.6, $\Gamma/2 = 0.2$		36
Dinitrophenyl Compounds					
2,4-DNP-acetic acid	345	14,000	0.1 M Tris-chloride, pH 7.6		35
2,4-DNP-L-alanine	360	14,430	1 N HCl, pH 1		37
	360	16,720	Bicarbonate, pH 8.3		
	360–365	17,200 (at $\lambda_{\max}$)	1 N NaOH	Criteria of purity in text	38
β-2,4-DNP-alanine	360	16,310	1 N HCl, pH 1.0	pK of carboxyl group in text	37
	360	17,940	Bicarbonate, pH 8.3		
2,4-Dinitroaniline	345($\lambda_{\max}$)	14,000	0.05 M phosphate, pH 7.4	$E = 12,400 \pm 600$ when bound to bovine serum albumin at $\lambda_{\max} = 340$–350 mμ	39
ϵ-2,4-DNP-aminocaproic acid	365($\lambda_{\max}$)	17,800	0.05 M phosphate, pH 7.4	$E = 15,000 \pm 200$ when bound to bovine serum albumin at $\lambda_{\max} = 350$ mμ	39

Compound	λ	ε	Solvent	Remarks	Ref.
2,4-DNP-L-arginine	360	15,630	1 N HCl, pH 1	pK's of carboxyl groups in text	37
2,4-DNP-L-aspartic acid	360	17,200	Bicarbonate, pH 8.3	Criteria of purity in text	38
	345(λ_{max})	17,600	4% NaHCO$_3$		37
	360	13,340	1 N HCl, pH 1		
	360	18,310	Bicarbonate, pH 8.3	Criteria of purity in text	38
m-Dinitrobenzene	360–365	18,200	1 N NaOH		40
m-Dinitrobenzene	241.5	16,300	Distilled water		39
	244(λ_{max})	14,300	0.05 M phosphate, pH 7.4		39
2,4-Dinitrobromobenzene	265(λ_{max})	10,300	0.05 M phosphate, pH 7.4		
3,4-Dinitrobenzoic acid	260	6,960	0.1 M Tris-chloride, pH 7.4		35
3,5-Dinitrobenzoic acid	238	16,770	0.1 M Tris-chloride, pH 7.4		35
S-2,4-DNP-cysteine	330	11,250	1 N HCl		41
2,4-DNP-L-cystine (bis)	355(λ_{max})	27,500	1 N NaOH	Criteria of purity in text	38
2,4-DNP-DL-glutamic acid	360	15,750	1 N HCl, pH 1	pK's of carboxyl groups in text	37
	360	17,960	Bicarbonate, pH 8.3	Criteria of purity in text	38
	360–365	17,400 (at λ_{max})	1 N NaOH		
2,4-DNP-glycine	360	12,840	1 N HCl, pH 1		37
	360	15,890	Bicarbonate, pH 8.3		
	325–330	7,900 (at λ_{max})	1 N NaOH	Elemental analysis and melting point in text	38

Small Molecules *(Continued)*

Chemical compound	λ (mμ)	E_M^{1cm}	Solvent	Comment	Ref.
Bis-2,4-DNP-L-histidine	360–365	21,500 (at λ_{max})	4% NaHCO$_3$	Criteria of purity in text	38
ϵ-N-2,4-DNP-L-lysine	360	17,470 17,530	1 N HCl, pH 1 Bicarbonate, pH 8.3	pK of carboxyl group in text	37
	360(λ_{max})	17,400	0.05 M phosphate, pH 7.4		39
	362(λ_{max})	14,400	1 M propionic acid	$E_M = 10,400$ at 378 mμ (λ_{max}) for ligand bound to antibody	42
Bis-2,4-DNP-L-lysine	355	28,600	4% NaHCO$_3$	Criteria of purity in text	38
2,4-DNP-norleucine	360	15,250	0.1 M Tris-chloride, pH 7.4		35
2,4-Dinitrophenol	358(λ_{max})	14,900	0.05 M phosphate, pH 7.4	$E_M = 15,000 \pm 170$ at λ_{max} when bound to bovine serum albumin	39
2,4-DNP-L-phenylalanine	360	13,740	1 N HCl, pH 1	pK of carboxyl group in text	37
	360–365	16,670 20,000	Bicarbonate, pH 8.3 1 N NaOH	Criteria of purity in text	38
2-(2,4-Dinitrophenylazo)-1-naphthol-3,6-disulfonate disodium salt	590(λ_{max})	35,800	Phosphate, pH 7.4, $\Gamma/2 = 0.2$	E_M at 590 mμ when bound to antibody = 3980	43

	λmax	Solvent	Value	λmax for dye bound to antibody = 486 mμ at pH 7.4, and E_M at λmax for bound dye = 26,600	Ref.
2,4-DNP-L-proline	390	1 N HCl, pH 1	15,640	pK of carboxyl group in text	37
	390	Bicarbonate, pH 8.3	18,970	Criteria of purity in text	38
	380–385	1 N NaOH	19,200 (at λmax)		38
2,4-Dinitrotoluene	250 (λmax)	0.05 M phosphate, pH 7.4	13,300		39
O-2,4-DNP-tyrosine	350	1 N HCl	290	λmax = 295–300 mμ	44
O,N-Bis-2,4-DNP-L-tyrosine	360–365 (λmax)	4% NaHCO₃	16,900 (λmax)	Criteria of purity in text	38
Nucleic Acid Components					
Adenine	262 (λmax)	0.1 N HCl	13,100		45
Cytidine	278 (λmax)	0.01 N HCl	13,000	$E_{260} = 6340$	45
Uridine	260 (λmax)	0.01 N HCl	9,900		45
Adenine	262.5 (λmax)	Dilute mineral acid	13,150	$E_{260} = 13,000$	46
Hypoxanthine	248 (λmax)	Dilute mineral acid	10,800	$E_{260} = 7350$	46
Guanine	275.5 (λmax)	Dilute mineral acid	7,350	$E_{260} = 8000$	46
	248.5 (λmax)	Dilute mineral acid	11,400		
Xanthine	260 (λmax)	Dilute mineral acid	9,150	$E_{260} = 9150$	46
	230.5 (λmax)	Dilute mineral acid	6,350		
Cytosine	276 (λmax)	Dilute mineral acid	10,000	$E_{260} = 6000$	46
	210 (λmax)	Dilute mineral acid	9,700		
5-Methylcytosine	283.5 (λmax)	Dilute mineral acid	9,790	$E_{260} = 3600$	46
	210.5 (λmax)	Dilute mineral acid	12,000		

SMALL MOLECULES (Continued)

Chemical compound	λ (mμ)	E_M^{1cm}	Solvent	Comment	Ref.
Thymine	264.5(λ_{max}) 207(λ_{max})	7,890 9,500	Dilute mineral acid	$E_{260} = 7400$	46
Uracil	260(λ_{max})	7,800	Dilute mineral acid		46
Adenosine monophosphate (5')	260	14,200	pH 2		46
Cytidine monophosphate (5')	260	6,200	pH 2		46
Uridine monophosphate (3')	260	10,000	pH 2		46
Thymidine monophosphate (5')	260	8,400	pH 2		46
Guanosine monophosphate (3')	260	11,800	pH 2		46
Penicillins					
Allylmercaptomethylpenicilloyl ε-aminocaproic acid	285(λ_{max})	23,900	0.05 M carbonate, pH 9.2	Criteria of purity, details of proteins conjugation and heavy metal titration in text	47
D-Benzylpenicillenic acid	322.5(λ_{max})	17,600	95% ethanol	$E_M = 17,800$ at 322.5 mμ for L isomer	48
S-(p-Mercuribenzoate)-benzylpenicillenate	327(λ_{max})	22,500		Elemental analysis in text	49
Trinitrophenyl Compounds					
2,4,6-TNP-L-alanine	340(λ_{max})	12,700	1 N HCl	Elemental analysis and melting point in text	50
2,4,6-TNP-ε-aminocaproic acid	350(λ_{max})	15,400	0.01 M phosphate, pH 7.4	Elemental analysis and melting point in text	51
2,4,6-TNP-ε-aminocaproic acid	348(λ_{max})	15,700	0.01 M phosphate, pH 7.4	Elemental analysis and melting point in text	52
2,4,6-TNP-L-arginine	350(λ_{max})	15,200	4% NaHCO$_3$	Elemental analysis and melting point in text	50

Compound	λ_{max}	ϵ	Solvent	Characterization	Ref.
2,4,6-TNP-L-aspartic acid	$350(\lambda_{max})$	13,400	4% NaHCO₃	Elemental analysis and melting point in text	50
2,4,6-Trinitrobenzoic acid	251	15,400	0.1 M Tris-chloride, pH 7.5		53
2,4,6-TNP-L-glutamic acid	$350(\lambda_{max})$	15,000	4% NaHCO₃	Elemental analysis and melting point in text	50
2,4,6-TNP-glycine	$345(\lambda_{max})$	14,990	0.01 M phosphate, pH 7.4	Elemental analysis and melting point in text. Very light-sensitive	52
2,4,6-TNP-L-histidine	$350(\lambda_{max})$	15,200	4% NaHCO₃	Elemental analysis and melting point in text	50
ε-N-2,4,6-TNP-L-lysine	$348(\lambda_{max})$	15,400	0.1 M phosphate, pH 7.4	Elemental analysis and melting point in text	52
	$346(\lambda_{max})$	14,500	4% NaHCO₃	Elemental analysis and melting point in text	50
α,ε-Bis-2,4,6-TNP-L-lysine	$350(\lambda_{max})$	26,200	4% NaHCO₃	Elemental analysis and melting point in text	50
2,4,6-Trinitrophenol	$355(\lambda_{max})$	14,400	0.02 M phosphate, pH 7.6	Elemental analysis and melting point in text	53
2,4,6-TNP-L-proline	$362(\lambda_{max})$	12,900	1 N HCl	Elemental analysis and melting point in text	50
2,4,6-Trinitrotoluene	$230(\lambda_{max})$	17,300	Distilled water	Elemental analysis and melting point in text	53
N-2,4,6-TNP-L-tyrosine	$340(\lambda_{max})$	13,800	1 N HCl	Elemental analysis and melting point in text	50
Mono-2,4-DNP-azo-N-chloracetyl-tyrosine	$350(\lambda_{max})$	18,500	pH 6.2	Elemental analysis and melting point in text	54
	$555(\lambda_{max})$	15,200	0.15 M NaOH		
	$360(\lambda_{max})$	13,000	0.15 M NaOH		

SMALL MOLECULES (*Continued*)

Chemical compound	λ (mμ)	E_M^{1cm}	Solvent	Comment	Ref.
Mono-p-nitrophenylazo-N-chloracetyl tyrosine	340(λ_{max})	20,700	pH 6.2		54
	520(λ_{max})	12,800	0.15 M NaOH		
	345(λ_{max})	13,400	0.15 M NaOH		
3-Iodopyridine	272	2,440			16
1-Dimethylaminonaphthalene 5-sulfonamide	329	4,050	Phosphate buffer		55
1-Dimethylaminonaphthalene-5-sulfonyl-glycine ethyl ester	246.5 (λ_{max})	15,900	20% dioxane-water (v/v)	Melting points and elemental analyses given in text	71
	328(λ_{max})	4,490	20% dioxane-water (v/v)		
1-Dimethylaminonaphthalene-5-sulfonyl-L-tryptophan ethylester	247.5 (λ_{max})	16,700	20% dioxane-water (v/v)	Melting points and elemental analyses given in text	71
	289 (λ_{max})	5,980	20% dioxane-water (v/v)		
	330 (λ_{max})	4,200	20% dioxane-water (v/v)		
1-Dimethylaminonaphthalene-5-sulfonamide	245 (λ_{max})	16,000	20% dioxane-water (v/v)	Melting points and elemental analyses given in text	71
	326 (λ_{max})	4,670	20% dioxane-water (v/v)		
2-p-Toluidinylnaphthalene-6-sulfonate (TNS)	223	47,000	Water	Fluorescence properties described in text	69
	263	24,500	Water		
	366	4,080	Water		
	317	18,900	Water		
1-Anilino-8-naphthalene sulfonate (Mg salt)	350	5,000	0.1 M phosphate pH 6.8		70
	265	19,200	0.1 M phosphate pH 6.8		
Fluorescein	490(λ_{max})	53,000	0.15 M NaCl, 0.02 M K phosphate, pH 7.4	Protein-bound dye has $\lambda_{max} = 495$ mμ	56

Substance	λ	ε	Solvent	Notes	Ref.
Lissamine rhodamine B disodium salt (RB200)	$573(\lambda_{max})$	73,000	0.15 M NaCl, 0.02 M K phosphate, pH 7.4	Protein bound dye has $\lambda_{max} = 575$ mμ	56
Benzene	$203.5(\lambda_{max})$	7,400	Distilled water		57
	$254(\lambda_{max})$	204	Distilled water		
Toluene	$206.5(\lambda_{max})$	7,000	Distilled water		57
	$261(\lambda_{max})$	225	Distilled water		
Tosyl ε-aminocaproic acid	$230(\lambda_{max})$	12,800	0.01 M phosphate, pH 7.4	Elemental analysis and melting point in text	51
Monoiodotyrosine	283	2,560	Low pH, 0.15 M KCl	At 295 mμ $E_M = 980$	58
	305	3,870	High pH, 0.15 M KCl	At 295 mμ $E_M = 3480$	
3,5-Diiodotyrosine	285	2,580	Low pH, 0.15 M KCl	At 295 mμ $E_M = 2410$	58
	311	5,830	High pH, 0.15 M KCl	At 295 mμ $E_M = 3640$	

MOLECULAR ABSORPTION COEFFICIENTS AND λ (mμ)[a]

Compound	In acid			In alkali		
	λ_{max}	λ_{min}	E_{mol}	λ_{max}	λ_{min}	E_{mol}
Tyrosine	274.5	—	1,340	293.5	—	2,330
		245.0	170	—	269.5	1,000
	223.0	—	8,200	240.0	—	11,050
Tryptophan	287.5	—	4,550	288.0	—	4,600
	278.0	—	5,550	280.5	—	5,430
		242.0	1,930	—	244.0	1,900
	218.0	—	33,500	221.5	—	34,600
Phenylalanine	267.1	—	92	267.6	—	124
	263.4	—	152	264.0	—	160
	260.3	—	144	261.0	—	176
	257.5	—	195	258.0	—	206
	251.6	—	154	252.2	—	172
	246.5	—	115	246.8	—	128
	241.5	—	81	241.5	—	84
		236.0	63	—	235.8	62
Cystine	248.0	—	345	—	—	—
		237.0	300	—	—	—

[a] Reprinted with permission from J. C. Greenstein and M. Winitz, "Chemistry of the Amino Acids," Vol. II, p. 1689, Wiley, New York, 1961.

1. L. Weil, T. S. Seibles, and T. T. Berskovitz, *Arch. Biochem. Biophys.* **111**, 308 (1965).
2. M. Sela, C. B. Anfinsen, and W. F. Harrington, *Biochim. Biophys. Acta* **26**, 502 (1957).
3. H. Neurath, *in* "The Enzymes" (P. Boyer, H. Lardy, and K. Myrbäck, eds.), Vol. 4, pp. 11–36. Academic Press, New York, 1960.
4. P. E. Wilcox, E. Cohn, and W. Tan, *J. Biol. Chem.* **228**, 999 (1957).
5. R. E. Canfield, *J. Biol. Chem.* **238**, 2691 (1963).
6. E. W. Davie and H. Neurath, *J. Biol. Chem.* **212**, 507 (1955).
7. E. W. Davie and H. Neurath, *J. Biol. Chem.* **212**, 515 (1955).
8. D. B. Wetlaufer, *Advan. Protein Chem.* **17**, 303 (1962).
9. R. L. Anacker and J. Munoz, *J. Immunol.* **87**, 426 (1961).
10. F. C. McDuffie and E. A. Kabat, *J. Immunol.* **77**, 193 (1956).
11. L. A. Steiner and S. Lowey, *J. Biol. Chem.* **241**, 231 (1966).
12. D. Gitlin, *J. Immunol.* **62**, 437 (1949).
13. F. Miller and H. Metzger, *J. Biol. Chem.* **240**, 3325 (1965).
14. T. Ikenaka, D. Gitlin, and K. Schmid, *J. Biol. Chem.* **240**, 2868 (1965).
15. R. H. Pain, *Biochem. J.* **88**, 234 (1963).
16. A. L. Grossberg, G. Radzimski, and D. Pressman, *Biochemistry* **1**, 391 (1962).
17. J. R. Little and H. N. Eisen, *Biochemistry*, in press (1968).
18. M. J. Crumpton and J. M. Wilkinson, *Biochem. J.* **88**, 228 (1963).
19. S. Utsumi and F. Karush, *Biochemistry* **3**, 1329 (1964).
20. M. E. Noelken and C. Tanford, *J. Biol. Chem.* **239**, 1828 (1964).

21. A. Nisonoff, *in* "Methods in Medical Research" (H. N. Eisen, ed.), Vol. 10, pp. 134–144. Year Book Medical Publishers, New York, 1964.
22. J. E. McGuigan and H. N. Eisen, *Biochemistry,* in press (1968).
23. F. S. Farah, M. Kern, and H. N. Eisen, *J. Exptl. Med.* **112,** 1195 (1960).
24. M. E. Koshland, F. M. Englberger, and S. M. Gaddone, *J. Immunol.* **89,** 517 (1962).
25. M. E. Koshland, F. M. Englberger, and R. Shapanka, *Biochemistry* **5,** 641 (1966).
26. F. Karush and R. Marks, *J. Immunol.* **78,** 296 (1957).
27. M. Tabachnick and H. Sobotka, *J. Biol. Chem.* **235,** 1051 (1960).
28. J. H. Phillips, Jr., S. A. Robrish, and C. Bates, *J. Biol. Chem.* **240,** 699 (1965).
29. D. S. Berns and S. J. Singer, *Immunochemistry* **1,** 209 (1964).
30. S. F. Velick, C. W. Parker, and H. N. Eisen, *Proc. Natl. Acad. Sci. U.S.* **46,** 1470 (1960).
31. A. Froese, A. H. Sehon, and M. Eigen, *Can. J. Chem.* **40,** 1786 (1962).
32. F. Karush, *J. Am. Chem. Soc.* **79,** 3380 (1957).
33. F. Karush, *J. Am. Chem. Soc.* **78,** 5519 (1956).
34. A. Froese and A. H. Sehon, *Immunochemistry* **2,** 135 (1965).
35. H. N. Eisen, unpublished observations, (1962).
36. J. D. Teresi, *J. Am. Chem. Soc.* **72,** 3972 (1950).
37. L. K. Ramachandran and L. V. S. Sastry, *Biochemistry* **1,** 75 (1962).
38. K. R. Rao and H. A. Sober, *J. Am. Chem. Soc.* **76,** 1328 (1954).
39. M. E. Carsten and H. N. Eisen, *J. Am. Chem. Soc.* **75,** 4451 (1953).
40. L. Doub and J. M. Vanderbelt, *J. Am. Chem. Soc.* **71,** 2414 (1949).
41. S. Belman and H. N. Eisen, unpublished observations, (1953).
42. H. Metzger and S. J. Singer, *Science* **142,** 674 (1963).
43. H. Metzger, L. Wofsy, and S. J. Singer, *Arch. Biochem. Biophys.* **103,** 206 (1963).
44. R. R. Porter, *in* "Methods in Enzymology" (C. P. Colowick and N. O. Kaplan, eds.), Vol. 4, pp. 221–237. Academic Press, New York, 1957.
45. H. S. Loring, *in* "The Nucleic Acids" (E. Chargaff and J. N. Davidson, eds.), Vol. 1, pp. 191–209. Academic Press, New York, 1955.
46. G. H. Beaven, E. R. Holiday, and E. A. Johnson, *in* "The Nucleic Acids" (E. Chargaff and J. N. Davidson, eds.) Vol. 1, pp. 493–553. Academic Press, New York, 1955.
47. B. B. Levine, *in* "Methods in Medical Research" (H. N. Eisen, ed.), Vol. X pp. 184–191. Year Book Medical Publishers, New York, 1964.
48. F. H. Carpenter, R. A. Turner, and V. du Vigneaud, *J. Biol. Chem.* **176,** 893 (1948).
49. J. A. Thiel, S. Mitchell, and C. W. Parker, *J. Allergy* **35,** 399 (1964).
50. T. Okuyama and K. Satake, *J. Biochem. (Tokyo)* **47,** 454 (1960).
51. B. Benacerraf and B. B. Levine, *J. Exptl. Med.* **115,** 1023 (1962).
52. J. R. Little and H. N. Eisen, *Biochemistry* **5,** 3385 (1966).
53. J. R. Little, unpublished observations, (1964).
54. H. Metzger, L. Wofsy, and S. J. Singer, *Biochemistry* **2,** 979 (1963).
55. G. Weber, *Biochem. J.* **51,** 155 (1952).
56. R. C. Nairn, "Fluorescent Protein Tracing." Livingstone, Edinburgh, 1964.
57. L. Doub and J. M. Vanderbelt, *J. Am. Chem. Soc.* **69,** 2714 (1947).
58. H. Fujioca and H. A. Scheraga, *Biochemistry* **4,** 2206 (1965).
59. J. J. Cebra and J. B. Robbins, *J. Immunol.* **97,** 12 (1966).
60. P. A. Small, Jr. and M. E. Lamm, *Biochemistry* **5,** 259 (1966).
61. A. Ghiretti-Magaldi, C. Nuzzolo, and F. Ghiretti, *Biochemistry* **5,** 1943 (1966).

62. J. J. Cebra and P. A. Small, Jr., *Biochemistry* **6**, 503 (1967).

63. J. F. Foster and M. D. Sterman, *J. Am. Chem. Soc.* **78**, 3656 (1956).

64. B. D. Polis, H. W. Schmukler, J. H. Custer, T. L. McMeekin, *J. Am. Chem. Soc.* **72**, 4965 (1950).

65. L. W. Cunningham and B. J. Nuenke, *J. Biol. Chem.* **234**, 1447 (1959).

66. H. Edelhoch, *J. Am. Chem. Soc.* **79**, 6100 (1957).

67. R. Arnon and G. E. Perlmann, *J. Biol. Chem.* **238**, 653 (1963).

68. H. S. Tenenhouse and H. F. Deutsch, *Immunochemistry* **3**, 11 (1966).

69. W. O. McClure and G. M. Edelman, *Biochemistry* **5**, 1908 (1966).

70. L. Stryer, *J. Mol. Biol.* **13**, 482 (1965).

71. D. A. Deranleau and H. Neurath, *Biochemistry* **5**, 1413 (1966).

72. M. E. Noelken, C. A. Nelson, C. E. Buckley, III, C. Tanford, *J. Biol. Chem.* **240**, 218 (1965).

73. H. F. Oettgen, R. A. Binaghi, B. Benacerraf, *Proc. Soc. Exptl. Biol. and Medicine* **118**, 336 (1965).

74. G. W. Siskind, W. E. Paul and B. Benacerraf, *J. Exptl. Med.* **123**, 673 (1966).

75. M. E. Kaplan and E. A. Kabat, *J. Exptl. Med.* **123**, 1061 (1966).

76. J. H. Rockey, *J. Exptl. Med.* **125**, 249 (1967).

77. L. W. Clem and P. A. Small, Jr., *J. Exptl. Med.* **125**, 893 (1967).

78. H. Fujio and F. Karush, *Biochemistry* **5**, 1856 (1966).

APPENDIX II

Buffers *

1. General Remarks

The advantages in studying charged substances under fixed conditions have long been recognized, and it has become common practice to add buffering substances that will correct for foreseeable extraneous sources of H^+ and OH^-. Some of the buffering solutions—usually partially dissociated salts of weak acids—can affect biological systems adversely. Trivalent ions, and to some extent divalent ions, added to saline can cause nonspecific agglutination of bacterial suspensions; buffers containing ethylenediaminetetraacetic acid will complex metals† in the environment—sometimes to disadvantage, but at other times advantageously (see buffers Nos. **20,21,21A**); some buffers may depress phosphorylation, others synthetic processes (1).‡ Buffer systems should be used in the lowest concentration that will take care of adventitious changes in the ionic environment. It is not wise to use buffers to supply H^+ or OH^- ions that may be required to bring a sample of product to "buffer pH." Rather, external sources of acid or alkali should be added to correct the pH of a solution so that the subsequently added buffering system will supply its full buffering capacity (see Section 9 of this Appendix).

Greatest buffering capacity occurs at the pK_a value of a given buffer acid (technically the negative logarithm of the dissociation constant), a value that corresponds to the pH of a mixture of equal moles of a weak acid and its salt ("half-neutralized" acid). Deviations in pH from the pK_a numerical value within the buffer range are accompanied by relatively less buffering capacity. The buffering capacity at a particular pH of a given buffer system is indicated by its "beta" value, which is defined as the amount of acid or alkali, in gram equivalents, necessary to change the pH by 0.1 pH unit (a slightly modified beta value is presented in ref. 2). Theoretical aspects of buffers are presented in refs. 2–5. Since ionic dissociation is frequently dependent on temperature and even on con-

* Appendix II was contributed by Merrill W. Chase.

† Complexing with metallic ions is discussed in ref. 2, p. 95.
‡ References are listed at the end of the Appendix. Reference numbers are given in parentheses in the text.

centration, the proportions of the buffering salts necessary to secure the desired pH at the chosen temperature often require adjustment from formulations designed for work at room temperature. The common practice of diluting buffers of ionic strength 0.1 to 0.05 can also result in minor changes in pH.

Buffer salts are listed in Table II, and buffer systems are given in Table III with references. A limited, numbered selection of buffer systems and particular buffers calculated to composition per liter follows, including acetate, barbital (Veronal), borate, carbonate, EDTA, glycine, phosphate, triethanolamine, and Tris(hydroxymethyl)aminomethane systems. The practical formulation of buffers and standardization of glass electrodes are considered in Section 2.

Buffers fall into several categories. The classical buffers, formulated on the basis of constant molarity, had relatively large buffering capacity. To stabilize pH values during biochemical reactions, a high buffering capacity is needed to combine, for example, with acids generated during cellular respiration. Under highly demanding conditions, one of the so-called "universal buffers," or a selected range thereof, can be employed; these consist of mixtures of overlapping buffer systems such that the capacity to absorb H^+ and OH^- is both relatively high and constant over nearly the whole buffer range—for example, pH 2.0 to 11.9. The formula of Prideau and Ward, employing phosphoric, phenylacetic, and boric acids, provides five acid groups; the buffer of Britton and Robinson provides seven acid groups by mixing barbital, citric acid, KH_2PO_4, and boric acid (ref. 3, pp. 364, 365, 370).

The class of buffers having fixed ionic strength or "ionicity" became much used with the advent of delicate work such as free boundary electrophoresis, chromatography, and selective precipitation of proteins by salt, pH, and temperature, with additives that further depress solubility, such as alcohol. Buffers of this class possess inconstant molarity from one pH value to another.

A third class, of very low ionic strength and conductance, became necessary for studying electrophoretic migration of proteins in liquids and in supporting media, in order to increase protein mobility (6) and to suppress heat effects. Formulations of this class often possess barely sufficient buffering capacity.

While the classical buffers have been mixtures of salts of weak acids or base, zwitterions (molecules bearing both acidic and basic groups) can function as buffers by partial neutralization of one or the other group. In this category fall glycine (buffers Nos. 22–26), glycylglycine, tris(hydroxymethyl)aminomethane (Tris) buffers Nos. 38–46), triethanolamine (buffers No. 37A and 37B), and ethylenediaminetetraacetic acid (EDTA) (buffers Nos. 20 and 21). A new set of buffers which can be viewed as de-rivatives of glycine or taurine has been developed (1,7) with the object of avoiding side effects in biological oxidation reactions; trivial names for some of these are Bicine, HEPES, MES, TES, and Tricine; the formulas are listed in Table II.

Various specialized buffers are devised for particular applications. Volatile buffers which can be removed by lyophilization (requiring especially efficient traps to avoid damage to the oil pump) have been formulated for recovery of amino acids from cation and anion exchange columns. These include pyridine–formate and pyridine–acetate (8a-c) for recoveries from cation exchangers, and collidine–pyridine–acetic acid (9) and N-ethyl morpholine–pyridine–acetic acid (10) for fractions from anion exchangers, and ammonium formate and—more difficult to remove —ammonium acetate.

For injection into tissues, buffers are chosen for compatibility with tissues and presented in isotonic concentration usually secured by adding sodium chloride. The added Na^+ ions depress dissociation when sodium buffer salts are present, and some correction in buffer composition may be needed in securing a desired pH. Simple "phosphate-buffered saline" (pH 7.0 to 7.2, usually at 0.01 or 0.02 M phosphate concentration) will often suffice (Section 8, buffers Nos. 35A–E, and No. 30 stock solution diluted 1:10). The latter, of only $M/150$ concentration, is usually sufficiently buffered (10a). For special purposes in which immediate local irritation must be minimal, the use of "balanced" solutions such as Hanks' solution and Eagle's solution can be advantageous for injection, although these are designed primarily for handling and maintenance of tissue cells *in vitro*.

2. The Formulation of Buffers

A desired pH will usually be sought by completing the mixing of acidic and basic components of a buffer system during monitoring by a glass electrode and a reference electrode. Because pH adjustment may be needed, the initial volume should not exceed 85% of the final volume. The buffer salts to be weighed out should be of reliable purity and free of extraneous water (see Table II); it is best to keep these sealed and separate from the common laboratory reagents that will be used by all workers. If one component is accurately known, the second component can be varied to secure the pH value without overshooting a desired ionicity. When solutions of two weighed components are to be combined, 90% of the one to be used in greater volume should be added, and balanced to pH by adding the one in lesser volume; from these relations, the buffer can be completed with assurance as to final volume and concentration. Table II gives solubility factors, useful in apportioning the volume of water between two weighed constituents.

The reliance placed on the reading by the glass electrode calls for its careful standardization (Section 3). When NaOH is a constituent of the buffer, its freedom from carbonate is often advantageous in attaining the theoretical end point (Section 4).

If large volumes of a particular buffer are required, it can be more expedient to calculate, from the various buffer tables, the amount of dry chemicals to be weighed out. It is suggested that carbonate-free 50% NaOH be employed rather than NaOH pellets, which are coated with carbonate (Section 4). Buffers are customarily stored in the cold room in polyethylene containers. Phosphate buffers for use or storage at cold room temperature at more than 0.1 M concentration should be made with dipotassium acid phosphate instead of the di-sodium salt.

Unless it is permissible to add preservative (thymol, toluol, chloroform, and the like), many of which have appreciable absorbancy in the ultraviolet range, the volume to be prepared should take into account the expected rate of use and the probability of bacterial growth. Phosphate and cacodylate buffers, for example, sustain growth of organisms readily. Microbial growth can be much less obvious in opaque plastic containers. It is recommended that buffers lacking preservative and held at 4° be checked weekly for growth (Chap. 2,C,4,f, Vol. I). As microbial contaminants develop and new solutions are needed, the container should be sterilized to prevent seeding of fresh batches of buffer. After thorough mechanical cleaning, chemical disinfection can be used, but it is helpful to use plastic jugs and screw caps from the autoclavable formulations, such as polypropylene plastic with linear polyethylene closures.

3. Use of Reference Standard Buffer Solutions

Simply prepared solutions that exhibit rather slight variations with temperature can be used to calibrate glass electrodes (see Table I). For short-term shelf-life (4 weeks), the use of polyethylene bottles and addition of a crystal of thymol are recommended. Sterile solutions preserved as small portions in containers of resistant glass will last for more than 2 years; add thymol whenever a portion is brought into use.

Each glass electrode put into service should be tested for its individual responses over a wide pH range. For use with a particular unknown, tests should be made with two appropriate standards, such as those listed in Table I, which "bracket" the pH of the unknown. If the particular electrode does not give the theoretical readings of two standards, say pH 2.0 and 7.0, the temperature compensator of the instrument should be

TABLE I
STANDARD BUFFER SOLUTIONS[a]

Solute at 25° in deionized water[b,c]	pH values at:							
	0°	5°	15°	20°	25°	35°	38°	45°
1. Potassium tetroxalate, 0.1 M					1.48		1.50	
2. HCl, 0.01 M + KCl, 0.09 M					2.07		2.08	
3. Potassium hydrogen tartrate, satd. at 25° (ca. 0.034 M)					3.56	3.55	3.55	3.55
4. Potassium hydrogen phthalate, 0.05 M	4.01	4.01	4.00	4.00	4.01	4.02	4.03	4.04
5. Acetic acid, 0.01 M + sodium acetate, 0.01 M					4.70		4.71	
6. KH$_2$PO$_4$, 0.025 M + Na$_2$HPO$_4$, 0.025 M	6.98	6.95	6.90	6.88	6.86	6.84	6.84	6.83
7. Borax, 0.01 M	9.46	9.39	9.27	9.22	9.18	9.10	9.08	9.04
8. Sodium bicarbonate, 0.025 M + sodium carbonate, 0.025 M					10.00			

[a] Chemicals are described in Table II. Data are derived from ref. 4.

[b] Specific conductance should be less than 2×10^{-6} ohm^{-1} cm^{-1} at 25°.

[c] Solutions 3, 4, 6, 7 are "primary" standards; 1, 2, 5 are "secondary" standards to complement the scale.

adjusted until the two standards give their theoretical values before reading the unknown (ref. 4, p. 94). Although it is common practice to rely on commerical "standard buffers," the possibility of deterioration is seldom kept in mind. Commercial buffers in the alkaline range—pH 8.0 and 9.0, in particular—are apt to deteriorate. When question arises as to validity of a stock buffer, the buffers of Table I should be used to allow decision.

In the particular problem posed in determining blood pH, special reference standards of KH_2PO_4 and Na_2HPO_4 closely approximating the reaction of blood at 37° have been proposed, either a molar ratio of 1:3.5 ($\Gamma/2 = 0.1$) or a ratio of 1:4 ($\Gamma/2 = 0.13$; see ref. 4, p. 86).

4. Sodium Hydroxide for Use in Buffers

The presence of sodium carbonate in NaOH alters the effective composition of many buffers prepared by adding alkali to weak acids (ref. 5, p. 370). Carbonate is usually removed by the method of Sørenson, preparing saturated NaOH (about 50%, or 17 N) in which carbonate is insoluble, allowing it to settle in sealed containers, and decanting the upper fluid through glass wool or especially treated hardened filter paper (5). The concentrated solutions must be stoppered tightly to exclude CO_2. Commercially available solutions of NaOH are recommended for preparation of buffers. To prepare small volumes, sealed carbonate-free concentrates are reconstituted to 1 liter of exactly 1.0 N by adding boiled and cooled distilled water. For large-scale operations, clear solutions of 50% NaOH (specific gravity 1.525) are available, the exact composition being stated on the label. Handling of such concentrated caustic should be done by skilled persons. Transfer of concentrated NaOH must be done without spattering by pouring it into a graduate (promptly wiping outside the rim of the bottle with disposable tissue) or by using mechanically controlled pipet, such as by the Propipette or the Caulfield safety pipettor. Protective goggles should be worn. Strong caustic will burn and scar eyes and mucous membranes, and mouth-operated pipets are to be avoided.

To prepare an approximately normal solution of NaOH, 26.5 ml (40.2 gm), if the concentration of NaOH is 50% (w/w), is diluted to 500 ml with boiled-out and cooled distilled water, mixed well, and titrated against standard acid (HCl or benzoic acid or potassium acid phthalate) with phenolphthalein. When accurate dilutions have been used, further solutions of NaOH suitable for buffer preparation may be made from the same lot of 50% NaOH. Also, the volume of concentrate to represent 1 gm of NaOH (theoretically, 1.31 ml) can be learned, useful in making buffers by weight.

Only exceptionally should laboratory preparation of cabonate-free NaOH be required. Weigh 200 gm of low-carbonate NaOH pellets (A.C.S.) into a 1-liter Erlenmeyer flask, and set in a metal pan as a precaution if breakage should occur by heat of solution or by stirring rod. Add 240 ml of cold distilled water carefully, and stir to dissolve the pellets. The time to effect solution is longer, but hot NaOH dissolves borosilicate glass. Close with a soda-lime tube until the solution cools to room temperature. Pour into a glass-stoppered cylinder, and leave at room temperature for 3 or 4 days. A small amount of carbonate should settle out. Decant the supernatant through glass wool, and store in polyethylene bottles, sealed tightly. If Pyrex bottles are used, glass stoppers should be replaced by Vaseline-coated tapered Teflon stoppers.

Dilute solutions of NaOH attack glass and absorb CO_2 from the air. Amounts of 1 liter or more should be stored in polyethylene bottles or in paraffin-coated Pyrex bottles with Vaseline-coated glass stoppers or Teflon stoppers. When dropping bottles are used in the laboratory to contain $1\ N$ and $0.1\ N$ NaOH solutions, the contents should be replaced periodically, since carbonate will be taken up from the air.

A simple test for the presence of carbonate (3) consists in adding phenolphthalein to a side portion of the dilute NaOH. Add sufficient HCl to approach the point of disappearance of pink color ($CO_3^{--} \rightarrow HCO_3^-$). Then add a neutral solution of barium chloride. If the light pink color fades when $BaCl_2$ is added, bicarbonate is present.

5. Hydrochloric Acid for Use in Buffers

Commercially available standardized concentrated solutions, to be diluted quantitatively to 1 liter, are preferable for small-scale work. When full accuracy is wanted in making large volumes of buffer, constant-boiling HCl (Chap. 12,A,3) can be used at the rate of 180.17 gm per liter of normal acid. A closely approximate normal HCl results from diluting 86.2 to 90 ml (101.7 to 110.7 gm) of concentrated hydrochloric acid (36%) to 1 liter. Standardization is performed by titration against sodium carbonate.

6. Chemicals for Preparation of Buffers

Table II lists chemicals used in preparing buffers with respect to formulas, molecular weights, solubility in water, and notes on chemical and physical properties. Values of pK_a and dissociation constants are given at 25° unless indicated; pK_a values are derived largely from refs. 2 and 11. For preparation of sodium hydroxide, see Section 4; for hydrochloric acid, see Section 5.

TABLE II
Chemicals for Preparation of Buffers

Compound	pK_a	Molecular weight	Water to dissolve 1 gm of solid	Notes
Acetic acid CH_3COOH	4.75	60.05	Miscible	Ca 57.5 ml glacial AcOH in 1 liter for M solution. Titrate with HCl vs. phenolphthalein. Dissociation constant, 1.76×10^{-5}. $1.0\ N$ solution has pH 2.4; $0.1\ N$, pH 2.9; $0.01\ N$, pH 3.4.
Aconitic acid (1,2,3-propenetricarboxylic acid) $HOOC(H)C:C(CH_2COOH)COOH$	3.8, 5.45	174.11	5.5 ml	Dry in vacuum desiccator. Dissociation constants, first hydrogen, 1.58×10^{-3}; second hydrogen, 3.5×10^{-5}
2-Amino-2-methyl-1,3-propanediol (Ammediol) $(CH_2OH)_2C(CH_3)NH_2$	8.79	105.14	0.4 ml	Recrystallize from absolute ethanol (100 gm/200 ml). M.p. 109°–111°. Dry *in vacuo.*
Ammonium acetate CH_3COONH_4		77.08	1.0 ml	Deliquescent. Store in cold room, sealed. Dissolve in CO_2-free water.
Ammonium chloride NH_4Cl		53.50	4.0 ml	Sublimes.
Ammonium hydroxide NH_4OH	9.24	35.05	—	Ammonium buffers require a closed system.
Barbital (5,5-diethylbarbituric acid; barbitone: Veronal) $NHCONHCOC(C_2H_5)_2CO$	7.98	184.19	130 ml	Dry *in vacuo* over P_2O_5. M.p. 188.0°. Dissociation constant, 3.7×10^{-8}
Barbital sodium $NNaCONHCOC(C_2H_5)_2CO$		206.18	5 ml	Dry *in vacuo* over P_2O_5. Dissolve in CO_2-free water. Aqueous solutions decompose slowly at room temperature. Recrystallization described in ref. 2, p. 42.

Barbitone, *see* Barbital				
Bicine (N,N-*bis*(2-hydroxyethyl)glycine) (HOCH$_2$CH$_2$)$_2$NHCH$_2$COOH	8.35	164.14	5.5 ml°	Refs. 1, 11a.
Borax, *see* Sodium tetraborate (decahydrate)				
Boric acid (boracic acid) H$_3$BO$_3$	9.23	61.84	18 ml	Dry in thin layers over CaCl$_2$. Polymerizes at high concentrations. Borate buffer values are highly concentration-dependent. Dissociation constants (20°), first hydrogen, 7.3 × 10^{-10}; second hydrogen 1.8 × 10^{-13}; third hydrogen, 1.6 × 10^{-4}.
Cacodylic acid (dimethylarsinic acid) (CH$_3$)$_2$AsO·OH	6.25	137.99	0.5 ml	Poisonous. Hygroscopic. Recrystallize in warm ethanol (100 gm/300 ml), dry *in vacuo* over CaCl$_2$. Dissociation constant, 6.4 × 10^{-7}.
Calcium lactate Ca[CH$_3$·CH(OH)COOH]$_2$·5H$_2$O		308.30	20 ml	Commercial product has less water than pentahydrate formula; becomes anhydrous at 120°.
(Carbonic acid)	6.4, 10.4			
Citric acid, anhydrous HOOC·CH$_2$C(OH)(COOH)CH$_2$COOH (anhyd)	3.128, 4.761, 6.396	192.12	<1.7 ml	Dissociation constant (18°), first hydrogen, 8.4 × 10^{-4}; second hydrogen, 1.8 × 10^{-5}; third hydrogen, 4 × 10^{-6}. 0.1 N solution has pH 2.2.
Citric acid, monohydrate C$_6$H$_8$O$_7$·H$_2$O		210.14	<1.7 ml	Titrate with 0.2 N Ba(OH)$_2$ vs. phenolphthalein.
s-Collidine (2,4,6-trimethylpyridine) (CH$_3$)$_3$C$_5$N	5.68	121.18	Miscible	$d = 0.9166_4^{22}$. Should be colorless; otherwise redistill under reduced pressure. Dissolve ca. 135 ml in CO$_2$-free water to 1 liter. Titrate with HCl vs. methyl orange.
Diethylbarbituric acid, *see* Barbital				

TABLE II (*Continued*)

Compound	pK$_a$	Molecular weight	Water to dissolve 1 gm of solid	Notes
3,3-Dimethylglutaric acid HOOC·CH$_2$·C(CH$_3$)$_2$CH$_2$COOH	4.24	160.17	Miscible	
Disodium citrate, *see* Sodium citrate				
EDTA				
Ethylenediaminetetraacetate, disodium (NaOCOCH$_2$)$_2$N(CH$_2$)N(CH$_2$COOH)$_2$·2H$_2$O	1.99, 2.67, 6.16, 10.26(20°)	372.254	0.97 ml	Purification when necessary as anhydrous acid prepared from disodium salt (12). Nonhealted EDTA estimated in ultraviolet at pH 9.0, total EDTA after adding Cu$^-$ ions at pH 5 (13).
Ethylenediaminetetraacetate, tetrasodium (NaOCOCH$_2$)$_4$N(CH$_2$)N		380.20	0.97 ml	pH of 1% solution, 11.8.
Ethanolamine HOCH$_2$CH$_2$NH$_2$	9.50	61.08	Miscible	Absorbs CO$_2$.
Ethanolamine hydrochloride C$_2$H$_7$NO·HCl		97.55	Freely soluble	Deliquescent; m.p. 75°–77°.
N-Ethyl morpholine C$_2$H$_5$·NCH$_2$CH$_2$OCH$_2$CH$_2$	7.65	115.18	Miscible	
Formic acid HCOOH	3.75	46.02	Miscible	Caustic to skin. Pungent. For *M*, dissolve approx. 38.5 ml "98–100%" in 1 liter. Titrate with NaOH vs. phenolphthalein. Dissociation constant (20°), 1.76×10^{-4}; 0.1 *N* solution has pH 2.3.

Substance	pK	Mol. wt.	Solubility	Remarks
2-Furoic acid (2-furanecarboxylic acid) $OC_4H_3 \cdot COOH$	3.17	112.08	26.0 ml	M.p. 132°. Can be recrystallized from hot water, then from chloroform. Dissociation constant, 6.76×10^{-4}. Dry at 110° for 1–2 hours.
Glycine (aminoacetic acid) NH_2CH_2COOH	2.35, 9.78	75.07	4.0 ml	Relatively large change in pH with temperature differences.
Glycylglycine $NH_2CH_2CONHCH_2COOH$	3.14, 8.25	132.00	<5.0 ml	
Hydrochloric acid HCl		36.47	—	For M solution, approx. 90 ml 36% HCl in 1 liter. Titrate with NaOH vs. methyl red.
(constant boiling mixture, 20.24% $HCl + H_2O$)			—	For M solution, 180.17 gm in 1 liter.
HEPES (N-2-hydroxyethyl-piperazine-N'-2-ethanesulfonic acid) $HOCH_2CH_2NHC_4H_8NCH_2CH_2SO_3H$	7.55	237.29	1.9 ml°	Ref. 1.
Lithium chloride LiCl		42.40	1.3 ml	Deliquescent; crystallizes also with 1 H_2O. Anhydrous m. 613°.
Lithium hydroxide LiOH		23.95	7.8 ml	Absorbs CO_2 from air. Strongly alkaline; pH of 1.0 N solution is ca. 14.
$LiOH \cdot H_2O$		41.96	4.3 ml	
Maleic acid $HOOCCH:CHCOOH$	1.92, 6.23	116.07	1.3 ml	Dissociation constants, first hydrogen, 1.42×10^{-2}; second hydrogen, 8.57×10^{-7}.
Maleic anhydride $OCOCH:CHCO$		98.06	Insoluble	
MES (2-(N-morpholino)ethanesulfonic acid $CH_2CH_2OCH_2CH_2NHCH_2CH_2SO_3H$	6.15	196.24	7.9 ml°	Ref. 1.

TABLE II (Continued)

Compound	pK_a	Molecular weight	Water to dissolve 1 gm of solid	Notes
Phenol C_6H_5OH	10.0	94.11	14.9 ml	Crystals may be preserved with 0.15% H_3PO_4, but not the chromatography grade.
Phenylacetic acid (α-toluic acid) $C_6H_5CH_2COOH$	4.87	136.14	56.0 ml	M.p. 76°. Dissociation constant (18°), 5.2×10^{-5}
Phosphoric acid (orthophosphoric acid) $(HO)_3PO$	2.15, 7.2, and (38°) 11.8	98.00	85% solution is miscible	85% H_3PO_4. Keep at room temperature, or warm above 30% if crystals appear in the cold. D_{25}, 1.864. Concentrated solution is irritating to skin. Dissociation constants, first hydrogen, 7.52×10^{-3}; second hydrogen, 6.34×10^{-8}; third hydrogen, 2.2×10^{-13}.
Piperazine $HNCH_2CH_2NHCHCH$	(5.68?) 9.82	86.14	Very soluble	M.p. 106°. Absorbs CO_2. Protect from light. Dissociation constant, 6.4×10^{-5}.
Potassium biphthalate (potassium acid phthalate) $HOOC \cdot C_6H_4 \cdot COOK$		204.22	12 ml	Dry at 110° for 1–2 hours.
Potassium chloride KCl		74.55	2.8 ml	Dry at 160° for several hours.
Potassium phenolsulfonate $C_6H_4(OH)SO_3K$ (anhydrous)		212.27	Very soluble	Recrystallize from H_2O at 90° with charcoal until white; dry at 110° for 24 hours to render anhydrous. Dissolve in CO_2-free water. Keep above 20°.
$C_6H_4(OH)SO_3K \cdot H_2O$		230.28	Very soluble	

Name		Mol. wt.	Volume	Remarks
Potassium phosphate, monobasic (potassium acid phosphate) KH_2PO_4		136.09	$7.0\ ml_{0°}$ $4.0\ ml_{7°}$ $3.3\ ml_{25°}$	Sulfate- and chloride-free grade. Dry at 110° for 1–2 hours.
Potassium phosphate, dibasic (dipotassium phosphate) K_2HPO_4		174.18	$3.1\ ml_{25°}$	Somewhat hygroscopic.
Potassium bitartrate (potassium acid tartrate) $KHC_4H_4O_6$		188.18	162 ml	Dry at 110° for 1–2 hours.
Potassium tetroxalate (potassium quadroxalate) $KHC_2O_4 \cdot H_2C_2O_4 \cdot 2H_2O$		254.19	60 ml	Do not dry above 60°. Total crystal formation must occur below 50° for theoretical dihydrate ($2H_2O$).
Pyridine $N{:}CHCH{:}CHCH{:}CH$	5.17	79.10	Miscible	Disagreeable odor. Reagent grade contains ca. 0.1% water (b.p. 115–116°). Forms azeotropic mixture with 3 moles water (b.p. 92°–93°). Dissociation constant, 2.3×10^{-9}.
Sodium acetate, anhydrous CH_3COONa		82.04	2 ml	Hygroscopic.
Sodium acetate, trihydrate $CH_3COONa \cdot 3H_2O$		136.09	0.8 ml	Becomes anhydrous at 120°.
Sodium acid maleate $NaOOCOH{:}CHCOOH$		138.07	NaOH used	Made by treating maleic acid or maleic anhydride with NaOH. See ref. 2, p. 41
Sodium bicarbonate (sodium acid carbonate) $NaHCO_3$		84.0	10.0 ml	Do not heat over 40°. Dissolve in CO_2-free water, and store below 20°. CO_3^{--}—HCO_3^- buffers require a closed system. 0.1 N solution has pH 8.4.
Sodium barbital, see Barbital sodium				
Sodium borate, see Sodium tetraborate				
Sodium cacodylate (sodium dimethylarsonate) $Na(CH_3)_2AsO_2 \cdot 3H_2O$		214.02	0.5 ml	Can be recrystallized from ethanol-water. Titrate with HCl vs. methyl orange.

TABLE II (*Continued*)

Compound	pK$_a$	Molecular weight	Water to dissolve 1 gm of solid	Notes
Sodium carbonate anhydrous Na$_2$CO$_3$ (anhydrous)		106.00	3.5 ml	Hygroscopic. Heat to 270° before use (do not exceed 360°), and dissolve in CO$_2$-free water. Avoid use of monohydrate, heptahydrate, and ("washing soda") decahydrate. 0.1 N solution has pH 11.6.
Sodium carbonate monohydrate Na$_2$CO$_3\cdot$H$_2$O		124.02	3.0 ml	
Sodium chloride NaCl		58.46	2.8 ml$_0$°	Dry at 160°.
Sodium citrate Na$_3$C$_6$H$_5$O$_7\cdot$2H$_2$O		294.12	1.3 ml	Dissolve in CO$_2$-free water.
Sodium citrate, acid (disodium citrate) Na$_2$C$_6$H$_6$O$_7\cdot$1½H$_2$O		263.13	2.0 ml	Also used as anticoagulant in blood banks.
Sodium formate HCOONa		68.02	1.3 ml	Deliquescent.
Sodium phosphate, dibasic, anhydrous Na$_2$HPO$_4$ exsiccated		141.98	8.0 ml	Hygroscopic, taking up 2 to 7 moles H$_2$O. Keep well closed. Dry at 110°–130° for 2 hours.
Sodium phosphate, dibasic, dihydrate Na$_2$HPO$_4\cdot$2H$_2$O		178.01		"Sørensen's phosphate." Uncertain stability. Becomes anhydrous at 95°.
Sodium phosphate, dibasic, heptahydrate Na$_2$HPO$_4\cdot$7H$_2$O		268.09	4.0 ml	Stable at room temperature if sealed.
Sodium phosphate, dibasic, dodecahydrate Na$_2$HPO$_4\cdot$12H$_2$O		358.17	23.3 ml$_0$° 16.1 ml$_5$° 3.3 ml$_{25}$°	Loses 5 moles H$_2$O on exposure to air. Keep sealed and in cold room.

Name and formula	Mol. wt.	pK	ml	Remarks
Sodium phosphate, monobasic, anhydrous (sodium biphosphate, sodium dihydrogen phosphate) NaH_2PO_4	120.01			Monohydrate can be dried at 100° to prepare anhydrous salt. Can replace KH_2PO_4 in buffers without introducing errors (3).
Sodium phosphate, monobasic, monohydrate $NaH_2PO_4 \cdot H_2O$	138.01		1.52 $ml_{0°}$ 1.0 $ml_{25°}$	
Sodium succinate, dibasic $NaOOC(CH_2)_2COONa$	162.02			Acid + theoretical amount carbonate-free NaOH evaporated to dryness; recrystallize from aqueous ethanol; dry at 120° for 6 hours or longer.
Sodium hydrogen succinate	140.01			Mix equal volumes of molar solutions of succinic acid and disodium succinate.
Sodium tetraborate decahydrate (borax) $Na_2B_4O_7 \cdot 10H_2O$	381.43		16.0 ml	Keep sealed to avoid partial dehydration. Do not heat. Dry to constant weight over deliquescent NaBr. Dissolve in CO_2-free water; stopper tightly. Toxic; acute and chronic borism. 0.1 N solution has pH 9.2.
Sodium p-toluenesulfonate	194.10			Prepared from p-toluenesulfonate and recrystallized from aqueous alcohol. (14) (Formation of buffer by adding NaOH to acid is recommended.)
Succinic acid $HOOC(CH_2)_2COOH$	118.09	4.21, 5.64	14.7 ml	Recrystallize from acetone. Dry at low temperature to avoid forming anhydride. M.p. 185°–185.5°. Dissociation constants, first hydrogen, 6.89×10^{-5}; second hydrogen, 2.47×10^{-6}.

TABLE II (Continued)

Compound	pK_a	Molecular weight	Water to dissolve 1 gm of solid	Notes
TES, see N-Tris(hydroxymethyl)-2-aminoethane-sulfonic acid				
p-Toluenesulfonic acid CH$_3$·C$_6$H$_4$SO$_3$H·H$_2$O		190.12	1.5 ml	Dry over KOH and CaCl$_2$. Somewhat deliquescent. M.p. 105°–106° in sealed tube.
Tricine, see N-Tris(hydroxymethyl) methylglycine				
Triethanolamine N(CH$_2$CH$_2$OH)$_3$	7.90	149.19	Miscible	Very hygroscopic; viscous. $D_4^{20} = 1.124$. Keep from air and light.
Triethanolamine·HCl (CH$_2$CH$_2$OH)$_3$N·HCl		185.65	Hardly soluble	M.p. 177°.
Trimethylamine·HCl (CH$_3$)N·HCl		95.58	Soluble	Monoclinic deliquescent crystals from alcohol; sublimes 200°; m.p. 278.5–280 (decomposes). Dissociation constant of free base, 7.4×10^{-5}.
Tris Tris(hydroxymethyl)aminomethane (HOCH$_2$)$_3$CNH$_2$	8.08	121.14	1.25 ml	Recrystallization from water as in ref. 2 (p. 42). Dissolve in CO$_2$-free water. Titrate with HCl vs. methyl orange. Relatively large change in pH with temperature differences.
N-Tris(hydroxymethyl)-2 amino-ethanesulfonic acid (TES) (HOCH$_2$)$_3$NHCH$_2$CH$_2$SO$_3$H	7.5	217.25	1.5 ml°	Ref. 1. Moderate change in pH with temperature differences.
N-Tris(hydroxymethyl)methylglycine (Tricine) (HOCH$_2$)$_3$CNH$_2$CH$_2$COOH	8.15	180.18	7.0 ml°	Refs. 1, 7.
Veronal, see Barbital				
Versene, see EDTA				

7. Various Buffer Systems, with References

TABLE III

Buffer	pH range	Buffer numbers[a] and references
Acetic acid–sodium Acetate	3.7–5.6	**Nos. 1–3;** 15, p. 140; 3, p. 357 (Table 93); 17, p. 314
$\Gamma/2 = 0.05, 0.1, 0.2$ at $0°$ and $25°$		2, p. 31 (Table 5D)
$\Gamma/2$ given variously at $18°$		5
Mole fraction as sodium acetate		16, p. 80; 5
Acetic acid–NaOH		**No. 4**
Acetic acid–NH$_4$OH	3.5–5.5	Author's experience
Acetate (Na)–HCl	0.65–5.2	18
Acetate (Na)–KCl + (HCl–KCl) buffer	4.0–5.5	**No. 5**
Constant ionic strengths of 0.05, 0.1, 0.15, 0.2, 0.25, room temperature		
Aconitic acid–NaOH	2.5–5.7	2, p. 37 (Table 5P); 15, p. 139; 17
"Ammediol"		
2-Amino-2 methyl-1,3-propane-diol–HCl	7.8–10.0	15, p. 145
0.05 M at $23°$ and $37°$		2, p. 40 (Table 5Y)
$\Gamma/2 = 0.05, 0.1, 0.2$ at $0°$ and $25°$		2, p. 35 (Table 5J)
Ammonium chloride–NH$_4$OH	8.3–10.8	4
$\Gamma/2 = 0.05, 0.1, 0.2$ at $0°$ and $25°$		2, p. 35 (Table 5K)
Ammonium chloride– KCl + (NaOH–KCl)	8.2–9.2	4
Constant ionic strengths of 0.05, 0.1 0.15, 0.2, 0.25		
Barbital–NaOH		
pH 8.6, $\Gamma/2 = 0.1$		**No. 9**
Barbital–NaOH–sodium acetate		
pH 8.6, $\Gamma/2 = 0.125$		**No. 10**
Barbital–barbital sodium	8.2–8.9	
$\Gamma/2 = 0.1$		**No. 9**
Barbital–barbital sodium–NaCl	7.4–9.4	2, p. 33 (Table 5H)
$\Gamma/2 = 0.05, 0.1, 0.2$ at $0°$ and $25°$		2, p. 33 (Table 5H)
$\Gamma/2 = 0.05, 0.1$ at $25°$ between pH 7.4 and 8.9		**No. 6A**
Special formulation with Ca^{++} and Mg^{++}	7.3	**No. 6B**
Barbital–barbital sodium–sodium acetate		
pH 8.6, $\Gamma/2 = 0.1$		**No. 11A**
Barbital–barbital sodium–calcium lactate	8.6	18a, p. 230
Barbital sodium–sodium acetate–HCl	2.6–9.4	**No. 8;** 19
pH 8.6, $\Gamma/2 = 0.1$		**No. 11B**

[a] Numbers shown in boldface type refer to buffer formulations of Section 8 below.

TABLE III (*Continued*)

Buffer	pH range	Buffer numbers and references
Barbital sodium–HCl	6.8–9.6	**No. 7**; 20; 15, p. 144; 3, p. 360 (Tables 101, 102); 17, p. 314
pH 8.2 Γ/2 = 0.05		**No. 12**; 21, p. 23
pH 8.4 Γ/2 = 0.05		**No. 13**
Barbital sodium–HCl–NaCl with Ca^{++} and Mg^{++}	7.3	**No. 6B**
Barbital sodium–HCl–Na$_2$CO$_3$	7.5–10.4	
Formulas for 22° and 37°		3 (Table 105)
Barbital sodium–KCl + (HCl–KCl)	7.0–9.0	4
Constant ionic strength of 0.05, 0.1, 0.15, 0.2, 0.25		
Boric acid–borax	7.6–9.2	**No. 14**; 15, p. 145; 3, p. 361 (Table 103)
Boric acid–NaOH–HCl	5.2–10.0	5
pH values given at 10°, 20°, 30°, 40°, 50°, 60°, 70°		
Boric acid–NaOH–KCl, 0.05 *M*	8.1–10.1	**No. 15**; 2, p. 40 (Table 5Z); 3, p. 362 (Table 107)
Boric acid–NaOH	7.4–10.0	
pH values given at 12.5°, 25°, 34°, 53°, 63°, 75°, 91°		3, p. 361 (Table 104); 5
pH 7.9, 8.5, 8.9 for gel electrophoresis		**Nos. 18A, B, C**; 23, 23*a*
Boric acid–KCl	7.8–10.0	17, p. 314
Boric acid–LiOH·H$_2$O		
pH 8.1, for starch gel electrophoresis		**No. 17**; 24
Boric acid–LiCl–NaOH	8.6	18*a*, p. 52
Borax–HCl	7.6–9.24	3, p. 362 (Table 106)
Borax–NaOH	9.28–12.3	15, p. 145; 3, p. 364 (Table 112)
pH values given at 10°, 20°, 40°		3, p. 363 (Table 109)
Borax–Na$_2$CO$_3$	9.2–11.0	5 (Table 46)
Borax–KCl + (HCl–KCl)	9.0–10.0	**No. 16**; 4
Constant ionic strengths of 0.05, 0.1, 0.15, 0.2, 0.25		
Borax–KH$_2$PO$_4$	5.8–9.2	17, p. 314
Borax–succinic acid, *see* Succinic acid		
Cacodylate (Na)–HCl	5.0–7.4	15, p. 142; 17, p. 314
Cacodylic acid–NaOH	5.2–7.2	
Γ/2 = 0.05, 0.1, 0.2 at 0° and 25°		2, p. 31 (Table 5E)
Carbonate (Na$_2$)–bicarbonate (NaH)	9.2–10.8	**No. 19**; 2, p. 36 (Table 5M); 15, p. 146 (Table 20); 17, p. 314
Γ/2 = 0.05, 0.1, 0.2 at 0° and 25°		2, p. 36 (Table 5M)
Carbonate (Na$_2$)–HCl	10.1–11.3	3, p. 363 (Table 110); not recommended, *see* 25

TABLE III (*Continued*)

Buffer	pH range	Buffer numbers and references
Citric acid–sodium citrate	3.0–6.2	2, p. 38 (Table 5Q); 15, p. 140; 18a, p. 193; see also Chap. 6,D,3,c
Citric acid–NaOH	2.2–6.5	3, p. 355 (Table 87); 17, p. 140; 18a, p. 184
pH values highly constant between 12.5° and 90°		17, p. 140; cf. 5
Citric acid–NaOH–HCl	1.1–4.9	5
Citric acid–Na$_2$HPO$_4$	2.4–7.6	15, p. 141 (Table 7); 3, p. 356 (Table 89); 5; 18a, p. 182; "McIlvaine's buffer"
Citrate (Na$_2$H)–HCl	1.1–4.8	17, p. 314
Citrate (Na$_2$H)–NaOH	5.0–6.3	3, p. 358 (Table 96)
s-Collidine–HCl 0.05 M, 23° and 37°	6.4–8.3	15, p. 39 (Table 5W)
Collidine–pyridine–acetic acid	3.0–8.5	9
Dimethylglutaric acid–NaOH	3.2–7.6	17, p. 314
EDTA, (NH$_4$)$_2$, Mg·3H$_2$O		12
EDTA, trisodium	7.4	**No. 20;** *see* **Nos. 33A, 33B**
EDTA, Na$_2$, Mg	7.4	**No. 21**
Ethanolamine–HCl	8.6–10.4	4
Ethanolamine·HCl–KCl + (NaOH–KCl)	8.6–10.4	4
Constant ionic strengths of 0.05, 0.1, 0.15, 0.2, 0.25		
N-Ethylmorpholine–pyridine–acetic acid	4.4–9.3	10
Formic acid–NaOH	2.6–4.8	2, 4
Γ/2 = 0.05, 0.1, 0.2 at 0° and 25°		2, p. 30 (Table 5C)
Formic acid–ammonium formate	3.4	23b; see p. 338
Formate (Na)–KCl + (HCl–KCl)	3.0–4.5	4
Constant ionic strengths of 0.05, 0.1, 0.15, 0.2, 0.25		
Furoic acid–NaOH	2.9–4.1	26; low buffer capacity
Furoic acid–sodium furoate	2.9–4.1	3, p. 356 (Table 90); low capacity
Glycine–HCl	2.0–3.4	**No. 22**
Glycine–HCl–NaCl	1.2–3.0	**No. 23**
Glycine–H$_2$SO$_4$ Γ/2 = 0.35	2.4	**No. 24**
Glycine–NaOH	8.8–10.8	**No. 25B**; 15, p. 145
Γ/2 = 0.05, 0.1, 0.2 at 0° and 25°		**No. 25A**; 2, p. 36 (Table 5L)
Glycine–NaOH–NaCl	8.2–10.1	**No. 26**; 17, p. 134; 3, p. 363 (Table 108)
pH values given for 10°, 40°, 70°		3
pH values for 2° temperature differences 10°–34°; 37°; 40°–70°		5

TABLE III (*Continued*)

Buffer	pH range	Buffer numbers and references
Glycine–NaOH–Na₂HPO₄	8.3–11.9	4
Hydrochloric acid–KCl	1.0–2.2	2, p. 30 (Table 5A); 15, p. 138; 17, p. 314
$\Gamma/2 = 0.1$, 25°		2, p. 37 (Table 5N)
Maleate (NaH)–NaOH	5.2–6.8	2, p. 38 (Table 5T); 15, p. 142
p-Phenolsulfonate (K)–NaOH	8.2–9.8	
$\Gamma/2 = 0.05, 0.1, 0.2$ at 0° and 25°		2, p. 34 (Table 5I); 5
Phenylacetic acid–NaOH	3.4–5.2	26; low buffer capacity
Phenylacetic acid–Na phenylacetate	3.4–5.1	3, p. 357 (Table 92); low buffer capacity; from (14)
Phenylacetate (Na)–KCl + (HCl–KCl)	3.5–5.0	4, p. 121
Constant ionic strengths of 0.05, 0.1, 0.15, 0.2, 0.25		
Phosphate-buffered saline		**No. 35A–E; No. 30** (a)
Phosphate: KH₂PO₄–K₂HPO₄	5.0–6.3	**No. 27**
Phosphate: KH₂PO₄–Na₂HPO₄	5.0–8.2	**Nos. 28, 29;** 17, p. 314;
$\Gamma/2 = 0.05, 0.1, 0.2$ at 0° and 25°		2, p. 32 (Table 5F)
Phosphate: KH₂PO₄–Na₂HPO₄–NaCl		
$\Gamma/2 = 0.1$	7.0	**No. 30**
Phosphate: KH₂PO₄–NaOH	5.8–7.9	**Nos. 31, 32;** 2, p. 39 (Table 5V); 4, p. 157
Very constant values from 12.5°–90°		3, p. 358, 359 (Tables 97, 99)
Phosphate: KH₂PO₄–borax	5.8–9.2	3, p. 359 (Table 98); 4
Phosphate: NaH₂PO₄–Na₂HPO₄	5.7–8.0	**Nos. 33A, 33B;** 15, p. 143
pH 7.0, with EDTA and sodium azide	7.0	**No. 36**
Phosphate: Na₂HPO₄–NaOH	10.8–11.4	3, pp. 363, 364 (Tables 111, 113)
Phosphate–trisodium EDTA	7.4	**No. 34**
Phthalate (KH)–HCl	2.2–3.8	2, p. 37 (Table 5 O); 15, p. 139; 17, p. 314
Phthalate (KH)–NaOH	4.2–6.2	2, p. 38 (Table 5S); 15, p. 142; 3, p. 358 (Table 94); 17, p. 314
Piperazine·HCl–NaOH	4.8–7.0	17, p. 314
Piperazine–glycylglycine	4.4–10.8	17, p. 314
Pyridine–acetate	3.1–5.2	8a–c
Pyridine–formate	1.2–3.4	8b; author's experience
Succinic acid–NaOH	3.8–6.0	2, p. 38 (Table 5R); 17, pp.141, 314
Succinic acid–borax	3.0–5.8	3, p. 357 (Table 91); 17, p. 314
Succinic acid–succinate (Na₂)–NaOH	5.0–6.0	26; low buffer capacity
Succinate (Na, H)–succinate (Na₂)	4.8–6.2	3, p. 358 (Table 95); low buffer capacity; from (14)
Sulfosalicylate (KH)–NaOH	2.0–4.0	4

TABLE III (*Continued*)

Buffer	pH range	Buffer numbers and references
p-Toluenesulfonic acid–NaOH	1.2–3.3	26
p-Toluenesulfonic acid–toluenesulfonate (Na)	1.2–3.3	3 (Tables 83, 84, 88); 14
Triethanolamine-buffered saline with Ca^{++} and Mg^{++}	7.3–7.4	**No. 37A**; 27
Triethanolamine–HCl	6.7–8.7	4
Triethanolamine·HCl–NaOH $\Gamma/2 = 0.1$	7.6	**No. 37B**; 18*a*
Triethanolamine·HCl–KCl + (NaOH–KCl) Constant ionic strengths of 0.05, 0.1, 0.15, 0.2, 0.25	7.0–8.5	4
Trimethylamine·HCl–NaOH	10.0	39
Tris–acetic acid pH 8.15, 0.1 *M* Tris, 0.05 *M* AcOH	8.15	**No. 40A**
Tris–boric acid—EDTA	8.9	**No. 44**
	8.5	**No. 45**
	8.4	Chap. 6,C,5,c,*ii*
Tris–citric acid pH 7.8, 8.0, 8.2 for gel electrophoresis		**No. 40B**; 23*a*, 24, 28
Tris–citric acid–Na$_2$HPO$_4$	8.4	18*a*, p. 347
Tris–glycine	7.7–9.0	Author's experience
	8.3	Table II, Chap. 6,C,4,d,*ii*
Tris–HCl	7.2–9.0	**No. 38**; 15, p. 144; 17, p. 314
0.05 *M* values at 23° and 37°		2, p. 40 (Table 5X)
$\Gamma/2 = 0.05, 0.1, 0.2$, at 0° and 25°		2, p. 33 (Table 5G)
pH 8.0 at 25°, $\Gamma/2 = 0.05$	8.0	**No. 41**
pH 8.0 at 25°, $\Gamma/2 = 0.058$	8.0	**No. 42**
Tris–HCl–0.2 *M* NaCl, pH 8.0 at 25° (0.1 *M* Tris, 0.06 *M* HCl, 0.2 *M* NaCl)	8.0	**No. 43**
Tris·HCl–KCl + (NaOH–KCl) Constant ionic strengths of 0.05, 0.1, 0.15, 0.2, 0.25	7.2–9.0	4
Tris–maleate–NaOH	5.2–8.6	**No. 39**; 15, after 29; 2, p. 39 (Table 5U); 17, p. 314
Tris–phosphoric acid	8.6	**No. 46**

8. Composition of Selected Buffers

A. Acetate Buffers

1. Acetate, 0.1 M, pH 3.6–5.6*

Solution A: acetic acid, 0.2 M (11.55 ml glacial acetic acid/liter).

Solution B: sodium acetate, 0.2 M (Na acetate·3H$_2$O, 27.2 gm/liter).

pH	Solution A (ml/liter)	Solution B (ml/liter)	pH	Solution A (ml/liter)	Solution B (ml/liter)
3.6	463	37	4.8	200	300
3.8	440	60	5.0	148	352
4.0	410	90	5.2	105	395
4.2	368	132	5.4	88	412
4.4	305	195	5.6	48	452
4.6	255	245			

2. Acetate, 0.2 M

As above, but read column headings as (ml/500 ml).

3. Acetic acid–sodium acetate, pH 3.7–5.6, $\Gamma/2 = 0.1$†

Solution A: acetic acid, 1 M (glacial acetic acid, ca. 57.5 ml/liter).

Solution B: sodium acetate, 1 M (AcONa·3H$_2$O, 136.07 gm/liter).

To 100 ml of solution B, prepared freshly, add the following amounts of solution A and dilute to 1 liter.

pH	Solution A (ml/liter)	pH	Solution A (ml/liter)
3.7	900	4.6	105
3.8	725	4.7	86
3.9	576	4.8	64
4.0	450	4.9	52
4.1	350	5.0	43
4.2	275	5.1	35
4.3	211	5.2	27
4.4	163	5.4	16
4.5	135		

4. Acetic acid–NaOH, pH 3.8–5.8, $\Gamma/2 = 0.1$‡

Solution A: acetic acid, 1 M, as in Buffer No. 3

Solution B: NaOH, 1 M.

* Walpole's acetate buffer (18). See refs. 15, p. 140; 17, p. 314. For an acetate buffer of constant ionicity, see buffer No. 3.

† An acetate buffer of constant molarity is given in buffer No. 1.

‡ Ref. 2, p. 31 for 25°.

pH	Solution A (ml/liter)	Solution B (ml/liter)
3.8	828	100
4.0	559	100
4.2	389	100
4.4	283	100
4.6	215	100
4.8	173	100
5.0	146	100
5.2	129	100
5.4	118	100
5.6	112	100
5.8	107.3	100

5. Acetate (sodium acetate–KCl + HCl–KCl), pH 4.0–5.5, $\Gamma/2 = 0.1$*
   Solution A: hydrochloric acid, 0.2 M, plus potassium chloride, 0.1 M (7.45 gm/liter).
   Solution B: sodium acetate, 0.05 M (AcONa·3H$_2$O, 6.8 gm/liter), plus potassium chloride, 0.05 M (3.72 gm/liter).
Solutions A and B both have $\Gamma/2 = 0.1$, and may be mixed in all proportions between pH 4.0 and 5.5.

B. BARBITAL (VERONAL) BUFFERS

According to recent federal legislation, purchase invoices of barbiturates must be retained and an inventory maintained of the supply; further, some states require that a perpetual inventory be kept by the user.

Barbital and barbital sodium (0.1 M) are bacteriostatic, and the two solutions can be kept separately for some weeks at room temperature. Before use, such solutions must be inspected carefully for full clarity. Aqueous solutions undergo slow decomposition.

Barbital buffers made without sodium chloride are highly useful for electrophoresis of proteins, both in paper and in agar, but the relative insolubility of barbital limits the pH range from 8.2 to 8.9 (cf. buffers Nos. 8 and 9).

Barbital at pH 8.6 shows a high absorption spectrum at 2800 A, but barbital is not ionized at pH 2.0, and protein concentrations can be determined by scanning at 280 mμ after addition of 1.0 N H$_2$SO$_4$ to pH 2.0; the blank to be used consists of barbital buffer treated similarly (reading of blank against water, ca 0.070^{280}_{1cm}). Clarify by centrifugation

* From ref. 4, p. 121. Other proportions are given for $\Gamma/2 = 0.05, 0.15, 0.2, 0.25$.

if crystals of barbituric acid form. Otherwise, the biuret or Folin–Ciocalteu reaction must be used to determine protein, since there is 15.2% of nitrogen in barbital.

6A. Barbital–barbital sodium–NaCl, pH 7.4–9.0*
  Solution A: barbital, 0.025 M (4.605 gm/liter).
  Solution B: barbital sodium, 0.05 M (103.09 gm/liter).
  Solution C: NaCl, 0.5 M (29.2 gm/liter).

	$\Gamma/2 = 0.05$ at 25°C			$\Gamma/2 = 0.1$ at 25°C		
pH	A (ml/liter)	B (ml/liter)	C (ml/liter)	A (ml/liter)	B (ml/liter)	C (ml/liter)
7.4	648	10	90	639	10	190
7.6	409	10	90	403	10	190
7.8	645	25	75	636	25	175
8.0	814	50	50	401	25	175
8.2	514	50	50	506	50	150
8.4	648	100	0	639	100	100
8.6	409	100	0	403	100	100
8.8				509	200	0
8.9				321	200	0

6B. Barbital (0.003 M)–barbital sodium (0.0018 M)–NaCl, with Ca++ and Mg++, pH 7.4 (22a)

Stock solution 1A, 1 liter†
  Barbital (2.875 gm)
  Barbital sodium (1.875 gm)
  NaCl (42.5 gm)

Alternate stock solution 1B, 1 liter†
  Barbital sodium (5.095 gm)
  1.0 N HCl (17.29 ml)
  NaCl (41.5 gm)

Stock solution No. 2 (2.5 ml) Stock solution No. 2 (2.5 ml)

Stock solution 2: 20.33 gm of $MgCl_2 \cdot 6H_2O$ (1 M) and 4.41 gm of $CaCl_2 \cdot 2H_2O$ (0.3 M) in 100 ml.

Working solution (prepare daily), pH 7.3, $\Gamma/2 = 0.15$: Dilute 1 volume of stock solution 1A or 1B with 4 volumes of water. Specific conductance should be 0.00817 ohm⁻¹ cm⁻¹ (22a). This buffer supplies the proper balance of Mg++ (5×10^{-4} M) and Ca++ (1.5×10^{-4} M) for optimal activity of guinea pig serum complement, as does buffer No. 37A. It is recommended that 0.1% gelatin be added to the working solution to assist in the integrity of erythrocytes (22a).

* From ref. 2, p. 33 (Table 5H). Other data are given for $\Gamma/2 = 0.2$ and proportions for preparing buffers having ionic strengths of 0.05, 0.1, and 0.2, at 0°C.
† Batches of 2 liters should be prepared. Use not less than 400 ml of water for 3 gm of barbital, and warm to dissolve.

7. Barbital sodium–HCl, pH 6.8–9.6*
Solution A: barbital sodium, 0.5 M (103.09 gm/liter).
Solution B: HCl, 1.0 N.

pH	Solution A (ml/liter)	Solution B (ml/liter)	pH	Solution A (ml/liter)	Solution B (ml/liter)
6.8	104.2	47.8	8.4	164.7	17.8
7.0	107.2	46.4	8.6	174.2	12.9
7.2	110.8	44.6	8.8	181.6	9.2
7.4	116.2	41.9	9.0	187.2	6.4
7.6	123.2	38.5	9.2	190.4	4.8
7.8	132.4	33.8	9.4	194.8	2.6
8.0	143.2	28.4	9.6	197	1.5
8.2	153.8	23.1			

8. Barbital sodium–sodium acetate–HCl, pH 2.6–9.4†
Solution A: barbital sodium, 0.16 M (29.43 gm/liter), and sodium
 acetate, 0.143 M (19.43 gm trihydrate/liter).
Solution B: HCl, 1.0 N.
Solution C: 8.5% NaCl (1.46 M).
Mix 200 ml of solution A, 80 ml of solution C, and n ml of solution
B, and bring to 1 liter.

pH	Solution B (ml/liter)	pH	Solution B (ml/liter)
2.62	64	7.25	22
3.62	56	7.42	20
4.66	40	7.66	16
5.32	32	7.90	12
6.12	28	8.18	8
6.5	27	8.55	4
6.99	24	8.68	3

9. Barbital, $\Gamma/2 = 0.1$

pH	Barbital (gm/liter)	Barbital sodium (gm/liter)
8.4	4.9	17.4
8.6	3.41	18.95
8.8	2.34	20.62
8.9	1.48	20.62

* After Michaelis (20).
† From Michaelis (19). When solution C is omitted, the ionic strength is 0.15 at pH
4.93 and drops progressively toward the alkaline side. The formula can be recalculated, using two-thirds of solution A and variable amounts of solution C, to produce
an isotonic buffer extending from below pH 4.9 to 9.4. For $\Gamma/2 = 0.1$ at pH 8.6,
bring 340 ml of solution A and 6.44 ml of N HCl to 1 liter.

Dissolve the barbital sodium in 850 ml of warm water, dissolve the barbital completely, let cool, and bring the solution to 1 liter. These buffers are usually diluted with an equal volume of water ($\Gamma/2 = 0.05$) for immunoelectrophoresis: pH 8.2 buffer can be prepared directly at ionic strength $= 0.05$ by using 3.44 gm of barbital and 7.57 gm of barbital sodium per liter.

The pH 8.6 buffer can be made alternatively by dissolving 22.09 gm of barbital in 800 ml of hot distilled water; add 20.5 ml of 5 N NaOH; cool a portion, and correct the pH if necessary. Cool and bring volume to 1 liter.

10. Barbital–NaOH–sodium acetate, pH 8.6, $\Gamma/2 = 0.125$

Dissolve 8.712 gm of barbital in 350 ml of hot distilled water, add 47.32 ml of M NaOH, 6.476 gm of sodium acetate·3H$_2$O, and 60 ml of 0.1 M HCl, and bring to 1 liter.

This buffer is recommended for paper electrophoresis.

11A. Barbital–barbital sodium–sodium acetate, pH 8.6, $\Gamma/2 = 0.1$

Barbital, 0.01 M (1.842 gm), barbital sodium, 0.05 M (10.309 gm), and sodium acetate·3H$_2$O, 0.05 M (6.804 gm). Weights per liter of solution are given.

This buffer is used for paper electrophoresis.

11B. Barbital sodium–sodium acetate–HCl, pH 8.6, $\Gamma/2 = 0.1$

An alternative preparation of buffer No. 11A consists of barbital sodium (9.78 gm), sodium acetate·3H$_2$O (6.47 gm), and HCl (60 ml, 0.1 N) per liter. The ratio of components is similar to that of buffer No. 8.

12. Barbital sodium–HCl, pH 8.2, $\Gamma/2 = $ ca. 0.05

10 gm barbital sodium plus 15.8 ml N HCl per liter.

An ionic strength of 0.05 is suited to immunoelectrophoresis on large agar plates (21). Other workers using 3 × 1-inch slides reduce the ionicity to about 0.04 (22) with 8 gm of barbital sodium and 12.6 ml of N HCl per liter.

13. Barbital sodium–HCl, pH 8.4, $\Gamma/2 = 0.05$

8.5 gm barbital sodium plus 8.9 ml N HCl per liter (ref. 18a, p. 68).

C. BORATE BUFFERS

Borate ions are complex and associate in solution, making borate buffers highly dependent on concentration. Borate ions complex with adjacent −OH groups in the *cis* configuration, such as are present on sugars, and thereby a "charge" is imposed on sugars by borate buffers, allowing movement in an electrical field. Subsequently, borate can be removed by special procedures. Similarly, borate complexes with the hydroxyl groups of agarose, making other buffers more suitable for gel electrophoresis. Note also that borate buffers must be handled carefully owing to toxicity.

14. Boric acid–borax, pH 7.6–9.2*

    Solution A: boric acid, 0.2 M (12.4 gm/liter).

    Solution B: sodium tetraborate·10H$_2$O, 0.05 M, 19.05 gm/liter (equivalent to sodium borate, 0.2 M NaBO$_2$).

    Use 250 ml of solution A, add n ml of solution B, and dilute to 1 liter.

pH	Solution A (ml/liter)	Solution B (ml/liter)	pH	Solution A (ml/liter)	Solution B (ml/liter)
7.6	850	150	8.6	450	550
7.8	800	200	8.7	400	600
8.0	700	300	8.84	300	700
8.2	650	350	9.0	200	800
8.4	550	450	9.1	100	900

15. Boric acid–NaOH–KCl, 0.05 M borate and 0.05 M KCl, pH 8.1–10.1†

    Solution A: H$_3$BO$_3$, 0.2 M (12.4 gm/liter), and KCl, 0.2 M (14.91 gm/liter).

    Solution B: NaOH, 0.2 M.

    To 250 ml of solution A, add n ml of solution B, and dilute to 1 liter.

pH	Solution B (ml/liter)	pH	Solution B (ml/liter)
8.1	24.5	9.1	118
8.2	30.0	9.2	132
8.3	36.0	9.3	146.5
8.4	43.0	9.4	160.5
8.5	50.5	9.5	173
8.6	50.9	9.6	184.5
8.7	68.5	9.7	194.5
8.8	79.0	9.8	203
8.9	90.5	9.9	211
9.0	104	10.0	218.5

---

* Holmes, 1943, recalculated from the original Palitzsch buffer.

† Clark and Lubs' buffer, according to refs. 2, p. 40; 3, p. 362; 4, p. 158; slightly emended from ref. 5.

16. Borax–KCl + (HCl–KCl), pH 9.0–10.0, $\Gamma/2 = 0.1$*

Solution A: borax, 0.0125 M (4.768 gm of decahydrate/liter) and KCl, 0.05 M (3.72 gm/liter).

Solution B: hydrochloric acid, 0.2 M, and KCl, 0.1 M (7.45 gm/liter).

Solutions A and B both have $\Gamma/2 = 0.1$, and may be mixed in all proportions between pH 9.0 and 10.0.

17. Boric acid–lithium hydroxide, pH 8.1, for discontinuous starch gel electrophoresis

	H_3BO_3	$LiOH \cdot H_2O$
(A)	0.38 M (23.5 gm)	0.1 M (4.196 gm)
(B)	0.192 M (11.89 gm)	0.05 M (2.1 gm)

Solutions A and B are tank, or electrode-compartment, buffers; values are grams per liter. They are added also, in 10% volume, to complete the corresponding gel buffers: gel buffer for Solution A is No. 40B (b), ref. 24; gel buffer for solution B is No. 40B (c), ref. 28.

18. Boric acid–NaOH, for starch gel electrophoresis

	pH	H_3BO_3	NaOH
(A)	7.9	0.3 M	0.06 M
(B)	8.48	0.03 M	0.012 M
(C)	8.9	0.03 M	0.12 M

Solution A is tank buffer for use with gel buffer No. 40B (a), ref. 23a. In Smithies' original work (23), solution A was employed with gel buffer 40B (b); buffer pairs 45A and 45B were introduced later. Solution C is another formulation for immunoelectrophoresis (ref. 18a, p. 228).

D. CARBONATE BUFFERS

Carbonate buffers, unless used within a gastight chamber, show marked shift in pH, especially during mechanical stirring when CO_2 is absorbed rapidly from the air and the pH shifts to the acid side: this shift is nearly always encountered in preparing fluorescein–isothiocyanate-coupled antibody preparations. Carbonate–bicarbonate buffers are a usual part of "balanced ion" buffering systems used with living cells (Tyrode's solu-

---

* From ref. 4, p. 122. Other proportions are given for $\Gamma/2 = 0.05, 0.15. 0.2, 0.25$. Note that the concentration of borax must remain between 0.01 M and 0.05 M.

tion, Hanks' solution, and so on). The concentration of bicarbonate buffer in Tyrode's solution is such that a marked alkaline pH occurs on exposure to air in thin, unstirred layers. Hanks' solution was designed largely with the purpose of overcoming a marked alkaline shift. In both cases, alkaline drift is corrected by adding CO_2 (preferably by passing 5% CO_2–air mixtures into buffer and making dropwise additions), and acid drift (arising by metabolism of glucose by cells) is countered as needed by adding isotonic 1.4% $NaHCO_3$.

An early extractive "buffer," once used extensively with defatted pollen grains, was "Coca's fluid," consisting of 4.5 gm of NaCl and 9 gm of sodium bicarbonate per liter, with sufficient CO_2 added to bring the reaction to faint pink with phenolphthalein, tested on a side portion. This fluid underwent alkaline shift and was unstable.

19. Sodium bicarbonate–sodium carbonate, pH 9.2–10.8

Solution A: sodium acid carbonate, 1.0 M ($NaHCO_3$, 84.0 gm/liter).

Solution B: sodium carbonate, 1.0 M (Na_2CO_3 anhydrous, 106.0 gm/liter).

| pH | $\Gamma/2 = 0.1$ at $25°$[a] | |
	Solution A (ml/liter)	Solution B (ml/liter)
9.0	76.8	7.74
9.2	67.6	10.8
9.4	56.8	14.4
9.6	45.3	18.2
9.8	34.3	21.9
10.0	24.6	25.1
10.2	17.0	27.6
10.4	11.2	29.5
10.6	7.06	30.8
10.8	4.07	31.7

[a] From ref. 2, p. 36 (Table 5M); $\Gamma/2 = 0.05$, 0.1, 0.15 at $0°$ and $25°$ are given.

E. EDTA BUFFERS

20. EDTA, NaOH (Na_3HEDTA), 0.15 M, pH 7.4

EDTA, disodium, 0.15 M (55.84 gm/liter) + NaOH, 1 M, to pH 7.4, giving a solution largely in the trisodium form. This buffer is used (30, 31) at a dilution of 1:18.75 (8×10^{-3} M) for inactivating C'1, C'4, and C'3 of complement by chelating Ca^{++} and Mg^{++} but permitting C'3 of complement to react. A concentration of 5×10^{-3} M is also employed i.e., a dilution of 1:30.

21. EDTA, disodium, monomagnesium, 0.15 M, pH 7.4

EDTA, disodium, monomagnesium (Na_2Mg EDTA), is set at pH 7.4 by adding 1 M NaOH (30). This buffer, used at a dilution of 1:9.38 (16×10^{-3} M), chelates Ca^{++} but not Mg^{++}, blocking activity of complement C'1 but permitting components C'2 and C'3 to react. A reaction of ca. pH 7.4 should be maintained for proper complexing.

F. GLYCINE BUFFERS

22. Glycine–HCl, pH 2.0–3.4
Solution A: glycine, 2 M (150.14 gm/liter).
Solution B: HCl, 1 M.

$\Gamma/2 = 0.1$ at $25°^a$			0.05 M glycine[b]	
Solution A (ml/liter)	Solution B (ml/liter)	pH	Solution A (ml/liter)	Solution B (ml/liter)
59.0	100	2.0	—	—
71.5	100	2.2	25	44.0
89.2	100	2.4	25	32.4
116	100	2.6	25	24.2
157	100	2.8	25	16.8
222	100	3.0	25	11.4
324	100	3.2	25	8.2
486	100	3.4	25	6.4
		3.6	25	5.0

[a] From ref. 2, p. 30 (Table 5B); formulas are given for $\Gamma/2 = 0.05, 0.1, 0.15$ at $0°$ and $25°$.

[b] From ref. 15, p. 139.

23. Glycine–HCl–NaCl, pH 1.2–3*
Solution A: glycine, 1.0 M (75.07 gm/liter), and NaCl, 1.0 M (58.5 gm/liter).
Solution B: hydrochloric acid, 1.0 N

* Sørensen's acid glycine at 18°. From ref. 17, p. 134. Note that the pH of glycine buffer is temperature-dependent; adjustment of the composition should be made for 0°, 37°, and so on.

pH	Solution A (ml/liter)	Solution B (ml/liter)	pH	Solution A (ml/liter)	Solution B (ml/liter)
1.2	15.0	85.0	2.6	70.2	29.8
1.4	28.7	71.3	2.8	75.6	24.4
1.6	38.2	61.8	3.0	80.8	19.2
1.8	45.7	54.3	3.2	85.6	14.4
2.0	52.3	47.7	3.4	90.3	9.7
2.2	58.3	41.7	3.6	94.5	5.5
2.4	64.5	35.5			

24. Glycine–H_2SO_4, pH 2.4, $\Gamma/2 = 0.35$*

Dissolve 32 gm of glycine in water, add 2.30 ml of 1.0 N H_2SO_4, and bring to 1 liter.

25A. Glycine–NaOH, pH 8.8–10.8, $\Gamma/2 = 0.1$ at 25°[a]

Solution A: glycine, 2 M (150.14 gm/liter).

Solution B: NaOH 1 N.

pH	Solution A (ml/liter)	Solution B (ml/liter)
8.8	467	100
9.0	313	100
9.2	216	100
9.4	155	100
9.6	116.1	100
9.8	91.7	100
10.0	76.3	100
10.2	66.5	100
10.4	60.3	100
10.6	56.4	100
10.8	53.8	100

[a] From ref. 2, p. 36 (Table 5L). Formulas for $\Gamma/2$ = 0.05, 0.1, 0.2 at 0° and 25° are given.

25B. Glycine–NaOH, pH 8.6–10.4.[a]

Solution A: glycine, 0.2 M (15.01 gm/liter)

Solution B: NaOH, 0.2 M

* Singer, Chap. 3,B,3, Vol. I.

25B. *Continued.*

pH	Solution A (ml/liter)	Solution B (ml/liter)
8.6	50	4.0
8.8	50	6.0
9.0	50	8.8
9.2	50	12.0
9.4	50	16.8
9.6	50	22.4
9.8	50	27.2
10.0	50	32.0
10.2	50	38.6
10.4	50	45.5

[a] From ref. 15, p. 145.

26. Glycine–NaOH–NaCl, pH 8.6–10.6*

Solution A: glycine, 1.0 M (75.07 gm/liter), and NaCl, 1.0 M (58.5 gm/liter).

Solution B: NaOH 1.0 N.

pH	Solution A (ml/liter)	Solution B (ml/liter)
8.6	94.8	5.2
8.8	92.1	7.9
9.0	88.5	11.5
9.2	84.2	15.8
9.4	79.0	21.0
9.6	73.2	26.8
9.8	67.7	32.3
10.0	63.0	37.0
10.2	59.0	41.0
10.4	56.1	43.9
10.6	53.7	46.3

G. Phosphate Buffers

Phosphate buffers are valuable particularly because they cover the physiological range of pH values and because phosphates are compatible with tissues. Microorganisms grow readily in these buffers, which must, accordingly, be made up every few days. Because preservatives are not suitable in many instances, and because there is a great advantage in being able to prepare small amounts of phosphate buffers on short notice, it is recommended that 0.2 M solutions of the two sodium salts (buffer No. 32) be kept on hand as sterile solutions, passed through Millipore filters, and dispensed in 15-ml and 100-ml sterile containers. The solutions

* Sørenson's alkaline glycine at 18°. From ref. 17, p. 134.

should be stored at room temperature. Since Na_2HPO_4 attacks ordinary glass, borosilicate bottles are recommended, with replacement about every 6 months. About four times the volume of Na_2HPO_4 relative to NaH_2PO_4 is needed.

Na_2HPO_4 is only slightly soluble at low temperatures, and phosphate buffers for cold room work should be made with K_2HPO_4 (as in buffer No. 37).

27. KH_2PO_4–K_2HPO_4, 0.1 M and 0.01 M, pH 5.8–7.7*

Solution A: KH_2PO_4, 0.5 M (anhydrous, 68.04 gm/liter).

Solution B: K_2HPO_4, 0.5 M (anhydrous, 87.09 gm/liter).

	0.1 M			0.01 M	
pH	Solution A (ml/liter)	Solution B (ml/liter)	pH	Solution A (ml/liter)	Solution B (ml/liter)
5.8	184	16	5.8	—	—
5.9	180	20	5.9	17.9	2.1
6.0	175.4	24.6	6.0	17.3	2.6
6.1	170	30	6.1	16.8	3.2
6.2	163	37	6.2	16.1	3.84
6.3	155	45	6.3	15.3	4.6
6.4	147	53	6.4	14.4	5.5
6.5	137	63	6.5	13.4	6.56
6.6	125	75	6.6	12.4	7.6
6.7	113	87	6.7	11.2	8.8
6.8	102	98	6.8	10.0	10.0
6.9	90	110	6.9	8.86	11.1
7.0	78	122	7.0	7.7	12.3
7.1	66	134	7.1	6.64	13.3
7.2	56	144	7.2	5.66	14.34
7.3	46	154	7.3	4.76	15.24
7.4	38	162	7.4	3.36	16.0
7.5	32	168	7.5	3.26	16.7
7.6	26	174	7.6	2.7	17.3
7.7	21	179	7.7	2.2	17.8

Diluting 0.01 M pH 7.4 buffer five-fold and adding 24 mg $MgSO_4$ per liter prepares the "RNP" buffer of W. C. Gillchriest and R. M. Bock, *in* "Microsomal Particles and Protein Synthesis" (R. B. Roberts, ed.), p. 1. Pergamon, New York, 1958 (cf. Vol. I, p. 15).

28. KH_2PO_4–Na_2HPO_4, 0.067 M, pH 5.0–8.2†

Solution A: KH_2PO_4, $M/15$ (9.078 gm/liter).

Solution B: Na_2HPO_4, $M/15$ (Na_2HPO_4 anhydrous, 9.47 gm/liter, or $Na_2HPO_4 \cdot 7H_2O$, 17.87 gm/liter, or $Na_2HPO_4 \cdot 12H_2O$, 23.88 gm/liter).

---

* Values shown follow author's experience. Composition of 0.1 M buffers is based on buffer No. 33A, since K and Na salts of phosphates are interchangeable on a molar basis.

† Sørensen buffer, ref. 17, p. 314.

28. *Continued.*

pH	Solution A (ml/liter)	Solution B (ml/liter)	pH	Solution A (ml/liter)	Solution B (ml/liter)
5.0	988	12	6.6	627	373
5.2	980	20	6.8	508	492
5.4	967	33	7.0	392	608
5.6	948	52	7.2	285	715
5.8	919	81	7.4	196	804
6.0	877	123	7.6	132	868
6.2	815	185	7.8	86	914
6.4	732	268	8.0	55	945
			8.2	33	967

29. KH_2PO_4–Na_2HPO_4, pH 5.8–7.8, $\Gamma/2 = 0.1$ at 25°*
   Solution A: KH_2PO_4, 0.5 M (KH_2PO_4, 68.04 gm/liter).
   Solution B: Na_2HPO_4, 0.5 M (anhydrous, 70.99 gm/liter, or $Na_2HPO_4 \cdot$ $7H_2O$, 134.04 gm/liter, or $Na_2HPO_4 \cdot 12H_2O$, 179.08 gm/liter).

pH	Solution A (ml/liter)	Solution B (ml/liter)
5.8	159	13.8
6.0	142	19.5
6.2	121	26.4
6.4	98.2	34.0
6.6	75.6	41.4
6.8	55.4	48.2
7.0	39.0	53.6
7.2	26.4	57.8
7.4	17.6	60.8
7.6	11.5	62.8
7.8	7.38	64.2

30. KH_2PO_4–Na_2HPO_4–$NaCl$, with or without 0.4% phenol (0.0067 M phosphate), pH 7.0, $\Gamma/2 = 0.1$†
   Stock solution, No. 1: $M/15$ phosphate; pH ca. 7.1 with 0.5% NaCl, $\Gamma/2 = 1.0$: KH_2PO_4 (3.63 gm/liter), Na_2HPO_4 ($Na_2HPO_4 \cdot 12H_2O$, 14.31 gm/liter), NaCl (50 gm/liter), pyrogen-free distilled water.
   Working solution, No. 2: (A) One part stock solution and 9 parts water gives a weakly but adequately buffered saline. (B) For making and diluting allergenic extracts intended for intradermal injection (31a, 32),

---

* From ref. 2, p. 32 (Table 5F). Note that 0.5 M Na_2HPO_4 is soluble only at room temperature.
† Stock solution No. 1 is derived from buffer No. 28 with addition of sodium chloride (31a). The ionic strength is calculated without the contribution of the phenol.

the stock solution is diluted with 8 parts water and 1 part 4% phenol.*
N.B. These dilutions can be autoclaved (once only) at 10 pounds steam
pressure for 20 minutes; sterile filtration is preferable.

31. KH_2PO_4–NaOH, pH 5.8–7.9†

Solution A: KH_2PO_4, 0.2 M (KH_2PO_4, 27.21 gm/liter).
Solution B: NaOH, 0.2 M.

To 250 ml of solution A, add n ml of solution B, and dilute to 1 liter.

pH	Solution B (ml/liter)	pH	Solution B (ml/liter)
5.9	23	7.0	145.5
6.0	28	7.1	160.5
6.1	34	7.2	173.5
6.2	40.5	7.3	185
6.3	48.5	7.4	195.5
6.4	58	7.5	204.5
6.5	69.5	7.6	212
6.6	82	7.7	217.5
6.7	96.5	7.8	222.5
6.8	112	7.9	226.5
6.9	129.5		

32. KH_2PO_4–NaOH, pH 5.8–7.8, $\Gamma = 0.1$ at 25°‡

Solution A: KH_2PO_4, 0.5 M (KH_2PO_4, 68.04 gm/liter).
Solution B: NaOH, 0.5 M.

pH	Solution A (ml/liter)	Solution B (ml/liter)
5.8	172.8	13.8
6.0	161.5	19.5
6.2	147.4	26.4
6.4	132.2	34.0
6.6	117.0	41.4
6.8	103.6	48.2
7.0	92.6	53.6
7.2	84.2	57.8
7.4	78.4	60.8
7.6	74.3	62.8
7.8	71.6	64.2

* Phenol is prepared from white phenol, in the form of crystals liquefied in the hood
in a water bath, *poured* into pyrogen-free water, and stirred until solution of phenol
in water is complete; for small-scale work, commercial 88% liquefied phenol can be
used (45.45 ml/liter), provided the product gives water-white solutions.
† Clark and Lubs buffer, from refs. 2, p. 39, (Table 5V) and 4, p. 157.
‡ From ref. 2, p. 32 (Table 5F).

33A. NaH_2PO_4–Na_2HPO_4, 0.1 M, pH 5.7–8.0*
Solution A: NaH_2PO_4, 0.2 M ($NaH_2PO_4 \cdot H_2O$, 27.6 gm/liter).
Solution B: Na_2HPO_4, 0.2 M ($Na_2HPO_4 \cdot 7H_2O$, 53.65 gm/liter, or $Na_2HPO_4 \cdot 12H_2O$, 71.64 gm/liter).

pH	Solution A (ml/liter)	Solution B (ml/liter)	pH	Solution A (ml/liter)	Solution B (ml/liter)
5.7	467.5	32.5	6.9	225	275
5.8	460	40.0	7.0	195	305
5.9	450	50.0	7.1	165	335
6.0	438.5	61.5	7.2	140	360
6.1	425	75.0	7.3	115	385
6.2	407.5	92.5	7.4	95	405
6.3	387.5	112.5	7.5	80	420
6.4	367.5	132.5	7.6	65	435
6.5	342.5	157.5	7.7	52.5	447.5
6.6	312.5	187.5	7.8	42.5	457.5
6.7	282.5	217.5	7.9	35	465
6.8	255	245	8.0	26.5	473.5

33B. NaH_2PO_4–Na_2HPO_4, pH 5.7–7.8, $\Gamma/2 = 0.1$†
Solution A: NaH_2PO_4, 0.2 M (as in buffer No. 33A).
Solution B: Na_2HPO_4, 0.2 M (as in buffer No. 33A).

pH	Solution A (ml/liter)	Solution B (ml/liter)	pH	Solution A (ml/liter)	Solution B (ml/liter)
5.7	417	27	6.8	125	124
5.8	395	34.5	6.9	104	131.5
5.9	375	41.5	7.0	86	137.5
6.0	354	49	7.1	71	143
6.1	325	58	7.2	56	147.5
6.2	298	67	7.3	45	151
6.3	270	77	7.4	36	154
6.4	238	87.5	7.5	29	156.5
6.5	205	97.5	7.6	24	159
6.6	177	107	7.7	19	160.1
6.7	151	116	7.8	16	161.2

* From ref. 15, p. 143, Na_2HPO_4 is only slightly soluble at 0°, making a 0.2 M buffer unsuitable for cold room use.
† Adapted from ref. 29.

34. Phosphate–trisodium EDTA, pH 7.4, $\Gamma/2 = 0.15$*

Solution A: NaH_2PO_4, 0.2 M (as in buffer No. 33A).

Solution B: Na_2HPO_4, 0.2 M (as in buffer No. 33A).

Solution C: $Na_3H \cdot EDTA$, 0.15 M (EDTA disodium, 55.84 gm/liter, titrated with 1 N NaOH to pH 7.4).

Mix 50 ml of solution A, 233.5 ml of solution B, and 6.67 ml of solution C, and dilute to 1 liter.

35. Phosphate-buffered saline (PBS) (see also buffer No. 30, solution 2A)

Solution A: NaH_2PO_4, 0.2 M ($NaH_2PO_4 \cdot H_2O$, 27.6 gm/liter).

Solution B: Na_2HPO_4, 0.2 M ($Na_2HPO_4 \cdot 7H_2O$, 53.65 gm/liter, or $Na_2HPO_4 \cdot 12H_2O$, 71.63 gm/liter).

Saline, 0.15 M (NaCl, 8.5 gm/liter).

A. 0.01 M phosphate in saline, pH 7.0, $\Gamma/2 = 0.16$: 16.5 ml of solution A (0.45 gm), 33.5 ml of solution B (1.8 gm), 8.5 gm of NaCl, water to 1 liter. This is the usual PBS; it is derived from buffer 33; cf. ref. 33.

B. 0.02 M phosphate in saline, pH 7.0, $\Gamma/2 = 0.2$: 33 ml of solution A (0.9 gm), 67 ml of solution B (3.6 gm), 8.5 gm of NaCl, water to 1 liter (ref. 33a).

C. 0.04 M phosphate in saline, pH 7.2, $\Gamma/2 = 0.15$: 56 ml of solution A (1.54 gm), 144 ml of solution B (7.73 gm), 3.04 gm of NaCl, water to 1 liter (ref. 30).

D. 0.05 M phosphate in saline, pH 7.1, $\Gamma/2 = 0.21$: 70 ml of solution A (1.93 gm), 180 ml of solution B (9.66 gm), 5.7 gm of NaCl, water to 1 liter. This solution is strongly buffered; cf. ref. 34.

E. 0.067 M phosphate in saline, pH 7.1, $\Gamma/2 = 0.23$: 113 ml of solution A (3.12 gm), 220 ml of solution B (11.8 gm), 4.5 gm of NaCl, water to 1 liter. This solution is strongly buffered.

36. Phosphate (NaH_2PO_4–Na_2HPO_4)–EDTA–sodium azide (Allison and Humphrey), pH 7

NaH_2PO_4, 0.2 M (130 ml), as in buffer No. 33A; Na_2HPO_4, 0.2 M (204 ml), as in buffer No. 33A; EDTA (1.86 gm); sodium azide (0.65 gm). Bring to 1 liter with distilled water. Used as solvent for dissolving high-grade agar of gel-diffusion quality. The composition was developed (35) for especial clarity of agar in gel diffusion studies.

H. TRIETHANOLAMINE BUFFER

37A. Triethanolamine-buffered saline with Ca^{++} and Mg^{++}, pH 7.3–7.4†

Stock solution (1 liter): triethanolamine, (28.0 ml), HCl, 1 N, (180.0

---

* From ref. 30. $Na_3H \cdot EDTA$, 1×10^{-3} M, used as chromatographic buffer with fractions of complement in DEAE-cellulose.

† From ref. 27. Employed as diluent for optimal activity of guinea pig complement (30).

ml), NaCl, (75.0 gm), $MgCl_2 \cdot 6H_2O$ (M.W. 203.31), (1.0 gm), and $CaCl_2 \cdot 2H_2O$ (M.W. 147.02), 0.2 gm.

Working solution, isotonic, $\Gamma/2 = 0.15$. Dilute stock solution with 9 volumes of water, to contain 0.05% gelatin as stabilizer, and provide 5×10^{-4} M in Mg^{++} and 1.5×10^{-4} M in Ca^{++}. This buffer is closer to the midpoint of the pH range than buffer No. 6B.

37B. Triethanolamine·HCl–NaOH buffer, pH 7.6, $\Gamma/2 = 0.1$*

Triethanolamine·HCl, (11.9 gm/liter); NaOH, 1.0 N (26.0 ml/liter). Dilute 1:2 for immunoelectrophoresis in agar gel.

I. TRIS(HYDROXYMETHYL)AMINOMETHANE (TRIS) BUFFERS

Tris is a highly useful buffer, extending from pH 5.2 to 9.0 in the various formulas shown below (Nos. 38, 39). There is a pronounced shift in pH value with temperature, illustrated in part in ref. 2 (pp. 33, 40), and the proportions should be adjusted for the temperature (0°, 20°, 37°) at which work will be carried out. Tris-buffered solutions at isotonic concentration (39) can be injected into tissues.

Tris is available in several grades. The least expensive grade will be entirely adequate for some purposes, although insoluble materials are often present, requiring filtration through paper. The better product (TRIZMA base of Sigma Chemical Company, THAM of Fisher Scientific Company, and so on) is more closely defined. For special purposes, Tris is available with an extremely low content of metal ions; deionized water should be used for dissolving this preparation. In the writer's laboratory, it has been found that Sephadex columns of G-150 and G-200 last much longer when Tris buffers, even of high commercial quality, are passed through Millipore filters (6 liters will pass a 142-mm membrane within 10 minutes at 4 pounds air pressure).

Tris buffers are bacteriostatic, but in limited degree. Although growth may not be obvious for some weeks, the shelf-life with respect to bacterial growth is not long, and bacterial counts often prove to be high. According to use, it may be advisable to practice sterile filtration (Chap. 2, C,4, Vol. I). Column effluents should be tested occasionally by allowing one or two drops to fall onto slants of nutrient agar and incubating the slants for 2 days at room temperature.

Other zwitterion-type buffers have been suggested as alternates to the use of Tris (1). Tris should be avoided for studies of oxidative phosphorylation and for use as an additive in phosphate-buffered solutions.

38. Tris-HCl buffer, 0.05 M Tris (pH 7.2–9.0)†

Solution A: Tris, 0.2 M (24.23 gm/liter).

Solution B: HCl, 1.0 M.

* From ref. 18a.
† From ref. 15, after 29.

To 250 ml of solution A add n ml of solution B per liter, and bring to 1 liter.

pH	B (ml/liter)	pH	B (ml/liter)
7.2	44.2	8.2	21.9
7.4	41.4	8.4	16.5
7.6	38.4	8.6	12.2
7.8	32.5	8.8	8.1
8.0	26.8	9.0	5.0

39. Tris–maleate–NaOH, pH 5.2–8.6*

Solution A: Tris, 0.2 M (24.23 gm/liter); maleate, 0.2 M (maleic acid, 23.2 gm/liter, or maleic anhydride, 19.6 gm/liter).

Solution B: NaOH, 1.0 M.

pH	A (ml/liter)	B (ml/liter)	pH	A (ml/liter)	B (ml/liter)
5.2	250	7.0	7.0	250	48.0
5.4	250	10.8	7.2	250	51.0
5.6	250	15.5	7.4	250	54.0
5.8	250	20.5	7.6	250	58.0
6.0	250	26.0	7.8	250	63.5
6.2	250	31.5	8.0	250	69.0
6.4	250	37.0	8.2	250	75.0
6.6	250	42.5	8.4	250	81.0
6.8	250	45.0	8.6	250	86.5

40A. Tris–acetic acid, pH 8.15. $\Gamma/2 = 0.05$†

Tris, 0.1 M (12.11 gm/liter); glacial acetic acid, 0.05 M (2.89 ml/liter).

40B. Tris–citric acid, for discontinuous starch gel electrophoresis

	pH	Tris	Citric acid · $2H_2O$
(a)	8.2	0.076 M (9.2 gm)	0.005 M (1.05 gm)
(b)	8.0	0.016 M (1.94 gm)	0.0033 M (0.639 gm)
(c)	7.8	0.052 M (6.29 gm)	0.0076 M (1.6 gm)

The figures show grams per liter of three "gel buffers." (a) Use with tank buffer No. 18A (23a); (b) Use with tank buffer No. 17A (24); (c) Use with tank buffer No. 17B (28). Each gel buffer is usually completed by adding 10% of its corresponding tank buffer.

* From ref. 15, after 29.
† Recommended for immunoelectrophoresis in agar.

41. Tris–HCl, pH 8.0 at 25°, $\Gamma/2 = 0.05$.*

Tris, 0.086 M (10.43 gm/liter or 86.1 ml 1 M Tris buffer); hydrochloric acid, 0.05 M (50 ml 1.0 N HCl per liter).

42. Tris–HCl, pH 8.0 at 25°, $\Gamma/2 = 0.058$.†

Conductivity equivalent to 0.17% aqueous NaCl $\simeq 1:5$ of normal saline.

Tris, 0.1 M (12.11 gm/liter); hydrochloric acid 0.06 M (60.0 ml 1.0 N HCl per liter).

43. Tris–HCl–0.2 M NaCl, pH 8.0 at 25°.

Tris, 0.1 M (12.11 gm/liter), and NaCl, 0.2 M (11.69 gm/liter), are dissolved in two-thirds of buffer volume using deionized distilled water; add 1.0 N HCl to pH 8 (ca. 60 ml/liter), with use of glass electrode. Check pH as final volume is approached.

Nonswelling buffer recommended for use with Sephadex G-150 and G-200. It has been found advisable to pass the completed buffer through one layer of filter paper and one glass fiber prefilter in a Millipore apparatus prior to use to assist in maintaining long life of the column. Ammonium sulfate (0.2 M) can replace NaCl (p. 137).

44. Tris–boric acid–EDTA, pH 8.9

Conductivity 3.0 millimhos.

Tris, 0.5 M (60.57 gm/liter); boric acid, 0.075 M (4.638 gm/liter); EDTA, 0.021 M (7.82 gm/liter for disodium salt).

High resolution buffer for serum proteins (36). Tris–borate gives good separation in the β-globulins, and EDTA improves separation of α_2-globulins. For paper electrophoresis, as on S&S No. 2043B, *acetylated*, run 6.5 volts/cm for 16 hours; for Oxoid cellulose acetate, use buffer 1.3 times as concentrated and lower voltage to 4.5 volts/cm for 16 hours.

45. Tris–boric acid–EDTA, pH 8.5‡

A. Gel buffer, stock solution: Tris 0.9 M (109 gm), boric acid, 0.5 M (30.9 gm), and EDTA, 0.02 M (5.76 gm), are dissolved in water to 1 liter.

B. Gel buffer, working solution: Dilute A with 19 volumes of water, pH 8.5.

C. Electrophoresis (tank) buffer: Tris, 0.05 M (65.4 gm), boric acid, 0.03 M (18.55 gm), and EDTA, 0.012 M (3.46 gm), are dissolved in water to 1 liter.

---

* Ref. 2, p. 33. Used for gel filtration on Sephadex or buffer for antigen-antibody diffusion studies through agar gel.

† Used as buffer 41, also for agar gel diffusion of hapten-protein complexes of limited solubility at pH 7.0.

‡ O. Smithies, personal communication to M. D. Poulik (Chap. 6,C,3, Vol. I). This buffer avoids formation of a "brown line" across the starch gel as the electrode buffer moves along the gel. Another formulation (pH 8.4) with increased boric acid is given in Chap. 6,C,5,c,*ii*.

46. Tris–phosphoric acid, pH 8.6*

Tris, 0.04 M (4.84 gm/liter), plus H_3PO_4, 0.005 M (85% phosphoric acid, 0.34 ml/liter).

9. Indicators

The use of indicator dyes to estimate pH values has declined with introduction of the glass electrode. Yet these dyes serve a useful function in the laboratory, permitting quick appraisal of shifts in pH of unbuffered solutions by testing split drops† of solutions, with avoidance of pH over-shoot and a privilege of immediate correction. The indicators also monitor well the approach to the neutral point, as when small volumes of con-centrated gamma globulin solution are being corrected to pH 7.0–7.2 after dialysis. It is well to correct the reaction by adding split drops of alkali on a 3.5 mm stirring rod with avoidance of high local concentration and to test by touching a rod to litmus paper, before testing a single or half-drop on a spot plate (adding 3 drops of saline and 1 drop of 0.02% phenol red). Finally, the pH is checked by immersing a fine-tipped combi-nation glass electrode in the solution.

Owing to salt errors and protein errors of indicator dyes, ultimate readings must rest on intelligent use of a standardized glass electrode. Yet too often the pH meter is not warmed or calibrated when a critical decision must be reached at once.

For coarse control and checking, three indicator papers are useful, Congo red paper (pH 3.0–4.5, blue to red), neutral litmus paper, and Brilliant Yellow paper (pH 7.0–9.0). The Brilliant Yellow paper is made by immersing sheets of filter paper in 0.15% aqueous solution and allowing to dry; it is an excellent aid in avoiding alkaline overshoot. One must practice using these papers while using the glass electrode and know the color changes intimately.

Phenol red, 0.02% aqueous (pH 6.8–8.2, yellow to red) is the single most useful indicator solution to have at hand, often used with a procelain spot plate. Other helpful indicator solutions could include chlorophenol red, 0.04% aqueous (pH 5.2–6.8, yellow to red), bromthymol blue, 0.04% aqueous (pH 6.2–7.6, yellow to blue), cresol red, 0.02% aqueous (pH 7.2–8.8, yellow to red), and phenolphthalein, 1% in alcohol (pH 8.0–10.0, colorless to red). The sulphonphthalein dyes mentioned above are best purchased as the water-soluble sodium salts. Alcohol-soluble phenol-

---

* From refs. 33 and 37. The "limit buffer" used in conjunction with this buffer for discharge from charged resins is 0.35 M Tris–H_3PO_4 (33).

† To secure split drops, let a drop of reagent fall on the terminal 15 mm of a dry 3.5-mm glass rod, shake to remove excess, plunge into the solution and stir rapidly.

TABLE IV
Isotonic Solutions[a]

Compound	Molecular weight	Solution in water (%)
Ammonium chloride	53.50	0.8
Ammonium sulfate	132.15	1.63
Calcium chloride		
$CaCl_2$	110.99	1.3
$CaCl_2 \cdot 2H_2O$	147.03	1.7
$CaCl_2 \cdot 6H_2O$	219.09	2.5
Calcium lactate $\cdot$ $5H_2O$	308.30	4.5
Citric acid, anhydrous	192.12	5.52
monohydrated	120.14	
Ethanol	46.07	1.29
Ethylene glycol	62.07	1.73
Glycerin	92.09	2.6
Lactic acid	90.08	2.3
Magnesium chloride, anhydrous	95.23	2.02
Magnesium sulfate, anhydrous	120.39	6.3
Phenol	94.11	2.8
Phosphates		
KH_2PO_4	136.09	2.18
K_2HPO_4	174.18	2.8
NaH_2PO_4	120.01	2.1
$NaH_2PO_4 \cdot H_2O$	138.01	2.45
Na_2HPO_4, exsiccated	141.98	1.75
$Na_2HPO_4 \cdot 7H_2O$	268.09	3.32
$Na_2HPO_4 \cdot 12H_2O$	358.17	4.45
Potassium chloride	74.55	1.19
Potassium iodide	166.02	2.59
Potassium oxalate, monohydrate	184.23	2.13
Propylene glycol	76.09	2.0
Sodium acetate, anhydrous	82.04	1.18
Sodium bicarbonate	84.0	1.39
Sodium carbonate, anhydrous	106.00	1.32
Sodium carbonate $\cdot$ $2H_2O$	124.02	1.56
Sodium chloride	58.46	0.9
Sodium citrate $\cdot$ $2H_2O$	294.12	3.02
Sodium lactate	112.07	1.72
Sodium propionate	96.07	1.47
Sodium sulfate $\cdot$ $10H_2O$	322.22	3.95
Sodium sulfate	142.06	1.61
Sugars		
Fructose	180.16	5.05
Galactose, anhydrous	180.16	4.92
Glucose, anhydrous (dextrose)	180.16	5.05
Glucose, monohydrate (the usual "dextrose")	198.2	5.51
Lactose	360.31	9.75
Sucrose	342.30	9.25
Urea	60.06	1.6

[a] These substances and many drugs are listed in ref. 38.

phthalein or thymolphthalein, 1% in ethanol (pH 9.3–10.5, colorless to blue), can be dropped onto filter paper and the solution for test applied by streaking a wetted glass rod across the area.

10. Isotonic Solutions

A listing of concentrations isoösmotic with normal saline solution reflects the extent of ionic dissociation and means that *aqueous* solutions at the concentrations shown can be mixed with normal saline or balanced salt solutions without altering the isoösmotic relations; but these simple mixtures can be injected into tissues in only a few instances. Table IV allows the calculation, for example, that addition of 0.4% phenol (buffer No. 30) is equivalent to 143 ml of aqueous 2.8% phenol (4 gm) per liter, and that 7.7 gm of NaCl (857 ml, 0.9%) will be required; or that addition of 0.25% phenol would require 8.0 gm of NaCl; or that a mixture of 50% glycerine and 50% saline should be diluted with 19 volumes of *distilled water* prior to injection into animals.

The concentrations listed are those that depress the freezing point of water to $-0.52°C$ (normal saline solution). In recent work, serum has been used as standard (0.305 ± 0.005 osmolar), and individual buffers and reagents have been measured by osmometer (39).

References

1. N. E. Good, G. D. Winget, W. Winter, T. N. Connolly, S. Izawa, and R. M. M. Singh, *Biochemistry* **5**, 467 (1966).
2. C. Long (ed.), "Biochemists' Handbook." Van Nostrand, New York, 1961.
3. H. T. S. Britton, "Hydrogen Ions," 3rd ed., Van Nostrand, New York, 1956.
4. R. G. Bates, "Determination of pH, Theory and Practice." Wiley, New York, 1964.
5. W. M. Clark, "The Determination of Hydrogen Ions." Williams & Wilkins, Baltimore, 1928.
6. B. S. Magdoff, *in* "A Laboratory Manual of Analytical Methods of Protein Chemistry," (P. Alexander and R. J. Block, eds.), Vol. 2, p. 199. Pergamon, New York, 1960.
7. N. E. Good, *Arch. Biochem. Biophys.* **96**, 653 (1962).
8. (a) H. Michl, *Monatsh. Chem.* **82**, 489 (1951); (b) E. Margoliash and E. L. Smith, *J. Biol. Chem.* **237**, 2151 (1962); (c) R. E. Caulfield and C. B. Anfinsen, *ibid.* **238**, 2684 (1963).
9. A. Tsugita, *et al., Proc. Natl. Acad. Sci. U. S.* **46**, 1463 (1960).
10. R. J. Hill and W. Konigsberg, *J. Biol. Chem.* **237**, 3151 (1962).
10a. A. C. Evans, *J. Infect. Diseases* **30**, 95 (1922).
11. A. Albert and E. P. Serjeant, "Ionization Constants of Acids and Bases." Wiley, New York, 1962.
11a. A. L. Remizov, *Biochemistry (U.S.S.R.)* **25**, 242 (1960).
12. R. W. McGilvery, *Anal. Biochem.* **1**, 141 (1960).

13. A. E. Martell and M. Calvin, "Chemistry of the Metal Chelate Compounds." Prentice-Hall, New York, 1952.
14. W. L. German and A. I. Vogel, *J. Chem. Soc.* **2**, 912 (1935).
15. G. Gomori, *in* "Methods in Enzymology" (S. P. Colowick and N. O. Kaplan, eds.), Vol. I, pp. 138–146. Academic Press, New York, 1955.
16. S. P. Colowick and N. O. Kaplan, (eds.), "Methods in Enzymology." Academic Press, New York, 1955.
17. K. Diem (ed.), "Documenta Geigy, Scientific Tables," 6th ed. Geigy Pharmaceuticals, Ardsley, New York, 1962.
18. G. S. Walpole, *Biochem. J.* **105**, 2501, 2521 (1914).
18a. R. J. Wieme, "Agar Gel Electrophoresis." Elsevier, New York, 1965.
19. L. Michaelis, *Biochem. Z.* **234**, 139 (1931).
20. L. Michaelis, *J. Biol. Chem.* **87**, 33 (1930).
21. P. Grabar and P. Burtin, "Immunoelectrophoretic Analysis." Elsevier, New York, 1964.
22. C. A. Williams, personal communication.
22a. M. M. Mayer, *in* "Kabat and Mayer's Experimental Immunochemistry," 2nd ed. p. 149, Thomas, Springfield, Illinois, 1961.
23. O. Smithies, *Biochem. J.* **61**, 629 (1955).
23a. M. D. Poulik, *Nature* **180**, 1477 (1957).
23b. E. Chargaff and J. N. Davidson (eds.), "The Nucleic Acids," Vol. 1, p. 273. Academic Press, New York, 1955.
24. R. J. Barrett, E. B. Astwood, and H. Friesen, *J. Biol. Chem.* **237**, 432 (1962).
25. G. E. Delory and E. J. King, *Biochem. J.* **39**, 245 (1945).
26. W. L. German and A. I. Vogel, *Analyst* **62**, 271 (1937).
27. J. F. Kent, A. G. Otero and E. E. Harrigan, *Am. J. Clin. Pathol.* **27**, 539 (1957).
28. A. Bearn, personal communication.
29. G. Gomori, *Proc. Soc. Exptl. Biol. Med.* **68**, 354 (1948).
29a. American Thoracic Society–Antigen Study Group, "Methodology Manual for Investigation of Mycobacterial and Fungal Antigens." American Thoracic Society, New York, New York, 1963. 1 v. (loose leaf); supplement, 1965.
30. I. H. Lepow, G. B. Naff, E. W. Todd, J. Pensky, and C. F. Hinz, *J. Exptl. Med.* **117**, 983 (1963).
31. L. Levine, M. M. Mayer, and H. J. Rapp, *J. Immunol.* **73**, 435 (1954).
31a. A. F. Coca and E. L. Milford, *J. Immunol.* **10**, 555 (1925).
32. W. B. Sherman and W. R. Kessler, "Allergy in Pediatric Practice," p. 286. Mosby, St. Louis, 1957.
33. E. A. Peterson, M. M. Wyckoff, and H. A. Sober, *Arch. Biochem.* **93**, 428 (1961).
33a. A. Tiselius and E. A. Kabat, *J. Exp. Med.* **69**, 119 (1939).
34. S. D. Chaperas and H. Baer, *Am. Rev. Respir. Dis.* **89**, 41 (1964).
35. A. C. Allison and J. H. Humphrey, *Immunology* **3**, 95 (1960).
36. T. Aronsson and A. Grönwall, *Scand. J. Clin. Lab. Invest.* **9**, 338 (1957).
37. A. J. L. Strauss, P. G. Kemp, Jr., W. E. Vannier, and H. C. Goodman, *J. Immunol.* **93**, 24 (1964).
38. P. G. Stecker (ed.), "The Merck Index of Chemicals and Drugs," 7th ed., p. 1545. Merck and Company, Rahway, New Jersey, 1960.
39. Levine, B. B., M. J. Fellner, and V. Levytska, *J. Immunol.* **96**, 707 (1966).

APPENDIX III

Powder Block Electrophoresis*

Technical details are provided to supplement the more general treatment of Chap. 6,D,1. Zone electrophoresis is carried out on supporting media in order to separate complex mixtures of proteins by virtue of different rates of migration in an electrical field. The purpose of the supporting media is essentially to minimize convection in the region of the solute–solvent zone (which may appear as a result of hydrostatic pressure differences) and to slow down boundary spreading by diffusion.

Preparation of mold: Great variation in sizes of blocks is possible. The actual molds in which the supporting material is to be poured may be constructed out of Plexiglass or $\frac{1}{4}$-inch plate glass which can be varied in width by placing Lucite or wooden bars on the plate. Several plates may prove useful according to the objective: for experimental runs, a block 10 cm wide $\times$ 30 cm long can be adequate, while for preparative runs 20 $\times$ 40 cm or 30–60 cm $\times$ 50 cm plates will be more suitable.

Powder blocks of too great depth result in heating and poorer resolution of the protein mixture. Blocks of 7–9 mm depth are suitable. The depth is readily established when Lucite bars, either resting on the plate or placed along the lateral edges, are machined to establish the wanted depth.

Besides the plate and side rails, six or eight lead or enamelled iron weights about 12 mm high $\times$ 4 cm wide $\times$ 15–20 cm long ($\frac{1}{2}$ inch $\times$ $2\frac{5}{8}$ inches $\times$ 6–8 inches) will be needed unless another system is available to provide side and end pressure in forming the mold.

The ends of the mold consist of heavy filter paper or the less expensive photographic quality blotting paper (Eastman Kodak 19 $\times$ 24 inch sheets); about 8 sheets $2\frac{1}{2}$ inches high, slightly longer than the block width, are needed at each end, butted against the ends by weights.

The base of the completed mold should be covered with a layer of polyethylene sheeting (0.0015 inch thick), precisely as long as the block and sufficiently wide to fold around and overlap on the top of the prepared block: a sturdy paper pattern is recommended for each size of block as a

* Appendix III was contributed by C. Kirk Osterland.

guide to cutting the sheeting. The surface of the plate is moistened slightly with distilled water and the sheeting is smoothed and pressed to provide sharp corners for the mold and the casting of a block which is rectangular in cross section.

Buffers. For most proteins, barbital buffer at pH 8.6 gives the least error in departure from ideality (Chap. 6,B,2). An ionic strength of 0.05 is usually suitable, and it keeps euglobulins in solution. A strength of 0.1 is sometimes appropriate, as when it is desired to keep α_1-globulin from running under the albumin peak. Barbital buffers No. 7 or No. 9 (Appendix II), diluted 1:2, provide an ionic strength of 0.05 at pH 8.6. With a higher ionicity, current flow is greater, which may result in more distorting convection currents and local heating within the block. One must not, however, lower the ionic strength to the point of producing euglobulin precipitation of the proteins being separated such as can occur with γM-globulin electrophoresis. Some other individual adjustment of temperature and ionic conditions may be necessary depending on the protein under study.

The outer vessels (Fig. 1), however, can contain pH 7.5 phosphate buffer of ionic strength = 0.2 (buffer No. 33B of Appendix II prepared at double strength). Such buffer is not only cheaper but it can accommodate more electrolysis during the run without pH change in block or inner electrode vessels.

Preparation of slurry. Granular potato starch and Pevikon C-870 (imported by Mercer Chemical Company, 11 Mercer Street, New York, New York) are suitable support media which cause little adsorption of

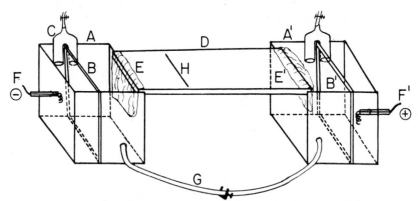

Fig. 1. Starch block electrophoresis apparatus. *A*, *A'*, Buffer chambers, containing 1–2 liters each. *B*, *B'*, Dividers between inner and outer buffer chambers. *C*, U-tube connecting inner and outer chambers (to be filled with buffer or agar plus buffer). *D*, Electrophoresis powder block plate support. *E*, *E'*, Wicks. *F*, *F'*, Platinum electrodes. *G*, Connective tubing between anode and cathode for buffer level. *H*, Point of application (origin) of sample. N.B. Polyethylene sheeting is not shown.

protein and allow for relatively easy recovery of protein from the block material. Potato starch takes up buffer and swells, whereas Pevikon takes up no buffer: practical amounts for preparing 250 cm³ of block are: starch, 200 gm, and Pevikon, 350 gm.

Washing of either material is carried out on a large Buchner funnel (2000 ml) with a coarse sintered glass disc, using first, large volumes of distilled water and later the buffer to be used in the electrophoresis. This washing procedure is necessary in order to wash out fine material and, with starch, some Folin-positive material that contaminates many preparations. Equilibration with starting buffer is carried out on the same sintered glass funnel. With Pevikon, the object of washing is to reduce the amount of a fine dustlike material that passes sintered filters; it is retained, however, by Millipore "SM" membranes of 5-μ pore size.

The final compacted cake is stirred into a slurry by adding small successive increments of electrophoresis buffer and stirring thoroughly with each addition. A wide-bladed (2½-inch) paddle is recommended when large blocks are to be poured. The proper consistency is attained suddenly with one small increment of buffer: it will be obvious that pouring can be accomplished, yet there is no excess of buffer.

Forming the block. The slurry is poured into the polyethylene-lined mold of plate and rails, closed at the ends with absorptive paper. Weights hold the rails and paper ends firmly in place. The extra liquid is drawn evenly through the Pevikon into the blotting pieces. As the strips become wetted, they may be inverted to provide fresh surface or replaced as needed. Pevikon blocks may show rough surfaces, but these can be smoothed over or even repaired by gentle pushing with a suitable spatula: one spatula should be long enough to rest on the Lucite side strips and establish an even depth of block. The block is ready when a small trial cut on the line selected for the origin stands clean and does not flow together. The blotting strips should then be removed and the block covered and placed in the cold room.

Starch does not attain the firmness of Pevikon, and permissible manipulation is more limited. Bubbles formed during the pouring process are removed by sharp instruments or by blotting the upper surface of the block with dry lint-free cloths. Much more time is required than for Pevikon in drawing the excess buffer into the blotting strips. A block is ready for application of the sample when it is dry enough to hold its shape well when a trough is cut in the block. When a drop of buffer is placed on such a block it almost immediately disappears into the substance of the supporting material.

Loading the block. The effective block length is the distance *between* the applied wicks. The position of the *origin* is established with regard to the nature of the material to be separated, the pH of the buffer, and the type of block. In the case of proteins run at pH 8.6, the only concern on the cathodal ($-$) end of the block is the extent of electroendosmosis, the result of cathodal buffer flow. For Pevikon, this cathodal movement of essentially uncharged material may be of the order of 6–8 cm on a large plate in 20 hours, whereas for starch about 12 cm should be allowed. In addition to protein analysis of block segments following the run, electro-endosmosis can be gauged by dissolving dextrose into the material to be fractionated, about 1.5 mg/ml, or by adding 0.05 ml of 3% dextrose in buffer per milliliter and analyzing segment eluates for dextrose by the anthrone test (Chap. 12,B,3,a).

Bromophenol blue can be added to the material to be applied to the block (0.05 ml of aqueous 0.5% dye per milliliter of serum) to delineate the movement of albumin and evenness of the advancing front, or a sample of dye–albumin can be placed in a separated small trench on the block. (Excess dye migrates ahead of albumin toward the anode.) The position of hemoglobin can be seen if it is present in the sample. Free hemoglobin migrates as a beta globulin, however. If $FeCl_3$ solution (0.1 ml of 0.6 mg/ml) is added to 10 ml of serum, the brownish transferrin band can also be observed in the beta region.

The material to be separated should be dialyzed overnight against the block buffer, replenished at least once. Protein concentrations of 5% can be used. The volume applied can be of the order of 0.3–0.4 ml per centimeter of slit trough.

To determine the position of the trough, a straightedge is laid across wooden strips (about 20 mm higher than the cast powder block and held firmly against the sides of the plate) to which rulers have been affixed as a guide for making the cut(s) by a rigid but narrow spatula. Alter-natively, a clear plastic (Keuffel and Esser, 30–60–90° triangles of Luxyl-ite) with a permanently attached strip of Lucite on the base of the tri-angle offer advantages over a movable straightedge. The trough is started 2.5 cm from the edge of the block. The length of one trough should be limited to 5–10 cm, hence for large blocks, several in-line troughs should be cut. The application troughs are kept as narrow as possible, and the block material is then pushed back with a spatula to widen the trough in a V-shape.

Some inequality of electrical contact and current can exist along the block width and cause the advancing protein front to become distorted. On subsequent elution of blocks containing long troughs, therefore, separated but adjacent protein peaks may be eluted to produce a mixture. For large blocks it is recommended to use several discontinuous troughs and to elute the corresponding segments separately. A few drops of buffer are allowed to fall on the block near each slit to avoid undue spreading of the introduced material into the nearly dry block. After loading the slit(s), as from a No. 23 needle attached to a hypodermic syringe; and allowing recession into the block, the sides of the trough are gently pushed together and smoothed over with a spatula.

Apparatus. Figure 1 shows one type of electrophoresis apparatus, as set up in a cold room close to a d.c. high voltage power supply. The buffer chambers must be as wide as the widest plate that will be used, since the buffer wicking must lay across the full width of the end of the block. The plate rests directly on the edge of the double tanks shown, and provision must be made for leveling these plate supports *in both directions.* Leveling can be done best by setting a spare plate in place. For smaller plates (e.g., up to 9 inches in width), the supporting plate can rest on wooden blocks, the inner electrode vessels can be plastic trays ($12\frac{1}{2} \times 3\frac{3}{4} \times 2\frac{1}{2}$ inches high), and the outer electrode vessels can be 1-quart square polyethylene refrigerator dishes ($3\frac{1}{4} \times 3\frac{1}{4} \times 5\frac{1}{2}$ inches high). In place of the desirable platinum electrodes, carbon electrodes ($6\frac{1}{2} \times 1 \times \frac{1}{2}$ inch) can be substituted.

The anode and cathode buffer chambers are connected by tubing (narrowed by pinchcock to reduce the alternate electric pathway) in order to equalize the buffer levels, since electroosmosis can cause sufficient fluid flow to produce a hydrostatic pressure head between the buffer chambers at anodal and cathodal ends.

When the outer chambers are to contain 0.2 ionic strength phosphate buffer, the outer chambers should be filled slightly less than the inner electrode chambers, which will contain barbital buffer. The wide-bore U-tubes (35–40 mm I.D.) are filled completely with barbital buffer by removing air and clamping off short lengths of gum rubber tubing attached to the evacuation port of the U-tube. By holding a small watch glass against the free ends of each filled U-tube, the U-tube is raised from the barbital buffer and used to join the two electrode compartments; only slight entry of air will occur; it is removed in turn. The final leveling will occur by automatic siphoning of some barbital buffer *into* the phosphate buffer owing to the initially unequal levels. The barbital buffer compartment should not contain any of the phosphate during the run.

Wicking. The wicks can be made of closely woven toweling material or several layers of filter or blotting paper laying across the *full width* of the block. These should be smoothed gently on to the outer ends of the block covering about 1 inch, with the other end hanging down into the buffer, and covers of polyethylene should be placed over the wicks to avoid evaporation. Since the wicks constitute the point of high electrical resistance in the system, the number of layers of wicking is important. Three layers of woven cotton toweling or the equivalent are appropriate. The interstitial water in the block constitutes the available space for the migrating proteins, and for best separation this water content is kept constant. The height of the block surface above the fluid level of the buffer chambers is an important factor. At about 7.5–10 cm for a starch block the water content stays at about 34%, a suitable content. At smaller height differences the block may take up more water and "melt." Increasing water content reduces the quality of protein separation. Some workers have found it useful to place a weighted glass plate cover on the block during the electrophoresis, but the cooling effect of the ambient air is reduced.

Control of evaporation: This must be attended to carefully. The polyethylene sheeting should be carried across the top of the block (avoiding the trapping of air bubbles) and overlapped, thereby securing also the polyethylene wick covers. Evaporation can cause local increases in salt (ionic) concentration and result in heating and further evaporation.

Electrical field. The power supply should not be plugged into source until the resistance system of block, wicks, and electrode vessels is complete and connections are made between the tank electrodes and the power supply. The block is allowed to cool to the temperature of the cold room before current is applied to it.

The current on the block should be 3.5 to 5.0 V/cm for a 20-hour run. Since the resistance offered by the wicks is variable, direct measurement is recommended. Platinum pins set 15 cm apart in a suspended Lucite bar can be introduced through small fissures in the polyethylene sheeting before the current is turned on, and direct reading of the d.c. current made by a d.c. voltmeter after 30–60 minutes, when the system has stabilized. During the run, appropriate high voltage warnings and/or physical barriers should be placed.

Serum albumin, having an electrophoretic mobility of about 5.8×10^{-5} cm^2 V^{-1} sec^{-1}, allows estimation of needed running time and voltage. For example, at 3.5 V/cm, albumin will move 17 cm in 23 hours.

After the run is concluded, samples should be withdrawn from each buffer compartment of Fig. 1 and the pH checked. The pH of the inner electrode compartments, A and A′, should be alike and essentially the same as the starting barbital buffer. The cathodal, left-hand, compartment will be quite alkaline and the anodal compartment fairly acidic. Deviations between pH values of A and A′ call the entire run into question. Insufficient ionic strength of barbital buffer or contamination from the outer phosphate chambers can be the cause.

Recovery of fractions is made as in Chap. 6,D,1,c,v. Fractions can be dialyzed and concentrated in a device modified from Fig. 5 of Chap. 8,C,4, in which a solid one-hole stopper is used and the Visking tubing of size 8DC is about 7 inches long. The tubing is attached to a glass tubing of 7 mm O.D. by slipping a 3-cm piece of Tygon tubing ($\frac{1}{4}$ inch I.D. $\times$ $\frac{3}{8}$ inch O.D. $\times$ $\frac{1}{16}$ inch wall) over the cellophane–glass jointure.

Author Index

Numbers in parentheses are reference numbers and indicate that an author's work is referred to although his name is not mentioned in the text.

Subject Index

Page numbers in italic type refer to figures, tables, or reaction schemes. Numbers in boldface type designate buffer formulations found in Appendix II.

A

A, mass number of isotopes, 185, *240*
Abderhalden drying pistol, 255
Absorbancy values
  azo compounds, 352, 353, 360
  benzene, 361
  dinitrophenyl compounds, 354–357, 359
  enzymes, *344*
  fluorescein, 360
  iodotyrosines, 361
  naphthalene derivatives, 360
  nitrophenyl compounds, 354
  nucleotides, 334
  penicillins, 358
  proteins
    native immunoglobulins, and fragments, purified antibodies, *344–350*
    purines, 320, 357, 358
    pyrimidines, 320, 357, 358
    rhodamine, 361
    toluene, 361
    trinitrophenyl compounds, 358, 359
Absorption coefficient of isotopes, *240*
Absorption spectra, *see also* Spectroscopy, Ultraviolet absorbancy
  absorbance, definition, 165
  absorption of light by organic molecules, 163, 165, 171
  aromatic amino acids in proteins, 167ff., 171
  bathochromic shift, 164, 172
  errors, 166
  extinction coefficient (E), 167, 171
  hyperchromic effect, 164, 334
  hypsochromic shift, 164, 172
N-Acetyl-D-allosamine (acetylhexosamine), 299
N-Acetylgalactosamine, *see also* Vol. I
  assays, 298, 299

relative color values, 299, 300
  of methyl derivatives, 299
N-Acetyl-D-glucosamine, *see also* Vol. I
  assays, 298, 299, 300
  color equivalents of methyl derivatives, 299
  relative reducing value, 285
N-Acetylhexosamines, 295ff., 298, *see also* Acetyl allosamine, Acetyl galactosamine, Acetyl glucosamine
  color value relative to hexosamine, 300
  identification, 295
  potassium borate assay, 299, 300
    chromogen absorbancy, 300
  sodium carbonate assay, 298, 299
    chromogen absorbancy, 299
Aconitic acid, 372
Acrylamide gel electrophoresis, 40, 42
  gels
    inertness, 48; large-pore, 39, 42, 43; small-pore, 39, 42
    molecular sieving, 48
    monomer mixture reactive with amino, OH⁻, and SH⁻ groups, 48
    properties, 47, 48, 53, 54
    variable gel density, 48
Acrylamide polymer chromatography, *see* Chromatography, polyacrylamide spheres
Adenine, absorbancy, 320, 357
Adenosine nucleotides, separation by zone electrophoresis, 75, *76*, 338
Adenosine-3-monophosphate, 292
  cysteine-H_2SO_4 test, 292
Adenosine-5-monophosphate (AMP), 76, 292
  absorbancy, 358
  cysteine-H_2SO_4 test, 292
Adenylic acid (yeast), cysteine-H_2SO_4 test, 292
ADP (adenosine diphosphate), 76

426

amino acid incorporation
 starvation enhancement of, 190, *see also* Vol. I
 disposal, radioactive corpses, 199
Anion exchangers, *see* Chromatography
Anthrone reaction for hexoses, 58, 288
 errors
  cotton fibers, lipids, sugar-tryptophane complex, 289
Antibodies, antigen-specific, *see also* Vol. I
 anti-levan, 290; anti-nuclear factors (Lupus patients), 317, 318; anti-ovalbumin (turbidimetry curve), 180
Antibodies, general, *see also* Antibodies, antigen-specific; Antibodies, purification of; Antitoxin; Vol. I
 bivalency, 14
 conjugation with ferritin, with fluorescein, 62
 denaturation: alkali: guanidine, 170; spectral shifts, 168; tryptophane degradation, 168, 170
 detection methods: turbidimetry (reaction with antigen), 174ff.
 immunoglobulins, 19S and 17S separated (ultracentrifugation), 100
Antibodies, purification, *see also* Antibodies, general; Vol. I
 absorbancy: differences among purified antibodies, 171; principles, 167ff., 170, 171
 extinction values: horse γG, γM, 351; human IgG, IgM, 351; mouse, 351; rabbit, 348, 351; of allotypic rabbits, 350
 purity criterion by absorption, 171
Antifoam agents, *see also* Vol. I
 octyl alcohol, 262
Antigen-antibody reactions, *see also* Vols. I, III
 equilibrium constants, 14
 lattice theory, 14
 methods
  turbidimetry, 174ff., *see also* Vol. III
 nitrogen values
  biuret, 272; Folin-Ciocalteu, 274, *see also* Vol. III; Kjeldahl, 261; Nessler, 266ff.; ninhydrin-hydrindantin, 275ff.

precipitates
 quantitative transfer, 254, *see also* Vol. III; radioactivity counted, 211
Anti-hapten sera, *see also* Vol. I
 antibody binding constant, 172
  spectral shifts, 172
 hapten associations
  equilibrium dialysis, 123; fluorescence quenching, 171, *see also* Vol. III; free electrophoresis, 16, 17
 ligand binding by spectroscopy of immune precipitates, 167
Anti-polyinosine serum, *322*
Antitoxin (diphtheria) fractionation by electrophoresis-convection, 80
AP (ammonium persulfate), 55
Apohemoglobin, absorbancy, *345*
Apomyoglobin, absorbancy, *345*
Apurinic acid preparation, 327
Apyrimidinic acid preparation, 327
Arabinose (pentose)
 cysteine-H_2SO_4 test, 292
 α-naphthol reaction, 285
 tryptophane test, 287
Archibald method (ultracentrifugation), 112, 117
Arlacel 83 (Sorbitan sesquioleate), 151, *152*
Arsanilate conjugates, 352, *see* Vol. I
Atomic Energy Commission (AEC), regulatory measures for radioisotopes, 196, 199
Atomic number (Z), 245, *247*
Atoms, *241*
ATP (adenosine triphosphate), 76
Attenuation of radiation, *240*
Autoradiography, 228ff., *see also* Radiolabeling for autoradiography
 applicable isotopes, *206*, 207
 barrier layers protecting film, 229, 231, 232
 control tissues, 230, 231
 darkroom planning, 232
 developing, 237
 exposure
  duration, 236, 237: fast pilot film, 237; humidity needed, 235
 fixatives, 230ff.

grain counting, 231, 235, 237, 239
histological preparations, 230
 solvent effects, 230, 231
liquid emulsion technique, 235
localization of emissions, 228, 239
photography
 emulsions: selection, 232, *233*, 237;
  shielding, 235
 records, 239
polyacrylamide gel slabs, 56
radioimmunoelectrophoresis, 228, *see
 also* Vol. III
sandwich technique and registration,
 232, 237
section thickness, 231
slides
 preparation, 231; storage and shielding, 232, 234, 235
 staining (contrast), 238
stripping film technique, 234, 237
p-Azobenzenearsonic acid-*N*-acetylhisti-
 dine, absorbancy, 352
p-Azobenzenearsonic acid diazo-ε-amino-
 caproic acid, absorbancy, 352
p-Azobenzenearsonic acid-*N*-chloro-
 acetyltyrosine, absorbancy, 352
p-Azobenzenecarboxylic acid-L-histidine,
 absorbancy, 352
p-Azobenzenecarboxylic acid-L-tyrosine,
 absorbancy, 352
p-Azobenzenesulfonic acid-*N*-acetylhisti-
 dine, absorbancy, 352
p-Azobenzenesulfonic acid-*N*-chloro-
 acetyltyrosine, absorbancy, 352
p-Azobenzoic acid-*N*-acetylhistidine, absorbancy, 352
p-Azobenzoic acid-*N*-chloroacetyltyro-
 sine, absorbancy, 352

B

Bacitracin, 123, *128*
Bacteria, *see also* Vol. I
 DNA
  extraction, 319: *E. coli, Proteus vulgaris*, 321, *322, 323*; immunogenicity: Brucella, *Salmonella typhimurium*, 317
 polysaccharide (pneumococcal), labeling by C^{14}-glucose, 184

protein synthesis (*E. coli*), 333
RNA
 E. coli, 337; hydrolysis, 335; sRNA
  species, 340; s-values, 337
sialic acid content, 303
somatic O antigen, *see* Lipopolysaccharides
Bacterial species, *see also* Bacteria; Vol. I
 Brucella, 317
 Diplococcus pneumoniae, 184, 317
 Escherichia coli, 321, *322, 323*, 333
 pneumococci, 184, 317
  immunogenicity of DNA, 317
 Proteus vulgaris, 321, *322, 323*
 Salmonella typhimurium, 317
Bacteriophage, *see also* Viruses, types of;
 Vol. I
 extraction of DNA, 319
 f$_2$ coliphage, mRNA of, 341
 λ coliphage, ultracentrifugation, *86*
 T$_4$ coliphage, DNA renaturation, 323,
  324, 325, *326*
 transducing phage, ultracentrifugation,
  86
Bacteriostatic agents (buffer additives),
 72
Barbital (5,5-diethylbarbituric acid), 372
 buffers, 61, 63, *372*, 387ff.
 legal requirements, 387
 proteins scanned, 387
Barbital sodium, for buffers, *372*
Barbitone, *see* Barbital
BBOT phosphor (2,5-bis-[2(5-*tert*-butyl-
  benzoxazolyl)]-thiophene)
 absorbancy, fluorescence, 212
 single solute in scintillation counting,
  205, 212
Beer's law (absorbance), 165
Bence-Jones proteins, *see also* Vol. I
 kappa, lambda chains, absorbancy, *345*
Bentonite, *see also* Vol. I
 adjuvant function, *see* Vol. I
 adsorption of viral antigens, *see* Vol. I
 cation exchange role, *see* Vol. I
 ribonuclease inhibitor, 330
 role in flocculation tests, *see* Vol. III
Benzene, absorbancy, 361
Benzylpenicillenic acid, absorbancy, 358
Beta particles, 241, *see also* Radiation
BGG, *see* Bovine gamma globulin

P

P³², *see* Radioisotopes

Palitzsch's borate buffer, 391(**14**)

Panose, relative reducing value, 285

Papain, 37, 38
 absorbancy, *344*

Paper electrophoresis, *see* Electrophoresis

Parlodion (collodion, celloidin) (nitrated
 celluloses), as barrier layer in autoradiography, 232

Partition systems for purification
 (Sephadex), 340

PBS, *see* Phosphate buffered saline

PC (proportional counter), 201, 206, 207
 windowless, low-energy β-emitters, 207

PCA (passive cutaneous anaphylaxis),
 see Vol. III (methods)

PCA (perchloric acid), 250, 275, 334, 335
 precipitation as K⁺ salt, 251, 335, 338

P-Cellulose (phosphoryl-), 155

PCyR (pentose-cysteine reaction), test
 for pentoses, 292

Penicillins, absorbancy, 358, *see also*
 Vol. I

Pentoses, 285–288, 290ff.
 cysteine-H_2SO_4 (PCyR) test, 291, 292
 indole reaction, 287
 α-naphthol reaction, 285
 orcinol-$FeCl_3$-HCl (Bial) test, 290ff.
 orcinol test, 286
  fucose correction, 286
 phenol-H_2SO_4 reaction, 288
 tryptophane reaction, 287

Pepsin, 347
 absorbancy, *344*

Pepsinogen, absorbancy, *344*

Peptide mapping, 19

Peptides, *see also* Vol. I
 fractionation on polyacrylamide
  columns, 142
 precipitation by phosphotungstic acid,
  251

Perchloric acid (PCA), 250, 275, 334, 335
 precipitation as K⁺ salt, 251, 335, 338

Permount, 237, 238ff.

Perspex (Lucite) solution, 232

Pevikon (polyvinyl chloride–polyvinyl
 acetate copolymer), 59, 61, 62, 65,
 410–412

pH, *see* Glass electrode

Phage, *see* Bacteriophage

Phenol, 331, *376*, 399, 406
 isotonic solution, *406*, 407

Phenolphthalein, 66
 as indicator, 405

Phenol red indicator, 405

Phenol-sulfuric acid test, carbohydrates,
 288
 interfering substances, 288

Phenyl-(*p*-benzeneazobenzoyl-amino)-
 acetic acid, absorbancy, 353

Phenylacetic acid, for buffers, *376*

Phenylalanine, absorbancy, 362

Phosphate-buffered saline (PBS), 367,
 384, 398(**30**), 401(**35**)

Phosphate buffers, 396ff.

Phosphatides, 305
 separation by TLC, 316

Phosphoric acid, for buffers, *376*

Phosphors, in scintillation counting of
 radioelements, *see* individual
 designations
 BBOT, POPOP, PPO, 204, 205, 212,
  213
 dimethyl-POPOP, 212
 gelled scintillator, 216

Phosphorus
 in lipids, 314
 inorganic, determination, 321
 terminal, in DNA, 320
 total, determination, 321

Phosphotungstic acid-HCl, precipitation
 of peptides, *251*

Photography
 autoradiographs, 239
 emulsions for autoradiography, *233*
 liquid emulsions, *233*
 starch gel photo records, 34

Photons
 detection by photocathode, 204
 emission counting, *245*
 gamma radiation, 185, *186*, *187*, 242,
  242
 quenching of light photons, *245*

Photronreflectometer, 176

Phycoerythrin (red algal glycoprotein),
 molecular weight standard, 143, 150

PI (preformed gradient isodensity), 105

Picocurie, definition, *241*